Talapoins
Miopithecus
Pp. 212-216

Mountain Monkeys
Allochrocebus
Pp. 242-249

Green Monkeys, Vervet Monkeys
Chlorocebus
Pp. 227-241

Forest Guenons
Cercopithecus
Pp. 250-333

Black and Black-and-White Colobus
Colobus
Pp. 382-411

Olive Colobus, Red Colobus
Procolobus
Pp. 335-381

Gorillas
Gorilla
Pp. 412-426

Chimpanzees
Pan
Pp. 427-450

Galagidae

Lorisidae

Cercopithecinae

Colobinae

Hominidae

Inquiries to the publisher should be directed to the following address:

Russell A. Mittermeier & Anthony B. Rylands
Editors, CI Tropical Field Guide Series
Conservation International
2011 Crystal Drive, Suite 500
Arlington, VA 22202
USA

ISBN 978-1-934151-48-8

Printed and bound by Panamericana Formas e Impresos S. A., Bogotá, Colombia

10 9 8 7 6 5 4 3 2 1

CONSERVATION INTERNATIONAL
TROPICAL FIELD GUIDE SERIES

PRIMATES
OF
WEST AFRICA
A Field Guide and Natural History

John F. Oates

Illustrated by
Stephen D. Nash

Series Editors
Russell A. Mittermeier & Anthony B. Rylands

Photo Editing and Layout
Paula K. Rylands

CONSERVATION
INTERNATIONAL

2011

Putu, Liberia, 2011 (photo by E. J. Greengrass)

John Oates is Professor Emeritus of Anthropology at Hunter College, City University of New York, where he was a member of the teaching faculty from 1978 to 2008. He has a PhD in Zoology from the University of London based on studies of the ecology and behavior of black-and-white colobus monkeys in Uganda, and has had research affiliations with Rockefeller University (New York), Cambridge University, the University of Benin (Nigeria), Njala University College (Sierra Leone) and Oxford Brookes University (England).

Oates first visited West Africa as an undergraduate at University College London in 1964, and since 1979 he has focused research and conservation efforts on that region. He has paid special attention to rainforest primates, undertaking field studies on a variety of prosimians, monkeys and apes. In the 1980s, he played a major role in establishing a research and conservation site at Tiwai Island, Sierra Leone, and he has assisted in the creation of several other protected areas, including the Cross River and Okomu national parks in Nigeria. In 2001–2004, he worked with the Nigerian Conservation Foundation and the Wildlife Conservation Society to establish a biodiversity research program in Cross River State, Nigeria.

Oates has been a member of the IUCN-SSC Primate Specialist Group (PSG) since 1978 and on behalf of the PSG he compiled the *Action Plan for African Primate Conservation: 1986–90* (published in 1986); a revised version of that plan appeared in 1996 as *African Primates: Status Survey and Conservation Action Plan*. Oates has also contributed to PSG conservation action plans for West African chimpanzees (2003), Cross River gorillas (2007) and Nigeria-Cameroon chimpanzees (2011). He is the author of *Myth and Reality in the Rain Forest: How Conservation Strategies Are Failing in West Africa* (University of California Press, 1999). He now lives in Kent, England.

Stephen D. Nash
A native of Great Britain and a graduate of the Natural History Illustration Department of the Royal College of Art in London, Stephen Nash has been Scientific Illustrator for Conservation International since 1989, producing images for conservation education and biological publications. Prior to this, he was part of the World Wildlife Fund-US Primate Program. Based at the State University of New York at Stony Brook, he is a Visiting Research Associate in the Department of Anatomical Sciences and an Adjunct Associate Professor in the Department of Art.

Paula K. Rylands
Paula K. Rylands is the Photo and Graphic Design Coordinator for the President's Office of Conservation International. She is also a photographer, artist and filmmaker. She has a BA in Social and Cultural Anthropology from the University of Maryland and has studied graphic arts in England and Washington, DC. Originally from Brazil, she has done fieldwork on African diaspora in the rural areas of Minas Gerais.

FOREWORD

It gives me great pleasure to introduce this new book on the Primates of West Africa, the latest in our Conservation International Tropical Field Guide series, which began in 1994. The Guinean Forests of West Africa, the principal focus of this book, rank high among the world's 35 Biodiversity Hotspots, the richest and most endangered of our planet's terrestrial systems. Indeed, many of us would regard this particular hotspot as one of the two or three at greatest risk and most prone to extinctions over the course of the next decade; others in this category are the Philippines and Madagascar and the Indian Ocean Islands. Among the most important and most visible of the vertebrate groups in this hotspot are the nonhuman primates, represented by an amazing 60 species and subspecies, of which 46, more than three-quarters, are endemic, including an endemic subgenus, the olive colobus. No less than 30 of the region's primates are threatened, including five in the Critically Endangered category, 16 in the Endangered category, and nine in the Vulnerable category. Of these, one, Miss Waldron's red colobus (*Procolobus waldroni*), may already be Extinct, while another, the roloway monkey (*Cercopithecus diana roloway*), may be on the verge of extinction. Since the Order Primates managed to come through the 20th century without the loss of a single taxon, these would represent the first primate extinctions in more than a century.

The pressures on non-human primate populations in this region are as severe as anywhere on Earth, and include habitat destruction in its many different manifestations and relentless bushmeat hunting, which threaten to push all but the most adaptable and widespread species to the brink of extinction. Indeed, this region could be the site of the first major primate extinction spasm of the 21st century if proper measures are not taken in the immediate future.

There are several ways in which we can combat the loss of primates and their habitats. One is to increase our knowledge of them and to stimulate more people to study and protect them through species-specific conservation projects. Another is to protect key areas of primate habitat through better management of existing parks and reserves and through the creation of new ones where necessary. A third is to ensure that protective legislation, which is already in place in most West African countries, is respected and strictly enforced. And yet another is to stimulate primate ecotourism to key sites.

In recent years, I have become a strong advocate for primate life-listing and primate-watching as strong incentives for primate conservation. By encouraging people both from within the region and from around the world to visit key sites in primate habitat countries, we can increase awareness of the importance of primates, develop a global constituency on their behalf, and raise more funds for primate conservation projects. And most important of all, we can provide income to local people living in the immediate vicinity of key protected areas through this new and emerging form of tourism. Giving local communities options of employment and the development of local businesses—the wherewithal to earn income by working as researchers, guides, and guards, from running hotels, restaurants, and other services, and by producing handicrafts for sale—will go a long way towards encouraging them to see primates as something other than a source of meat or a crop pest, to be shot on sight.

Although I have spent little time in West Africa compared to places such as Madagascar, Amazonia, and the Atlantic forest of Brazil, I have had the privilege of visiting the region 14 times, including trips to Ghana, Liberia, Côte d'Ivoire, Sierra Leone, Senegal, The Gambia, and the Island of Bioko in Equatorial Guinea. I have seen quite a few of the region's species in the wild, which gives me a good feel for the great potential for primate ecotourism that this region holds.

This amazing new book by John F. Oates will go a long way towards achieving all of these objectives. By summarizing what we already know in a convenient and attractive format, it will stimulate further research and conservation efforts on behalf of these animals—hopefully in the region itself, as well as internationally. By providing everything that we know on West African primate behavior and ecology, and where primates occur in each country, it will facilitate better protective legislation. And perhaps most of all, it will help develop a global cadre of primate watchers and primate life-listers who will become advocates for West Africa's primates, dedicate themselves to furthering awareness and knowledge of these animals, and help to ensure their long-term survival.

And who better to write such a book than John Oates. For more than 40 years John has been a globally recognized authority on this region, and one of its most articulate and dedicated advocates. His knowledge of West African primates, and his commitment to working there—sometimes under very difficult conditions—is simply extraordinary. I first encouraged him to write this book back in 2004, to make sure that all his vast knowledge of these remarkable prosimians, monkeys and apes could be summarized in one convenient place and made available to the world at large. It has been an immense task for John, who is otherwise still actively involved in diverse research and conservation efforts in the region, but I think that you will agree that it has been well worth the wait. What you have in front of you here is a remarkably comprehensive and detailed synthesis of our knowledge of this group of African primates, and we are both delighted and honored to be able to publish it for the benefit of current and future generations of primatologists, primate-watchers, conservationists, and the world at large.

What is more, we are very fortunate to have available once again the services of Stephen D. Nash, surely one of the world's greatest primate illustrators, who has produced here a series of unique and highly descriptive drawings of West African primates covering all known taxa. These are accompanied by the best available photographs taken in the wild and in captivity. It is very difficult to photograph West African primates in most areas because they are so heavily hunted, and we are most grateful to the photographers who have so generously contributed their work.

Lastly, I would like to thank Anthony B. Rylands, Deputy Chair of the IUCN/SSC Primate Specialist Group and Co-Editor of our Tropical Field Guide Series, for his outstanding editorial work, Paula K. Rylands for doing such a fine job of layout and design, Ella Outlaw and Jill Lucena for their administrative support, and the Margot Marsh Biodiversity Foundation and Conservation International for providing the financial resources to make all of this possible.

Thank you all for your interest in primates and in their long-term conservation. We hope that you enjoy this impressive book and use it to the fullest extent possible to help ensure the long-term survival of these wonderful animals.

Russell A. Mittermeier, Ph.D.
President, Conservation International
Chairman, IUCN/SSC Primate Specialist Group

TABLE OF CONTENTS

PREFACE

Russ Mittermeier gave me the idea for this field guide during discussions in late 2004. Writing the text for the book, and advising on the production of the illustrations, has helped me to organize the knowledge I have acquired on the primates of West Africa—and on its environment and political history—since I first set foot in this fascinating part of the tropics as a young undergraduate student in 1964. An old journal tells me that my earliest sighting of a West African primate in the wild was on the night of August 27th that year. With a fellow student, Graham Dunn, I was searching for nocturnal animals in Moka, in the southern mountains of the island of Fernando Po (now called Bioko). We heard cat-like cries from the undergrowth beside our path and soon we spotted the bright orange reflection from two eyes in our light beams. This proved to be an Allen's galago. Some days later we caught one of these primates and arranged for it to be sent to London Zoo; this particular animal is pictured on p. 120 of this book.

My attempts to continue studies on West Africa's primates were thwarted a few years later by the outbreak of the Nigerian civil war (see Oates, 1999, for an account). But my early experiences had got me hooked and, after spells in East Africa and India, I returned to West Africa in 1979. I have been back every year since then, sometimes for many months, sometimes for just a few weeks. My initial field work focused on learning about the natural history of Africa's forest primates, but I soon became equally involved with conservation efforts as I witnessed the huge pressures being put on wild primates and their habitats by the influences of a rapidly growing human population and of economic development.

There are several guide books dealing with the mammals of Africa as a whole, and one excellent account in French of the natural history of the primates of Central Africa (Gautier-Hion *et al.*, 1999). But up till now there has been no publication that not only illustrates every recognized species and subspecies of West African prosimians, monkeys and apes, but also gives a detailed summary of each primate's natural history along with references to the scientific literature about it.

I hope that providing such an account will encourage more interest in this region's rich but threatened primate fauna. Russ Mittermeier is firmly of the view that a series of field guides like this can help to create a cadre of primate watchers, similar to the armies of people who travel widely to see new birds and add them to their life lists. In the course of my own research and travels I have been fortunate to see the great majority of the primate species and subspecies described in this book. But a few have eluded me, and I am probably not now up to the challenge of ticking off every one of these. The challenge of seeing all of the region's primates has become more daunting as the number of forms that are rare and threatened with extinction has grown. I very much hope that this book will be used just as much by people in West Africa as by foreign visitors, and that it will spread a better knowledge of primates in the region. If this can make a contribution to conservation, it will justify Russ Mittermeier's support.

I must thank many people for their help along the way with this undertaking. Among early significant influences were my parents, who tolerated my childhood fascination with animals (and quite often even encouraged me in my interest), and several teachers and mentors, notably Geoffrey Creber, Peter Jewell and Tom Struhsaker, who helped me to develop proper habits of study and to ground my interests in a larger intellectual context. A number of close associates have provided important scientific or collegial support, notably Peter White, Pius Anadu and (before his untimely death) Peter Grubb, while colleagues and students I interacted with during almost 30 years at the City University of New York (CUNY) had a profound influence on my understanding of primatology.

Just as important as these colleagues in the academic world have been the many people that I have interacted and worked with in West Africa since 1964. In particular, I owe a debt of gratitude to all those guides and hunters who have led me through the forest or sat down with me in their villages to talk, and imparted their knowledge of the animals described here and their environments. I could not have learned what I have about West African primates without the assistance of these people, and I could not have managed to do field work without the assistance of all those others who kept camps or field posts functioning.

In the seven years it took me to assemble the material for this book I have been helped by another important set of people. I made frequent visits to the Mammal Collections at the Natural History Museum in London where I received valuable assistance from Paula Jenkins and her staff. I also made much use of the excellent resources of the Zoological Society of London's Library where again the staff have always been helpful. I asked questions of, and sought literature or illustrations from, a very large number of primatologists and conservation professionals, including Michael Abedi-Lartey, Lesley Ambrose, Kate Arnold, Christos Astaras, Lynne Baker, Simon Bearder, Richard Bergl, Sery Gonedelé Bi, David Brugière, Tom Butynski, Paul Buzzard, Janis Carter, Jan Decher, Andrew Dunn, Bernard Fosso, Roger Fotso, Liza Gadsby, Anh Galat-Luong, Jessica Ganas, Mary Glenn, Katy Gonder, Elizabeth Greengrass, Gail Hearn, Tatyana Humle, Ainare Idoiaga, Rebecca Kormos, Felix Lankester, Josh Linder, Boo Maisels, Bethan Morgan, Georges Nobimè, William Olupot, Elizabeth Pimley, Jill Pruetz, Caroline Ross, Noel Rowe, Eric Sargis, Katherine Silenga, Volker Sommer, Dawn Starin, Jacqui Sunderland-Groves, Julie Teichroeb, Nelson Ting, Zena Tooze, Tony Tosi, Ymke Warren (now sadly deceased), and Klaus Zuberbühler. Scott McGraw was especially generous in providing information from his long-term studies of monkeys in Côte d'Ivoire. Many thanks to all of these people, and to any others whose assistance may have slipped my mind.

The value of this book as a field guide will depend heavily on its illustrations and maps, into the preparation of which Stephen Nash has put a huge amount of effort. Stephen and I have been bouncing illustrations back and forth between us for many years and, although I must often have exasperated him, his good heart has allowed us to remain friends. The maps rely to some extent on a long-term West African forest primate mapping project that I undertook while at CUNY, which was assisted by several graduate students in New York, including Marian Dagosto, Richard Bergl and Ryan Raaum. The mapping data generated by that project were contributed to the Global Mammal Assessment which formed the basis of the 2008 IUCN Red List; in turn the Red List maps have been a valuable reference in preparing those that appear in this publication.

Bill Konstant helped to get this project off the ground and it has been brought to fruition by the hard and patient work of Anthony Rylands and Paula K. Rylands at Conservation International. Conservation International (CI) and the Margot Marsh Biodiversity Foundation provided grants which supported work on the guide, and I am grateful as ever to Ella Outlaw at CI for all her efficient assistance in administering these grants.

John F. Oates

Gautier-Hion, A., Colyn, M. and Gautier, J.-P. 1999. *Histoire Naturelle des Primates d'Afrique Centrale*. ECOFAC, Libreville, Gabon.
Oates, J. F. 1999. *Myth and Reality in the Rain Forest: How Conservation Strategies are Failing in West Africa*. University of California Press, Berkeley.

Fig. 1.1: Adult female and infant olive baboons (*Papio anubis*), Gashaka Gumti National Park, Nigeria (photo by R. A. Lodge).

1

INTRODUCTION

The countries of West Africa are home to a diverse and distinctive set of nonhuman primates. The aims of this book are, first, to illustrate and describe this diverse array of animals, providing a guide both for people resident in the region and for visitors that may help them distinguish between the different species and subspecies, and, second, to give a summary of the natural history of each primate, along with references to the larger literature on their biology. As the human population of the world and West Africa continues to grow and as economies expand, with consequent ever-greater demands for resources of land, food, materials and energy, most of the primates of this region face serious threats to their continued survival. A few are teetering on the brink of extinction and one, Miss Waldron's red colobus, may have become extinct in the last decade. It is hoped that, by spreading greater awareness of these animals, this book can contribute in some small way towards efforts to ameliorate the threats to their continued survival in the wild; it would be a tragedy if, not too many years from now, parts of this book serve only to catalogue facts about some fascinating organisms that have been lost forever. Conservation challenges are discussed further in section 6, and other introductory sections aim to provide further background to an understanding of the biology of the region's primates.

"West Africa" as defined here is the western bulge of the continent south of 20°N latitude, extending from the coast of Senegal in the west to Lake Chad and Cameroon's Sanaga River in the east (see Fig. 1.1). This definition works well in relation to primate distributions, but is not consistent with the most common geographical and political descriptions of West Africa. For instance, the United Nations regards the sub-region of West (or Western) Africa as including Nigeria, but not Cameroon or Equatorial Guinea; some other accounts consider all of Cameroon to be in West Africa. In this book I take a course between those positions, and place the boundary of West Africa within the nation of Cameroon, at the Sanaga River. I do this because the Sanaga forms a very marked boundary to the distribution of many forest-zone primates; several (such as the angwantibo, drill, and red-eared monkey) occur on both sides of the Nigeria-Cameroon border, across which their habitat is continuous, but do not extend south of the Sanaga River, where related but different species occur. Subspecies of several of the primates that live in the Nigeria-Cameroon border region are found on

Fig. 1.2: The country boundaries and major rivers of West Africa. The Sanaga River in Cameroon marks the eastern boundary of the region.

the island of Bioko, part of the nation of Equatorial Guinea, and the northern section of Bioko lies to the north of the mouth of the Sanaga; therefore, the primates of Bioko are also included in this guide.

Using the Sanaga River as a boundary is consistent with how Russell Mittermeier and others (1998) have defined the eastern and southern edge of the "Guinean Forests of West Africa" biodiversity hotspot. Perhaps even more importantly from the perspective of a book dealing with primate natural history, the benchmark publication *Histoire naturelle des Primates d'Afrique Centrale* by Annie Gautier-Hion *et al.* (1999) also considers the River Sanaga as the boundary between the faunas of Central and of West Africa, and in focusing on Central Africa does not include descriptions of the primates of the island of Bioko. Therefore, this book and that of Gautier-Hion *et al.* exactly complement each other geographically.

Even so, a potential reader might reasonably ask whether there are not already enough guides available to African primates and other mammals. However, although a range of guide books to the larger mammals of Africa (including the primates) has been published in the last 40 years, none focuses on West Africa. For instance, Jonathan Kingdon's excellent *The Kingdon Field Guide to African Mammals* (1997) and *The Kingdon Pocket Guide to African Mammals* (2004) deal comprehensively with the mammals of all of Africa, but in so doing they inevitably provide less detail on the natural history of particular West African primates than is given here, they do not provide information on the sources of statements about the animals' natural history, and they do not illustrate every one of the currently recognized subspecies in West Africa. Furthermore, Gautier-Hion's and Kingdon's treatments predate the publication of a new approach to the classification of Africa's primates that was published by Peter Grubb *et al.* in 2003, based on a workshop held by the IUCN/SSC Primate Specialist Group in Orlando, Florida, in 2000. The taxonomy used in this book is based on Grubb *et al.* (2003) with a few modifications discussed in section 3, which provides a detailed classification of West African primates.

According to the classification followed here, there are 60 different kinds of primate in this region, ranging in size from the tiny Demidoff's galago to the hulking Cross River gorilla. They occupy most of the region's great variety of habitats: swamps, rain forests, wooded savannas, wet and dry mountain ranges, and also many areas of farmland. These primates can be classified into two suborders, four families, 19-20 genera and 41 species; 15 of the species have more than one subspecies in West Africa (with a total of 34 subspecies among this group of 15).

Many of West Africa's primates are unique. Twenty-two of the 42 species (52%) are found only within the region (i.e., they are endemic to it). Thirteen West African primate subspecies are endemic, but have close relatives elsewhere on the continent. One West African primate is especially distinctive: the olive colobus monkey (*Procolobus verus*), which occurs in forests from Sierra Leone to Nigeria. It is the smallest of all the African and Asian colobine monkeys and the only anthropoid primate in which mothers carry their small young in their mouths as a matter of course. The genetic studies by Nelson Ting (2008) suggest that the ancestors of the olive colobus separated from those of the red colobus monkeys about 6 million years ago. While Ting and Grubb *et al.* (2003) treat the olive colobus and red colobus as different subgenera within the genus *Procolobus*, Groves (2001) included only the olive colobus in *Procolobus* and places the red colobus in the genus *Piliocolobus*. From Groves's perspective then, the olive colobus is a primate genus unique to West Africa.

Most of the primate species found in West Africa that are not unique to the region occur either in the more easterly forests (in eastern Nigeria and Cameroon) whose fauna and flora generally have much in common with those of Central Africa, or in the savanna zone. Across Africa as a whole, savanna-zone primate species tend to have much broader geographical ranges than those of the moist forest zone. The moist forests of West Africa, like those elsewhere on the continent,

Fig. 1.3: The olive colobus (*Procolobus verus*) is the smallest of all colobine monkeys and occurs only in West Africa (photo by W. S. McGraw).

contain larger numbers of primate species and more species with restricted geographical ranges. For instance, the forests of the Oban Division of Nigeria's Cross River National Park and of the adjacent Korup National Park in Cameroon are home to 14 different primate species. The vegetation of West Africa is discussed further in section 2.

The higher species-richness of moist forest habitats is probably a consequence of the less extreme seasonality of such ecosystems, which allows more ecological specialization to take place and therefore the coexistence of many species, most of which have relatively narrow niches. The restricted ranges of the forest primates are most likely a consequence both of modern ecology and of longer-term evolutionary history. Many forest species, especially if they are specialist tree-dwellers, cannot readily cross areas of savanna between forests, while the differentiation of unique forms in particular places will have been promoted historically by the shrinking of forest to small refuge areas at times of arid climate (a process explored further in section 4).

The "meat" of this book is the identification guide and summary of natural history provided in section 8, which is introduced in section 7. Following the species' descriptions, an appendix provides information about some of the most important sites, particularly national parks, where West Africa's primates can be observed in the wild.

2

WEST AFRICAN GEOGRAPHY AND ECOLOGY: TOPOGRAPHY, DRAINAGE, CLIMATE AND VEGETATION

Topography

A glance at a relief map shows that, considered as a whole, West Africa is the most low-lying area in all of tropical Africa. Almost all of the region lies below an elevation of 600 m (about 2,000 ft) and is relatively flat and featureless (see Fig. 2.1). The most mountainous area is in the far southeastern corner in the highlands of Cameroon, which include the active volcano of Mount Cameroon, West Africa's highest mountain at 4,095 m (13,435 ft). Mount Cameroon is located on a tectonic fault line that extends northeast to the Adamawa Highlands, and southwest into the Gulf of Guinea as far as the island of St. Helena. Also located on this fault are the two second-highest peaks in West Africa: Mt. Oku in Cameroon and Pico Basilé on the continental shelf island of Bioko, both of which reach 3,011 m above sea level. Apart from the Jos Plateau in Central Nigeria, which has maximum elevations of just over 1,800 m, the only other major mountainous areas in West Africa are the Fouta Djallon highland region of western central Guinea (average elevation about 900 m), and a string of mountains extending from eastern Sierra Leone through southeastern Guinea to western

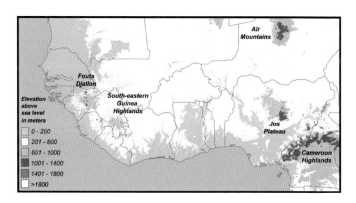

Fig. 2.1: This relief map of West Africa shows how low-lying is most of the region. The most mountainous area is the Cameroon Highlands in the far south-east of the region (map by R. A. Bergl and S. D. Nash).

Fig. 2.2: Part of the Mount Nimba range, where the boundaries of Côte d'Ivoire, Liberia and Guinea meet. At 1,752 m, Mount Nimba is one of the highest points in West Africa to the west of Mt. Cameroon. Parts of the range are protected by nature reserves: 200 km² in Liberia, 130 km² in Guinea and 50 km² in Côte d'Ivoire. The Nimba ecosystem has been seriously damaged by large-scale iron-ore mining and further mining is planned (photo by O. Langrand).

Côte d'Ivoire; these include Sierra Leone's Loma Mountains, with Mt. Bintumani (1,945 m), the highest peak in Africa west of Basilé, and Mount Nimba (1,752 m), which straddles the Guinea-Liberia-Côte d'Ivoire border. Except for the Cameroon Highlands there is little land in West Africa more than 1,000 m above sea level and this probably explains why few animal species are present that are specifically adapted to montane habitat, other than in the Cameroon Highlands. Only one West African primate, Preuss's monkey (*Allochrocebus preussi*) of Cameroon, Nigeria and Bioko, occurs mainly in mountains.

Rivers and Lakes

The highland regions are the source of West Africa's major rivers. Many of West Africa's longest rivers begin their journey to the sea by first draining northward. Tributaries of the Senegal and Gambia rivers rise in the Fouta Djallon and flow northwards before looping to the west and reaching the Atlantic. West Africa's longest river, the

Niger (4,180 km), rises in the mountains on the Sierra Leone-Guinea border. Initially, the Niger flows northeast into Mali and approaches the southern edge of the Sahara; it then bends, and flows southeast through Niger and Nigeria to finally disgorge into the Gulf of Guinea through Africa's largest river delta. The Niger's major tributary, the Benue, collects much of its present drainage from the northern slopes of the Adamawa Highlands.

Many rivers with shorter courses flow southeast or south to the Atlantic from inland hills and mountains. Mt. Nimba, for instance, feeds the Cavally River, which forms the border between Liberia and Côte d'Ivoire. The two main branches of the Volta River (the Black and White Voltas) rise in Burkina Faso and flow south to merge in central Ghana and feed the artificial Lake Volta (the world's largest reservoir by area), formed by a hydroelectric dam at Akosombo near the coast. The southern drainage of the Adamawa Highlands is into the Sanaga, which forms the biogeographical boundary of the West African region.

West Africa's largest natural lake is Chad, located in the arid zone where Nigeria, Chad and Cameroon meet. This shallow lake currently covers an estimated area of 1,500–2,000 km^2 (Carles and Petrella, 2009), and fluctuates in size annually and with the seasons. However, the present lake is a remnant of a much larger prehistoric lake:

Fig. 2.3: The Benue River, a major tributary of the Niger River, rises in the Adamawa Plateau of northern Cameroon. Over 1,000 km long, much of the river is shallow and only navigable for most of its length towards the end of the wet season (photo by J. F. Oates).

"Megachad". Around 7,000 years ago, at a time of high monsoonal rainfall, Megachad covered an area of about 360,000 km² and was then larger than any lake on the planet today (Drake and Bristow, 2006). Megachad has been shrinking for thousands of years. It probably had its original main outflow on its southern shore, into the Mayo Kébi River and from there into the Atlantic via the Benue (Hugueny and Lévêque, 1994; Drake and Bristow, 2006). Presumably the Benue and lower Niger would then have been much larger rivers than they are today. Intermittently, some water still reaches the Upper Benue from Lake Chad via the Logone and Mayo Kébi rivers (Brown, 2008).

Climate

Rainfall in West Africa has not only fluctuated greatly in a historical perspective, it is also extremely variable spatially and temporally today (Ojo, 1977). This has great implications for the kind of habitats available to primates and the foods present in those habitats at different times of year. There are essentially two major opposing air masses that affect climate in West Africa through their seasonal movements in relation to each other (Hopkins, 1974). The equatorial Atlantic produces a humid maritime air mass which typically blows from the southwest onto the West African coast, while the Sahara Desert produces a dry continental air mass whose northeasterly winds at times bring dry (and often cool) air to the lands to the south of the desert.

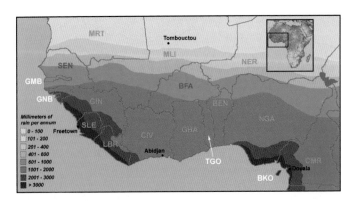

Fig. 2.4: The pattern of annual rainfall across West Africa. Data on the distribution of rainfall across months for the four cities marked on this map are given in Fig. 2.5.

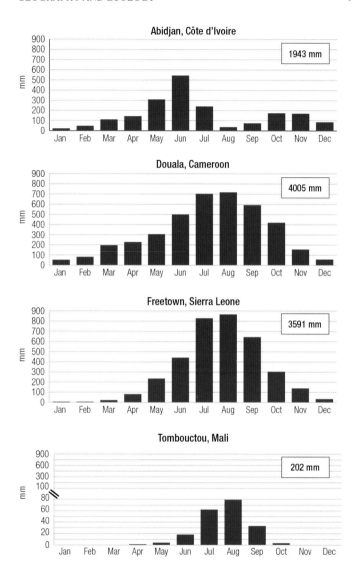

Fig. 2.5: Mean monthly rainfall at four localities in West Africa. Abidjan has two peaks of wet weather interrupted by an August dry spell. Mean total annual rainfall is shown in the boxes on the right of the chart. Source: WorldClimate (<http://www.worldclimate.com>) (Hoare, 2005) (graphics by K. Meek).

On the southern coast of Bioko Island and at the southwestern foot of Mt. Cameroon, average annual rainfall exceeds 10,000 mm per annum, making this one of the wettest areas on earth; a significant part of this rain falls during an intense southwest monsoon period between June and September. To the west of Cameroon, another rainfall maximum is reached in the coastal regions between Guinea and western Liberia; Freetown in Sierra Leone and Monrovia in Liberia each receive an average of more than 3,000 mm of rain each year. By contrast, average annual rainfall at Tombouctou (Timbuktu) on the Niger in Mali, close to the southern edge of the Sahara, is only about 200 mm; over 90% of this rain falls between June and September (see Fig. 2.5). The general pattern is that rainfall decreases with distance inland from the coast, but between the high coastal rainfall foci in eastern Nigeria-western Cameroon and in Guinea-Liberia there is a relatively dry coastal zone between eastern Ghana and the western edge of Nigeria, sometimes called the "Dahomey Gap".

Seasonality in the pattern of rainfall is apparent all over West Africa, even at the wettest sites, and this seasonality can be very pronounced. Tombouctou in the Sahel endures eight months with hardly any rain, but many coastal locations also experience several months when less than 50 mm of rain falls. Like Mt. Cameroon in the far west of our region, Freetown has a monsoonal rainfall pattern, with a single major peak of rain in June-October; in Freetown this is followed by a long dry season where it is normal for <50 mm of rain to fall each month from December through March. Between eastern Liberia and western Nigeria, a two-peak rainfall regime occurs: Abidjan in Côte d'Ivoire has a moderate 1,950 mm of rainfall per year, and less than 50 mm of rain falls monthly both in January-February and in August.

The whole region defined as West Africa in this book falls within the Tropics, so that warm temperatures with relatively low fluctuations across the year are the norm in the lowlands, especially in the more southerly parts of the region. For instance, the mean monthly temperature in Douala, Cameroon, only varies between 24°C (in August) and 27°C (January-April). At Tombouctou on the other hand, the average temperature in January is 23°C (with a mean minimum of 15°C), while the May and June average is 35°C. Almost all of West Africa is frost-free, but frost is not uncommon on the summit of Mt. Cameroon, where snow occasionally falls (Cable and Cheek, 1998).

Vegetation

Given the relative uniformity of the temperature regime across West Africa, it is the availability of water (from rain, or proximity to water bodies) that mostly determines the pattern of vegetation in the region. Elevation, through its influence not only on rainfall but also on evapotranspiration, also has an effect on vegetation.

As a result of the distribution of rainfall, the predominant natural vegetation pattern in West Africa is a series of latitudinal zones parallel to the coast, with dense forest in the high rainfall areas near the coast giving way to progressively drier and more open vegetation types (dry forest, savanna woodland, scrub, then desert) as you move north. In the far west of the region, however, where the coastline has a north-south orientation, the drier zones approach the coast, as they do in the low-rainfall Dahomey Gap of Bénin and Togo (see section 4). Superimposed on this general pattern are the special plant formations of upland areas, the mangrove swamps of some very low-lying coastal regions, the seasonally-flooded savannas of the Inland Niger Delta

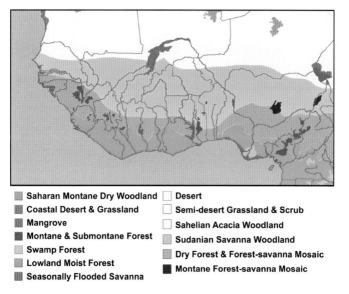

Saharan Montane Dry Woodland | Desert
Coastal Desert & Grassland | Semi-desert Grassland & Scrub
Mangrove | Sahelian Acacia Woodland
Montane & Submontane Forest | Sudanian Savanna Woodland
Swamp Forest | Dry Forest & Forest-savanna Mosaic
Lowland Moist Forest | Montane Forest-savanna Mosaic
Seasonally Flooded Savanna

Fig. 2.6: Natural vegetation zones of West Africa. Based on White (1983) and Burgess *et al.* (2004) (map courtesy of R. A. Bergl and S. D. Nash).

(or *Macina*) in Mali and the Lake Chad margins, and the freshwater swamps of the coastal Niger Delta (see Fig. 2.6).

The technical terms applied to the different vegetation types that make up this pattern, and the positions of the boundaries between them, vary from one authority to another. A major factor that complicates an understanding of West Africa's natural vegetation zones, and leads to disagreement among plant ecologists attempting to interpret the patterns on the ground, is the long-term influence that humans have had on the vegetation through their burning and farming activities; these have affected almost all of West Africa's landscapes with the exception of the steepest mountain slopes and the driest desert areas. Fires started by humans may well have been affecting African vegetation for hundreds of thousands of years, and agriculture has been practiced for several thousand years. Such human influence has had a particularly large influence on the drier types of forest and woodland, which have sufficient rainfall to support crops, but are also relatively easy to clear and to burn.

Given such strong human impact, how is the "natural" pattern to be discerned? Botanists and ecologists can make informed guesses based on rainfall patterns, historical records and the species-composition of vegetation remnants that appear to have escaped major damage. Ultimately, though, all the existing maps showing the natural vegetation of West Africa are based on a large amount of interpretation, and that is why they vary so much from one interpreter to another. While maps inevitably show a sudden transition from one vegetation type to another, the reality on the ground is that one vegetation type usually merges gradually into another, except where fire and cultivation produce a sharp boundary at a forest edge.

The map shown in Figure 2.6 relies heavily on the map of the "Terrestrial Ecoregions" of Africa produced by Burgess *et al.* (2004), which itself was based on the vegetation map of Africa compiled for UNESCO by White (1983).

Most of West Africa's primate species are forest dwellers, and many of these are restricted to the forests that lie within 300–400 km of the coast. Such forests are widely referred to as "rain forest". Figure 2.6 calls the forest type found in high-rainfall coastal areas of West Africa "Lowland moist forest." This kind of forest is termed "Lowland rain forest" by White, "Tropical moist broadleaf forest" by Burgess *et al.*, and simply "Tropical forest" by Hopkins (1974). Such forest, when mature, typically has a high multi-layered tree canopy (with the tallest trees reaching to a height of at least 40 m), high tree-species richness, and no more than four months of the year with less than 50 mm of rainfall. Some authorities subdivide this zone (or biome) into many subtypes; for instance, Poorter *et al.* (2004) recognize hyperwet, wet evergreen, moist evergreen, moist semi-deciduous and dry semi-deciduous forest types within the Upper Guinea forest zone of West Africa. These subdivisions recognize variations in rainfall patterns across the zone that produce differences in tree-species composition and in the seasonal behavior of the trees; for instance, in the semi-deciduous forests a high percentage of upper canopy trees typically shed their leaves during the dry season. Mapping and describing each of these subdivisions is beyond the needs of this book because most primates do not have their distributions restricted to a very narrow forest type. Most primatologists have not recognized these forest subdivisions in their accounts of natural history.

Immediately to the north of the coastal moist forest zone, Figure 2.6 portrays a zone referred to as "Dry forest and forest-savanna mosaic". This is called "Guinea-Congolia/Sudania regional transition zone" by White, "Guinean forest-savanna mosaic" by Burgess *et al.*, and "Forest-savanna zone" by Hopkins. Much of this area, which typically has a dry season lasting longer than four months, would most likely have supported dry forest vegetation before the appearance of agricultural humans, and it is now a mosaic of forest patches, farmland, and wooded grassland (or savanna) that has resulted from generations of clearing and burning forest by people. Where this zone reaches the coast in the Dahomey Gap (and where the vegetation has been protected from heavy human impact), patches of closed-canopy dry forest survive. Forest in this zone has lower tree-species richness than moist forest and the height of its canopy is lower. Dry-season fires, most often started by humans, typically sweep through habitats in this zone, especially those where grasses have become abundant; these fires suppress the growth of most trees, except for fire-resistant species such as *Lophira lanceolata*.

North of the dry forest zone, our map shows a broad zone of "Sudanian savanna woodland". This is referred to as "Sudanian woodland" by White and as "Sudanian savanna" by Burgess *et al.* Some authors (such as Lawson, 1966) refer to the southern part of this zone as "Guinea savanna." As in the dry forest zone, most of this vegetation has been profoundly modified by humans; in its natural state it would often appear as a woodland of medium-sized trees (among

Fig. 2.7: Canopy of lowland moist forest, Tiwai Island, Sierra Leone (photo by J. F. Oates).

Fig. 2.8: Dry forest, Outamba Kilimi National Park, north-western Sierra Leone (photo by J. F. Oates).

Fig. 2.9: Sudanian savanna woodland, near Pendjari National Park, Bénin (photo by M. Wegmann).

Fig. 2.10: Sahelian *Acacia* savanna woodland, Gadabeji Faunal Reserve, Niger (photo by T. Wacher).

Fig. 2.11: Lower montane forest at 800 m above sea level on Jideh Mountain, Putu, Liberia (photo by E. J. Greengrass).

which species of *Isoberlinia*, *Combretum* and *Terminalia* are common), with an understorey dominated by tall grasses. Rainfall in this zone is typically 600–1,000 mm per annum, with a dry season lasting at least six months; dry-season fires are common. A relatively small number of primate species inhabit this savanna zone, including baboons, patas, green and tantalus monkeys, and Senegal bushbabies.

Between the Sudan savanna and the semi-desert scrub that fringes the Sahara lies the zone called "Sahelian *Acacia* woodland" on our map. This is referred to as "Sahel *Acacia* wooded grassland" by White, and as "*Acacia* Sahelian savanna" by Burgess *et al*. This Sahelian zone has even less annual rainfall (500 mm or less) and a more prolonged dry season than the Sudanian zone. Tree-species richness is low, and trees are typically small and widely-spaced; at ground level, grass cover is relatively sparse and does not reach more than 1 m in height even after the rains. The dominant trees are spiny acacias such as *Acacia tortilis*, *A. senegal* and *A. seyal*. The Sudan and Sahel zones share the same non-human primate fauna.

A very important primate habitat in all the savanna zones is gallery forest. This is forest vegetation growing along the banks of rivers (and sometimes called riparian, riverine or fringing forest), with tree growth supported in dry seasons by groundwater. The alluvial soils in river valleys and the protection that the damp habitat provides against fire are other factors favoring tree growth along these rivers. Gallery forest is quite often inundated at the wettest time of year. These forests provide both sleeping sites and food sources for many primates.

As well as occurring in each of the major West African vegetation zones, some primates are also found in other habitats, such as coastal mangrove swamps, in the freshwater marsh forest of the Niger Delta (which has a unique primate, the Niger Delta red colobus, *Procolobus epieni*), and in montane forests. Montane forests are quite rare in West Africa because of the generally low relief of the region; they are most common in the Cameroon Highlands. Montane forest typically has a lower canopy of simpler structure than lowland forest, fewer tree species, and abundant epiphytes. The transition from lowland to montane forest often begins at 700–800 m elevation; a lower montane, or submontane, forest then gives way to upper montane (or "classic montane") forest at around 1,600–1,800 m (Oates *et al.*, 2004). Mist and low cloud are common in the upper montane forest zone, where the trees typically have small, simple leaves. In the western part of West Africa, the scattered montane forests at sites such as the Nimba and Loma Mountains are often dominated by one tree species, *Parinari excelsa* (Richards, 1996).

Fig. 3.1: Mainland drills (*Mandrillus leucophaeus leucophaeus*), Drill Ranch Afi Mountain, Cross River State, Nigeria (photo by A. Idoiaga). Drills occur only in West Africa, in Nigeria and Cameroon (Mainland drill) and on the island of Bioko, Equatorial Guinea (Bioko drill).

3

CLASSIFICATION OF LIVING WEST AFRICAN PRIMATES

Introduction

The names of particular primates have to be mentioned when describing their distribution, evolution and conservation in these introductory sections. To avoid confusion as to which species and subspecies these names refer to, a full classification of West Africa's primates, with their scientific and common English names, is therefore given here, before further discussion of their biology and status.

This book does not have as a major aim a revision of African primate taxonomy. Several accounts of primates generally, and of African primates in particular, published over the last 15 years have adopted novel classifications, with the result that non-specialist readers can become confused as to which names are appropriately applied to animals they encounter. It was with the goal of trying to reach a taxonomic consensus among primate experts that the IUCN/SSC Primate Specialist Group arranged a meeting in Orlando, Florida, in 2000. The consensus reached by the specialists on African primates who attended that meeting (the "Orlando taxonomy") was published in the *International Journal of Primatology* in December 2003, and that classification (Grubb *et al.*, 2003) will form the basis of the one used in this book. A few instances where that classification is not followed are explained later in this section.

In taxonomy (the science of classification), the primates are placed as an Order within the Class Mammalia, following the hierarchical system of classification that was invented by the Swedish botanist Carl Linnaeus in the 18th century, and which is well explained by Groves (2001). Under the Linnaean system, each species carries a two-part (binomial) Latinized name, such as *Cercopithecus campbelli* for the Campbell's monkey.

The most commonly used primate classifications divide the Order Primates into two suborders, using either the names Prosimii and Anthropoidea, or Strepsirrhini and Haplorrhini (sometimes spelled Strepsirhini and Haplorhini). These alternative schemes are based on whether the small, nocturnal tarsiers found on Southeast Asian forested islands are regarded as best classified with the galagos, lemurs and lorises (the prosimian/anthropoid scheme), or with the monkeys and apes (the strepsirrhine/haplorrhine scheme). The Orlando taxonomy preferred the latter scheme, and so that is what is followed here.

What is a Species?

A major point of contention within Systematics, the larger biological science of which taxonomy is a part, is the definition of a species. It surprises many non-biologists that biologists themselves do not all agree on what a species is, even though more than 150 years have passed since the publication of the first edition of Charles Darwin's *On the Origin of Species by Means of Natural Selection*. Many primatologists have tended to favor use of the so-called Biological Species Concept (BSC) formulated by Ernst Mayr, and described by him as follows:

> "A species consists of a group of populations which replace each other geographically or ecologically and of which the neighboring ones intergrade or interbreed wherever they are in contact or which are potentially capable of doing so (with one or more of the populations) in those cases where contact is prevented by geographical or ecological barriers" (Mayr, 1940).

But as Mayr (1942) has himself acknowledged, such a definition produces a difficulty in cases where populations are not geographically close to one another. Mayr said that in those cases (which are in fact common among African primates) it is left to the judgment of the individual systematist to consider whether or not two forms are "potentially capable" of interbreeding. This leads to a considerable degree of subjectivity in judging whether two populations are or are not members of the same species, especially when it comes to considering how successful might be any interbreeding between them.

This difficulty with applying the BSC in practice has led the leading primate taxonomist Colin Groves to favor the Phylogenetic Species Concept (PSC) of Cracraft (1983), by which populations are recognized as members of different species if, after taking account of age and sex differences, 100% of individuals in one population can be distinguished from members of another population through the sharing of a fixed characteristic, such as a color pattern, a size difference, a vocalization, or a DNA sequence (Groves, 2001, 2004).

Unfortunately, the "Orlando taxonomy" did not choose a particular operational species definition, but instead adopted what we have called "a relatively conservative view" for African primates (Grubb *et al.*, 2003), generally following common practice among our predecessors in deciding whether any two populations might be potentially capable of breeding successfully if they were to meet in the wild, taking into account such features as very similar or identical vocalizations. As a consequence, we had special difficulty in agreeing on where species boundaries lay among the red colobus monkeys, whose populations are generally widely separated geographically, show distinctly different color patterns, but have graded systems of vocalizations, so that a characteristic male loud call, for example, cannot be used to readily unite or separate two populations. In this book I will therefore follow Groves (2007b) in his PSC-based species-level classification of red colobus to help provide some clarity for a reader, but I will not apply the PSC rigorously to all African primates.

Subspecies

If the PSC is strictly applied, many commonly-recognized subspecies of primates become elevated to species rank. However, because this book takes a more traditional approach to taxonomy, it recognizes a large number of subspecies among the primates of West Africa. Subspecies are geographical segments of a larger species population that differ on average, but not absolutely, from other subspecies in their appearance, size and/or genetics; where the ranges of two subspecies meet, it is normal for interbreeding to occur. A subspecies carries a three-part (trinomial) Latinized name; *Cercopithecus campbelli lowei* for Lowe's monkey, for example. Groves (2004) notes a useful rule-of-thumb proposed by Ernst Mayr; that in a subspecies, at least 75% of individuals differ from all those in other populations of a species.

Classification Used in This Book

This classification of West African primates is based largely on the "Orlando taxonomy" of Grubb *et al.* (2003). Where a scientific name used here differs from the one used in that taxonomy, that name is preceded by an asterisk (*); these differences are discussed in the subsequent section.

SUBORDER STREPSIRRHINI	**Galagos, lemurs and lorises**
Family Galagidae Gray, 1825	**Galagos or bushbabies**
Genus *Galagoides* A. Smith, 1833	Dwarf galagos
G. demidovii (G. Fischer, 1808)	Demidoff's galago
G. thomasi (Elliot, 1907)	Thomas's galago
Genus *Galago* É. Geoffroy, 1796	Lesser galagos or bushbabies
G. senegalensis senegalensis É. Geoffroy, 1796	Senegal galago or bushbaby
Genus *Euoticus* Gray, 1863	Needle-clawed galagos
E. pallidus pallidus (Gray, 1863)	Bioko needle-clawed galago
E. pallidus talboti (Dollman, 1910)	Talbot's needle-clawed galago
Genus *Sciurocheirus* Gray, 1873	Allen's galagos
S. alleni alleni (Waterhouse, 1838)	Bioko Allen's galago
S. alleni cameronensis (Peters, 1876)	Cross River Allen's galago
Family Lorisidae Gray, 1821	**Lorises and pottos**
Genus *Arctocebus* Gray, 1863	Angwantibos
A. calabarensis (J.A. Smith, 1863)	Angwantibo
Genus *Perodicticus* Bennett, 1831	Pottos
P. potto potto (Müller, 1766)	Bosman's potto
**P. potto juju* Thomas, 1910	Benin potto
P. edwardsi Bouvier, 1879	Milne-Edwards's potto
SUBORDER HAPLORRHINI	**Tarsiers, monkeys, apes and humans**
Family Cercopithecidae Gray, 1821	**Old World monkeys**
Subfamily Cercopithecinae Gray, 1821	**Cheek-pouched monkeys**
Tribe Papionini	**Papionins**
Genus *Cercocebus* É. Geoffroy, 1812	White-eyelid mangabeys
C. atys (Audebert, 1797)	Sooty mangabey
**C. lunulatus* (Temminck, 1853)	White-naped mangabey
C. torquatus (Kerr, 1792)	Red-capped mangabey
Genus *Mandrillus* Ritgen, 1824	Drills and mandrills
M. leucophaeus leucophaeus (F. Cuvier, 1807)	Mainland drill
M. leucophaeus poensis Zukowsky, 1922	Bioko drill

Genus *Lophocebus* Palmer, 1903 — Crested mangabeys
    L. albigena (Gray, 1850) — Gray-cheeked mangabey
Genus *Papio* Erxleben, 1777 — Baboons
    P. papio (Desmarest, 1820) — Guinea baboon
    P. anubis (Lesson, 1827) — Olive baboon

Tribe Cercopithecini — **Guenons**

Genus *Miopithecus* I. Geoffroy, 1842 — Talapoins
    M. ogouensis Kingdon, 1997 — Northern talapoin
Genus *Erythrocebus* Trouessart, 1897 — Patas monkeys
    E. patas (Schreber, 1774) — Patas monkey
Genus **Chlorocebus* Gray, 1870 — Green and vervet monkeys
    C. aethiops sabaeus (Linnaeus, 1766) — Green monkey
    C. aethiops tantalus (Ogilby, 1841) — Tantalus monkey
Genus **Allochrocebus* Elliot, 1913 — Mountain monkeys
    A. preussi preussi (Matschie, 1898) — Cameroon Preuss's monkey
    A. preussi insularis (Thomas, 1910) — Bioko Preuss's monkey
Genus *Cercopithecus* Linnaeus, 1758 — Forest guenons
    C. diana diana (Linnaeus, 1758) — Diana monkey
    C. diana roloway (Schreber, 1774) — Roloway monkey
    C. neglectus Schlegel, 1876 — De Brazza's Monkey
    C. campbelli campbelli Waterhouse, 1838 — Campbell's monkey
    C. campbelli lowei Thomas, 1923 — Lowe's monkey
    C. mona (Schreber, 1775) — Mona monkey
    C. pogonias pogonias Bennett, 1833 — Bioko crowned monkey
    *C. pogonias subsp. — Golden-bellied crowned monkey
    C. petaurista petaurista (Schreber, 1774) — Eastern spot-nosed monkey
    C. petaurista buettikoferi Jentink, 1886 — Western spot-nosed monkey
    C. erythrogaster erythrogaster Gray, 1866 — Red-bellied monkey
    C. erythrogaster pococki Grubb, Lernould & Oates, 1999 — Nigerian white-throated monkey
    C. sclateri Pocock, 1904 — Sclater's monkey
    C. erythrotis erythrotis Waterhouse, 1838 — Bioko red-eared monkey
    C. erythrotis camerunensis Hayman in Sanderson, 1940 — Cameroon red-eared monkey
    C. cephus cephus (Linnaeus, 1758) — Red-tailed mustached monkey
    C. nictitans nictitans (Linnaeus, 1766) — Eastern putty-nosed monkey
    *C. nictitans stampflii Jentink, 1888 — Stampfli's putty-nosed monkey

C. nictitans insolitus Elliot, 1909   Nigerian putty-nosed monkey
C. nictitans ludio Gray, 1849   Red-rumped putty-nosed monkey
C. nictitans martini Waterhouse, 1838   Bioko putty-nosed monkey

Subfamily Colobinae Jerdon, 1867   **Colobine monkeys**

Genus *Procolobus* Rochebrune, 1887   Olive and red colobus monkeys
Subgenus *Procolobus* Rochebrune, 1887   Olive colobus
  P. verus (van Beneden, 1838)   Olive colobus
Subgenus *Piliocolobus* Rochebrune, 1887   Red colobus
  P. badius badius (Kerr, 1792)   Bay colobus
  P. badius temminckii (Kuhl, 1820) Temminck's red colobus
  **P. waldroni* (Hayman, 1936)   Miss Waldron's red colobus
  **P. epieni* Grubb & Powell 1999   Niger Delta red colobus
  **P. pennantii* (Waterhouse, 1838) Pennant's red colobus
  **P. preussi* (Matschie, 1900)   Preuss's red colobus
Genus Colobus Illiger, 1811   Black-and-white colobus monkeys
  C. polykomos (Zimmermann, 1780)   Western black-and-white colobus
  C. vellerosus (I. Geoffroy, 1834) White-thighed black-and-white
                        colobus
  C. guereza occidentalis   Western guereza
    (Rochebrune, 1887)
  C. satanas satanas Waterhouse, 1838 Bioko black colobus

Family Hominidae Gray, 1825   **Great apes and humans**

Genus *Gorilla* I. Geoffroy, 1852   Gorillas
  G. gorilla diehli Matschie, 1904 Cross River gorilla
Genus *Pan* Oken, 1816   Chimpanzees
  P. troglodytes verus Schwarz, 1934 Western chimpanzee
  **P. troglodytes ellioti* (Matschie, 1914) Elliot's chimpanzee

Points of Difference from the Taxonomy of Grubb *et al.* (2003)

Benin potto, *Perodicticus potto juju*.   Grubb *et al.* regard *P. p. juju* as being included within *P. p. potto*. However, Grubb himself had previously shown that pottos living between the Volta and Niger rivers (*P. p. juju*) can reasonably be regarded as subspecifically distinct from those found further west (*P. p. potto*) (Grubb, 1978b), and in morphological research for a doctoral thesis, Stump (2005) has found good evidence for the distinctiveness of *P. p. juju*. *P. p. juju*, called the

"Benin potto" in this book, is lighter in color and smaller than other West African pottos, and most individuals have tails that are much shorter than those of *P. p. potto*.

White-naped mangabey, *Cercocebus lunulatus*. Booth (1958b) regarded the *Cercocebus torquatus* group of white-eyelid mangabeys as being represented by two species in West Africa: *C. atys* (in the west) and *C. torquatus* (in the east). Booth considered *C. atys* to have two subspecies: *C. atys atys* west of the Sassandra-Nzo rivers, and *C. a. lunulatus* east of the main Sassandra. Between the main Sassandra River and its western tributary the Nzo, Booth encountered both subspecies. However, while noting that mangabeys hybridize in captivity, he admitted that he observed no natural hybrids between *atys* and *lunulatus* in the wild. Because I consider that these two forms are distinctive in their external appearance, they are regarded here as different species in light of Booth's field observations, pending further evidence of their relationship.

Genera *Chlorocebus* and *Allochrocebus*. Grubb *et al.* (2003) acknowledged genetic evidence suggesting that the Preuss's monkeys, green monkeys and patas monkeys were an evolutionary line divergent from members of the genus *Cercopithecus* in which they have often been placed (e.g., by Kingdon, 1997). "Pending more data", Grubb *et al.* retained the green monkeys and Preuss's monkeys in *Cercopithecus* but, following tradition, kept the patas monkeys separate in the genus *Erythrocebus*. Groves (2001), on the other hand, had retained *Erythrocebus*, placed the green monkeys (and vervets) in *Chlorocebus*, but left the Preuss's monkey group in *Cercopithecus*. Tosi *et al.* (2004, 2005) make a strong case (based on X- and Y-chromosome genetics) for the Preuss's monkeys, green monkeys and patas (the "terrestrial guenons") having had a single common ancestor that separated long ago (around 5 million years) from the arboreal guenons. Based on that evidence, either all of these terrestrial guenons should be placed in one genus (for which the oldest available name would be *Chlorocebus*), or each of them should be placed in its own genus. Given the degree of ecological divergence among these monkeys, I strongly favor the second option, which entails placing the Preuss's monkeys in *Allochrocebus*, the green monkeys in *Chlorocebus* and the patas in *Erythrocebus*. The genus *Cercopithecus* then consists entirely of the arboreal guenons.

Crowned monkey, *Cercopithecus pogonias*. Grubb *et al.* noted that Gautier-Hion *et al.* (1999) had regarded the form of this monkey living on the mainland between the Cross and Sanaga rivers as different from that found on Bioko Island, but Grubb *et al.* kept the name *C. pogonias pogonias* for mainland and island populations. The Bioko population does indeed differ from that on the mainland, with Bioko animals being smaller, having longer hair, and less intense coloration. It is reasonable, therefore, to consider these members of two different subspecies; however, because the original description of *C. pogonias pogonias* was based on a specimen from Bioko, the mainland form is left for now with no valid name.

Putty-nosed monkey, *Cercopithecus nictitans*. Grubb *et al.* listed only two subspecies of this monkey: *C. nictitans nictitans* and *C. nictitans martini*; their *C. n. martini* included western forms that Grubb *et al.* note have at various times been listed as the separate subspecies *martini*, *stampflii*, *insolitus* and *ludio*. The pelage characteristics of these monkeys, whose populations are scattered from Liberia to the Cross River, with a distinct population on Bioko (*C. n. martini*), have been further studied during the preparation of this book. I have concluded that the five subspecies listed above are reasonably considered distinct from one another; their individual features are described in the species accounts that make up section 8.

Red colobus, subgenus *Piliocolobus*. Grubb *et al.* noted that "the red colobus monkeys have long been one of the thorniest taxonomic problems among the African primates" and during the 2000 Orlando meeting they could not agree on appropriate species names for most Central African populations. However, they did manage to allocate all the West African populations to named species or subspecies. This book follows these allocations, except that each of the subspecies *waldroni*, *pennantii*, *preussi* and *epieni* recognized by Grubb *et al.* is elevated to species rank, as they are also by Groves (2007b) in his revision of all the African colobine monkeys.

Dandelot (1971) listed *waldroni* as a "potential species", rather than a subspecies of *P. badius*, because although it has a similar color pattern to *P. badius*, its nose is not raised on a fleshy base. In a recent study, Ting (2008) found that a single sample of mitochondrial DNA from *waldroni* showed major differences in the NADH4 gene from other West African red colobus. These suggestions that *waldroni* should be regarded as a distinct species are consistent with the field report of Booth (1954b) that, although he observed a mixed troop of *waldroni* and *badius* in a small area on the east bank of the Nzi (or Nzo) River, "no definite proof of hybridization" was found. On the other hand, Groves (2007b), who has examined the four specimens collected by

Booth from this locality, does find evidence of intermediate features in the skins and skulls. On balance, *P. waldroni* is best considered a species, although sadly it may now be extinct and further clarification of its taxonomic status may therefore be impossible.

Grubb *et al.* treated *pennantii*, *preussi* and *epieni* as subspecies of *P. pennantii*. However, these three forms can be easily distinguished by their different coat color patterns, while a recent study by Ting (2008) was also able to discriminate them on the basis of mtDNA sequences. Ting found that the mtDNA of *epieni* was more similar to that of Central and East African populations than to neighboring West African forms; although Ting found that *pennantii* and *preussi* showed a close relationship in their mtDNA, his analysis still suggested a divergence time of 300,000 years. Meanwhile, a thorough re-analysis of vocalizations by Struhsaker (1981, 2010) has found little overlap between the call repertoires of *pennantii* and *preussi*, and has found that the repertoire of *epieni* (like its mtDNA) is most similar to Central and East African red colobus. Based on this evidence I have confidence in treating *P. pennantii*, *P. preussi* and *P. epieni* as separate species.

Like Groves (2007b), this book treats *Procolobus badius* as having two subspecies, *P. b. badius* and *P. b. temminckii*, because individuals with intermediate pelage features have been found in the area between where typical members of *temminckii* occur near the River Gambia, and where typical *badius* occur in eastern Sierra Leone. Ting (2008) was also unable to discriminate between *badius* and *temminckii* based on their mtDNA.

Elliot's chimpanzee, *Pan troglodytes ellioti*. This is the subspecies called *P. t. vellerosus* by Grubb *et al.* Oates *et al.* (2009) have shown that the name *vellerosus* actually applies to a chimpanzee that came from Gabon, within the range of *Pan troglodytes troglodytes*, rather than from Mount Cameroon as had been assumed. From two alternative available names that had been given by Matschie (1914) to chimpanzees collected near Basho, Cameroon, in 1905, Oates *et al.* therefore chose the name *ellioti* for the chimpanzees of southern Nigeria and western Cameroon. The common name "Elliot's chimpanzee" is preferred to others in use, such as the "Nigeria chimpanzee" (in fact about half of the population lives in Cameroon) or "Nigeria-Cameroon chimpanzee".

Fig. 4.1: Pennant's red colobus (*Procolobus pennantii*), Bioko Island (photo by R. A. Bergl).

4

EVOLUTIONARY HISTORY OF WEST AFRICAN PRIMATES

Origins of the African Primate Fauna

Two major, large-scale environmental forces have influenced the evolution of Africa's primates: continental drift and global climate change. Until about 180 million years ago, in the Jurassic period, Africa was part of the southern supercontinent of Gondwanaland (along with Antarctica, India, Madagascar and South America). Then a tectonic fracture zone formed between the eastern and western parts of the supercontinent, splitting Africa and South America in the west from Antarctica, India, and Madagascar in the east (Eagles and Koenig, 2008). The South Atlantic Ocean began to form about 130 million years ago (MYA), in the Early Cretaceous period, and by around 105 MYA Africa had separated from South America. Africa (including what is now Arabia) became an isolated land mass; it drifted northward, finally establishing a new land connection with Eurasia 20–30 MYA.

For about 80 million years, therefore, Africa's land animals evolved on a very large island (sometimes referred to as Afro-Arabia). It is during this period (perhaps 70–80 MYA) that the first primates appeared, most likely not in Africa (Bloch *et al.*, 2007; Pozzi *et al.*, 2010; Steiper and Young, 2006). In the course of Africa's isolation, occasional migrations of animals in and out of the continent seem to have occurred, however, perhaps on drifting rafts of vegetation, perhaps via tenuous and transient land connections to Eurasia across the ancient Tethys Sea (of which the Mediterranean is a modern remnant).

The oldest known African primate so far is *Altiatlasius*, an animal about the size of a mouse lemur, the fossilized remains of which have been found in rocks of the late Paleocene epoch (60 MYA) in Morocco (Sigé *et al.*, 1990). From deposits laid down in the Eocene epoch (56–34 MYA) in North Africa come a variety of small primates, most of which were probably strepsirrhines. It is a matter of some contention as to whether anthropoid primates (monkeys and apes) evolved from prosimian ancestors in Africa, or originated outside Africa (for instance, in Asia) and migrated there later (Tabuce *et al.*, 2009; Seiffert, 2010), but anthropoids were definitely present in Africa towards the end of the Eocene. Fossils named *Catopithecus* have been found in late Eocene deposits in Jebel Quatrani, at Fayum in Egypt (Simons, 1990). *Catopithecus* is deduced to have been a small (400–800 g), diurnal, arboreal quadruped, with a mixed diet, and with males probably being larger than the females (Simons *et al.*, 1999). Genetic evidence suggests that the ape evolutionary lineage separated from the Old World monkey lineage about 30 MYA, in the early Oligocene epoch (Steiper and Young, 2009). This event most likely occurred in Afro-Arabia, which was probably still isolated from other continents; a recently-described fossil from 28-29 MYA Saudi Arabian deposits seems to represent a population ancestral to the ape-monkey split (Zalmout *et al.*, 2010). Apes migrated into Eurasia when a land-bridge was later established between Africa and Eurasia,. The oldest-known fossil colobine monkey is *Microcolobus* from Kenya, dated at about 9.5 MYA, while the oldest-known definite cercopithecines are *Parapapio* of 6–8 MYA from Kenya, and a macaque-like fossil from Algeria (Benefit *et al.*, 2008; Nakatsukasa *et al.*, 2010).

Probably due mainly to the absence of suitable sedimentary rocks, no ancient primate fossils are known from West Africa. But from west-central Chad, just outside the area covered by this book, hominid fossil remains dated to 6–7 MYA have been found that have been named *Sahelanthropus tchadensis* (Brunet *et al.*, 2002). *Sahelanthropus* has been interpreted as lying on or close to the evolutionary line from which the ancestors of chimpanzees and humans diverged 4–6 MYA. This find hints that important events in primate evolutionary history could have taken place in West Africa.

Climate and African Primate Evolution

Today, large areas of tropical Africa have less annual rainfall and longer dry seasons than tropical America and Asia. As a result, Africa has a smaller proportion of moist forest, and more dry forest, woodland, savanna and desert than these other major tropical areas. The savannas and dry woodlands of Africa are relatively rich in primate species, with parts of the West African savanna zone supporting baboons, patas monkeys, green monkeys and Senegal bushbabies, along with several forest-zone species in gallery forests along watercourses.

The relative aridity of Africa is probably an ancient phenomenon, and cycles of aridity must have had major evolutionary effects on the primate fauna, a point that has been stressed by Jonathan Kingdon in his book *Island Africa* (Kingdon, 1990). Kingdon has argued that many of Africa's monkeys (along with its hyraxes and squirrels) probably have terrestrial or semi-terrestrial ancestors. The ability to move on the ground would have been an advantage during periods of dry climate when tree growth thinned.

An example of ancient aridity in Africa and of its consequences for primate evolution is given by the Sahara Desert. The Sahara probably began to form in the middle of the Miocene Epoch about 14 MYA, when there was global cooling and an East Antarctic ice sheet formed, bringing cooler and dryer climates to mid-latitude continental regions (Doaudy *et al.*, 2003); mean summer temperatures in Antarctica cooled by at least 8°C (Lewis *et al.*, 2008). Around this time, mitochondrial genetic evidence indicates that colobine and cercopithecine monkey lineages diverged from each other, probably in Africa (Stewart and Disotell, 1998; Raaum *et al.*, 2005). From rocks laid down near Lake Victoria in East Africa about 15 MYA, and therefore just before that time, come fossils of *Victoriapithecus*, an early Old World Monkey, which has been interpreted to have been part of an evolutionary radiation that preceded the cercopithecine-colobine split (Benefit, 1993).

As the Miocene progressed, there was a further deterioration in climate, and an expansion of the early Sahara. Around 11.5 MYA, the guenon and baboon lineages diverged, and the ancestors of today's North African elephant shrew became separated from those of Central African elephant shrews (Douady *et al.*, 2003; Tosi *et al.*, 2005). Africa has continued to become drier over the last 3 million years, with increasing dryness on the continent likely underlying the ecological processes and evolutionary pressures that led to the emergence of the genus *Homo* from australopithecine ancestors some 2.6 MYA, when savanna vegetation spread at the beginning of the Pleistocene Epoch.

Rain-forest Refuges

Climatic drying in Africa has been both progressive and cyclical (deMenocal, 2004). During cyclical peaks of arid climate, the vegetation and associated fauna typical of moist forests will have become restricted to limited areas, which are now widely-known as rain forest "refugia" or refuges (Booth, 1958b). For instance, pulses of forest-tree speciation separating East and Central African species appear to have occurred at about 33, 17, 8 and 5 million years ago (Couvreur *et al.*, 2008). From the beginning of the Pleistocene Epoch there has been a series of Ice Ages, or glaciations, when ice sheets spread from high latitudes and glaciers moved lower on tropical mountains. Cool glacial maxima have also been times of globally dry climate, when sea levels fell and tropical moist forest would have become restricted to refuges, such as areas at high elevation and areas that have particularly high rainfall today (Vanzolini, 1973; Maley, 1996). Over the last 800,000 years, glacial maxima have occurred at intervals of approximately 100,000 years, producing repeated cycles of forest retraction followed by expansion. The last glacial maximum occurred between 19,000 and 26,500 years before present (BP), when global sea levels were at minimum levels and ice sheets at maximum extents (Clark *et al.*, 2009). Dramatic warming began 14,700 BP, and the ice age is often considered to have ended at around 10,000 BP (Schaefer *et al.*, 2006). At the peak of the last glacial maximum, sea levels are estimated to have been 120 m below today's levels; starting about 19,000 BP, the oceans have risen in pulses until about 6,000 BP, when they stabilized close to present levels (Gornitz, 2007).

When forest fauna became restricted to refuges at times of dry climate, evolutionary differentiation between fragmented populations of a formerly more widespread species would almost certainly have occurred, as a result of some combination of mutation, adaptation to local conditions, and genetic drift. This is the basis of the refuge hypothesis for the differentiation of subspecies and species as developed and elaborated by Aubréville (1949), Booth (1958a, 1958b), Haffer (1969) and Vanzolini (1973).

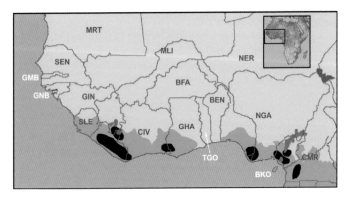

Fig. 4.2: Locations (in black) of hypothesized forest refuges at the time of the last glacial maximum, in relation to approximate present extent of lowland moist forest zone (dark green). Modified from Grubb (2001) and Maley (2001).

Current evidence suggests that during periodic episodes of global cooling and drying in the Pleistocene, forest in West Africa became restricted to quite small fragments in a few areas of high rainfall near the coast, and on mountains such as those in the Cameroon and Guinea Highlands. The most recent of those episodes occurred around 20,000 BP, at the time of the last glacial maximum, with the episodes previous to that occurring around 160,000 and 250,000 BP. On occasions during these arid periods, desert sand dunes reached as far south as 6°N in West Africa (Nichol, 1999).

Based on present rainfall patterns, topography and, crucially, the present distribution of plant and animal taxa, lowland moist forest refuges are reckoned to have persisted in what is today Liberia, in the eastern Côte d'Ivoire and western Ghana border region, and in the western Cameroon-eastern Nigeria border region; montane refuges were probably located in the vicinity of Mt. Nimba where Guinea, Liberia and Côte d'Ivoire meet, and in the Cameroon Highlands (Maley, 1996, 2001) (see Fig. 4.1). Analysis of the distribution of forest primate distribution patterns generally supports this refuge model, but also indicates the presence of a secondary refuge in south-western Nigeria (Booth, 1958a, 1958b; Grubb, 1990, 2001).

Regional Communities of Primates in West Africa

Distinct regional communities of primates are found in different forest areas of Africa, each containing unique (or endemic) species and/or subspecies; the origins of these distinct communities may well lie in a series of Pleistocene refuges, which are centers of mammalian endemism (Grubb, 1978a, 1982, 1990, 2001; Gautier-Hion *et al.*, 1999). The existence of these regional primate communities, and their roots in past climatic events, was recognized in the compilation of the *IUCN-SSC Action Plan for African Primate Conservation: 1986-90* (Oates, 1986a, 1986b). In West Africa, that action plan recognized major forest primate communities in the Upper Guinea region (with West and East subregions) and in Cameroon (including eastern Nigeria and Bioko); more minor distinct communities were identified in the Casamance and Fouta Djallon region (in southern Senegal, the Gambia, Guinea-Bissau and western Guinea) and in southern Nigeria. With some modifications from the 1986 proposal, these are mapped in Fig. 4.2, which shows Upper Guinea (West and East), Western Cameroon (with Bioko as a distinct subregion), Southwestern Nigeria, and Fouta Djallon-Casamance.

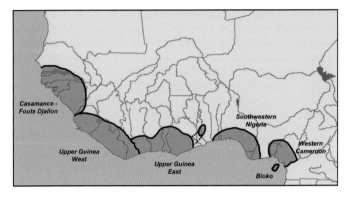

Fig. 4.3: Regional communities of forest primates in West Africa.

Upper Guinea West. The Upper Guinea West subregional community is presumed to have its evolutionary origins in a Pleistocene refuge area in the vicinity of Liberia. It is home to the following endemic primates: *Cercocebus atys*, *Cercopithecus diana diana*, *Cercopithecus campbelli campbelli*, *Cercopithecus petaurista buettikoferi*, *Procolobus badius badius* and *Colobus polykomos*. *Cercopithecus nictitans stampflii*, whose present distribution is centered in northern Liberia, might perhaps have differentiated in a montane refuge on Mt. Nimba, which lies on the edge of Upper Guinea West.

Upper Guinea East. This subregional community seems to have its origins in a refuge in the western Ghana-eastern Côte d'Ivoire area, referred to by Booth (1958a) as "Gold Coast". This community includes the following endemics: *Cercocebus lunulatus*, *Cercopithecus diana roloway*, *Cercopithecus campbelli lowei*, *Cercopithecus petaurista petaurista*, *Procolobus waldroni* (likely recently extinct) and *Colobus vellerosus*. The range of *C. vellerosus* once extended into western Nigeria but its current western range limit is uncertain.

Western Cameroon. The mainland portion of this forest region extends between the lower Cross River in eastern Nigeria and the lower Sanaga River in Cameroon. Primate taxa restricted to this subregional community are *Euoticus pallidus talboti*, *Sciurocheirus alleni cameronensis*, *Arctocebus calabarensis*, *Mandrillus leucophaeus leucophaeus*, an as yet unnamed form of *Cercopithecus pogonias*, *Cercopithecus erythrotis camerunensis*, *Cercopithecus nictitans ludio*, *Procolobus preussi* and *Gorilla gorilla diehli*. *Allochrocebus* *preussi preussi* occurs in montane forests in the Western Cameroon region and may have evolved in a past Cameroon Highland refuge close to a lowland refuge in this region; Grubb identifies a Bamenda Highland Center of Endemism immediately to the north of a lowland West Cameroon Center. Booth (1958a) describes an "Eastern Nigeria" region extending from the Niger to the Sanaga, but several of the primates listed above do not occur (at least in the present day) between the Niger and the Cross; between those rivers is an endemic guenon, *Cercopithecus sclateri*, whose evolution I will discuss later.

Bioko. Primates restricted to Bioko are *Euoticus pallidus pallidus*, *Sciurocheirus alleni alleni*, *Mandrillus leucophaeus poensis*, *Allochrocebus preussi insularis*, *Cercopithecus pogonias pogonias*, *Cercopithecus erythrotis erythrotis*, *Cercopithecus nictitans martini*, *Procolobus pennantii* and *Colobus satanas satanas*. This subregion of the Western Cameroon region has been created as a result of Bioko Island's cycles of connection and disconnection from the mainland during sea level rises and falls coincident with warming and cooling episodes in the Pleistocene. Although some of the island subspecies most similar to mainland forms may have only diverged since the end of the last glacial maximum when Bioko last became isolated by sea-level rise, more distinctive forms could have differentiated during earlier periods of isolation. For instance, Ting (2008) has calculated a divergence time between *Procolobus pennantii* of Bioko and *P. preussi* of the mainland of 300,000 ±100,000 years, while Ting *et al*. (2011) have shown that the mainland and Bioko drill populations diverged much more recently. Castelo (1994) has described the littoral platform connecting Bioko to the mainland as being 50–100 m in depth; any parts of this platform currently 100 m below the surface would likely have been submerged until about 14,000 BP, and areas now 50 m below the surface would have been under water until about 10,000 BP, based on the currently-understood pattern of sea level rise since the end of the last glacial maximum (Gornitz, 2007).

Southwestern Nigeria. Long ago, Booth (1954a) presciently recognized that the mammals of western Nigeria (where the endemic monkey *Cercopithecus erythrogaster* occurs) belong to a distinct community; later he suggested that a small Pleistocene forest refuge may have existed in the area of Benin (i.e., Benin City) or on the right bank of the Niger River (Booth, 1958a, 1958b). Grubb (1978a) initially followed Booth in suggesting the presence of a refuge west of the Niger River in Nigeria, but he later (Grubb, 1990, 2001) expanded this to a "Niger River Center" that includes the Niger Delta; Grubb notes that also found in this area are a distinctive potto (*Perodicticus potto juju*), an endemic form of pygmy hippopotamus (*Hexaprotodon liberiensis heslopi*), and some subspecies of squirrel. In 1993 an endemic form of red colobus monkey (referred to as *Procolobus epieni* in this book) was discovered in the Niger Delta (Grubb and Powell, 1999), and recent phylogenetic studies have revealed a new species of small duiker antelope (*Philantomba walteri*) restricted to the Dahomey Gap and Niger Delta region (Colyn *et al.*, 2010). In 2009, S. Bearder, F. Dowsett-Lemaire and J. Oates noticed that tree hyraxes in the forests of western Nigeria and the Dahomey Gap have a different call to those found to the east and west. Other primates found in western Nigerian forests are *Cercocebus torquatus*, *Cercopithecus mona* and *Cercopithecus nictitans insolitus*; each of these monkeys also occurs to the east of the Niger River (and the range of *C. torquatus* extends as far south as the Republic of Congo), but it seems possible that they originated in western Nigeria or the Niger Delta and quite recently dispersed from there. Neither *C. mona* nor *C. torquatus* occurs on Bioko, suggesting that these species might not have been present on the adjacent mainland around 10,000 years ago when the island last had a land bridge to the continent.

Fouta Djallon-Casamance. This area is not usually considered as the likely location of a Pleistocene refuge area, but it is home to a couple of special primates. The elevated Fouta Djallon Plateau of Guinea, today a mosaic of agricultural land, savanna and patches of forest, would once probably have been largely covered by forest, and it supports an endemic bat species, *Rhinolophus maclaudi* Fahr *et al.*, 2002. West of the Fouta Djallon an area of dry forest and forest-savanna mosaic extends to the Atlantic coast of Guinea and north into Guinea-Bissau, the Casamance area of Senegal, and the Gambia. In this region are found a unique form of red colobus monkey, *Procolobus badius temminckii*, and the Guinea baboon, *Papio papio*, suggesting that there may have been some kind of refuge there—at least of gallery forest—in which they differentiated. The green monkey, *Chlorocebus aethiops sabaeus*, is another characteristic primate of this area. Although its range extends eastward to Ghana, its origins may lie in this far western part of West Africa. Also to be found in the gallery forests of this region are several monkeys that have probably spread north from an origin in Upper Guinea West: *Cercocebus atys*, *Cercopithecus campbelli campbelli*, *Cercopithecus petaurista buettikoferi*, and *Colobus polykomos*.

Rivers as Zoogeographic Barriers

Booth (1958a) suggested that rivers could act to impede the spread of fauna out of forest refuges as climate ameliorated following dry episodes, and forest advanced. Booth suggested that in West Africa the Niger was particularly important as a zoogeographic barrier of this kind, with the Volta also being significant (see Fig. 1.1). In a second paper focusing on primates, Booth (1958b) notes that many primate species or subspecies are limited in their distribution by the Sanaga River in Cameroon. Several subsequent analyses have highlighted the importance of the Sanaga as a distributional limit for many components of the West African forest primate fauna (e.g., Grubb, 1990; Sarmiento and Oates, 2000; Gonder *et al.*, 2006). However, rivers are semi-permeable, not absolute, barriers for many primates. Monkeys, especially members of the Cercopithecinae, can swim; many West African rivers are not very long, and their headwaters are quite narrow, especially in dry seasons; and rivers change course. This makes quite puzzling the major apparent significance of the Sanaga as a distributional barrier to forest primates, as the Sanaga is not today a very large river. It is possible that the Sanaga is located in an area that had little forest during one or more periods of arid climate, so that the present course of the river merely marks or is acting to reinforce an ecological barrier of long-standing. Alternatively, or additionally, perhaps the Sanaga has been a larger river in the past.

Dahomey Gap

Between the western edge of Nigeria and the central coast of Ghana there is an obvious discontinuity in the zone of moist forest that, until it became fragmented and degraded by human activities, extended along the West African coast from the Guinea-Sierra Leone border to Cameroon. This discontinuity (described in section 2) is known as the "Dahomey Gap", from the former name of the country now known as the Republic of Bénin within which it lies. The absence of moist forest in the Dahomey Gap is a result of low rainfall that is apparently caused by the combined influences of nearby ocean currents, wind patterns and the orientation of the coast line (Oates, 1988a; Vollmert *et al.*, 2003); the coastal city of Lomé in Togo in the middle of the gap has an average annual rainfall of less than 900 mm, and Accra, Ghana, towards the western end of the gap, has an average annual rainfall of about 800 mm (World Weather Information Service, 2010). The natural vegetation of the Dahomey Gap is probably a mosaic of dry forest and savanna woodland, with ribbons of gallery forest extending along rivers; however, much of the Dahomey Gap today is farmland or farm fallow growth, with only small patches of forest remaining.

In one of his earliest published papers on the biology of West Africa, Angus Booth argued for the significance of the Dahomey Gap in separating the different forest mammal faunas that occur on either side of it (Booth, 1954a). The forest gap would have been much wider during episodes of cool, dry climate in the Pleistocene, but when climate became warmer and wetter it appears that the gap still acted as a barrier to the spread of many moist-forest mammals dispersing from refuges. The Dahomey Gap has not been an absolute barrier to primates, however, because *Procolobus verus* and *Colobus vellerosus* are known from forests on both sides of the gap and from remnant forests within it (Oates, 1988a), while some primates characteristic of western Nigerian forests (*Perodicticus potto juju*, *Cercopithecus mona*, *Cercopithecus erythrogaster*) also occur in the gap; indeed evidence is growing that in terms of their fauna the Dahomey Gap forests may best be regarded as an extension of the Southwestern Nigerian community.

Forest Monkeys That Don't Fit

Two species of uniquely West African forest primates have distributions that are not readily explained as resulting from some historical process of isolation in forest refuges during dry phases of the Pleistocene, followed by subsequent spreading that may have been limited by the presence of river barriers or the dry zone of the Dahomey Gap. One is the olive colobus monkey (*Procolobus verus*) and the other is Sclater's monkey (*Cercopithecus sclateri*).

The olive colobus is found in forests south of 8°N from south-eastern Sierra Leone to just east of the lower Niger in Nigeria, and it has been observed in forests in the Dahomey Gap (Campbell *et al.*, 2008b). Unlike any other forest monkeys across this range, this species shows no evidence of obvious evolutionary diversification; although there may be some small average size differences across its range, no subspecies are recognized. Genetic research by Ting (2008) indicates that the evolutionary lineages of the olive colobus and red colobus diverged from each other on the order of 6.4 MYA, in the late Miocene Period. It is very unlikely that the modern olive colobus has been living unchanged in West Africa since that time, especially given the vicissitudes that the West African forest has experienced. Whatever

Fig. 4.4: Sclater's monkey (*Cercopithecus sclateri*), Lagwa, Nigeria (photo by L. R. Baker).

the long-term history of its ancestors may have been, it seems likely that the olive colobus species of today has no subspecies or close living relatives because it has spread relatively recently from a place in which it was isolated during either the last glacial maximum or at most the previous maximum. For want of any obvious clues to this place of isolation, a guess can be made that it was mid-way between the species' current eastern and western limits; that would be in the vicinity of the Ghana-Côte d'Ivoire border, which is the location of the proposed Upper Guinea East Pleistocene forest refuge.

Sclater's monkey is another puzzle. This member of the *Cercopithecus cephus* species group is found only in southern Nigeria from east of the Niger River to the western bank of the Cross River. No other species of mammal is known to be confined to this area, and the nearest proposed Pleistocene refuge area (in western Nigeria and/ or the Niger Delta) is occupied by its close relative *Cercopithecus erythrogaster*. At times in the past, *C. sclateri* has been regarded as a subspecies of *C. erythrotis* (e.g., by Dandelot, 1971). Indeed, it shares features with both *C. erythrogaster* to its west and *C. erythrotis* to its east. One possible explanation of its origin is that it arose as a result of hybridization between those other two species. If *C. erythrogaster* and *C. erythrotis* speciated in refuges in southwestern Nigeria and Western

Cameroon respectively during a Pleistocene glacial maximum, their populations might have met in the Niger-Cross area when they spread out during a warming period, and hybridized. In a subsequent dry phase, perhaps a population of these hybrids managed to hang on in a small area of coastal or riverine forest somewhere between the Cross and Niger, evolved into the monkey now called *C. sclateri*, and later expanded towards those river barriers (for instance, after the end of the last ice age). Populations of *C. erythrogaster* and *C. sclateri* now meet on the eastern edge of the Niger Delta, where a small area of hybridization between them has been found (Baker, 2005).

The Savanna Primates

Unlike most of the forest primates of West Africa, the savanna-zone primates (with the exception of the Guinea baboon) have very wide geographical distributions. The habitat to which they are adapted was probably not reduced to such small remnants as was lowland moist forest during episodes of arid climate; these primates have the ability to disperse over long distances because they are typically at home on the ground as well as in trees, and they are ecologically flexible animals. Thus the olive baboon, the patas monkey and the Senegal galago are found over large parts of West Africa's woodlands and savannas, with no very marked local forms, at least in their external appearance. However, the isolated populations of olive baboons and patas monkeys that occur in the Aïr Mountains in central Niger, on the southern edge of the Sahara, are sometimes regarded as distinct subspecies.

Even though these savanna primates appear superficially to show less geographical variation than those of the forest zone, they are almost certainly more varied than they appear at first glance, and they too have probably been affected by historical changes in the African environment. For instance, Zinner *et al.* (2010) show that there are two different mitochondrial forms (or clades) of olive baboons in West Africa whose distributions appear to meet in the vicinity of north-western Nigeria. The most westerly of these clades may have diverged from other olive baboons at a time of Saharan expansion, and Zinner *et al.* suggest they could have been joined later by olive baboons from further east that dispersed into West Africa from the north, skirting the ancient Megachad lake and its presumed large outlet through the Benue-Niger river system.

A similar division into eastern and western savanna forms is found in the green monkey group (*Chlorocebus*). The green monkey itself (*C. aethiops sabaeus*) can be quite readily distinguished from the tantalus monkey (*C. aethiops tantalus*) by its pelage, and these two forms are often placed in different species (e.g., by Dandelot, 1971, by Kingdon, 1997, and by Butynski *et al.*, 2011). In Ghana, the two forms seem to be separated by the White Volta River, although the tantalus is found to the west of the lower Volta, while to the north of Ghana there is no obvious geographical barrier separating these monkeys, which are known to be good swimmers. Because *Chlorocebus* tends to favor moister habitats than the other savanna primates (and is particularly associated with gallery forest) its differentiation may well be another consequence of habitat fragmentation during a glacial maximum, with *sabaeus* evolving in an isolated region in the west of its current range (perhaps near the Guinea Highlands, or on the coast) and *tantalus* somewhere to the west, with the two forms spreading out post-glacially to meet in the center of West Africa. Although this is speculation, the tantalus might also have spread from a refuge further east around Megachad.

Thus, although African savanna-zone habitats may not have suffered such extreme fragmentation as moist forest habitats during past episodes of dry climate, they were almost certainly subject to some level of restriction, producing their own faunal refuge areas. The savanna fauna of Africa has its own geographical patterning that, like the more obvious patterning of rain-forest animals, is almost certainly a consequence of past climate change.

Superspecies and Geospecies

I have described distinct regional communities of primates in West Africa as typically containing species or subspecies closely related to, but different from, similar forms living in the same kind of ecosystem elsewhere on the continent. These different related forms, separated geographically, are known as vicariants, and are presumed to have differentiated as a result of historical events such as glacial periods that affected and isolated whole ecosystems. Two such related species occurring in different geographical areas are referred to as "allopatric" species, and a series of allopatric species have been called a "superspecies", defined by Mayr (1942) as "a monophyletic group of geographically representative (allopatric) species which are morphologically too distinct to be included in one species." Such superspecies are a prominent feature of the African primate fauna; obvious examples are the small forest guenons related to *Cercopithecus cephus*, the mona group of guenons, the savanna baboons and the red colobus monkeys.

Superspecies such as *C. cephus* are sometimes referred to as "species groups" (e.g., by Grubb 1990, and Grubb *et al.*, 2003), but as Peter Grubb discusses in one of his last published papers (Grubb, 2006a), several African primate species have different geographical forms that are commonly regarded as subspecies rather than species (an example is *Cercopithecus diana*), or are single species that have no allopatric sister-species and no recognized subspecies (such as *Cercopithecus neglectus*). Grubb (2006b) points out that these are examples of zoogeographical entities, contributing to particular regional faunas, and he therefore chooses the term "geospecies" from Eck (1996) (an abbreviation of "zoogeographical species") as a way to partition the entire African primate fauna, and to compare the fauna of Africa with those of Asia, tropical America and Madagascar. Grubb also makes the illuminating point that when centers of endemism in Africa not previously known to contain members of a particular primate geospecies have been carefully explored, new taxa have often been found (such as *Procolobus epieni* in the Niger Delta).

Table 4.1 shows, with a few modifications, how Grubb (2006b) allocated African primate species to different geospecies. Grubb recognized 33 geospecies, but had included the recently-discovered mangabey-like kipunji of southern Tanzania in the *Lophocebus albigena* geospecies. The kipunji is now generally accepted as belonging to a distinct genus, *Rungwecebus* Davenport *et al.*, 2006, and recognizing that genus produces a list of 34 African primate geospecies. With that exception, Table 4.1 shows the same set of geospecies listed by Grubb, but the species within the geospecies follow the taxonomy used in section 4 of this book.

The species descriptions in section 8 are grouped according to Grubb's geospecies arrangement. West Africa is home to 25 of the 34 African geospecies, although a couple of these (*Miopithecus talapoin* and *Cercopithecus neglectus*) are only found in a small area in the far southeast of this geographical area.

Table 4.1. Geospecies of African primates, modified from Grubb (2006b). Species occurring in West Africa are shown in bold.

SENIOR SPECIES NAME IN GEOSPECIES	OTHER SPECIES INCLUDED IN GEOSPECIES
Galagoides demidovii	
Galagoides thomasi	
Galagoides orinus	*G. rondoensis*
Galagoides zanzibaricus	*G. cocos, G. granti, G. nyasae, Galagoides* spp. nov. 1, 2, 3
Galago senegalensis	*G. gallarum, G. matschiei, G. moholi*
Euoticus elegantulus	**E. pallidus**
Sciurocheirus alleni	*S. gabonensis, Sciurocheirus* sp. nov.
Otolemur crassicaudatus	*O. garnetti, O. monteiri*
Arctocebus calabarensis	*A. aureus*
Perodicticus potto	**P. edwardsi**
Macaca sylvanus	
Cercocebus torquatus	**C. atys, C. lunulatus**, *C. galeritus*
Mandrillus sphinx	**M. leucophaeus**
Lophocebus albigena	*L. aterrimus*
Rungwecebus kipunji	
Papio cynocephalus	**P. anubis**, *P. hamadryas*, **P. papio**, *P. ursinus*
Theropithecus gelada	
Allenopithecus nigroviridis	
Miopithecus talapoin	**M. ogouensis**
Erythrocebus patas	
Chlorocebus aethiops	
Allochrocebus preussi	*A. lhoesti, A. solatus*
Cercopithecus diana	
Cercopithecus dryas	
Cercopithecus neglectus	
Cercopithecus mona	**C. campbelli, C. pogonias**
Cercopithecus hamlyni	

SENIOR SPECIES NAME IN GEOSPECIES	OTHER SPECIES INCLUDED IN GEOSPECIES
Cercopithecus cephus	*C. ascanius*, **C. erythrogaster**, **C. erythrotis**, **C. petaurista**, **C. sclateri**
Cercopithecus nictitans	*C. mitis*
Procolobus verus	
Procolobus badius	**P. pennantii**, *P. kirkii*, *P. rufomitratus*, *P. tholloni*, *P. bouvieri*, *P. foai*, **P. preussi**, *P. gordonorum*, *P. oustaleti*, *P. tephrosceles*, *P. langi*, **P. waldroni**, *P. parmientieri*, *P. semlikiensis*, **P. epieni**
Colobus polykomos	*C. angolensis*, **C. guereza**, **C. satanas**, **C. vellerosus**
Gorilla gorilla	*G. beringei*
Pan troglodytes	*P. paniscus*

Fig. 4.5: Adult and infant western guereza (*Colobus guereza occidentalis*), Kibale, Uganda (photo by N. Ting). Newborn are white and turn grayish at three weeks old.

5

THE PEOPLE OF WEST AFRICA AND THEIR HISTORY

Section 2 alluded to the fact that human activity has profoundly modified the "natural" vegetation of West Africa. *Homo sapiens* is itself a primate species of African origin and therefore, in a sense, a part of African nature. In most parts of Africa, non-human primates must always have lived in the presence of humans, or of human ancestors, and almost every primate habitat in West Africa, with the exception of some impenetrable swamps or steep mountain slopes, must be to some extent "anthropogenic". For hundreds of thousands of years, the drier habitats have probably been affected by fires set by humans or their immediate ancestors, while most habitats will have been impacted for several thousand years by farming or grazing activities. In a significant footnote to his classic treatise on tropical rain forest, Paul W. Richards (1952, p.29) says: "Forest which has never at any time been cultivated exists in West Africa on swampy sites, but elsewhere only on extremely limited areas, mostly on steep rocky slopes, etc."

In addition to farming and burning primate habitats, people have long interacted with the non-human primates in Africa by hunting them. For instance, there is evidence of humans butchering giant geladas at Olorgesailie in Kenya more than 500,000 years ago (Shipman *et al.*, 1981). As with farming and forest clearance, the ability of people to hunt other primates will have changed as technology has changed (and especially once firearms became widely available), but humans in West Africa can be assumed to have long hunted wild primates, along with other mammals, for their meat. The recent impacts of humans on primates and their habitats will be discussed further in the next section of this book (section 6, Conservation). Here, I want to give a brief outline of the demographic, socio-political and historical background to human influence on the West African environment.

Based on United Nations estimates, the total number of people living in West Africa in 2010 was about 315 million (United Nations Secretariat, 2008); that estimate includes the total population of all the countries covered in this book, except for Cameroon (for which I have included just half of the population) and Equatorial Guinea (where only Bioko Island is considered, with an estimated population of about 100,000).[1] One country, Nigeria, contains approximately 50% of all the people living in West Africa. West Africans belong to a host of different ethnic groups, in the sense of groups of people with a distinct language (or dialect) and culture. Nigeria alone, for instance, is generally considered to have more than 250 different ethnic groups (Central Intelligence Agency, 2009), and West Africa has been described as the most multilingual area in the world (Berry, 1970). Most of the indigenous languages of West Africa are classified by linguistic anthropologists as being members of the large Niger-Congo group, which includes the Bantu languages of central and southern Africa (Williamson and Blench, 2000). Some major Niger-Congo languages in West Africa are Yoruba, Igbo, Fula (or Fulfulde), Akan and Mòoré. In northern parts of the region, and across much of the Sahara, people speak so-called Afro-Asiatic languages; Arabic is an Afro-Asiatic language, and so is Hausa of northern Nigeria. West Africa also has a scattering of people speaking Nilo-Saharan languages, in particular the Songhai (or Songhay) along the Niger River in Mali and Niger. Today, the official languages throughout West Africa are English or French, except in Guinea-Bissau (Portuguese) or Bioko, Equatorial Guinea (Spanish). This is, of course, largely a consequence of colonial history, as are the boundaries of the modern nation-states of the region.

A book that is primarily a guide to the primates of West Africa and their biology is not the appropriate place for a detailed analysis of history, but to have a proper understanding of the modern West African environment it is important to realize that people (and people who were connected to the world beyond West Africa) must have been having profound influences on this environment and its wildlife for a long time. West Africa was not recently some primeval wilderness, and given its long history of developed human settlement and resource exploitation it is not surprising that it is not an area famous in recent times for supporting abundant and widespread populations of large mammals. In this region, humans and other larger mammals have been coexisting in a complex mosaic landscape for thousands of years.

From 7,000 years ago, pastoralist people with cattle, sheep and goats occurred widely in northern West Africa, and from about 3,500 years ago millet cultivation was widespread in the grassland zone. By 2,500 years ago, metal working was occurring in several parts of West Africa, and bananas (native to Southeast Asia) had reached southern

---

[1] The northern regions of Mauritania, Mali and Niger lie outside the limits of West Africa as mapped in this book; these are, however, desert regions with a very low human population density.

Cameroon (McIntosh, 2006). Commerce between West Africa and Mediterranean states (including ancient Egypt) probably occurred from at least as early as the first millennium BC, and by 2,000 years ago major urban settlements with long-distance trade networks had been established in the Inland Niger Delta (where the Niger River divides into many channels in present-day Mali).

West African trade expanded with the introduction of the camel from western Asia, and caravans regularly travelled to and from North Africa through cities such as Timbuktu and Gao on the northern bend of the Niger, and Kano in what is today northern Nigeria. By late medieval times hundreds of thousands of camels were probably engaged in crossing the Sahara (Oliver, 1991). Salt, gold, ivory, slaves and manufactured goods featured in this trade, which apparently had three principal routes: a western one from Morocco to the northern bend of the Niger, a central route south from Tunisia to the region between the Niger and Lake Chad, and an eastern route from Libya and Egypt (Fage, 1962).

Fig. 5.1: Lee J. T. White inspecting fragments of charcoal in a soil pit in Okomu Wildlife Sanctuary (now a national park), Nigeria, in 1994 (see White and Oates, 1999). Pieces of charcoal (especially from oil palm nuts) and pottery occur in the soil under much of this forest, which at one time was a rich source of mahogany timber. Radiocarbon analysis on charcoal from this particular pit indicates that it dates to about the year 1300 AD, when most of the Okomu area, which lies to the east of Benin city, was probably densely settled by people (photo by J. F. Oates).

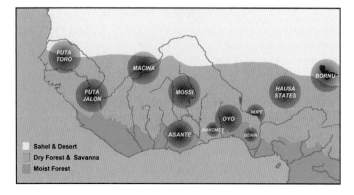

Fig. 5.2: Approximate locations of some major kingdoms and states in West Africa in 1800 (modified from maps in Webster and Boahen, 1967).

Fig. 5.3: Elmina Castle, on the coast of Ghana, is the oldest surviving European building in sub-Saharan Africa. The original structure, named São Jorge da Mina, was erected by the Portuguese in 1482 using stone carried from Europe, and its primary purpose was to protect merchandise used in the important gold trade ("da Mina" refers to the local gold mines). Elmina later came to play a major role as a base in the Atlantic slave trade (photo by J. F. Oates).

A succession of kingdoms and empires flourished in West Africa before the coming of Europeans in the 15th century, and some of these states continued to exercise power up until the colonial partitioning of Africa. Timbuktu and Gao were part of the Songhai Empire which dominated much of the Upper Niger valley (and therefore part of the trans-Sahara trade) in the 15th and 16th centuries, and Songhai itself had taken control of this area from the earlier Mali (or Mandinka) Empire which had expanded from what is now northern Guinea and southern Mali in the 13th century. Other major West African states of the pre-colonial period included the Oyo Empire of the Yoruba, based in western Nigeria and powerful between the 15th and 18th centuries; the Benin Empire of the 15th to 19th centuries, also in western Nigeria; Dahomey, which rose to power at the end of the 17th century in what is now the Republic of Bénin; the Asante Empire, which dominated much of modern Ghana and beyond in the 18th and 19th centuries; and the Sokoto Caliphate in northern Nigeria in the 19th century (Webster and Boahen, 1967).

The colonial era in West Africa had its beginnings with systematic Portuguese explorations for new trading opportunities and a search for Christian allies in the 15th century (Fage, 1962). In 1445, Portuguese navigators reached the coastal region of modern Senegal, and in 1472 Fernão do Pó reached Bioko, naming it "Formosa Flora" ("Beautiful Flower"). By the end of the 15th century, Portuguese trading posts had been established on the West African coast, beginning with Elmina in modern Ghana, a stone castle whose construction began in 1482. These events, and Columbus's voyage of discovery to the Caribbean in 1492, led to the opening of the Atlantic slave trade; Columbus himself had visited Elmina in the 1480s.

Until around 1800, however, Europeans largely confined themselves to trading with West Africans from bases on the Atlantic coast. For nearly 300 years this trade was dominated by slave traffic, many of them captured in warfare between local kingdoms, others enslaved through kidnapping or judicial procedures. After 1550, captive West Africans began to be shipped in large numbers to the Americas (Manning, 2006). This Atlantic slave trade has had very large effects on West Africa at several levels, but the full and exact nature of these effects is still being debated. While many analyses conclude that the slave trade must have depopulated large areas (because of both the numbers of people captured and the general disruptions to society, especially in the southern part of the savanna zone), some scholars suggest that coastal areas experienced a population increase (Oliver, 1991).

Fig. 5.4: Village and urban life in West Africa today. Above, a village in southern Guinea; below, Siaka Stevens Street, Freetown, Sierra Leone (photos by J. F. Oates).

As efforts to halt the Atlantic slave trade started to take effect in the early 19th century, European explorers and traders began to move inland from the coast. This expanded activity became more successful after the introduction of quinine to suppress malaria around 1850 (Webster and Boahen, 1967). In southern Nigeria in particular, the trade in palm-oil grew rapidly, replacing that in slaves. With military expeditions, the making of commercial and political treaties, and missionary activity, the "Scramble for Africa" had begun (Pakenham, 1991). Indigenous kingdoms that still existed were defeated or their influence diminished, and at the Berlin Conference of 1884-85 European powers agreed to formally recognize the areas of influence of each of their nations in Africa on the basis of whether they had established political administrations. However, actual territorial boundaries were not fully settled until about 1900. Through this process of partition, France and Britain became the main colonial administrators in West Africa, but Germany took control of Togo and Cameroon, Portugal retained a small colony in Guinea, and Spain retained its toehold on Bioko (then called Fernando Po, part of Spanish Equatorial Guinea).

Liberia was an exception to this pattern. As a nation it has its roots in an endeavour to settle former slaves and other free black Americans on the coast of Africa, following the British model of Freetown in Sierra Leone. The first settlement was founded in 1821, the colonies were christened "Liberia" in 1824, and in 1847 the several coastal settlements declared themselves the independent Republic of Liberia (Johnston, 1906); through the rest of the 19th century this state expanded its territory inland and along the coast.

The arrangement of West African territorial borders established by the beginning of the 20th century as a result of European colonial activities is essentially what survives to the present day, with only small changes. After the defeat of Germany in World War I, Togo and Cameroon were each divided into two Trust Territories, one under French and one under British control, with the administrating powers accountable to the League of Nations. That part of Togo administered by Britain after World War I is now integrated into Ghana, and the northern part of formerly British-administered Cameroon is now integrated with Nigeria.

The colonial era brought major changes to most of West Africa, but especially to the coastal regions where European administration and commerce were based. Towns and cities grew, and roads, railways and ports were built; new agricultural crops were introduced, along with plantation-style cultivation (for instance, of rubber, oil palm, cocoa and bananas); mines were developed, and logging activities became more systematic. All of these "development" activities, along with a growing human population, inevitably led to increased pressures on natural resources. Not all areas developed to the same degree or in the same fashion, however. The nature of the political regime in each territory influenced the languages and practices of government, education and business and these in turn had influences on patterns of resource exploitation and conservation policy.

From the beginning of the colonial era there was, of course, resentment of foreign rule by many of the peoples of Africa (as there had also been in Asia). Pressures from Africans for freedom from colonial regimes grew after World War II, and the European powers themselves had been weakened by the conflict. The freedom movement, which found strong support in the United States, culminated in the independence of British-ruled Gold Coast as the new nation of Ghana in 1957. By the end of 1961, most of the countries of West Africa had their independence. The Gambia followed in 1965, Equatorial Guinea in 1968 and (following an armed conflict) Portuguese Guinea in 1974. The main period of European colonial rule over much of West Africa had therefore lasted less than 100 years.

6

CONSERVATION: THREATS TO PRIMATE SURVIVAL, AND STRATEGIES FOR PROTECTION

Since the ending of colonial rule over most of West Africa in the 1960s there have been major political changes and considerable further economic development. However, armed conflicts in several of the countries in the region, especially in the coastal forest zone, have sometimes seriously disrupted development and the rule of law. In spite of those disruptions, the human population of West Africa has continued to grow rapidly, so that the same United Nations database that estimates the current population of the region at about 315 million people gives an estimate of only 86 million people in 1960 (United Nations Secretariat, 2008), suggesting an increase of more than 250% over 50 years.

An increase in local population, coupled with economic development that has led to an expansion of road networks and an increase in demand for land, water and other material resources, has resulted in hugely increased pressures on the wildlands of West Africa and their fauna. These pressures have been accentuated by greatly rising demands from the world beyond West Africa for products such as oil, minerals, timber, cocoa, bananas and other commercial crops.

Forests: Destruction and Protection

It is the primates of the coastal moist forests that have suffered most from the rising pressures on the West African environment. The savanna-zone primates are in general widespread, ecologically flexible species that often tolerate quite large disruptions to their habitat; indeed, in some places they are regarded as agricultural pests. By contrast, natural selection tends to operate in tropical rain-forest ecosystems to produce ecological specialists that have relatively narrow niches, while the impact of Pleistocene glacial cycles has led to the evolution of forest primate species and subspecies that have restricted geographic distributions. Primates with small geographical ranges and narrow habitat requirements are inevitably very vulnerable to the conversion of their habitat. As high, closed-canopy moist forest has been progressively lost from West Africa, almost all forest primate

Fig. 6.1: A stream in the rainforest of Korup National Park, Cameroon (photo by J. F. Oates).

species have seen declines in their abundance and in the area over which they occur.

A striking and well-documented case of forest loss in West Africa is that of Côte d'Ivoire. Myers (1980) notes that, judging from climate patterns, moist forest probably once covered about 150,000 km² of the country, about half of its land area. A careful survey in 1966 found that just under 90,000 km² of relatively undisturbed forest remained, along with 57,000 km² of secondary and severely degraded forest; by 1974, the figures were 54,000 km² of undisturbed forest and 32,000 km² of secondary forest. An all-weather road system expanded rapidly after Côte d'Ivoire's independence in 1960 and this led to a great increase in the extent and rate of logging, which in turn led to the spread of farming in the harvested forest by subsistence cultivators. A very similar pattern of forest conversion was followed in Ghana and Nigeria.

Since 1980, forest loss has continued in West Africa, although the rate of loss is slowing as remaining intact forest becomes more and more restricted to areas managed by government for forestry and conservation purposes. The Food and Agriculture Organization of the United Nations has estimated that total forest land in the 11 West African coastal states of Bénin, Côte d'Ivoire, The Gambia, Ghana, Guinea, Guinea-Bissau, Liberia, Nigeria, Senegal, Sierra Leone and

Togo declined in extent from 688,110 km² in 1990 to 538,060 km² in 2010, with the greatest loss, in terms of both total and percentage area, occurring in Nigeria (FAO, 2005). All West African countries have forest management policies, and categories of land that are set aside for the safeguarding of forests whose main designated purpose is timber production (and sometimes watershed protection). These are called Forest Reserves in former British-administered countries, Forêts

Fig. 6.2: Rain forest cleared to plant oil palms, Okomu, Nigeria (above), and logs felled in the Gbanraun area, Niger Delta, waiting to be towed in rafts to a saw mill (photos by J. F. Oates).

Classées in francophone countries, and National Forests in Liberia. In many places these production forest areas have not been successful in maintaining an ecosystem that can sustainably produce timber; many of their forests have been heavily degraded by intensive logging, fire and/ or the incursion of farmers and cattle-herders; some have been entirely converted to farmland or plantations. Forest has generally survived best where it is contained in an area established mainly or totally to protect a natural ecosystem, for example a National Park, Strict Nature Reserve or Wildlife Sanctuary.

The first important protected area in the forest zone of West Africa was the strict nature reserve established at Mt. Nimba in Côte d'Ivoire and Guinea in 1943–44; the reserve initially covered 171 km² and was later extended. The main period of forest national park creation in West Africa was between 1972 and 1990, beginning at a time when there was growing concern for the future of Africa's rain forests because of the intensification of destructive forces (Struhsaker, 1972). Taï National Park (3,300 km²) was established in Côte d'Ivoire in 1972, followed by Bia (305 km²) and Nini-Suhien (166 km²) in Ghana in 1974 and 1976, respectively; unfortunately, Bia was reduced in size to 77 km² in 1976 and the rest of the park was opened to loggers. Sapo National Park (1,804 km²) was created in Liberia in 1983, Korup (1,260 km²) in Cameroon in 1986, and Cross River (around 4,000 km², in two disjunct sections) in Nigeria in 1990. These important parks, together with several others created since 1990 and some small wildlife sanctuaries, have generally held back logging and farming, but they have not had great success in deterring hunting. Furthermore, they comprise a set of highly dispersed fragments, most of which are not connected to other strictly protected areas (see Fig. 6.7, p.70); they are at risk of losing species over the long term because of the vulnerability of small populations of organisms to extinction through local catastrophes, disease epidemics, inbreeding and climate change. Bioko Island, with a total area of 2,017 km² (smaller than some of the region's national parks) has retained a fauna of 11 forest primates since it was cut off from the mainland by sea-level rise at the end of the last glaciation. However, no mammals larger than a drill or duiker are now present on Bioko. Chimpanzees have not been recorded from the island since it was first explored zoologically in the 19th century; they are present on the adjacent mainland and therefore might have gone extinct on the island at some point since its isolation; forest buffalo were once present on Bioko and apparently went extinct around 1900, probably from overhunting (Basilio, 1962; Hearn *et al.*, 2006).

Hunting

The forest-zone primates of West Africa have been badly impacted not only by the loss and fragmentation of their habitat, but also by human hunting for their meat. Hunting has had an even more devastating impact on forest primates than habitat conversion. Some quite large tracts of lowland moist forest still survive in West African protected areas, but in many of these very few monkeys or other wild mammals have been detected in the course of surveys (McGraw, 1998a; Oates, 1999); this is the "empty forest" syndrome, as described for parts of Amazonia by Redford (1992).

Wild game has long had an important place in the diet of people living in the forest regions of West and Central Africa, where large-scale livestock-rearing is not generally practicable; in anglophone West Africa, this meat is usually called "bushmeat." Although many of the people inhabiting the savanna and semi-desert regions of West Africa are Muslims who traditionally avoid consuming primate meat (although this tradition is dwindling in some areas), the people of the coastal forest regions of West Africa tend to be predominantly Christian and in this region few taboos surround the eating of primates (with the exception, in places, of great apes).

Fig. 6.3: Bushmeat. Red-eared monkeys (*Cercopithecus erythrotis erythrotis*) and Preuss's monkeys (*Allochrocebus preussi insularis*) in the Malabo market, Bioko, Equatorial Guinea (photo by J. F. Oates).

When forests covered large areas of coastal West Africa, human populations were much smaller than today, and efficient firearms were not widely available, most forest primate populations were probably not badly affected by human hunting, which would have been conducted mostly for subsistence. In the last 100 years the balance has tilted strongly against the non-human primates. The larger species that are most dependent on high, closed-canopy forest, such as colobus and Diana monkeys, have found their habitats reduced to relatively small patches, while hunting pressure on them has increased. There are many more people, there are more effective transport and trading networks, ammunition and locally-made shotguns often can be readily obtained, and there are very large numbers of people in towns and cities prepared to pay for the meat of monkeys and other wildlife. In Liberia, Côte d'Ivoire, Ghana, Nigeria and Cameroon especially, these factors have led to great increases since World War II in the amount of hunting directed at forest primates to supply a commercial bushmeat trade.

Fig. 6.4: (Left) Hunter with a female *Cercopithecus erythrogaster pococki* in Okomu National Park, Nigeria (photo by J. F. Oates). (Right) Boy selling a carcass of an eastern spot-nosed monkey (*Cercopithecus petaurista petaurista*), Ghana (photo by R. A. Mittermeier).

How hunted meat reaches an ultimate consumer in West Africa is quite complicated, and varies considerably from place to place. The simplest situation involves a farmer with traps on his land, or a gun, taking carcasses home, where they are either consumed by his household, sold to someone else in the community, or—where his village is on a road—marketed as fresh meat at the roadside by his family. Where, within easy reach of a village, a significant commercial bushmeat market exists (either as an actual market, or in the form of restaurants), then a farmer-hunter or commercial hunter may travel with his kill to that market with fresh carcasses, or he may use an intermediary to sell the carcasses for him. The first pattern is found with hunters supplying chop-bars in Takoradi, Ghana (Cowlishaw *et al.*, 2005), and the second pattern on Bioko, where hunters use taxi drivers to carry their bushmeat for them to the one major bushmeat market in the island's capital, Malabo (Fa, 2000). Hunting in West Africa is a male occupation. A small proportion of commercial hunters work at this trade full-time, but most hunters have other occupations such as farming or mining. Traders in bushmeat, on the other hand, tend to be almost exclusively women (Anadu *et al.*, 1988; Fa, 2000).

When a hunting site is far from a road, market or town, West African hunters typically establish a camp inside the bush and stay there for days, butchering and smoking their kill at camp, then carrying a consolidated load of smoked meat out of the forest, from where they either carry it to market themselves, or sell it to middlemen. Such smoked meat may enter long transport chains, and has increasingly been turning up in Europe and North America; for instance, a study in 2008 by Chaber *et al.* (2010) has estimated that 270 tonnes of African bushmeat were passing each year through Charles de Gaulle Airport in Paris.

Bushmeat arriving in Europe is only the tip of a very large iceberg, however. In the late 1970s the amount of bushmeat eaten annually in Nigeria was estimated at 188.7–314.9 million kg (or 188,700–314,900 metric tonnes) (Martin, 1983); in Bioko in 1990–1991 it was estimated that 112 tonnes of bushmeat were being marketed annually, at a time when the human population of the island was 62,000 (Fa *et al.*, 1995; Fa, 2000); 100,000 tonnes of wild meat was estimated to enter markets in Côte d'Ivoire in 1996 (H.-U. Caspary and J. Momo, 1998, cited in Refisch and Koné, 2005a); in the Ghanaian coastal city of Takoradi, the estimated monthly volume of bushmeat sales by market traders and chopbars in 2000 was 15,859 kg (equivalent to 190 tonnes annually) (Cowlishaw *et al.*, 2005); and in the region between the Cross River in

Fig. 6.5: Olive colobus (*Procolobus verus*) and hornbills on sale by the roadside, Konobo District, Grand Gedeh, Liberia (photo by J. F. Oates).

Nigeria and the Sanaga River in Cameroon, Fa *et al.* (2006) estimated that 12,221 tonnes of terrestrial vertebrates were traded annually in 2002–2003, including 11,702 tonnes of undressed meat.

The impact of commercial hunting on forest wildlife, including primates, initially raised concerns in Ghana (Booth, 1956; Jeffrey, 1970), but by the mid-1980s these concerns had become widespread in West Africa (e.g., Ajayi, 1971 [commenting on Nigeria]; Robinson, 1971 [Liberia and Sierra Leone]; Verschuren, 1982 [Liberia]; Martin, 1983 [Nigeria]). This was some years before the "African Bushmeat Crisis" came to general public attention in Europe and America in the 1990s, when logging activity was intensifying in Central Africa and photographic documentation of the consumption of great apes gained wide publicity (Pearce and Ammann, 1995; Bowen-Jones and Pendry, 1999). By the 1990s, Miss Waldron's red colobus, unknown to science until 1933, was probably already extinct in Ghana as a result of many years of overhunting (Oates *et al.*, 1997, 2000a).

The forest primates most badly impacted by hunting are species such as red colobus that are relatively large, that predominantly use the upper part of the forest canopy, and that typically live in large social groups; such species are the most profitable for hunters to target and are the most easily detected and shot. Even when particular species get reduced to very small numbers, they will still be hunted because of the opportunistic nature of forest hunting in West Africa. A hunter typically moves quietly and alone along established pathways in the forest and shoots at what he encounters, depending on the size and visibility of the quarry. In this way, vulnerable species may become completely extirpated. Another technique used to hunt drills in the forests of Cameroon and Nigeria involves the use of a small pack of dogs; on locating a group of drills, the dogs drive them into trees, where many can be readily picked off by the hunter's gun (Gartlan, 1975); this technique obviously has the potential to devastate populations.

The Most Threatened Primates

The first really systematic and comprehensive analysis of the threats facing all African primates, both species and subspecies, took place as part of the IUCN Global Mammal Assessment of 2003–2008 (Schipper *et al.*, 2008). This formed the basis of the threat ratings that were incorporated into the IUCN Red List for 2008; the IUCN threat ratings for African primates have not been revised since then.

Table 6.1 shows how the Red List rates the status of West African primates, adjusted to the taxonomy employed in this field guide. Of the 42 species regarded here as inhabiting West Africa, four are Critically Endangered, six are Endangered, and eight are Vulnerable; all these threatened species (43% of the total) are forest dwellers.

The West African primates that are rated as Critically Endangered in the Red List are three forms of red colobus monkey (treated in this book as *Procolobus waldroni*, *P. preussi* and *P. epieni*) and the Cross River gorilla. *Procolobus waldroni* (Miss Waldron's red colobus monkey) is probably now extinct. The roloway monkey (*Cercopithecus diana roloway*) is rated as Endangered in the Red List, but at the time of writing it had been confirmed to survive in only one location, the Tanoé Forest in south-eastern Côte d'Ivoire, a site without formal protected status; this monkey must be considered as Critically Endangered.

Table 6.1. Conservation Status of West African Primates in the 2008 IUCN Red List.

LC = Least Concern; NT = Near Threatened; VU = Vulnerable; EN = Endangered; CR = Critically Endangered; na = not assessed due to the use of a different taxonomy.

SPECIES	STATUS	SUBSPECIES	STATUS
Galagoides demidovii	LC		
Galagoides thomasi	LC		
Galago senegalensis	LC	*G. s. senegalensis*	LC
Euoticus pallidus	LC	*E. p. pallidus*	EN
	LC	*E. p. talboti*	LC
Sciurocheirus alleni	LC	*S. a. alleni*	EN
		S. a. cameronensis	LC
Arctocebus calabarensis	LC		
Perodicticus potto	LC*	*P. p. potto*	LC**
		P. p. juju	LC**
Perodicticus edwardsi	LC*		
Cercocebus atys	NT*		
Cercocebus lunulatus	EN*		
Cercocebus torquatus	VU		
Mandrillus leucophaeus	EN	*M. l. leucophaeus*	EN
		M. l. poensis	EN
Lophocebus albigena	LC		
Papio papio	NT		
Papio anubis	LC		
Miopithecus ogouensis	LC		
Erythrocebus patas	LC		
Chlorocebus aethiops	na	*C. a. sabaeus*	LC†
		C. a. tantalus	LC†
Allochrocebus preussi	EN	*A. p. preussi*	EN
		A. p. insularis	EN

SPECIES	STATUS	SUBSPECIES	STATUS
Cercopithecus diana	VU	*C. d. diana*	VU
		C. d. roloway	EN
Cercopithecus neglectus	LC		
Cercopithecus campbelli	LC	*C. c. campbelli*	LC
		C. c. lowei	LC
Cercopithecus mona	LC		
Cercopithecus pogonias		*C. p. pogonias*	VU**
		C. pogonias (mainland)	VU**
Cercopithecus petaurista	LC	*C. p. petaurista*	LC
		C. p. buettikoferi	LC
Cercopithecus erythrogaster	VU	*C. e. erythrogaster*	EN
		C. e. pococki	VU
Cercopithecus sclateri	VU		
Cercopithecus erythrotis	VU	*C. e. erythrotis*	VU
		C. e. camerunensis	VU
Cercopithecus cephus	LC	*C. c. cephus*	LC
Cercopithecus nictitans	LC	*C. n. stampflii*	VU**
		C. n. insolitus	VU**
		C. n. ludio	VU**
		C. n. martini	VU**
		C. n. nictitans	LC
Procolobus verus	NT		
Procolobus badius	EN	*P. b. temminckii*	EN
		P. b. badius	EN
Procolobus waldroni	CR§		
Procolobus preussi	CR*		
Procolobus epieni	CR*		
Procolobus pennantii	EN*		
Colobus polykomos	VU		
Colobus vellerosus	VU		

SPECIES	STATUS	SUBSPECIES	STATUS
Colobus guereza	LC	*C. g. occidentalis*	LC
Colobus satanas		*C. s. satanas*	EN
Gorilla gorilla	CR	*G. g. diehli*	CR
Pan troglodytes	EN	*P. t. verus*	EN
		P. t. ellioti	EN

*   Regarded as a subspecies on the Red List
†   Treated as a full species on the Red List
**   Combined as a single subspecies on the Red List
§   Treated as a subspecies of *P. badius* on the Red List; probably extinct

Each of the distinct regional primate communities in the moist forest zone (see section 4) contains five or more threatened primates. Every one of the subspecies endemic to Bioko, including the two larger galago species, is regarded as threatened by IUCN because of the small size of the island and the pressures of habitat loss and hunting.

The survival of all the Endangered and Critically Endangered monkeys and apes of West Africa has been put at risk not so much by habitat loss, although that has been a factor in their decline, but by hunting, and especially by hunting for trade. This point was stressed by Oates *et al.* (1990) in describing the probable extinction of Miss Waldron's colobus.

Conservation Action Plans

The Primate Specialist Group of the IUCN Species Survival Commission has produced a series of plans that provide recommendations on priorities for action if further declines in primate populations are to be minimized and extinctions averted. The first of these was the *Action Plan for African Primate Conservation: 1986-90* (Oates, 1986b); this was updated and re-issued in a second edition (Oates, 1996b). Plans dealing specifically with West African primates are *West African Chimpanzees: Status Survey and Conservation Action Plan* (Kormos *et al.*, 2003a), *Regional Action Plan for the Conservation of the Cross River Gorilla* (Oates *et al.*, 2007), and *Regional Action Plan for the Conservation of the Nigeria-Cameroon Chimpanzee* (Pan troglodytes ellioti) (Morgan *et al.*, 2011).

The original 1986 action plan noted that the Primate Specialist Group felt that the loss of primates in the face of increasing human impact could best be mitigated by: 1) Setting aside protected areas for endangered and vulnerable species; 2) creating large national parks and reserves in areas of high primate diversity and/or abundance; 3) maintaining and increasing the effectiveness of parks and reserves that already exist; and 4) creating and increasing public awareness of the need for primate conservation.

The plan defined a set of distinct regional primate communities in Africa and recommended that at least two reserves be supported or created in each special region, noting that it is forest primates that are under the most pressure. In West Africa, the plan identified several

Fig. 6.6: Action plans for African primates and the West African great apes produced by the IUCN/SSC Primate Specialist Group in collaboration with partner conservation organizations.

existing or planned parks as important in this context, as follows: 1) Taï, Côte d'Ivoire; 2) Sapo, Liberia; 3) Gola and Tiwai Island, Sierra Leone; 4) Ankasa/Nini-Souhien and Bia, Ghana; 5) Okomu, Nigeria; and 6) Korup, Cameroon.

Surveys to locate potential new protected areas were also recommended in: 1) The Republic of Guinea; 2) the Lofa-Mano area of western Liberia; 3) Eastern and central Côte d'Ivoire; 4) Ondo and Ogun States, Nigeria; 5) the area between the Niger and Cross rivers, Nigeria; 6) Oban Hills, Nigeria; 7) the region between Mamfe, Cameroon, and Obudu, Nigeria, including the Takamanda Forest Reserve; and 8) Bioko Island, Equatorial Guinea.

All of the parks that existed or were planned in 1986 have subsequently had investment in their development, although not always particularly for primate conservation. There have also been surveys in all the areas recommended for investigation for new reserves; several of these surveys had a specific focus on primates, and were stimulated by the publication of the action plan. Since 1986, new protected areas have been established in Guinea, in Oban and Okwangwo in Nigeria, at Takamanda in Cameroon, and on Bioko Island.

However, many of the new and formerly existing protected areas have not fulfilled their potential to safeguard primate populations. In a paper on the fate of Miss Waldron's red colobus, Oates *et al.* (2000) warned that what had happened to that monkey in the forests of eastern Côte d'Ivoire and western Ghana could be the first manifestation of an extinction spasm that would soon affect other large mammals in the region unless more rigorous protection was put in place. Unfortunately that warning was not significantly heeded. Hunting continued at a high level, especially in the forests of Ghana, so that recent surveys have not managed to locate any roloway monkeys in the Ankasa and Bia conservation areas. Although the roloway monkey is still known to survive at one site in Côte d'Ivoire, it may now have followed Miss Waldron's colobus to extinction in most of Ghana.

Parks, People and Conservation Policies

National parks and similar reserves were once widely regarded as the best means to protect nature from the ravages of humans. From the 1950s onwards, as the growing human pressures on wild nature in Africa became of concern to many conservationists, moves were made to expand the network of national parks on the continent, along the lines of the parks established to preserve wilderness areas in the United States, Australia and Canada in the latter part of the 19th century. The Virunga National Park was Africa's first national park, created in 1925 as the Albert National Park in the colonial Belgian Congo (now the Democratic Republic of Congo); the Kruger National Park in South Africa followed in 1926. Although several game reserves were established in West Africa before World War II, the first national parks in this region were not established until 1954, and these were in the savanna zone (W National Park in Niger and Niokolo Koba in Senegal). The first rain-forest national park in West Africa was not established until 1972, with the declaration of Taï National Park in Côte d'Ivoire.

In West Africa, however, national parks have often faced multiple challenges and many have proved ineffective in adequately protecting their fauna and flora. This is one of the most densely settled parts of the African continent, so that most parks could not be established in true wilderness areas in which long-resident people did not already hold rights to the land, where they traditionally farmed and hunted. Because wildlife conservation is not generally seen by the people of West Africa as a high personal or national priority, political will to support parks has tended to be low. Given the demands that governments have faced to assist national development, therefore, they have usually not devoted sufficient resources to properly protecting parks from the pressures to which they have inevitably been exposed, exacerbated particularly by the high rate of human population growth in the region. Periods of political instability in many countries in the region have sometimes led to a breakdown of law and order, during which park regulations have been largely unenforced, sometimes for years. Meanwhile, although national laws generally protected certain threatened animal species wherever they occurred, inside or outside parks, such laws have rarely been strongly enforced, and are generally ignored.

The extent to which the bushmeat trade has flourished in West Africa (and still relies to a significant extent on the activities of commercial hunters operating inside national parks), is testimony to the widespread lack of effectiveness of conservation that relies on state legislation and management. On the other hand, and in spite of these failings, West Africa's protected areas still usually retain more natural vegetation cover than other areas (and in the moist forest zone they have generally been spared from major farming and logging activities) and often still contain more wildlife. Several of West Africa's parks are the main strongholds or last refuges for many of the region's threatened large mammals.

Because of the challenges faced by national-park management in West Africa, many of the region's parks have received material support from foreign conservation organizations and from foreign-aid programs, given international concerns about wildlife and rain-forest conservation. This trend increased in the 1980s, and was influenced by the *World Conservation Strategy*, published by IUCN, UNEP and WWF (1980). Compared to the first wave of park establishment, which was driven largely by a concern to hold on to special pieces of nature before they were overwhelmed by human activity, the new policy enshrined in the World Conservation Strategy argued that nature conservation should be seen as a component of a process of sustainable development, with the establishment and management of protected areas being "one of the most important ways of ensuring that the world's natural resources are conserved so that they can better meet the material and cultural needs of mankind now and in the future" (MacKinnon *et al.*, 1986). I have argued elsewhere (1999) that this strategy was the result of a political compromise influenced by the perceived need to listen to powerful voices in less-developed countries arguing that development should not be held back by the concerns of environmentalists and conservationists.

In any event, from the late 1980s onwards, the establishment and management of national parks in West Africa, especially where these were supported by external funding, tended to de-emphasize efforts to control poaching (even though hunting pressures were rising) while including efforts to promote the economic development of people living in proximity to parks. Part of the theory behind this approach was that if people were assisted to live better material lives they would be less likely to illegally exploit resources in the parks. In time, this approach came to take on board the key United Nations Millennium Development Goal of eradicating poverty (United Nations General Assembly, 2000), leading many conservation projects to attempt to build poverty alleviation measures into their planning (Oates, 2006a). Although the goal of eradicating poverty is indisputably important, incorporating poverty alleviation into park management strategies has not generally been successful in West Africa in terms of bringing the hunting of endangered primates under better control.

Elsewhere (Oates, 1999, 2006a), I have argued that in the short term much more emphasis needs to be placed on the basic protection of the wildlife still surviving in the parks and other reserves of West Africa, places that are often some of the last refuges for many endangered species. On the other hand, only very large parks can provide adequate long-term protection for viable populations of species that live at low population densities and where individuals or social groups have large home ranges. Great apes have those characteristics, and yet only a small number of parks in the West African forest zone are sufficiently large to potentially sustain a viable ape population for a long time. This indicates the need for the proper enforcement of laws that protect such species wherever they occur, inside and outside national parks.

The better management of parks and a better general respect for wildlife laws are difficult to achieve without widespread public support. To gain such support, increased efforts will be needed to bring about change in attitudes at all levels of society, including efforts to inculcate an appreciation of wildlife and wild places for their intrinsic value, quite apart from their potential to contribute to material development. Such changes in attitude can be assisted by nurturing in young people the inherent interest they usually have in animals and plants. However, changes in societal attitudes rarely occur quickly. We can work steadily to bring about long-term change, but West Africa's most endangered primates require the most rigorous protection now if they are to survive and to be appreciated by future generations of people within the region and in the wider world. It is hoped that this book may in some small way promote greater interest in the region's primates, and encourage efforts to give them better protection.

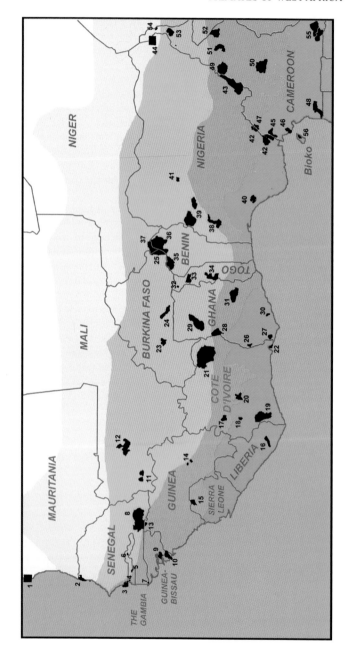

Fig. 6.7: National parks in West Africa, 2010 (map courtesy of R. A. Bergl and S. D. Nash).

Key:

1. Banc d' Arguin, Mauritania; 2. Diawling, Mauritania; 3. Delta du Saloum, Senegal; 4. Kiumi, The Gambia; 5. Kiang West, The Gambia; 6. River Gambia, The Gambia; 7. Basse Casamance, Senegal; 8. Niokolo Koba, Senegal; 9. Lagoas de Cufada, Guinea Bissau; 10. Cantanhez Forest, Guinea Bissau; 11. Kouroufing and Wongo, Mali; 12. Boucle du Baoulé, Mali; 13. Badiar, Guinea; 14. Haut Niger, Guinea; 15. Outamba Kilimi, Sierra Leone; 16. Sapo, Liberia; 17. Mont Sangbe, Côte d'Ivoire; 18. Mont Peko, Côte d'Ivoire; 19. Taï, Côte d'Ivoire; 20. Marahoué, Côte d'Ivoire; 21. Comoé, Côte d'Ivoire; 22. Iles Ehotile, Côte d'Ivoire; 23. Deux Bales, Burkina Faso; 24. Kabore Tambi, Burkina Faso; 25. W, Burkina Faso; 26. Ankasa/Bia, Ghana; 27. Ankasa/Nini Suhien, Ghana; 28. Bui, Ghana; 29. Mole, Ghana; 30. Kakum, Ghana; 31. Digya, Ghana; 32 Fosse aux Lions, Togo; 33. Kéran, Togo; 34. Fazao Malfakassa, Togo; 35. Pendjari, Bénin; 36. W, Bénin; 37. W, Niger; 38. Old Oyo, Nigeria; 39. Kainji, Nigeria; 40. Okomu Forest Reserve and National Park, Nigeria; 41. Kamuku, Nigeria; 42. Cross River, Nigeria; 43. Gashaka Gumti, Nigeria; 44. Chad Basin, Nigeria; 45. Korup, Cameroon; 46. Mount Cameroon, Cameroon; 47. Takamanda, Cameroon; 48. Campo Ma'an, Cameroon; 49. Faro, Cameroon; 50. Mbam & Djerem, Cameroon; 51. Bénoué, Cameroon; 52. Bouba Ndjida, Cameroon; 53. Waza, Cameroon; 54. Kalamaloué, Cameroon; 55. Boumba Bek, Cameroon; and 56. Pico de Basilé, Bioko Island, Equatorial Guinea.

▓ Lowland moist forest	▒ Sahelian acacia woodland
▒ Dry forest and forest-savanna mosaic	☐ Desert and semi-desert
▒ Sudanian savanna woodland	

Fig. 7.1: Simon K. Bearder carrying out surveys in Okomu National Park, Nigeria in 2009 (photo by J. F. Oates). During this survey, Bearder noticed that the vocalizations of tree hyraxes in Okomu were very different from those in eastern Nigeria, supporting the notion that there was once a Pleistocene forest refuge in this area (see p. 36).

7

IDENTIFYING AND STUDYING WEST AFRICAN PRIMATES

Arrangement of This Book

The next part of this book will provide descriptions of each West African primate, written as an aid to identifying them in the field, rather than as specimens in museums. Following a listing of biological and common names, each species or subspecies description is followed by information under a series of main headings: **Identification**, providing a description of the visual appearance of the primate including size, proportions and coloration, along with a sub-heading comparing the primate to *similar species* with which it might be confused; **Taxonomic Note**, describing any issues affecting the biological name of the primate; **Geographic Range**; **Natural History**; **Conservation Status**; and suggestions about where the primate may be most readily seen in the wild, **Where to See It**. These main headings (except for "Similar Species") broadly follow those used in other books in this series: *Lemurs of Madagascar* (First edition, Mittermeier *et al.*, 1994) and *Primates of Colombia* (Defler, 2004).

Unlike those other volumes, this book organizes quite extensive natural history information under a series of sub-headings. The sub-headings vary slightly in the different accounts, depending on the amount of information available for or relevant to a particular taxon. For instance, *Association with other species* is provided for monkeys that are often seen moving with others, but not for the much more solitary nocturnal prosimians. Sometimes an adaptation or behavior that is characteristic of the species in question, but not found in other primates (such as the "infant parking" behavior of some of the prosimians), is given a special sub-heading. In all cases a section on *Field studies* describes the sources of information from which our knowledge of natural history has come. Illustrations by Stephen Nash of each species and subspecies are provided, as well as a photograph (if this is available) of each species. Maps show the geographical distribution of each taxon.

The species accounts are grouped under short accounts of the Suborders, Families, Subfamilies and Geospecies in which they are classed, as described in section 3.

Identifying Your Primate

By starting with a description of the external appearance of each primate, this book is written with the presumption that most of those who use it as a field guide will be trying to see wild prosimians, monkeys or apes. After seeing a wild primate with which you are unfamiliar and then trying to identify it, you will probably turn first to the illustrations to find out which looks most similar to the animal you have observed. If you find that one or more pictures resembles the animal you've seen, you can then check the written descriptions for "fit", as well as looking at the information on distribution and habitat to find out whether the primate you have seen is really likely to be in the place you saw it. If this doesn't lead you to a confident identification, study the material on similar species. In many forest situations, and especially where humans have been hunting primates and they are wary, you may hear primates calling but fail to get a really good view of them. In these cases, and also to provide supplementary confirmation of your original ID, it is a good idea to study the material on *Vocalizations* in the description of Natural History, along with the material on *Habitat use* and *Activity pattern*.

Finding and Observing Primates

Driving or walking around national parks or other reserves in the West African savanna zone, you will probably not have much trouble encountering wild primates, or at least one of the open-country monkey species. In some places you may also meet these monkeys outside reserves, including farms or plantations, around settlements and crossing roads. In all cases a good view of the animals' appearance and behavior will be greatly assisted by using a pair of binoculars.

Observing primates can be much more challenging in West African forests, not just because of the thick vegetation, but also because relentless hunting for bushmeat has made many of the primates (except for the small nocturnal species) very wary of people. An excellent account, in French, of how to go about finding monkeys in an African forest is given in the book *Histoire Naturelle des Primates d'Afrique Centrale* by Gautier-Hion *et al.* (1999, pp.18–19) that complements this volume. Unless you are already experienced, and familiar with a particular forest, it is usually best to recruit a guide, preferably a hunter, from a nearby village to lead you into the forest along existing paths; as Gautier-Hion *et al.* advise, tell the hunter to leave his gun at home.

Try to walk slowly and quietly, stopping frequently, and listening—as Gautier-Hion *et al.* say, hearing is often the best way to initially "see" forest primates. Listen not only for calls, but for the sounds of leaves and branches moving as monkeys run and jump; a characteristic noise in the African forest is the sound of vegetation brushing or crashing against other vegetation as a monkey leaps from one tree crown to another. Be very still when you hear these sounds and try to get a glimpse of an animal, then focus your binoculars on the spot where you've seen it. You can try creeping closer, but if the animals are very shy they may well detect you and either hide or escape. The best times to encounter forest monkeys are in the early morning and late afternoon, when they tend to be most active.

To detect the small nocturnal prosimians (the galagos and pottos) you need to go out at night, again with a local guide (especially if you are unfamiliar with the area), and to use a battery-powered headlamp (a variety of useful models are made by the *Petzl* company). The prosimians have a reflective tapetum behind their retina; if one of them is caught in the beam of your lamp you should easily see the bright orange reflections from their eyes. Using a handheld torch (flashlight) is less effective because a reflection will not come back directly to your

Fig. 7.2: Eyeshine of Thomas's galagos (*Galagoides thomasi*), Okomu National Park, Nigeria (photo by A. P. Leventis).

eyes unless you hold the torch by your head. The best way to get a better look at the animal and attempt an identification is to keep it in the beam of your lamp (or that of a companion), and focus binoculars on it.

It hardly needs saying that making careful notes of your observations (size, color, length of any tail, position of the animal in relation to the ground, patterns of movement, social behaviors, and calls) can help to confirm your identifications after you get back from the field, as well as being a potentially useful scientific record. Modern Global Positioning System (GPS) units can be quite inexpensive, and some models now work quite well under a forest canopy; co-ordinates from a GPS add to the scientific value of observations.

History of Primate Studies in West Africa

Careful, systematic observation of wild primates has provided the information on natural history given in the next section. One of the earliest attempts at the scientific study of any wild primates was made in West Africa in 1930, when Henry W. Nissen of the Laboratories of Primate Biology at Yale University visited Guinea to collect observations on chimpanzees, under the direction of Robert M. Yerkes. Nissen spent nine weeks in the field—very short by the standards of a modern field study —and his fragmentary observations were able to provide only a very incomplete picture of the behavior of wild chimpanzees (Nissen, 1931; Peterson, 2006); but in terms of West African field primatology, Nissen was a pioneer. It was another member of the Yerkes Laboratories, Clarence Ray Carpenter, who was to conduct the first really long-term observational study of wild primates, on the howler monkeys of Barro Colorado Island, Panama; Carpenter's first study began on Christmas Day 1931, and continued until May 26 1932 (Carpenter, 1965). Carpenter is widely regarded as having established the ground rules for field primatology, attempting to disturb his study animals as little as possible, while carefully gathering repeated

Fig. 7.3: Henry W. Nissen (1901-1958), who carried out pioneering fieldwork on chimpanzees in Guinea in 1930.

observations. This process is greatly aided by the "habituation" of the primates being studied where, as a result of being approached in a quiet, nonthreatening manner, they become accustomed to the close presence of an observer, so that behavior observed can be regarded as having been minimally affected by human presence (Schaller, 1963).

After Nissen's pioneering work, few scientific observations of West African primates were made until the 1950s, when Angus H. Booth travelled widely from his base at the University College of the Gold Coast (now the University of Ghana), collecting vertebrates in Ghana and neighboring Côte d'Ivoire. Booth had a special interest in primates and, although his main interest was collecting specimens and documenting distribution patterns, he also made extensive notes on the natural history of the animals he encountered. This allowed Booth to publish the first account, after Nissen's, of the natural history of a West African primate, the olive colobus monkey (Booth, 1957). Unfortunately, Booth died in mysterious circumstances in Ghana in 1958, not long after his olive colobus account was published (Oates, 1999); in his short professional life he had, however, laid important foundations for the understanding of West African primate zoogeography.

The "modern age" of African field primatology began in 1958–1960 when K. R. L. Hall, Sherwood Washburn and Irven DeVore began a series of baboon studies in southern and eastern Africa (DeVore and Hall, 1965), George Schaller began studies of the mountain gorillas in the Virunga Volcanoes (Schaller, 1963), and Jane Goodall commenced her work on the chimpanzees of Gombe (Goodall, 1963, 1965). In West Africa, Adriaan Kortlandt followed Nissen's footsteps to Guinea in 1960, making short-term observations of unhabituated chimpanzees. In 1964, I made my first visit to West Africa, watching galagos in the mountains of Bioko in the course of an undergraduate expedition, and nurturing my subsequent fascination with the region and its primates. Following a second visit to Equatorial Guinea in 1965, I was able to make more systematic observations of prosimians in the forests of eastern Nigeria in 1966–1967 (Jewell and Oates, 1969b; Oates, 1999). Around the same time, in late 1966, Tom Struhsaker began 17 months of observations on the forest monkeys of western Cameroon, where he was joined by Steve Gartlan in 1967 (Struhsaker, 1969; Gartlan, 1970; Gartlan and Struhsaker, 1972).

None of the early studies in West Africa involved observations on habituated animals, however. This region has proved more challenging for primatologists than eastern and southern Africa. Because West Africa has such a dense human population and because primate meat has long been an accepted part of the diet of people living in the forest zone, wild primates are wary and difficult to habituate in most places: in the savanna zone because they are often harassed as farm pests, and in the forest zone because they are hunted. Only in a few places, where there are effective protected areas, or where for some reason primates are rarely harmed by people, has it proved possible to habituate (or semi-habituate) primates and study them for prolonged periods. In 1975–1976, studies of that kind were initiated at four West African sites: Bia National Park in Ghana, Bossou in Guinea, Niokolo Koba National Park in Senegal, and Taï National Park in Côte d'Ivoire.

The first of these studies to be launched was in 1975 at Bia, which had been declared a national park in the previous year. A team from the University of California, Berkeley, supported locally by the

Fig. 7.4: Anh Galat-Luong and the author at Taï Forest in 1979 (photo by G. Galat).

Ghana Department of Game and Wildlife, collected observations on colobus and roloway monkeys through 1977, and these observations were continued into 1978 by Claude Martin, the senior park warden at Bia (Olson, 1986; Martin, 1991; Curtin, 2002). Unfortunately a large part of Bia National Park was de-gazetted in 1977 and opened for logging, and around this time the once-prosperous Ghanaian economy was collapsing (Oates, 1999). Bia became neglected and hunting was little controlled; by the time new surveys were conducted in 1993, no evidence of any red colobus or roloway monkeys surviving in the park could be found (Struhsaker and Oates, 1995).

In 1976, Yukimaru Sugiyama began the habituation of a small community of chimpanzees that were using forest, savanna and cultivated land around Bossou village in Guinea (Sugiyama and Koman, 1979), and studies of that community have continued to the present day (Hockings *et al.*, 2009). Also in 1976, a team from the University of Stirling began research at Niokolo Koba on chimpanzees (which became partially habituated) (McGrew *et al.*, 1978; Tutin *et al.*, 1983). Dunbar and Nathan (1972) carried out a short study of baboons at this site in 1969, followed by researchers from the University of St. Andrews (Byrne, 1981; Sharman, 1981).

Following early pilot studies in the Taï Forest, habituation of monkeys by Anh Galat-Luong and Gérard Galat commenced in 1978 (Galat and Galat-Luong 1985) and of chimpanzee by Christophe Boesch in 1979 (Boesch and Boesch, 1989). These studies evolved into the Taï Monkey Project and the Taï Chimpanzee Project, both of which continue today and have yielded a wealth of information (see, for example, Boesch and Boesch-Achermann, 2000; McGraw *et al.*, 2007).

After some months attempting to study baboons at Niokolo Koba, Dawn Starin of the City University of New York began a study of red colobus monkeys in the Abuko Nature Reserve in The Gambia in early 1978. Starin followed a particular social group from dawn until dusk and recorded information on activity patterns, diet, ranging and social behavior using methods that had become standardized by field workers in Africa over the previous decade (Clutton-Brock, 1974; Altmann, 1974; Struhsaker, 1975; Starin, 1991). In 1982, habituation of a similar primate community to that of Taï began at Tiwai Island in Sierra Leone (Oates and Whitesides, 1990). In 2000, a long-term study of black-and-white colobus monkeys began at the Boabeng-Fiema Monkey Sanctuary in Ghana, where the monkeys are protected from

Fig. 7.5: Researchers Maikanti Hassan and Emily Lodge studying baboons, Gashaka Gumti National Park, Nigeria (photo by R. A. Lodge).

hunting by traditional taboos and can therefore be readily observed (Teichroeb *et al.*, 2003; Saj *et al.*, 2006). Also in 2000, attempts began to study chimpanzees at Gashaka Gumti National Park (6,700 km²) in Nigeria (Sommer *et al.*, 2004). Although it has not yet been possible to habituate chimpanzees at this site, olive baboons have been habituated and studied (Warren, 2003), and guenon calling behavior has also been investigated (Arnold and Zuberbühler, 2006).

Beyond those I have listed above, few other sites in West Africa have proved amenable for traditional primate field studies involving the persistent following of habituated animals. Instead, and especially in the forest zone, much of the information we have on primate natural history has been gleaned from fleeting encounters with unhabituated animals, often made in the course of survey projects. This contrasts rather strongly with the situation in East Africa, where primates have been habituated at many sites. Regrettably, several West African primates are now threatened with extinction, before their biology has been well investigated.

A Note on Common Names

The descriptions of each primate in this guide are preceded by their common and scientific names. The first common name given is an English name; I have used the names given by Grubb *et al.* (2003) as a primary guide, but I have also consulted the paper by Grubb (2006a), in which he provided an exhaustive list of the English common names given to every species and subspecies of African primate, and noted which of these names he preferred. For the primary common names used in this guide, I have sometimes chosen the simplest version of a name from Grubb's list, rather than his preferred name. Therefore, for example, I have chosen "Senegal bushbaby" rather than "Senegal lesser galago" and "angwantibo" to "Calabar angwantibo." Several of the alternative names listed by Grubb (2006a) are listed under *Other English* names.

For names in other non-African languages I have listed French, Spanish and Portuguese names, the other official languages of West African nations. A French common name is given for every taxon, because French is very widely used in West Africa and a majority of taxa occur in at least one francophone country; for these French names I have mostly referred to Dorst and Dandelot (1970) and Gautier-Hion *et al.* (1999). Spanish and Portuguese names are given only for those

Fig. 7.6: Michael Abedi-Lartey searching for primates in the Ankasa Conservation Area, southwest Ghana, 2006 (photo by J. F. Oates).

taxa occurring in Spanish-speaking Bioko and Portuguese-speaking Guinea-Bissau. For Spanish names I have referred to the website of the Bioko Biodiversity Protection Program (<www.bioko.org>) and to Basilio (1962); Portuguese names are primarily from Frade and Silva (1980).

It would be impossible to list all the indigenous names for different primates in West Africa given that this region has well over 1,000 languages and that only in some of these languages have animal names been well-documented. I have chosen only a selection of indigenous names, which tend to be those in languages used by large numbers of people, or those used at a site of special importance for primate observation or conservation. For these names I have used information (a) garnered during my own travels in West Africa; (b) generously provided to me as personal communications by M. Abedi-Lartey [Liberia, Ghana], A. Bitty and W. S. McGraw [Côte d'Ivoire], G. Campbell [Bénin and Togo], P. A. Anadu, L. R. Baker and K. Williamson [Nigeria], J. M. Linder, F. Maisels, B. Morgan and J. Sunderland-Groves [Cameroon]; and (c) found in publications and reports by Gatinot (1974 [Senegal]), Monard (1938 [Guinea-Bissau]), Waitkuwait (2001 [Liberia]), Tahiri-Zagrët (1976 [Côte d'Ivoire]), and Dunn (1999 [Nigeria]).

Maps in this Guide

The maps of geographic range for each taxon described in this book follow the format of many field guides. They portray what might be called a generalized historic range: the area over which a species or subspecies was most likely distributed before humans strongly modified its natural habitat, or eliminated it from part or most of its range by hunting. From knowledge of a primate's habitat preference, and from distribution records culled from the literature, from museum specimens and from my own observations, it is possible to get a reasonably good idea of the general area over which this primate was spread in the past. For most West African primates there have not been adequately fine-grained and comprehensive surveys to allow accurate maps to be drawn of present distribution; in most cases attempts to draw such maps would probably be misleading, so I have avoided doing that.

The maps used here are similar, but not identical to, those in the IUCN Red List, which are themselves based on the results of the Global Mammal Assessment (GMA) that was completed in 2008; I began a project to map the distribution of West African forest monkeys in 1980 and contributed data from that project to the GMA (Oates, 1981).

In a few cases, a distribution other than an historic range is shown, or that presumed range is shown along with a more recent range. For the Critically Endangered Miss Waldron's red colobus (probably now extinct) and the Endangered roloway monkey (a taxon that clearly deserves Critically Endangered status), their last confirmed locality in the wild is shown, along with their presumed historic range. For the Critically Endangered Preuss's red colobus and Cross River gorilla of Cameroon and Nigeria, their approximate current range is shown; these two taxa probably had considerably wider ranges in the past, but the evidence on which to construct a former range is poor. For most of the primates of Bioko, their historic range probably encompassed most of that island, but the monkeys there have for long had much more restricted ranges; therefore, the approximate ranges of these monkeys in the mid-1980s are portrayed, as mapped by Butynski and Koster (1994).

Demidoff's Galago
Galagoides demidovii

Thomas's Galago
Galagoides thomasi

Senegal Bushbaby
Galago senegalensis
senegalensis

Fig. 8.1.

8

THE PRIMATES OF WEST AFRICA

FAMILY GALAGIDAE
Galagos or bushbabies

The galagos, or bushbabies, are small nocturnal primates with long bushy tails and large flexible ears that are found only in wooded habitats in sub-Saharan Africa. Their legs are considerably longer than their arms, and their long legs enable them to make powerful leaps. Together with the pottos of Africa, lorises of Asia, and lemurs of Madagascar they belong to the suborder Strepsirrhini, characterized by having soft, dense fur, and (used in grooming this fur) a comb-like arrangement of the lower front teeth and an elongated claw-like nail on the second toe. Another strepsirrhine feature is a prominent muzzle with naked skin around the nostrils, which have a narrow, curved shape. In their *A Handbook of Living Primates*, Napier and Napier (1967) placed all of the galagos in the single genus *Galago*, whereas Grubb *et al.* (2003) recognize five genera (*Galagoides*, *Galago*, *Euoticus*, *Sciurocheirus* and *Otolemur*) and 24 species, five of which occur in West Africa.

Galagoides A. Smith, 1833
Dwarf galagos

These are the smallest primates found on the mainland of Africa. Smith created the genus *Galagoides* in 1833 to separate both the dwarf and Senegal galagos from other species, based on their dentition, but since then the dwarf galagos have been moved back and forth in classifications between *Galagoides* and *Galago*. Schwarz (1931) lumped the dwarf galagos with most other species in *Galago*, leaving only the needle-clawed galagos in a separate genus, *Euoticus*. Hill (1953) revived *Galagoides* for the single species *G. demidovii*. Napier and Napier (1967) then downgraded *Galagoides* to a subgenus of *Galago*, but *Galagoides* was used by Dorst and Dandelot (1970), Hill and Meester (1971), and Kingdon (1997) for these tiny primates. Groves (2001) carried out his own character-analysis of all the galagos and on that basis decided that it was "unsafe" to recognize any genera beyond *Otolemur*, *Euoticus* and *Galago*.

While bearing in mind the reservations of Groves, Grubb *et al.* (2003) considered that a range of biological information justified

recognizing *Galagoides* as a genus, within which four groups of species
could be identified. Only one of these groups, the *G. demidovii* group,
occurs in the region covered by this book. The other three groups
(*orinus*, *zanzibaricus* and *granti*) are restricted to East Africa.

Galagoides demidovii and *G. thomasi* geospecies

Grubb *et al.* (2003) place two species, *G. demidovii* itself and *G.
thomasi*, in the *G. demidovii* group. Thomas's galago had originally
been named as a full species (*Galago thomasi*) by Elliot in 1907 from
specimens collected in the forests of the Congo-Uganda border region.
Although Hill (1953) regarded Thomas's galago as only a subspecies
of *G. demidovii*, he did note that it was the largest and most distinct
subspecies. Eventually, a thorough taxonomic review of the galagos was
made by Olson (1979), who highlighted the distinctiveness of Thomas's
galago, which he elevated to species rank in the genus *Galagoides*,
alongside *G. demidovii* (which he referred to as *G. minutus*) and *G.
zanzibaricus*. Subsequent classifications have retained *thomasi* as a
species and recognized its close affinity to *demidovii*. One important
feature uniting *G. demidovii* and *G. thomasi*, and separating them from
other species, is their use of a characteristic call, which has phrases
that increase in intensity and speed of repetition to a marked crescendo
(Bearder *et al.*, 1995); their close relationship is also supported by
the genetic analysis of Masters *et al.* (2007). Grubb (2006b) treats
G. demidovii and *G. thomasi* as two distinct geospecies; their ranges
broadly overlap across large areas of the African forest zone.

Local Representatives

When Todd Olson resurrected the species *G. thomasi* in 1979, this
galago was regarded as a species (or subspecies) restricted to eastern
Africa, except for a seemingly isolated population on Mount Oku
in the Cameroon Highlands (Eisentraut, 1973). It took some years
before it became generally appreciated, especially through the work of
Simon Bearder's research group, that *G. thomasi* also occurs widely in
western Africa (e.g., Bearder and Honess, 1992; Wickings *et al.*, 1998;
Ambrose, 1999). Prior to the 1990s, therefore, most observations
of dwarf galagos in the forests of western Africa were assumed to
be attributable to only one species, *Galagoides demidovii*, when in
fact these observations could have been of either *G. demidovii* or *G.
thomasi*. The author is one of the observers who failed to discriminate
between these two galago species in the wild (e.g., Jewell and Oates,

1969b), and the same mistake was made by Pierre Charles-Dominique during his classic studies of prosimian behavior at Makokou in Gabon (e.g., Charles-Dominique, 1977). Therefore, it is often impossible to know from most accounts of field studies in West Africa published before 1990 and referring to *G. demidovii* whether the author was observing *G. demidovii*, *G. thomasi*, or both species.

Although *Galagoides demidovii* and *G. thomasi* are now recognized to co-occur across much of the West African forest zone, subspecies within these species remain poorly defined. Hill (1953) recognizes three subspecies of *G. demidovii* in West Africa: *G. d. demidovii* from Senegal to the Niger River; *G. d. murinus* from the Niger to the Congo; and *G. d. poensis* on Bioko Island. However, given great variation among museum specimens both within and between different local regions, Grubb *et al.* (2003) consider that insufficient evidence is yet available to judge which geographical clusters of *G. demidovii* are validly regarded as belonging to different subspecies. Much further work is also needed to determine whether different subspecies (or even species) are usefully recognized among those small galagos now being referred to as *G. thomasi*. This book will therefore follow Grubb *et al.* (2003) in referring only to two species, *Galagoides demidovii* and *G. thomasi*, and will not recognize different subspecies in West Africa, pending further research.

Demidoff's galago
Galagoides demidovii (G. Fischer, 1808)

Other English: Demidoff's dwarf galago, Demidoff's dwarf bushbaby, Demidoff's bushbaby, Prince Demidoff's bushbaby
French: Galago de Demidoff
Spanish: Gálago de Demidoff, gálago enano
West African languages: G'neh (Bassa, Liberia); Eme (Yoruba, Nigeria); Akhekhe (Edo, Nigeria); Eboo (Bakossi, Cameroon) (The same names are almost certainly used for both *G. demidovii* and *G. thomasi.*)

Identification (see Fig. 8.1, p.84)

This very small nocturnal forest primate has a long tail that is not particularly bushy, a short, pointed, slightly upturned nose, large eyes (but not relatively as large as in other forest galagos), large ears, and a soft dense coat. The coloration of the coat of Demidoff's galago varies greatly across its range. The body's dorsal surfaces and the tail are typically brown (but vary in shade from gray-brown to reddish-brown to dark brown), while ventral surfaces are creamy-white or yellow, sometimes with a bright sulphury wash. There is an obvious white stripe along the bridge of the nose between the eyes. The tail is sometimes darker than the body.

Demidoff's galagos are typically found low down in dense undergrowth, where they move in a scuttling fashion on small supports. They are most often detected by their high-pitched rising crescendo call (but see the account for *Galagoides thomasi*), given at intervals throughout the night, and used to maintain contact between individuals; two animals are often heard exchanging the call as they become active at dusk or before they sleep at dawn. The crescendo or "rolling" call consists of a series of closely-spaced repeated units that become more closely-spaced and louder as the call proceeds, before ending abruptly (Bearder and Honess, 1992).

This is the smallest primate found on the mainland of Africa. Males are more variable in size than females, but are on average larger. Males have a head and body length of 12–17 cm, a tail length of 16–19.5 cm, and body weight of 55–80 g; females have a head and body length of 12–15.5 cm, a tail length of 15.5–18.5 cm, and body weight of 45–68 g (Eisentraut, 1973; Ambrose, 1999; specimens in Natural

History Museum, London, and JFO pers. obs.). Charles-Dominique (1977) describes a class of "Central A" males at Makokou in Gabon as averaging 75 g in weight, compared to "Central B" males that averaged 56 g and had little contact with females.

Similar species. Demidoff's galago is broadly sympatric with Thomas's galago (*Galagoides thomasi*), with which it is quite easily confused. Thomas's galagos in West Africa are typically a little larger than *G. demidovii*; they are reddish-brown dorsally and, unlike Demidoff's galagos, often have gray rather than cream or yellow ventral surfaces; their tail is typically darker and often a little more bushy. The obvious white nose stripe of *G. demidovii* is less distinct in Thomas's galago, but *G. thomasi* does have a patch of light hair on its forehead; *G. thomasi* has a more prominent muzzle than *G. demidovii*, larger ears, and often has dark circles around its eyes. *G. thomasi* uses a range of heights and supports in the forest canopy, but is commonly seen relatively high up; it leaps much more often than does

Fig. 8.2: Demidoff's galago (*Galagoides demidovii*), Agenebode, Nigeria (photo by A. P. Leventis).

G. demidovii. Both *G. demidovii* and *G. thomasi* make crescendo calls, but in *G. thomasi* the crescendo call is commonly given in multiples of three or more, rather than singly as in *G. demidovii*. Demidoff's galago sometimes makes a distinctive buzzing call as a threat or alarm, a call not heard from Thomas's galago. In eastern Nigeria, western Cameroon and Bioko the dwarf galagos share their habitat with the northern needle-clawed galago (*Euoticus pallidus*) and Allen's galago (*Sciurocheirus alleni*). The Allen's and needle-clawed galagos are much larger than Demidoff's galago and make very different calls (in *Euoticus* a common call is a shrill yap, while Allen's galago gives croaks and whistles). Demidoff's galago is frequently encountered in young secondary forest and farmbush, whereas the other three species are more typical of older forest.

Taxonomic Note

Jenkins (1987), Nash *et al.* (1989), Kingdon (1997) and Groves (2001) refer to this species as *Galago* (or *Galagoides*) *demidoff*. Grubb *et al.* (2003) have shown that *Galagoides demidovii* (Fischer, 1808) is the valid name.

Geographic Range

If all the local forms usually included in *G. demidovii* (with the exception of *thomasi*) are truly members of the same species, then Demidoff's galago may occur over most of the African forest zone from southern Senegal to Uganda, including all the moist forests of West Africa and the Congo Basin. However, some populations

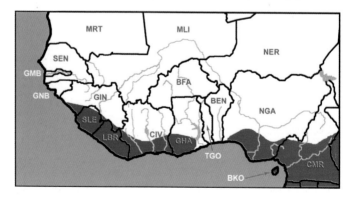

Fig. 8.3: Distribution of *Galagoides demidovii* in West Africa.

included in this range, especially in drier areas of West Africa, may actually belong to *G. thomasi*. For instance, Ziegler *et al.* (2002) report finding small galagos in a bushmeat market in the Guinea savanna-deciduous forest mosaic landscape of central Guinea, which they described as *Galagoides* cf. *thomasi*; they did not report *G. demidovii* from this locality.

Natural History

Habitat. Demidoff's galago is a species typical of moist forest; the extent to which it occurs in drier, semi-deciduous forest is unclear because of long confusion with Thomas's galago. In the moist forest zone, Demidoff's galago is most abundant in young secondary forest and farmbush, including especially edge habitats such as roadsides, river banks and clearings caused by tree falls (Ambrose, 1999). It is uncommon above an elevation of 1,000 m.

Field studies. The most reliable sources of information on the natural history of *G. demidovii* are those conducted after 1990, by which time the differences between *G. demidovii* and *G. thomasi*, and their broadly overlapping distributions, had become widely recognized. The most important of these studies for West Africa is that of Lesley Ambrose (1999), who observed *G. demidovii* in the Taï Forest, Côte d'Ivoire, in 1995, in southwestern Cameroon in 1996–1997, and on Bioko Island in 1997. There are also observations from surveys in Korup National Park, Cameroon, in 1991–1992 by Simon Bearder and Paul Honess (Bearder and Honess, 1992), and by Bearder and Oates in Nigeria in 2009 (Bearder and Oates, 2009a, 2009b). Pierre Charles-Dominique (1971, 1977) included "*Galago demidovii*" in his long-term study of nocturnal prosimians in the forests of Makokou, Gabon, in 1965–1973, but it is now clear that some of the observations he reports for this species include information on *G. thomasi*. The same problem affects the studies conducted on *G. demidovii* in the Republic of Congo by François Vincent in 1963–1969 (Vincent, 1969; and see comments by Ambrose, 1999).

Population. Demidoff's galago can be uncommon in mature forest, yet very abundant in edge habitats. Ambrose (1999) encountered this species in Gabon, Cameroon, Côte d'Ivoire and on Bioko at an average rate of 0.48 animals/hr, but the encounter rate was much higher in the Taï Forest, Côte d'Ivoire, (about 1.3/hr) than on Mt. Cameroon (0.22/hr). At several sites in and near Korup National Park in Cameroon, Bearder and Honess (1992) encountered Demidoff's galago 351 times during 214 hours of searching along an estimated 168 km of transects (2.1 encounters/km). Bearder and Oates (2009b) obtained 0.9 sightings/hr in surveys in Okomu National Park, Nigeria.

Habitat use. Demidoff's galago frequently uses thick growth below a height of 5 m and is almost always found below 12 m (Ambrose, 1999; Bearder and Oates, 2009b). It travels on fine branches and lianas of 1 cm or less in diameter, and typically uses narrow lianas when it climbs from the understorey.

Locomotion and posture. *Galagoides demidovii* typically scurries rapidly on narrow supports rather than leaping, whereas *G. thomasi* often leaps.

Activity pattern. Demidoff's galagos are nocturnal, but their activity patterns have not been carefully studied. Their rolling crescendo calls at dusk are often the first sign of prosimian activity as night falls in the West African forest.

Vocalizations. In addition to their distinctive single-crescendo (or "rolling") call used to maintain contact among groups, *G. demidovii* also makes "unit yaps" (or "chips") as a mild signal of arousal or alarm, "rapid yaps" (delivered in multi-unit sequences) to signal higher-intensity alarm, and insect-like "buzzes" as a threat or when disturbed by humans (Bearder and Honess, 1992; Ambrose, 1999).

Nesting behavior. By day, Demidoff's galagos sleep together in groups, sometimes huddled in dense foliage, but often in leaf nests that frequently contain 2 or 3 animals and may contain up to 10. Nests may contain more than one adult female (as well as young), but only rarely contain adult males (Charles-Dominique, 1977). Struhsaker (1970b) describes observing a *G. demidovii* nest in secondary forest at Idenau, southwest Cameroon; the nest was a ball of dead vegetation about 25 cm in diameter in a liana thicket about 2 m above ground. In the first 15 days of observation the nest was used by either 2 or 3 galagos; it was then apparently abandoned, but persisted for at least two months. Bearder and Honess (1992) describe two nests at heights of 3.5 and 4.5 m in Korup, Cameroon; one in good condition was constructed of finely woven fibrous bark, with a round entrance on one side; it was wedged in the fork of a tree and camouflaged by a leafy covering.

Social organization. Although Charles-Dominique (1977) did not distinguish between *G. demidovii* and *G. thomasi* in his studies at

Makokou in Gabon, his account of *G. demidovii* social and ranging behavior almost certainly is based on data from this species (and not on observations of *G. thomasi*) because the data were mostly obtained by trapping animals in an area of secondary forest; *G. demidovii* prefers second-growth vegetation and is much easier to trap than *G. thomasi*. Charles-Dominique describes *G. demidovii* as living in small matrilineal groups (based on a mother with offspring); females remain in the area in which they are born and there is overlap in the ranges of adult females. Males disperse away from their natal area at puberty, and different kinds of sexually-mature males occur: large "Central A" males whose ranges may overlap those of several females; smaller "Central B" males occurring in the same area as Central A males but having little contact with females; medium-sized peripheral males with large ranges adjacent to females and who can move to Central A status and increase their bodyweight; and nomadic, or vagabond, males that have undergone puberty but are still young and have not yet settled down.

Social behavior. Male and female Demidoff's galagos deposit urine on their hands and feet and in this way mark their range as they forage. During courtship, males and females groom each other by mutual licking and become marked with each others' urine (Charles-Dominique, 1977).

Reproduction. Details on reproduction in West African populations are not available. In Gabon, the gestation period in *G. demidovii* is about 16 weeks and births take place throughout the year, but there is a peak in the first four months of the year (from the short dry season into the beginning of a short rainy season) when insects and fruits are most abundant (Charles-Dominique, 1977). In Congo Republic, Vincent (1969) found that most births among female *G. demidovii* brought into captivity occurred either in September–October (early rains) or in January–February (mid wet season), suggesting that there can be a post-partum estrus. Birth and early development of Demidoff's galago in Gabon have been described by Charles-Dominique (1977); mothers separate themselves from other group members to give birth in a nest; the newborn is relatively helpless, and between three and seven days following its birth the mother carries it in her mouth from the nest at dusk, and "parks" it in vegetation while she forages, moving the infant from one feeding area to another during the night and carrying it back to the nest at dawn. The infant begins to move around independently at 2–3 weeks of age and to take solid food after about 1 month; weaning occurs at about 45 days and adult weight is reached after 6 months.

Ranging patterns. Sleeping groups of Demidoff's galagos disperse from their day nests to forage, but keep in contact throughout the night by calling (Ambrose, 1999). Range sizes have not been measured in West Africa, but in Gabon the ranges of females average 0.8 ha in size, while the ranges of Central A males average 1.8 ha, and those of Central B males only 0.5 ha (Charles-Dominique, 1977).

Diet. The diet of *G. demidovii* in West Africa has not been studied. Charles-Dominique (1977) reports a diet of 70% insects and 19% fruits in Gabon based on a study of stomach contents, but some of the animals studied may have been *G. thomasi*. Ambrose (1999) reports seeing Demidoff's galagos in captivity in Gabon grabbing insects in their hands after listening for them and chasing them, and fruits being picked up in the mouth or with one hand.

Predators. Predation on Demidoff's galagos in West Africa has not been documented. Struhsaker (1970b) describes *G. demidovii* fleeing from and giving alarm calls to a large green mamba at Idenau is southwest Cameroon; the mamba was crawling on the ground.

Conservation Status

Galagoides demidovii is listed as of Least Concern in the IUCN Red List. This is a widespread and often common species that tends to be most abundant in disturbed habitats rather than mature forest. Because of its small size it is not normally targeted by hunters.

Where to See It

Demidoff's galago can be encountered throughout the moist forest zone of West Africa where at least secondary forest remains, including plantations and areas of regrowth from farming. Its presence is most often revealed by its crescendo call, especially at dusk and dawn, but it can be quite hard to observe clearly (even with a headlamp) because of its small size and rapid, scuttling movement.

Thomas's galago
Galagoides thomasi (Elliot, 1907)

Other English: Thomas's dwarf galago, Thomas's dwarf bushbaby,
Thomas's bushbaby
French: Galago de Thomas
West African languages: G'neh (Bassa, Liberia); Eme (Yoruba,
Nigeria); Akhekhe (Edo, Nigeria) (The same names are almost
certainly used for both *G. demidovii* and *G. thomasi.*)

Identification (see Fig. 8.1, p.84)

A small nocturnal forest primate with a long and somewhat bushy
tail, large eyes, very large ears, and a soft dense coat. Coat coloration
varies across the range, but the body's dorsal surfaces are typically
brown or reddish brown, while ventral surfaces are usually gray; the
tail is darker brown than the back. There are often thin dark rings
around the eyes.

Unlike the related (and superficially similar, but smaller)
Demidoff's galago, Thomas's galago typically uses the forest canopy,
and has leaping as an important component of its locomotion. Like
Demidoff's galago, *G. thomasi* makes a crescendo contact call, but
the Thomas's crescendos are commonly given in multiples of three or
more, and individuals will engage in extended counter-calling.

Galagoides thomasi is a small animal, but not as small as Demidoff's
galago. On average, males may be slightly larger than females, but
few dimensions are available from West African populations. A male
from Mt. Oku, Cameroon, had a head and body length of 15.9 cm, a
tail length of 17.8 cm, and weighed 100 g; a female pregnant with a
relatively large fetus had a head and body of 14.1 cm, a tail of 18.1
cm, and weighed 130 g (Eisentraut, 1973; referring to "*demidovii
pr. thomasi*"). One female measured in Gabon had a head and body
length of 17.4 cm and a tail of 16.5 cm (Ambrose, 1999); males caught
in Gabon had a mean weight of 82 g, compared to 71 g for females
(Wickings *et al.*, 1998).

Similar species. This species is easily confused with Demidoff's
galago. Similarities and differences between the two species, and
between them and needle-clawed and Allen's galagos, are described
under *G. demidovii*. Among other differences between *demidovii* and

thomasi are that *thomasi* is larger and has proportionately larger ears, and that the "buzz" arousal call made by *demidovii* has not been heard in *thomasi*.

Taxonomic Note

This galago was long regarded as a localized subspecies of *Galagoides demidovii* (= *Galago demidoff*) (e.g., Jenkins, 1987). Only following the publication of a synopsis of galago species characteristics by Nash *et al.* (1989) did the specific distinctiveness of Thomas's galago (pointed out by Olson and Nash, 2003) become generally accepted. It is now recognized that each species has a wide distribution across the African forest zone and that the two occur together in many places. Because of the wide distribution of the galagos now being referred to as *G. thomasi*, and variation in the pelage and vocalizations of populations being placed in that taxon, it seems very likely that deeper study will reveal that the populations being referred to as "*Galagoides thomasi*" represent more than one species. For instance, the galagos from the Haut Niger National Park in Guinea, described by Ziegler *et al.* (2002) as resembling *G. thomasi*, have bright ochre-orange, rather than gray, undersurfaces and longer tails than other populations (see Fig. 8.6, p.99). Individuals from Mount Kupé, Cameroon, are described by

Fig. 8.4: Thomas's galago (*Galagoides thomasi*), Okomu National Park, Nigeria (photo by A. P. Leventis).

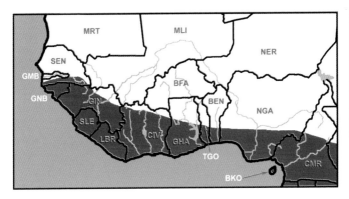

Fig. 8.5: Distribution of *Galagoides thomasi* in West Africa.

Ambrose (1999) as being larger, with redder pelage, than those from Gabon.

Geographic Range

Because any observations or collections of small forest galagos were long assigned to *G. demidovii*, the distribution of *G. thomasi* is not known with confidence. Since 1990, field studies in the African forest zone by experts have found *G. thomasi* to be present in most localities (e.g., Bearder and Honess, 1992; Ambrose, 1999, 2002; Bearder and Oates, 2009a, 2009b). This galago may be found throughout the forest zone, and has been noted to be present in some dry or higher-elevation forests where *G. demidovii* is rare or absent; for instance, the forest-savanna mosaic of central Guinea (Ziegler *et al.*, 2002), the dry forests of the Dahomey Gap (F. Dowsett, pers. comm., 2009), and the Kibale Forest, Uganda (Ambrose, 2002).

Natural History

Habitat. Thomas's galago has been reported from lowland and montane rain-forest, and semi-deciduous and dry forests. Assuming that the galagos on Mt. Oku described by Eisentraut (1973) as "*demidovii pr. thomasi*" belong to this species, then it occurs as high as 2,100 m. Small galagos that almost certainly belong to this taxon have also been observed in montane forest at 1,900 m on Chappal Waddi in the Gotel Mountains of northeastern Nigeria (Dowsett and Dowsett-Lemaire, 1989).

Field studies. No field study has focused on Thomas's galago, but observations on this species were almost certainly included in the studies by François Vincent on *G. demidovii* in the Republic of Congo in 1963–1969 (Vincent, 1969) and by Pierre Charles-Dominique on the prosimians of Makokou, Gabon, in 1965–1973 (1971, 1977). Some information on the natural history of *G. thomasi* in West Africa has been gathered during survey studies conducted after 1990, by which time the differences between *G. demidovii* and *G. thomasi* had become widely recognized. These studies include those of Simon Bearder and Paul Honess in Korup National Park, Cameroon, in 1991–1992 (Bearder Honess, 1992); of Lesley Ambrose (1999), who observed *G. demidovii* in the Taï Forest, Côte d'Ivoire, in 1995, in southwestern Cameroon in 1996–1997, and on Bioko Island in 1997; and of Bearder and Oates in Nigeria in 2009 (Bearder and Oates, 2009a, 2009b). There are also a few observations from Gabon (Wickings *et al.*, 1998) and Uganda (Ambrose, 2002). In general, however, this remains a poorly-known species.

Population. Thomas's galago can be abundant. In Korup National Park in Cameroon, Bearder and Honess (1992) encountered *G. thomasi* at a rate of 1.9/km, compared with 2.1/km for *G. demidovii*. Ambrose (1999) encountered this species in Gabon, Cameroon, Côte d'Ivoire and on Bioko at an average rate of 0.23 animals/hr, with the highest encounter rate (0.37/hr) being in montane areas of southwest Cameroon and Bioko. Bearder and Oates (2009b) obtained 3.0 sightings/hr in surveys in Okomu National Park, Nigeria, compared with 0.9 sightings/hr for *G. demidovii*.

Habitat use. Unlike Demidoff's galago, which is most often below a height of 5 m, Thomas's galago is usually seen high in the forest canopy, usually above a height of 10 m and often above 20 m (Ambrose, 1999; Bearder and Oates, 2009a, 2009b).

Locomotion and posture. *G. thomasi* uses branches of different sizes, but is commonly seen on medium-sized and large branches, running rapidly and leaping, rather than scurrying like *G. demidovii*.

Activity pattern. Activity patterns in Thomas's galagos have not been carefully studied, but Bearder and Honess (1992) report that in Korup they return to their sleeping places 30 minutes earlier than Demidoff's galago. Ambrose (1999) reports that Thomas's galagos call almost exclusively when there is bright moonlight and only rarely call on dark or stormy nights.

Vocalizations. Through the studies of Ambrose (1999), the vocal behavior of *G. thomasi* is the best understood aspect of this species' natural history. Ambrose describes seven call types: "multiple crescendos", "trills", "grunts", "rapid yaps", "rapid yap sequences", "shriek yaps", and "wail yaps". Rapid yaps (or "chips") are the most frequently heard call; they are given in situations of alarm; they are short, high-frequency calls given in sequences that very in intensity and speed of repetition depending on the level of alarm (this call is well described by Kingdon [1997] as a "scolding chitter"). Multiple crescendos are the second most common call type; like the single crescendo of *G. demidovii*, these contact calls are exchanged at dusk between individuals as they leave sleeping nests and are then heard at intervals through the night. They are most often given in sequences of three or more, and individuals may counter-call for up to five minutes.

Social organization and nesting. The social system of *G. thomasi* may be similar to that of *G. demidovii*, but very little reliable information on the social behavior and organization of this species is available. Ambrose (1999) reports that she usually encountered individuals alone, but that two were sometimes found in the same location and up to five animals were observed gathering at dawn before sleeping. Bearder *et al.* (2003) report that *G. thomasi* (like *G. demidovii*) builds nests; therefore, groups of *G. thomasi* very likely sleep together in nests.

Fig. 8.6: A small galago in Haut Niger National Park, Guinea, that is probably *Galagoides thomasi* or a closely related form (photo by T. Humle).

Reproduction. Reproductive behavior in *G. thomasi* is not known in any detail. Bearder *et al.* (2003) report that, as in *G. demidovii*, small infants are carried in the mother's mouth, and that mothers "park" their infants while they forage.

Ranging patterns. Ranging behavior in this species has not been studied.

Diet. The diet of *G. thomasi* is not well known, but is thought to be similar to that of *G. demidovii*, which is dominated by insects but also includes some fruit and a little gum. Ambrose (1999) describes a captive individual in Gabon as frequently hunting moths, moving its large ears to pick up moth sounds, then running (or leaping) and grabbing the insect with both hands, sometimes hanging bipedally to eat the prey.

Predators. There is no reliable information available on the predators of *G. thomasi*.

Conservation Status

Galagoides thomasi is listed as of Least Concern in the IUCN Red List. Thomas's galago appears to be a widespread and often common species, occupying a broad range of forest habitats, but its distribution and ecology are still relatively poorly known. Its preferred habitat seems to be the canopy of tall forest, and abundance will therefore be affected by the clearing of mature forest. Because of its small size it is rarely targeted by hunters, but Ziegler *et al.* (2002) report seeing galagos resembling this species in a local market in central Guinea; small squirrels were also seen in local markets in the same region, suggesting that larger game may have been becoming scarce, at which point even quite small mammals become vulnerable to hunting.

Where to See It

Thomas's galago can be seen by "night shining" with a headlamp in many forests in West Africa. Among sites where it has been observed are the Haut Niger National Park (Guinea); Taï National Park (Côte d'Ivoire); Tafi Atome Monkey Sanctuary, Ghana; the Lama Forest, Bénin; Okomu National Park, Cross River National Park and Afi Mountain Wildlife Sanctuary (Nigeria); Korup National Park, Mount Cameroon and Mount Kupé (Cameroon); and the Gran Caldera and Southern Highlands Scientific Reserve (Bioko, Equatorial Guinea).

Galago É. Geoffroy, 1796
Lesser galagos or bushbabies

This is the oldest generic name still in use for any of the galagos. As explained previously, on some occasions over the last 50 years all of the galagos have been "dumped" into this genus—as a "wastebasket" taxon—because of uncertainties about relationships within the family Galagidae. However, Grubb *et al.* (2003) restrict *Galago* to a set of medium-sized species that occur in a range of woodland and forest habitats, and that are united by a range of morphological characteristics (Olson, 1979); these species are *G. senegalensis* of the Sudanian savanna woodland, *G. gallarum* of northeastern Africa, *G. moholi* of southern central Africa, and *G. matschiei* from forests near the western Rift Valley in East Africa. Genetic studies also group members of this genus closely together, and suggest that they have a close relationship to the needle-clawed galagos, *Euoticus* (Masters *et al.*, 2007).

Galago senegalensis was the first species of galago to be scientifically described and, despite all the upheavals in the taxonomy of the galago family, this species still retains the name given to it by Étienne Geoffroy Saint-Hilaire in 1796.

Galago senegalensis geospecies

Grubb (2006b) treats all members of the genus *Galago* as one geospecies. *Galago senegalensis*, *G. gallarum*, *G. moholi* and *G. matschiei* are allopatric, each occurring in a different geographical area.

Local Representatives

Only one species of this group, *Galago senegalensis* itself, occurs in the West African region. Groves (2001) and Grubb *et al.* (2003) recognize four subspecies of *G. senegalensis*: *G. s. senegalensis*, *G. s. braccatus*, *G. s. sotikae* and *G. s. dunni*; only one of these subspecies, *G. senegalensis senegalensis*, is found in West Africa.

Senegal bushbaby
Galago senegalensis É. Geoffroy, 1796

Other English: Senegal galago, Senegal lesser galago, western lesser
bushbaby, northern lesser bushbaby
French: Galago de Sénégal
West African languages: Mbet (Bamoun, Cameroon)

Identification (see Fig. 8.1, p.84)

A small nocturnal primate of savanna woodland; the Senegal
bushbaby has a rounded head and short muzzle, large eyes, very large
ears and a long tail. The first part of the tail has relatively short hair, but
it becomes bushier towards the tip. In West African populations (*G. s.
senegalensis*) the dorsal surfaces of the coat are a uniform silvery gray,
and the ventral surfaces have creamy-tipped hairs with light gray bases,
giving a silvery-cream appearance; the tail is gray, getting darker and
browner towards the tip. The anterior outer surfaces of the arms and
legs, and the neck, have a striking pale yellow-ochre wash. There are
distinct dark circles around the eyes, the inner surfaces of the ears are
pinkish yellow-brown, and there is a stripe of white hair on the nose
between the eyes.

Males are somewhat larger than females. Head and body length
averages about 160 mm in adult females and about 170 mm in adult
males, but tail length is about 250 mm in both sexes (specimens in the
Natural History Museum, London); wild-caught East African males (*G.
s. braccatus*) averaged 315 g compared with 250 g in females (from R.
W. Cooper, in Izard and Nash, 1988).

Similar species. The Senegal bushbaby is the only nocturnal
primate present across the drier parts of its extensive range in the
savanna zone in West Africa. Where the savanna grades into forest,
however, its geographical range overlaps with the dwarf galago
species: Demidoff's galago (*Galagoides demidovii*) and Thomas's
galago (*Galagoides thomasi*). The two dwarf species are not always
easy to distinguish from each other, except by their calls, and their
geographical ranges have yet to be well established; they may be
encountered in forest patches and galleries on the fringes of the forest
zone; they are smaller than the Senegal bushbaby, have darker, browner
dorsal pelage, and a pointed muzzle. *Galagoides thomasi* uses a range
of heights and supports, but *G. demidovii* is usually low down in thick

growth, scuttling about on twigs and thin branches. While the most common call of the Senegal bushbaby is a single, low-pitched "woo" uttered at a regular tempo, the dwarf galagos make characteristic high-pitched "crescendo" calls: these are rapidly-pulsed calls that increase in pulse-rate and pitch during delivery; they are uttered as single 3–10 sec calls by *G. demidovii* and as short (1.5–3 sec) repeated, multiple units by *G. thomasi* (Zimmermann *et al.*, 1988; Bearder *et al.*, 1995).

Taxonomic Note

Until the research on galago systematics by Olson (1979), most accounts grouped the taxa *gallarum*, *granti*, *moholi* and *zanzibaricus* with the Senegal bushbaby in the species *Galago senegalensis*. Such an approach was still being followed by Jaclyn Wolfheim in 1981. Olson placed *senegalensis*, *gallarum* and *moholi* as different species within the genus *Galago*, and considered *zanzibaricus* and *granti* to be forms of *Galagoides*. The view that these five galagos are not all members of one biological species only began to become widely accepted after the publication of a "Synopsis of galago species characteristics" by Nash, Bearder and Olson in 1989, and is now reflected in the taxonomies of Groves (2001) and Grubb *et al.* (2003). Older accounts of the natural history of *Galago senegalensis*, therefore, often include information

Fig. 8.7: Senegal bushbaby (*Galago senegalensis senegalensis*) at Yankari, Nigeria (photo by A. P. Leventis). In 2006, Yankari reverted from its status as a national park to that of a state-managed game reserve.

Galagidae

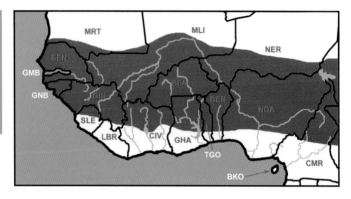

Fig. 8.8: Distribution of *Galago senegalensis senegalensis* in West Africa.

about populations (such as *moholi*) that differ in a number of significant respects in their biology from *G. senegalensis* as it is treated here.

Geographic Range

Galago senegalensis occurs from Senegal and The Gambia east through the savanna zone to Sudan, western Ethiopia and northern Tanzania. The West African subspecies *G. senegalensis senegalensis* is found as far east as Sudan, and also in Uganda and western Kenya (if the subspecies *G. s. albipes* of Uganda and Kenya is regarded as synonymous with *G. s. senegalensis*, following Groves [2001]). Masters (1998) has pointed out that the range center of *G. senegalensis* falls within the Sudanian (savanna) center of plant endemism.

Natural History

Special adaptations. The Senegal bushbaby appears to be primarily adapted to a life eating gums and insects in dry Sudanian and Sahelian savanna woodland, often harvesting gum from *Acacia* trees. It shares its use of gums with other members of its geospecies (including *G. moholi* and *G. matschiei*), and with the related needle-clawed galagos (*Euoticus*). Butler (1966) notes that structural adaptations for water conservation in the kidneys of the Senegal bushbaby help its survival in a 4–5-month dry season.

Habitat. In West Africa, *Galago senegalensis senegalensis* is found in Guinean and Sudanian savanna. In Ghana it is said to prefer "orchard bush" country (Booth, 1960), while in Sudan, Butler (1966) described its typical habitat in the Nuba Mountains as "fairly dense gum forest" of *Acacia* and *Balanites*. On Mt. Elgon in Uganda, Ambrose (2002) observed Senegal bushbabies at 2,600–2,800 m in low-stature montane forest. In Laikipia, Kenya, *G. s. braccatus* is associated with open *Acacia* woodland and bushland (Off *et al.*, 2008).

Field studies. Although this species was one of the first nonhuman primates to come to the attention of western science, quite little is known about its behavior and ecology; no results from a careful long-term field study of *Galago senegalensis* have been published, and hardly any information is available on West African populations. Some short-term observations have been made on *G. senegalensis* in eastern Africa: on *G. s. albipes* (= *G. s. senegalensis*) in Uganda (Haddow and Ellice, 1964; Ambrose, 2002) and southern Sudan (Butler, 1966, 1967), and on *G. s. braccatus* in Kenya (Nash and Whitten, 1989; Off *et al.*, 2008). Most of the detailed information on the natural history of the *G. senegalensis* geospecies comes from studies of *G. moholi* in southern Africa (e.g., Bearder and Doyle, 1974; Bearder and Martin, 1980; Pullen *et al.*, 2000). Bearder (1999) says that *G. senegalensis* and *G. moholi* have apparently identical ecological niches and locomotor styles, but show consistent differences in other biological characteristics.

Population. No information is available on population densities of *G. senegalensis senegalensis* in West African savannas, but Butler (1966) describes it as "extremely common" in the Nuba Mountains, Sudan. From censuses of *G. s. braccatus* in Laikipia, Kenya, Nash and Whitten (1989) estimated a density of 1.5 individuals/ha in a small area of *Acacia* woodland near the Suguroi River at Mutara Ranch, while Off *et al.* (2008) encountered these galagos at estimated densities ranging from 0.4–2.4 individuals/ha in a variety of *Acacia* woodlands and bushlands along the Ewaso Nyiro River at Mpala Ranch. The highest density at Mpala was found in *Acacia xanthophloea* woodland.

Habitat use and locomotion. Almost nothing has been published about patterns of locomotion and habitat use in West African populations. On Mt. Elgon, Ambrose (2002) observed *G. s. senegalensis* using all levels of montane forest from 0–14.5 m, and hopping on branches with the kangaroo-like locomotion which members of this geospecies use when travelling on the ground. In Laikipia, Kenya, *G. s. braccatus* has been seen at heights of 0–18 m (and at an average height of 7.4 m) (Off *et al.*, 2008). Bearder and Doyle (1974) describe rapid leaping as the primary locomotor mode in *Galago moholi*, with slower stepping as a secondary mode.

Activity pattern. Senegal bushbabies are nocturnal, but their activity pattern has not been studied in West Africa. On Mt. Elgon, Ambrose (2002) saw these galagos emerging at dusk, before it was fully dark. In northern Karamoja, Uganda, Haddow and Ellice (1964) found *G. senegalensis* to be most active in the two hours after sunset and just before sunrise.

Vocalizations. Zimmerman *et al.* (1988) describe 19 different calls made by *G. s. senegalensis* in a captive colony that was founded by individuals collected in western Africa. The most frequently heard call is a single-unit "woo" repeated in series that can last up to an hour that is exchanged by dominant animals in different groups and by individuals in the same group synchronizing their movements. Three other variants of the "woo" call are reported by Zimmermann *et al.* (1988), one used only in courtship and mating, and one made by mothers communicating with infants. Other common calls are a "ga" in situations of mild anxiety, a "cht" used in agonistic interactions, a "ft" used in reaction to agonistic calls, and "fwa" and "hfut" alarm calls.

Nesting behavior. In *Acacia xanthophloea* woodland in Kenya, Nash and Whitten (1989) observed that one group of *G. s. braccatus* slept in a tree hole, while in *Acacia drepanolobium* woodland the galagos slept in dense *Grewia* shrubs. In northern Karamoja, Haddow and Ellice (1964) found that Senegal bushbabies preferred to use tree holes (especially of *Terminalia brownii*) 4–5 ft (1.2–1.5 m) above ground, as well as uninhabited bee hives. The related *G. moholi* in southern Africa was found to sleep mostly on nests of flat leaves or branch forks, selecting dense thorny *Acacia* trees as sleeping sites; tree hollows are also used (Bearder and Doyle, 1974).

Social organization. The social behavior and organization of *G. senegalensis* are very poorly known, especially in West Africa. A small number of galagos commonly sleep together in a tree hole or nest, and these sleeping groups probably split up for much of their foraging. From observations of foraging Senegal bushbabies in northern Karamoja, Haddow and Ellice (1964) report that 56% of encounters were with single animals, 36% with 2–3 individuals, and 8% with four. However, more than 50% of Karamoja nesting groups consisted of two or more animals and 69% of these groups contained one adult male; a majority of solitary nesters were adult males. In Laikipia, Kenya, Nash and Whitten (1989) found small groups of 2–3 individual *G. s. braccatus* sleeping together; these groups each included at least two adults which were guessed to be a male and female pair. Elsewhere in Laikipia, Off *et al.* (2008) observed solitary individuals in 81% of census encounters, pairs in 16% and groups of 3–5 individuals in 3% of encounters.

Reproduction. Studies on the reproductive condition of females collected in northern Uganda and southern Sudan indicate that *G. s. senegalensis* has two annual breeding seasons in eastern Africa (Haddow and Ellice, 1964; Butler, 1967); the same may apply to West African populations. Gestation length in captive *G. s. senegalensis* is 144–146 days (Manley, 1966) and in *G. s. braccatus* 142 days (Izard and Nash, 1988). Females may have a post-partum estrus if an offspring is lost, but otherwise ovulate about one cycle later (mean cycle length 32 days) (Manley, 1966). Females usually give birth to singletons (only 8% of litters in captive *G. s. braccatus* were twins, compared to 41% in *G. moholi*), and the young take one year to reach sexual maturity (Izard and Nash, 1988). The penis of *G. senegalensis* has a more bulbous shape than that of *G. moholi* and is sparsely covered with fine, small spines, compared with dense, thick spines in *G. moholi* (Anderson, 1998).

Ranging patterns. In a 17-day study of *G. s. braccatus* in Kenya, members of the same sleeping group used an area of 1–2 ha (Nash and Whitten, 1989).

Diet. In a study of the gut contents of Senegal bushbabies collected in northern Uganda, Haddow and Ellice (1964) found insects in all samples, with beetles and caterpillars most frequently represented; plant material was only recognizable in about one-quarter of the samples, but the authors acknowledge that they could not have recognized acacia gum in their macerated samples. In their 17-day study at Laikipia in July–August 1984, Nash and Whitten (1989) saw *G. s. braccatus* eat only arthropods, and the gum of *Acacia xanthophloea* and *A. drepanolobium*; fruits were not available in that habitat at that time. Bearder and Martin (1980) report a diet consisting only of arthropods (mostly insects) and *Acacia* gum for *G. moholi* in southern Africa; gum was particularly important in the diet during the cold, dry winter months.

Predators. Remains of *G. s. senegalensis* have been found in the feces of chimpanzees in Niokolo Koba National Park, Senegal (McGrew *et al.*, 1978) and in 2005–2006 Pruetz and Bertolani (2007) observed chimpanzees at Fongoli, to the east of Niokolo Koba, fashioning sharpened sticks which they jabbed inside tree hollows, apparently to capture Senegal bushbabies; one galago was seen to be captured and eaten by this method, and on two other occasions chimpanzees were seen eating galagos. Only part of the range of *G. senegalensis* is occupied by chimpanzees, and otherwise little is known about predation on this species.

Conservation Status

Galago senegalensis and the West African subspecies *G. s. senegalensis* are listed as of Least Concern in the IUCN Red List. The Red List notes that *G. s. senegalensis* is widespread and relatively common, and that at present there are no major threats to this subspecies. Where trees in savanna woodland become sparse through the spread of pasture and farmland, or through cutting for firewood, there must be negative impacts on these galagos, but large areas of suitable habitat currently remain. Senegal bushbabies are not a significant target of human hunters.

Where to See It

The Senegal bushbaby probably occurs in all or most of the savanna-zone protected areas between Senegal and Cameroon, as well as in many places outside parks and other reserves.

Galagidae

Bioko Allen's Galago
Sciurocheirus alleni alleni

Bioko Needle-clawed Galago
Euoticus pallidus pallidus

Talbot's Needle-clawed Galago
Euoticus pallidus talboti

Cross River Allen's Galago
Sciurocheirus alleni cameronensis

Fig. 8.9.

Euoticus Gray, 1863
Needle-clawed galagos

Galagidae

Needle-clawed galagos get their name from the sharply-pointed, ridged (or keeled) nails on their fingers and toes. Other specializations in their dentition and digestive system are described below, all of which are related to their gum feeding habits.

The name *Euoticus* was proposed as a subgenus of *Otogale* (the greater galagos) by Gray in 1863 for a needle-clawed galago collected on Fernando Po (Bioko) by Richard Burton, the British Consul on the island. Hill (1953) also used *Euoticus* as a subgenus for the needle-clawed galagos, but within the genus *Galago*, and he was followed in this course by Napier and Napier (1967). On the other hand, Schwarz (1931), in a review of the taxonomy of the galagos, placed all the species except the needle-clawed forms in the genus *Galago*, separating the needle-clawed galagos into the genus *Euoticus* based on the anatomy of their teeth and nails. Hill and Meester (1971) and Groves (1989) followed the same course as Schwarz. Subsequently, Groves (2001) published a cladistic analysis of morphological, pelage, locomotor, life-history, genetic and vocal characters of all the galagos, concluding that the needle-clawed species form a sister group to all the other smaller forms of galago, while these two groups are themselves a sister group to the greater galagos (genus *Otolemur*). Masters *et al.* (2007), on the other hand, found that the molecular data groups *Euoticus* within a clade that includes *Galago senegalensis, G. moholi* and *G. matschiei,* and on this basis argued that *Euoticus* should be moved back to a subgenus of *Galago*, supporting the results of an earlier morphological analysis by Olson (1979) that was also followed by Nash *et al.* (1989). Because of the distinctive morphology and behavior of the needle-clawed galagos, related to their diet, they are retained in their own genus in this guidebook, with the recognition that their taxonomy is not well settled.

Euoticus is restricted in its distribution to the moist forests of western equatorial Africa between the Niger and Congo rivers, and the island of Bioko.

Euoticus elegantulus geospecies

Grubb *et al.* (2003) follow Groves (1989, 2001) and Kingdon (1997) in recognizing two species of needle-clawed galagos: *E. elegantulus,* which occurs in southern Cameroon, Gabon, Rio Muni, the Republic of Congo and the Central African Republic; and *E. pallidus*, which occurs in Cameroon north and west of the Sanaga River, in eastern Nigeria, and on Bioko. In her thorough study of diversity in West and Central African galagos, Ambrose (1999) found that *E. elegantulus* and *E. pallidus* have significant differences in their calls, and she notes that there are also differences in the morphology of their penises. Grubb (2006b) considers that these two species together comprise the geospecies *Euoticus elegantulus*, which is the senior of the two species names.

Local Representatives

Only the species *E. pallidus* occurs in the region covered by this book, to which it is endemic. Within *E. pallidus,* two subspecies are recognized by Groves (2001) and by Grubb *et al.* (2003): *E. pallidus pallidus* on Bioko Island, and *E. pallidus talboti* on the mainland, between the lower Niger River and the Sanaga River.

Galagidae

Northern needle-clawed galago
Euoticus pallidus (Gray, 1863)

Other English: Northern needle-clawed bushbaby, pale (or pallid)
needle-clawed bushbaby, pale galago
French: Galago mignon du nord
West African languages: Ettebu (Bubi, Bioko)

Identification (see Fig. 8.9, p.109)

A small nocturnal forest primate with a very long and bushy tail,
a rounded head with a short muzzle and very large eyes, a soft, dense,
woolly coat, large hands and feet, and a pink muzzle. They are strong
runners and leapers, typically seen moving rapidly on horizontal or
diagonal branches high up in trees. Needle-clawed galagos make
characteristic shrill yapping calls and high-pitched "tsic" calls.

The dorsal surfaces of the coat in the Bioko form (*E. p. pallidus*)
are reddish gray-brown, slightly redder on the lower back than on the
arms, shoulders, neck and crown. Most of the tail is light brownish
gray, with little red tone. The undersurfaces are ashy gray. There
is no distinct mid-dorsal stripe, but the coat is slightly redder in the
midline of the back. Individuals of the mainland form, Talbot's need-
clawed galago (*E. p. talboti*), are quite variable in the coloration of
their coat. Dorsally they are typically a grayish red-brown (slightly
more red than the Bioko form) and often (but not always) they have a
distinct reddish spinal stripe; some individuals are much redder in color
than others. The undersurfaces of *E. p. talboti* are a light creamy-gray,
lighter than the Bioko animals, and often have a yellowish tinge; the
light gray color extends onto the flanks under the fore and hind limbs,
and onto the sides of the neck, much more obviously than it does in *E.
p. pallidus*. The nose is yellowish pink. The coat of *E. p. pallidus* is
longer than that of *E. p. talboti*.

Males and females are about the same size. Head and body length
of adult *E. p. talboti* is 17-21 cm, tail length is 28–33 cm, and body
weight is 230–280 g (Ambrose, 1999; JFO unpubl. obs.). *E. pallidus
pallidus* may be slightly larger, with two measured individuals having
head and body lengths of 19 and 25 cm, and tails of 31 and 35 cm
(Eisentraut, 1973; Ambrose, 1999).

GALAGO ELEGANTULUS PALLIDUS

Fig. 8.10: The northern needle-clawed galago (*Euoticus pallidus*) as portrayed in *A Review of the Primates* by D. G. Elliot (1913).

Similar species. The needle-clawed galago shares its forest habitat with three other species of galago: Allen's galago (*Sciurocheirus alleni*), Thomas's galago (*Galagoides thomasi*) and Demidoff's galago (*Galagoides demidovii*). An observer searching for galagos will most likely first detect them from the reflection of a head-lamp beam from the tapetum in the animal's eyes ("eyeshine"); the eyeshine of *Euoticus* is typically a bright golden orange, coming from relatively widely-spaced eyes, and this galago is often seen higher up than the other species. *Galagoides demidovii* and *G. thomasi* are much smaller and make crescendo calls (high-pitched calls that rise in pitch and in the speed of intervals between their component subunits); *G. demidovii* is found mostly in low, thick undergrowth, moving only on fine branches. *S. alleni* is of similar size to *E. pallidus*, but has a brown or black tail and rich reddish color on the arms and legs. Allen's galago is often seen low in the understorey of open forest, leaping between small vertical supports, and quite often descending to the ground; but is occasionally seen higher in the canopy, at heights of up to 15 m. The most characteristic call of Allen's galago is a long mewing whistle.

Taxonomic Note

In many older classifications (e.g., Jenkins, 1987) the northern needle-clawed galago is listed as a subspecies of a single needle-clawed species (*Galago elegantulus pallidus*, or *Euoticus elegantulus pallidus*).

Geographic Range

Euoticus pallidus talboti occurs in the forest zone from the lower Niger River and the eastern edge of the Niger Delta in Nigeria east to the lower Sanaga River in Cameroon, and *E. pallidus pallidus* is found on Bioko Island, Equatorial Guinea.

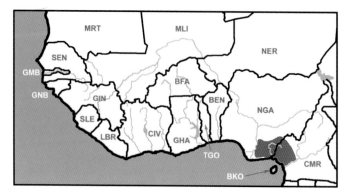

Fig. 8.11: Distributions of *Euoticus pallidus pallidus* (yellow) and *E. pallidus talboti* (red).

Natural History

Special adaptations. Needle-clawed galagos have a number of specializations related to exploiting the gums of trees and lianas as a major source of energy. Their pointed nails allow them to gain purchase on tree trunks, especially when moving head downwards. Their lower incisor and canine teeth form a forward-pointing (procumbent) comb that is longer and narrower than in the other galago species with which *Euoticus* shares its habitat; the toothcomb is used in scraping gum from branches; under the tongue is a well-developed sublingua, a cartilaginous structure, used to clean the toothcomb and in grooming. Canine-like premolar teeth are likely used to gouge bark to promote gum flow. *Euoticus* has a large caecum in which the long-chain carbohydrates of gums are digested (Chivers and Hladik, 1980).

Habitat. Needle-clawed galagos prefer old secondary or mature moist forest and are only occasionally found in young secondary forest. They occur in both lowland and montane forest. On Mt. Kupé and Mt. Cameroon on the mainland, Ambrose (1999) encountered them more frequently at high elevations (>1,000 m) than in lowlands; on Bioko they occur from coastal areas (near Riaba [= Concepción]) to highlands, where they have been observed at almost 1,600 m above Moka (Eisentraut, 1973; Schlossman, 2006).

Field studies. There has not been an extended field study of *Euoticus pallidus*, but a good deal of information has accumulated during short-term surveys in eastern Nigeria in 1966–1967 by Jewell and Oates (1969b); in southwest Cameroon in 1992 by Bearder and Honess (1992), and in 1996–1997 by Ambrose (1999); and on Bioko Island in 1997 by Ambrose and Perkin (2000) and in 2006 by Schlossman (2006). Longer-term observations were made on the closely-related *Euoticus elegantulus* in the forests of Makokou, Gabon, in 1965–1973 by Charles-Dominique (1971, 1977).

Population. The abundance of pallid needle-clawed galagos varies considerably from site to site, presumably related to forest structure and food abundance. In Korup National Park in Cameroon, Bearder and Honess (1992) obtained 232 sightings along 168 km of survey trail in mostly mature forest (1.38/km), and in the Mamu Forest Reserve, Nigeria, Jewell and Oates (1969b) had 13 sightings on approximately 20 km of trail in old secondary forest (0.65/km). In Korup and on Mt. Cameroon, Ambrose (1999) encountered *E. pallidus* at a rate of about 0.2 animals/hr when surveying at an average speed of 0.45

km/hr, equivalent to 0.44 sightings/km, but on Mt. Kupé the sighting rate was 0.89/hr, or 1.98/km. In montane forest at Moka, Bioko, Ambrose and Perkin (2000) had an encounter rate of 0.25 animals/hr, while Schlossman (2006) reports an encounter rate of 0.33 animals/hr. Charles-Dominique (1977) reports a density of 15-20/km² for the *Euoticus elegantulus* in the forests of Makokou, Gabon.

Habitat use. Needle-clawed galagos typically use large branches in the upper part of the forest canopy. Ambrose (1999) notes that a majority of observations of *E. pallidus* were made above 15 m, but that the galagos may come as low as 4 m. In Nigeria, they have been seen at heights of 3–23 m (JFO pers. obs.). In Gabon, the related *E. elegantulus* is seen usually at heights of 5–35 m, but sometimes as high as 50 m (Charles-Dominique, 1977).

Locomotion and posture. Needle-clawed galagos are strong runners and leapers, moving rapidly in the forest canopy and often making large leaps between tree crowns. Charles-Dominique (1977) has observed *E. elegantulus* in Gabon moving between some 100 gum-collection sites each hour, stopping briefly at each site to lick or scrape droplets of gum. Leaps between trees (which may cover >5m horizontally) are often done in a "parachuting" fashion, with the animal's motion slowed by spread-eagled arms and legs, its long bushy tail, and opened skinfolds between the limbs and the trunk of the body; the galago may fall several meters in the course of such a leap, making a soft landing in foliage (Charles-Dominique, 1977). The large hands and feet of *Euoticus*, and its sharply-pointed nails, allow it to use wide supports such as tree trunks, and it will forage head downwards on trunks for gum.

Activity pattern. Although needle-clawed galagos are nocturnal, in Gabon they become active earlier than other prosimian species at dusk, and they are one of the last of these species to return to a sleeping site at dawn (Charles-Dominique, 1977). This long activity period may be related to maximizing food-gathering time for a species that is exploiting a low-energy and highly-dispersed food source (gum). *Euoticus elegantulus* in Gabon sleeps in tight clusters of several individuals, on branch forks in dense foliage (Charles-Dominique, 1977).

Vocalizations. *Euoticus pallidus* is a relatively quiet galago. The most frequent calling heard by Ambrose (1999) was in the high-density population at Mt. Kupé, where 0.76 calls were heard per hour. Ambrose describes the most common *E. pallidus* call as a shrill "yap" or "t'ya", high-pitched single units that are sometimes interspersed with grunts; yaps are used as a contact call between individuals and, at higher intensities, as an alarm. Other calls are long drawn-out screeches, possibly associated with sexual behavior, and shrieks. Bearder and Honess (1992) note a brief, high-pitched "tsic" exchanged between individuals during dawn movement to a sleeping site.

Social organization. Very little is known about the social behavior of *E. pallidus*; these galagos are usually seen foraging alone, but sometimes in pairs; at dusk, up to four may be observed together, suggesting that they sleep in groups (Ambrose, 1999; JFO pers. obs.). In Gabon forests, *E. elegantulus* is also most often seen foraging alone (76% of sightings), but sometimes two animals are seen (17% of sightings); *E. elegantulus* congregate in sleeping clusters of 2–7 individuals, with varying combinations of adult females, adult males, and young (Charles-Dominique, 1977).

Reproduction. Few data are available on reproduction in this species. *Euoticus pallidus* probably does not have a restricted breeding season because pregnant individuals have been collected in November, January, May and June in southwestern Cameroon and eastern Nigeria (Sanderson, 1940; Jewell and Oates, 1969b). In Gabon, births in *E. elegantulus* are also spread across the year; small infants may be parked by the mother while she forages (and moved from place to place carried in her mouth); and adult weight is attained at the age of 8–10 months (Charles-Dominique, 1977). Unlike other galagos, needle-clawed galagos have only one pair of teats.

Ranging patterns. Nothing is known about the ranging behavior of *E. pallidus*. In Makokou, Gabon, *E. elegantulus* individuals of a sleeping cluster separate at dusk and move off in different directions to feed, visiting 500–1,000 gum-producing sites each night; the galagos are seen most frequently in areas where the gum-producing liana *Entada gigas* is common; one female was found to cover 200 m in 1.5 hours (Charles-Dominique, 1977).

Diet. *Euoticus pallidus* probably feeds mostly on gum (Oates, 1969), supplementing this diet with insects to provide protein; however, this species' feeding patterns have not been studied. The diet of *E. elegantulus* in Makokou, Gabon, comprises 75% gums, 20% insects (especially orthopterans and beetles), and only 5% fruits. In using their hands to grab insects as these take off from branches, they may end up hanging from a branch by their legs, before returning to a squatting position on the branch and transferring the prey to their mouth (Charles-Dominique, 1977; Ambrose, 1999).

Predators. There is no information about predation on needle-clawed galagos. Their agility, and rapid movements while foraging, would make them difficult prey during the night; they are probably most at risk when sleeping in the daytime. Charles-Dominique (1977) notes that *E. elegantulus* in Gabon did not respond to African wood owls (*Strix woodfordi*) hunting for insects only a few meters away from them.

Conservation Status

Euoticus pallidus is listed as of Least Concern in the IUCN Red List. With respect to the two subspecies, the Red List regards the mainland form, *E. p. talboti* as of Least Concern, but categorizes the Bioko form, *E. p. pallidus* as Endangered on the basis of the relatively small total area over which it occurs, the fragmentation of the animal's forest habitat, and continuing decline in the area and quality of the habitat. Because of its small size, the needle-clawed galago is not usually a target of human hunters, but it occasionally gets caught in snares set for other species. This galago is typically associated with large trees and is rarely found in young secondary forest or farmbush; therefore it is deleteriously affected by the loss of old forest to agriculture.

Where to See It

Talbot's needle-clawed galago can be seen in Nigeria in the Afi Mountain Wildlife Sanctuary, in Cross River National Park, and at the Centre for Education, Research and Conservation of Primates and Nature (CERCOPAN) Rhoko field site; in Cameroon it can be seen in Korup National Park, Takamanda National Park, and on Mount Kupé. On Bioko Island, the subspecies *E. pallidus pallidus* can be observed in forests around the settlement of Moka, and in the nearby Gran Caldera and Southern Highlands Scientific Reserve.

Galagidae

Sciurocheirus Gray, 1872
Allen's galagos

The genus *Sciurocheirus* was proposed in 1872 by Gray for the Allen's galago of Fernando Po (Bioko), a species originally named *Galago alleni* by Waterhouse in 1838. However, most subsequent authors retained the name *Galago alleni*, including in this species the populations living in the mainland forests of Cameroon, Nigeria and western equatorial Africa. Olson (1979) proposed a significant taxonomic revision of the galagos; he revived *Sciurocheirus* as a subgeneric name for Allen's galagos, and placed them in the genus *Galagoides*. Ambrose (2003) notes that evidence from studies of locomotor anatomy and genetics separate Allen's galagos from other species, and she suggests that they could either be grouped with the greater galagos in the genus *Otolemur*, or placed in their own genus, *Sciurocheirus*. The latter course was taken by Grubb *et al.* (2003), and is supported by the genetic analysis of Masters *et al.* (2007); this is therefore the arrangement followed in this book.

Careful studies by Bearder *et al.* (1995) and by Ambrose (1999) show that three distinct types of Allen's galago can be recognized on the basis of their vocalizations: *Sciurocheirus alleni* found on Bioko, and in western Cameroon and eastern Nigeria; *S. gabonensis* of southern Cameroon (south of the Sanaga River), Rio Muni and northern Gabon (probably extending into southern Central African Republic and northern Republic of Congo); and a species found south of the Ogooué River in Gabon, the Makande galago, that has not yet been formally named. These three species can also be distinguished by differences in their pelage. These three types are recognized as full species by Grubb *et al.* (2003), and that is the arrangement followed here.

Sciurocheirus alleni geospecies

Grubb (2006b) considers that the three allopatric species of *Sciurocheirus* comprise one geospecies, for which the senior name is *S. alleni*.

Local Representatives

Sciurocheirus alleni is the only species of this group found in the West African region. Two subspecies of *S. alleni* are recognized by Grubb *et al.* (2003): *S. alleni alleni* on Bioko Island, and *S. alleni cameronensis* on the mainland, between the lower Niger River in Nigeria and the Sanaga River in Cameroon. Groves (2001) regards these two forms as separate species, but their degree of difference is relatively small; they have the same call repertoires, but differ in the frequency with which the different calls are given (Ambrose, 1999); as noted by Groves, the Bioko animals are considerably larger.

Fig. 8.12: Bioko Allen's Galago (*Sciurocheirus alleni alleni*) in London Zoo in 1964. This individual was captured in Moka, as described in the Preface (photo by J. F. Oates).

Allen's galago
Sciurocheirus alleni (Waterhouse, 1838)

Other English: Allen's bushbaby, Allen's squirrel galago
French: Galago d'Allen
Spanish: Gálago de Allen
West African languages: Itebbo (Bubi, Bioko)

Identification (see Fig. 8.9, p.109)

A small nocturnal forest primate with a long bushy tail, a pointed muzzle, large eyes, very large ears, long, slender fingers and toes, and a soft, dense dark-colored coat. Allen's galagos are frequently seen low down in the forest canopy, where they make powerful leaps between thin vertical supports, and often gather food on the ground. They make distinctive whistling calls.

The Bioko Allen's galago (*S. alleni alleni*) is the darkest of all the forest galagos. The back is dark reddish-brown, and the outer arms, knees and upper surfaces of the thighs are a bright rusty red-brown; the hairs of these dorsal surfaces have gray bases. The tail is dark gray, sometimes almost black, with a slight brown tinge. The crown of the head is a dark brownish gray with a slight red tinge. The undersurfaces are pale gray, and there is a pale gray nose stripe. The skin of the muzzle, hands and feet is grayish pink. The large, thin flexible ears are dark brownish gray.

The mainland subspecies, the Cross River Allen's galago (*S. alleni cameronensis*), has an overall lighter coat than the Bioko subspecies, but with the same general pattern. The dorsal surfaces are a lighter red-brown (with lighter gray hair bases) and, although the arms and legs are redder than the back, the overall coloration is more even than in the Bioko population. Tail color varies, but is typically a mid gray with a slight brownish tinge, getting darker towards the tip; however, in some individuals the tail is dark gray, and in some it becomes lighter towards the tip. The hair is not as long as in Bioko animals. Some individuals on Mt. Cameroon have brown tails and little rusty coloration (Ambrose, 1999).

Males and females are about the same size. *S. alleni alleni* from Bioko is considerably larger than the mainland form; head and body length is 20–28 cm, tail length is 22–30 cm, and body weight is 395–455 g (Eisentraut, 1973; Ambrose, 1999; JFO pers. obs.). *S. alleni cameronensis* has a head and body length of 17–27 cm, a similar tail length of 22–30 cm, but a body weight of only 240–320 g (Eisentraut, 1973; Ambrose, 1999; Pimley, 2002; JFO pers. obs.). The average head and body length of 11 specimens of *S. alleni alleni* measured by Eisentraut (1973) was 227 cm, compared with only 188 cm in 10 specimens of *S. alleni cameronensis*.

Similar species. Allen's galago shares its habitat with three other galago species: the northern needle-clawed galago (*Euoticus pallidus*), Thomas's galago (*Galagoides thomasi*) and Demidoff's galago (*Galagoides demidovii*). The needle-clawed galago is similar in size, but its eyeshine is more orange than the bright red eyeshine of Allen's galago; *G. demidovii* and *G. thomasi* are much smaller. *Euoticus* is not as dark in color as Allen's galago and has a light brownish-gray tail rather than a mid to dark gray, or black, tail. *Euoticus* is often seen running on large branches high in the forest, while Allen's galago is typically low down, leaping between vertical supports; *G. thomasi* uses a range of heights and supports in the canopy, but *G. demidovii* is usually low down in thick growth, scuttling about on twigs and thin branches. *Galagoides demidovii* and *G. thomasi* make high-pitched crescendo calls, *Euoticus* makes shrill yaps, while Allen's galago gives croaks and whistles.

Taxonomic Note

In much of the older literature (e.g., Napier and Napier, 1967; Wolfheim, 1983; Jenkins, 1987) all Allen's galagos are treated as a single species, *Galago alleni*, with no subspecies.

Geographic Range

Sciurocheirus alleni alleni is restricted to Bioko Island, Equatorial Guinea, while *S. alleni cameronensis* occurs in the forest zone from the lower Niger River and the eastern part of the Niger Delta in Nigeria, east to the lower Sanaga River in Cameroon. South and east of the Sanaga in Cameroon, *S. gabonensis* is found, which often (but not always) has a white tail tip.

Natural History

Field Studies. Lesley Ambrose (1999, 2003) gave considerable attention to Allen's galagos in her study of vocalizations and diversity

Fig. 8.13: Cross River Allen's galago (*Sciurocheirus alleni cameronensis*), at Rhoko, Cross River State, Nigeria (photo by O. Brattström).

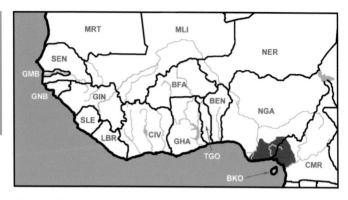

Fig. 8.14: Distributions of *Sciurocheirus alleni alleni* **(yellow) and** *S. alleni cameronensis* **(red).**

in the forest galagos of western Africa, making observations on Mt. Cameroon, Mt. Kupé and in Korup National Park (Cameroon) and at Moka on Bioko Island in 1996–1997. Further observations were made by Elizabeth Pimley at Mt. Kupé in 1999–2000 (Pimley, 2002; Pimley *et al.*, 2005b). In the course of short-term surveys, observations of *S. alleni* have been made in eastern Nigeria in 1966–1967 by Jewell and Oates (1969b), on Bioko Island in 1986 by Butynski and Koster (1994), and in Korup National Park, Cameroon, in 1992 by Bearder and Honess (1992). Pierre Charles-Dominique (1971, 1977) conducted a major long-term study of all the nocturnal prosimians in the forests of Makokou, Gabon, in 1965–1973; one of these species was the Gabon Allen's galago (*Sciurocheirus gabonensis*), referred to by Charles-Dominique as *Galago alleni*. Additional observations were made from 1969 to 1975 on *S. gabonensis* in secondary forest at Nkolnguem near Yaoundé, Cameroon, by Nicole Molez (Molez, 1976).

Habitat. Allen's galago is an animal of moist lowland and montane forest and may be encountered both in secondary and mature forest. It occurs from sea level up to 2,250 m; a higher elevation than any other West African galago species (Ambrose, 1999; Butynski and Koster, 1994; Schlossman, 2006). It sometimes crosses open pasture in Bioko's Moka highlands (1,300 m) to forage in bushes (Jewell and Oates, 1969b; Butynski and Koster, 1994).

Population. Allen's galagos vary greatly in abundance across their range; they tend to be most common in montane forest. In Korup National Park in Cameroon, Bearder and Honess (1992) had

214 sightings along 168 km of survey trail in mostly mature lowland forest (1.27/km), while in the Oban Hills of Nigeria, to the west of Korup, Jewell and Oates (1969b) had 4 sightings along approximately 6.5 km of trail in mature forest (0.6/km). In Korup, Ambrose (1999) encountered *S. alleni* at a rate of 0.83 animals/hr when surveying at an average speed of 0.45 km/hr, equivalent to 1.84 sightings/km, while in montane forest the sighting rate was 1.92/hr, or 4.27/km. In her study area on Mt. Kupé, Cameroon, Pimley (2002) found a density of 15 animals/km².

Habitat use. Although Allen's galago is sometimes observed as high as 20 m in the canopy, it is typically found in the forest understorey below a height of 5 m, and often gathers food on the ground (Ambrose, 1999; Pimley, 2002; JFO pers. obs.). Open understorey is preferred, where these galagos characteristically leap between narrow vertical supports, both thin tree trunks and the vertical bases of lianas. Pimley (2002) found that *S. alleni* at Mt. Kupé most frequently used supports of 2–5 cm diameter, and in more than half of all sightings they were on vertical supports.

Locomotion and posture. Sciurocheirus alleni is a powerful leaper. These galagos commonly leap 2–4 m from one vertical support to another in the understorey, or elsewhere in the forest canopy. They characteristically leap from an upright clinging posture on their support, pushing off with their legs and grasping the landing support with their hands (Ambrose, 1999). Charles-Dominique (1977) describes how *S. gabonensis* then rotates rapidly around the landing support and leaps to the next trunk, thereby covering as much as 12 m in 5 seconds with 5–6 leaps.

Activity pattern. Allen's galagos are nocturnal, but details of their activity patterns have not been described. At Mount Kupé, Pimley (2002) found that *S. alleni* sleeps by day in hollows in trees and large lianas, and in tangles of vines and lianas; Pimley notes that the galagos peered out of their sleeping holes for 5–20 minutes at dusk before leaving the sleeping sites. In Gabon, *S. gabonensis* also sleeps during the day in tree hollows that are sometimes lined with leaves; a succession of different hollows is used (Charles-Dominique, 1977). Molez (1976) reports that at Nkolnguem, Cameroon, *S. gabonensis* wakes up about 20 minutes before sunset, and sleeps 15 minutes after sunrise; at Nkolnguem the galagos were most active in the first part of the night and showed peaks of feeding activity at 3–4 hour intervals.

Vocalizations. These are noisy galagos, and their calling behavior is one of the best studied aspects of their biology (Ambrose, 1999, 2003). Foraging individuals keep in contact with each other via low-frequency croaking and long drawn-out "mew whistles." Especially on Bioko, mew whistles may be uttered in counter-calling phrases of several units, especially in situations of mild alarm (Ambrose, 2003). Croaking is used for long-distance communication, and when individuals meet they exchange mew whistles, twitters, chirps and whirrs (Pimley, 2002). Young *S. alleni* probably make high-pitched "click" or "tsic" calls to communicate with the mother, as reported for *S. gabonensis* by Charles-Dominique (1977).

Social organization. Ambrose (1999) observed that although Allen's galagos disperse to forage, they are quite often seen together; 50% of observations on Bioko and 44% in southwest Cameroon were of 2–4 individuals in close proximity, exchanging calls, with this behavior being particularly common at the beginning of the night. Pimley (2002) found a very similar pattern: about half of her observations of *S. alleni* at sleeping sites on Mt. Kupé were of solitary individuals, while the other half were of 2–4 individuals together. Although they typically foraged on their own, the galagos kept in touch with sleeping partners through exchanging mew whistle calls. In Gabon, Charles-Dominique (1977) found that certain pairs of female *S. gabonensis* had extensively overlapping home ranges and often slept together in the same tree hollow, while adult males used larger ranges overlapping those of several females, and slept alone. *Sciurocheirus gabonensis* marks its range with urine deposited on its hands and feet.

Reproduction. Evidence from Cameroon suggests that *S. alleni* does not have a restricted breeding season, because pregnant females and small young have been found throughout the year (Sanderson, 1940; Ambrose, 1999; Pimley, 2002). Females typically produce single offspring once a year; small infants are carried in the mother's mouth, but when older are parked in dense vegetation while the mother forages (Ambrose, 1999). In Gabon, *S. gabonensis* has births spread across the year; there is a 133-day gestation period; and adult body weight is attained at an age of about 10 months (Charles-Dominique, 1977).

Ranging patterns. From radio-tracking at Mt. Kupé in Cameroon, Pimley *et al.* (2005) determined that, on the basis of measuring a minimum convex polygon occupied, four adult females had home ranges of 0.82–19.32 ha, and one adult male had a range of 12 ha; one juvenile female and one subadult male each used an area of over 40 ha. Small home ranges with an average size of 0.82 ha are reported for *S. gabonensis* at Nkolnguem, Cameroon (Molez, 1976), but in Gabon Charles-Dominique (1977) found female ranges of 8–16 ha in this species, and very much larger male ranges of up to 50 ha.

Diet. Fruits and small animals are the main foods of Allen's galago. Ambrose (1999) describes *S. alleni* gathering fallen fruit from the forest floor, and catching insects flushed by columns of driver ants. Pimley (2002) did not have a large sample of feeding observations for this galago at Mt. Kupé, but more than 50% of her observations of feeding involved insects (especially moths). In mature forest at Makokou, Gabon, *S. gabonensis* has a diet comprising 73% fruits and 25% small animals, based on stomach contents (Charles-Dominique, 1977), with the animal part of the diet including beetles, snails, moths, frogs, ants and spiders. In secondary forest at Nkolnguem, Cameroon,

Fig. 8.15: Bioko's Allen's galago (*Sciurocheirus alleni alleni*) in the Gran Caldera de Luba (photo by R. A. Bergl).

Galagidae

the diet of *S. gabonensis* (again based on stomach contents) was found by Molez (1976) to be strongly animal-based: 66% small animals (especially orthopterans, snails and slugs), 34% fruits, and very small traces of gums.

Predators. Almost nothing is known about predation on Allen's galagos. Their habit of feeding on the ground likely puts them at risk of predation by a variety of carnivores and by owls. Pimley (2002) suggest that snakes may be a threat. These galagos occasionally appear in the bushmeat market in Malabo, Bioko (Oates *et al.*, 2004).

Conservation Status

Sciurocheirus alleni is listed as of Least Concern in the IUCN Red List. The Red List treats the two subspecies differently; the mainland form, *S. a. cameronensis* is listed as of Least Concern, but the Bioko form, *S. a. alleni,* is listed as Endangered based on the relatively small total area over which it occurs, the fragmentation of its habitat, and continuing decline in the area and quality of this habitat. Because this galago tends to be associated with older forest it is threatened by the continuing loss and degradation of such forest outside protected areas. Montane forest is a particularly important habitat for *S. alleni*; this habitat is suffering heavily from conversion to agriculture in many parts of the Cameroon-Nigeria border region, and is poorly represented in protected areas; *S. a. cameronensis* would benefit by an upgrading of the conservation status of several mountain areas in western Cameroon (Oates *et al.*, 2004). By contrast, montane forest is relatively secure on Bioko. Although *S. alleni* is occasionally shot by hunters or caught in traps set for other species, bushmeat hunting is not a major threat to this primate.

Where to See It

The Cross River Allen's galago, *Sciurocheirus alleni cameronensis*, can be seen in Nigeria at Afi Mountain Wildlife Sanctuary, Cross River National Park, and the CERCOPAN organization's Rhoko field site. In Cameroon it can be seen in Korup National Park, Takamanda National Park, and on Mounts Cameroon and Kupé. On Bioko Island, the subspecies *S. a. alleni* can readily be observed in forests around the settlement of Moka, as well as in the nearby Gran Caldera and Southern Highlands Scientific Reserve.

Family Lorisidae
Lorises and pottos

The lorises and pottos are small, forest-living nocturnal primates with short or very short tails; compared to galagos they have relatively shorter legs and smaller ears. They are highly arboreal, they do not jump, and their characteristic style of movement is deliberate quadrupedal climbing and walking, with only occasional running. Like the galagos, lorisids have the strepsirrhine features of a naked snout, soft dense fur, a toothcomb and an elongated nail on the second toe. Lorises are found in forest habitats in South and Southeast Asia, while the pottos are restricted to African forests. There are two living genera of pottos, *Perodicticus* and *Arctocebus*. *Perodicticus* is larger and more robustly built than *Arctocebus*, and has an obvious, but short tail; three species are recognized by Groves (2001), spread across the forest zone and its outliers from southern Senegal to Kenya. The more gracefully-built *Arctocebus* has a very short tail; two species are recognized, restricted to western equatorial forests between the Niger and the Congo.

Arctocebus Gray, 1863
Angwantibos

Angwantibos have small, compact but relatively slender bodies, very short tails, large eyes, rounded ears, and a pointed snout. Their hands and feet are adapted for strong grasping; the hands have a pincer-like appearance, with the second finger represented by just a small tubercle and the third shortened. Two species are recognized by Kingdon (1997), Groves (2001) and Grubb *et al.* (2003): *A. calabarensis* from north of the Sanaga River in Cameroon and eastern Nigeria, and *A. aureus* from south of the Sanaga. The name "angwantibo" is derived from the indigenous name for these lorisids in the part of the world from where the type specimen came: Calabar in Nigeria.

Arctocebus calabarensis geospecies

Grubb (2006b) regards the two allopatric forms of angwantibo as one geospecies, *Arctocebus calabarensis*.

Local representative

The only species of *Arctocebus* in the region covered by this book is *A. calabarensis*.

Angwantibo
Arctocebus calabarensis

Lorisidae

Bosman's Potto
Perodicticus potto potto

Benin Potto
Perodicticus potto juju

Milne-Edwards's Potto
Perodicticus edwardsi

Fig. 8.16.

Angwantibo
Arctocebus calabarensis (J. A. Smith, 1863)

Other English: Calabar angwantibo, Calabar potto
French: Arctocèbe, potto de Calabar
West African languages: Anwantibo (Efik, Nigeria); Ikiri (Igbo, Nigeria)

Identification (see Fig. 8.16, p.130)

In adults, the dorsal surfaces (including the outer limbs) are brown, varying among individuals from a grayish-yellow khaki to a warm reddish tan; the hairs on the ventral surfaces are dirty or creamy white, with gray bases. Some individuals have a white stripe on the nose, but this is not a feature of all angwantibos. Infants are born with a long, fluffy coat that has two dorsal hair types; scattered among the gray-based, reddish-tipped hairs are longer gray "guard" hairs about 1.5 cm long with white tips, giving the young animal a "frosted" appearance for the first six months of life. The ventral surface of the infant is gray, becoming paler with age.

Males and females are about the same size, with adults having a head and body length of 22–26 cm, a tail a little less than 1 cm long, and a weight of 300–380 g (Sanderson, 1940; Jewell and Oates, 1969a; JFO pers. obs.).

Similar species. The most similar species with which the angwantibo shares its habitat is the potto. The species within the range of the angwantibo is Milne-Edwards' potto, *Perodicticus edwardsi*. Milne-Edwards' potto is considerably larger than the angwantibo, with a head and body length of about 33 cm, and a body weight of up to 1.6 kg (but averaging 1.1 kg) (Charles-Dominique, 1971, 1977). The potto has a shorter muzzle and relatively smaller eyes and ears, long black guard hairs on the nape of the neck, and darker dorsal pelage. The potto's second finger is much reduced in size, but is not as vestigial as it is in *Arctocebus*.

Taxonomic Note

Some classifications (e.g., Jenkins, 1987) place the Calabar angwantibo as a subspecies (*A. calabarensis calabarensis*) of a species which also includes the golden angwantibo (*A. calabarensis aureus*).

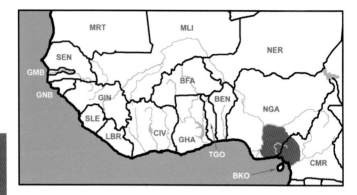

Fig. 8.17: Distribution of *Arctocebus calabarensis*.

The golden angwantibo occurs south of the Sanaga River in Cameroon, and in Gabon, mainland Equatorial Guinea and the Republic of Congo; it is a smaller (average adult weight about 200 g), more slender animal than the Calabar angwantibo, and has more golden-reddish dorsal pelage.

Geographic Range

Arctocebus calabarensis occurs in the forest zone from the lower Niger River and the eastern edge of the Niger Delta in Nigeria, east to the lower Sanaga River in Cameroon. It occurs not only in the moist forest zone but also in the mosaic derived savanna and woodland zone north of the moist forest, at least as far north as 7°41'N, close to the Benue River near its confluence with the Niger (Oates and Jewell, 1967). It has not been found in montane forests in this region, nor on the island of Bioko.

Natural History

Habitat. Although the angwantibo is a forest zone species, it is rarely seen in closed high-canopy rain forest. Most often it is encountered in young secondary forest, including forest edges, and in forest patches surrounded by other vegetation. In Nigeria, a large part of its habitat between the Cross and Niger rivers is a mosaic of farmland, young forest regrowth, and derived savanna, with small scattered patches of forest (Oates and Jewell, 1967; Jewell and Oates, 1969b).

Field studies. There has been no extended field study of *Arctocebus calabarensis*. Observations were collected on transect surveys in Nigeria in 1966–1967 (Jewell and Oates, 1969b) and in Cameroon in 1992 (Bearder and Honess, 1992). Some behavioral and reproductive information is available from captive studies in Nigeria, which included observations on individuals maintained in an open-air enclosure close to their natural habitat (Jewell and Oates, 1969a, 1969b). More in-depth research was conducted on the golden angwantibo (*A. aureus*) in 1965–1973 in Gabon by Pierre Charles-Dominique (1971, 1977). Charles-Dominique considered his study animals to be representatives of the subspecies *A. calabarensis aureus*.

Population. Twenty-seven sightings of angwantibos were made in 36 night walks, each of about 800 m, in forest fragments in the mosaic landscape between the Cross and Niger rivers (Jewell and Oates, 1969b). This is an encounter rate of approximately 1 per km. By contrast, in Korup National Park in Cameroon, only three sightings came from surveying 168 km of trail; these sightings were in secondary forest in a predominantly mature forest landscape (Bearder and Honess, 1992). In Gabon, Charles-Dominique (1977) found *A. aureus* living at a density of 2/km² in mature rain forest, where the animals were concentrated in patches of dense vegetation produced by tree falls.

Fig. 8.18: Juvenile angwantibo (*Arctocebus calabarensis*), Nsukka, Nigeria (photo by P. A. Jewell).

Habitat use. Angwantibos typically use dense growth near the ground. In eastern Nigeria they are usually seen below a height of 3 m, but may range up to 10 m (Jewell and Oates, 1969b); in Korup, Cameroon, they have only been observed below 5 m (Bearder and Honess, 1992). They travel on the ground between suitable foraging sites. In Gabon, Charles-Dominique (1977) discovered that in mature forest the closely related *Arctocebus aureus* occurs especially in tree-fall zones, which have dense low vegetation and are rich in lianas. It is most often seen below a height of 5 m and never higher than 15 m; a pattern of abundance and habitat use consistent with that for *A. calabarensis*. *Arctocebus aureus* uses small-diameter lianas to move from bush to bush in the understorey, and explores twigs when searching for food.

Locomotion and posture. Like other lorisine primates, angwantibos walk and climb in a gliding manner, without pauses, maintaining a grip on supports with at least two limbs on opposite sides of the body, while moving along lianas, small branches and twigs. This movement is well described for *A. aureus* by Charles-Dominique (1977). When threatened, angwantibos grip their support tightly, hunch their body, and often rock up and down with the mouth open, producing a hissing sound; in this position they will attempt to bite another angwantibo or a potential predator by pushing their head downwards and backwards, striking from under an arm. Despite the suggestion by Sanderson (1940) that angwantibos sleep suspended beneath horizontal branches, Jewell and Oates (1969b) only observed them to sleep in upright positions, clinging to fine supports, with the rump sometimes resting on a fork between two branches, and the head buried between the arms.

Activity pattern. Angwantibos are fully nocturnal and only become active when it is completely dark. During the day they sleep in the cover of dense vegetation.

Vocalizations. Wild angwantibos have not been heard to call, but *A. calabarensis* has not been the subject of a long-term behavioral field study. In captivity, hissing is heard from threatened animals, and squeaking calls from males when fighting (Jewell and Oates, 1969b). In *A. aureus*, Charles-Dominique (1977) notes high-pitched "tsic" contact calls made by isolated infants and mothers searching for them, "groaning" from threatened or fighting individuals, and a squeaky whistling "wheet" call in situations of distress.

Fig. 8.19: Angwantibo (*Arctocebus calabarensis*), Ahoada, Nigeria (photo by A. P. Leventis).

Social organization and behavior. Except for mothers with dependent young, angwantibos almost always forage and sleep alone. In captivity, adult males fight if introduced to each other; a male shows interest in an introduced female, but the female may show aggression to the male if approached (Jewell and Oates, 1969b). Males scent-mark foliage with urine and will search for females by following scent trails.

Reproduction and life history. Manley (1974) notes (from studies of captive angwantibos) that both males and females have small areas of naked, tessellated, glandular skin in the genital area; during courtship a male will mark an estrous female with secretions from this glandular area (on the scrotum) by climbing over her back, using three of his limbs in locomotion, and cocking one leg. Angwantibos in eastern Nigeria do not have a distinct breeding season; the gestation period is about 130 days and females can become pregnant during a post-partum estrus soon after giving birth, so they may breed twice in a year (Jewell and Oates, 1969a). Females have three pairs of nipples but have only been observed to give birth to singletons. Infants start to feed themselves at about six weeks of age and may be weaned at about four months; they can attain full size after only seven months (Charles-Dominique, 1966a; Jewell and Oates, 1969a). Thus, angwantibos demonstrate features of an *r*-selected life-history strategy, possibly related to their use of unpredictably available pioneer vegetation.

Infant parking. In angwantibos and pottos (and in the related lorises of Asia), females "park" their infants during the night while they forage (Jewell and Oates, 1969b; Charles-Dominique, 1977). Very young infants are carried clinging to the mother's belly, but several days after birth the mother will leave her infant holding on to a small support in dense foliage after grooming it extensively with her tongue. Before dawn the mother recovers the infant after an exchange of "tsic" calls. When larger infants are with their mother they are carried on her back.

Ranging patterns. The ranging behavior of *A. calabarensis* has not been studied.

Diet. Although angwantibos eat some fruit, their diet is dominated by insects, especially slow-moving, soft-bodied forms such as caterpillars. From 65% to 85% of the contents of stomachs of *A. aureus* in Gabon contained caterpillars (Charles-Dominique, 1966b, 1977). Food is located predominantly by smell.

Predators. The natural predators of angwantibos are not certainly known, but probably include viverrid carnivores and possibly owls.

Conservation Status

Arctocebus calabarensis is listed as of Least Concern in the IUCN Red List. Because *A. calabarensis* is more abundant in young secondary growth than in mature forest, the conversion of mature forest that has proceeded apace in eastern Nigeria and western Cameroon may have actually increased the amount of habitat available for this species, which is very rarely seen in mature forest. Because of its small size it is not a special target of hunters, but may still be caught and eaten where larger mammals are scarce or absent.

Where to See It

Angwantibos can be encountered in the farm-regrowth mosaic that is widespread in southeastern Nigeria, including the Rhoko field research site of the CERCOPAN organization in Cross River State.

Perodicticus Bennett, 1831
Pottos

Like angwantibos, pottos are nocturnal primates with compact bodies and soft woolly coats. However, they are larger than angwantibos, and their tails, while still short, are longer; they have rounded heads with a short muzzle, large protruberent eyes (although the eyes are smaller than in other African prosimians), and small, rounded ears. Pottos are cautious, arboreal, quadrupedal climbers that never jump. The hands and feet are adapted for strong grasping, with the second (index) finger reduced to a stump.

The taxonomy of the pottos is not well resolved. For many years, all pottos have been regarded as belonging to a single species, *Perodicticus*

Lorisidae

Fig. 8.20: Benin potto (*Perodicticus potto juju*), Okomu, Nigeria (photo by A. P. Leventis).

potto (e.g., Hill, 1953; Napier and Napier, 1967; Hill and Meester, 1971; Jenkins, 1987; Groves, 2001). However, Grubb *et al.* (2003) suggested that further study might show that *Perodicticus* contains several valid species. Such a study has been conducted by Stump (2005). Stump's study, focusing on morphology, provides support for recognizing at least three species, equivalent to the subspecies recognized by Jenkins (1987) and Groves (2001): *Perodicticus potto*, *P. edwardsi* and *P. ibeanus*; it also suggests that the pottos found between the lower Volta River in Ghana and the lower Niger River in Nigeria are distinctive. Grubb (1978b) showed that the Volta-Niger potto is reasonably regarded as the distinct subspecies *P. potto juju*, and Stump (2005) notes that an argument can be made for elevating this taxon to a full species. Butynski and de Jong (2007) have described a new subspecies of potto from Mount Kenya, *P. potto stockleyi*, which might also justify species status, but at the time of writing it was known from only one old museum specimen.

Perodicticus potto geospecies

In this guidebook, a classification of the pottos into several species is accepted. All these forms of potto are members of the single *P. potto* geospecies as identified by Grubb (2006b).

Local Representatives

Two potto species occur in West Africa: *Perodicticus potto* (found from southern Senegal to the Niger) and *P. edwardsi* (found from the Niger east to the Ubangi River). Within *P. potto*, two subspecies are recognized: *P. p. potto* (from southern Senegal to the Volta River in Ghana) and *P. p. juju* (found from the Volta to the Niger).

How this Guide Treats the Pottos

This account begins by describing the appearance and distribution of each of the three kinds of potto in West Africa. Almost all the careful field observations conducted on West African pottos have been made on just one of these forms, Milne-Edwards's potto, *Perodicticus edwardsi*. Therefore, following the basic description of the three forms, one consolidated account is presented that reviews knowledge on the natural history of all the West African pottos, with an emphasis on the best-known, *P. edwardsi*.

Bosman's potto
Perodicticus potto potto (Müller, 1766)

Other English: Western potto
French: Potto de Bosman
West African languages: Condeh (Mende, Sierra Leone); Ja'an (Bassa, Liberia); Akoutaginei (Twi, Ghana)

Identification (see Fig. 8.16, p.130)

Lorisidae

Bosman's potto has a longer tail than any other form of potto; adults have a head and body length of 30–35 cm and a tail length of 7–10 cm; the typical tail length of 8–9 cm is as long as the legs (Jenkins, 1987; Stump, 2005). There is no reliable, published information on the body weight of this form of potto, but the average weight is almost certainly less than 1 kg; males and females are about the same size.

In adults of *P. p. potto*, the dorsal surfaces (including the outer limbs) are reddish gray-brown, with distinctly darker coloration in a band along the midline of the back, especially in the shoulder region. Undersurfaces have a creamy-gray appearance as a result of hairs with mid-gray bases and creamy-white tips. Infants are born with pink skin and a mostly white coat that has a light brown strip down the middle of the back (Grand *et al.*, 1964); the skin and pelage gradually darken, but retained white guard hairs give the dorsal surfaces of young animals a "frosted" appearance for the first 5–6 months of life (Rahm, 1960).

Fig. 8.21: A juvenile Bosman's potto (*Perodicticus potto potto*), Kumasi, Ghana (photo by J. F. Oates).

Female pottos examined in the hand can readily be mistaken for males because of their prominent, stout clitoris and the presence of a "pseudo-scrotum," a raised area of fissured, glandular skin posterior to the clitoris, closely resembling the similar glandular surface of the male's scrotum (Manley, 1966).

Similar species. No very similar species occurs within the range of *P. p. potto.* Within its range, the only other nocturnal forest primates with similar "eyeshine" are the Demidoff's and Thomas's galagos; each of these is considerably smaller than the potto, has a long tail and large ears, and typically moves more rapidly, often running and frequently jumping. Sometimes confused with Bosman's potto is the arboreal palm civet (*Nandinia binotata*). The palm civet has a long tail and is about double the size of the potto; it has a brown, spotted coat and the tail has black rings.

Geographic Range

Perodicticus potto potto is known from the moist forest zone from at least Sierra Leone to the vicinity of the Volta River in Ghana. The western limit of its range is uncertain. Although museum specimens do not seem to exist from west of Sierra Leone, there are accounts in the literature of pottos from as far north and west as Senegal and The Gambia (Grubb *et al.*, 1998). McGrew *et al.* (1978) found potto remains in chimpanzee feces from Niokolo Koba National Park, Senegal. However, the potto is not listed in descriptions of the primates of Guinea-Bissau (Monard, 1938; Gippoliti and Dell'Omo, 2003).

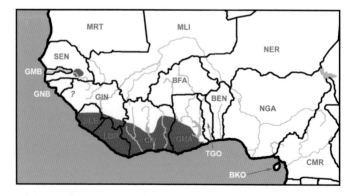

Fig. 8.22: Distribution of *Perodicticus potto potto*.

Lorisidae

Benin potto[1]
Perodicticus potto juju Thomas, 1910

French: Potto de Togo-Sud
West African languages: N'dazala (Tem, Togo); Assididohë (Gen, Togo); Iki (Yoruba, Nigeria); Atakolode (Edo, Nigeria)

Identification (see Fig. 8.16, p.130)

The Benin potto is the smallest and lightest-colored of the West African pottos. Although the length of the tail in the Benin potto is variable, most individuals have very short tails which average 6–7 cm in length but are often only 5 cm long, little more than half the length of the *P. p. potto* tail (Baudenon, 1949; Stump, 2005; specimens in the Natural History Museum, London). Adults of *P. p. juju* have a head and body length of about 30 cm (range 29–34 cm). Body weights of individuals measured in southern Togo ranged from 720 to 1,050 g, with a mean of 840 g (Baudenon, 1949).

The Benin potto differs from Bosman's potto (*Perodicticus potto potto*) in its paler dorsal coloration, which is typically a light silvery gray-brown with a slight reddish or yellowish tint; in *P. p. juju*, the dark dorsal stripe characteristic of *P. p. potto* is thin and relatively indistinct, or absent (Stump, 2005). Rather than a dark "saddle" of hair on the shoulder there is sometimes a dark "smudge" at the base of the neck (Grubb, 1978b), but even this can be absent. Ventral surfaces have a silvery-cream appearance resulting from hairs with silvery-gray bases and creamy tips.

Similar species. As with Bosman's potto, no very similar species lives in the same forests as the Benin potto, but possible confusion might occur during night observations with the Demidoff's and Thomas's galagos and with the two-spotted palm civet (see comments under *P. p. potto* above).

---

[1] This potto has not had a commonly-used English name. "Benin potto" is chosen here because: (a) the species occurs in the forests of the Dahomey Gap, and Bénin is the current name for the country formerly known as Dahomey; (b) the forests where it occurs are adjacent to the Bight of Benin in the Gulf of Guinea; (c) the species also occurs in forests in Nigeria near the historic city of Benin, once the capital of a powerful kingdom, that has given its name to the Bight of Benin, which in turn led to the choice of name for the Bénin Republic.

Fig. 8.23: Benin potto (*Perodicticus potto juju*), Okomu, Nigeria (photo by A. P. Leventis).

Geographic Range

Perodicticus potto juju occurs in the forests of southwestern Nigeria, southern Bénin Republic and Togo (i.e., the Dahomey Gap), and probably southeastern Ghana. Grubb (1978b) regards the affinities of the only two museum specimens of pottos he located from southeastern Ghana as "uncertain".

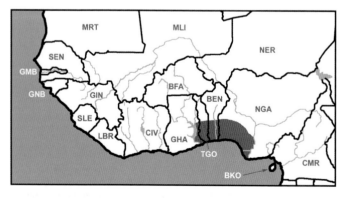

Fig. 8.24: Distribution of *Perodicticus potto juju*.

Milne-Edwards's potto
Perodicticus edwardsi Bouvier, 1879

Other English: Cameroon potto, central potto, Central African potto
French: Potto de Milne-Edwards
West African languages: Dachai (Iko, Nigeria); Half-a-tail (Pidgin, Cameroon)

Identification (see Fig. 8.16, p.130)

Lorisidae

Milne-Edwards's potto differs from Bosman's and Benin pottos in its larger size (especially the larger size of its skull and molar teeth) and darker coat. The tail is short, but not quite as short as that of the Benin potto. Males and females do not differ in size. *Perodicticus edwardsi* from the Mamfe region of southwestern Cameroon have head and body lengths of 26–42 cm (mean 37 cm) and tail lengths of 6–8 cm (mean 7 cm) (Sanderson, 1940). Adults from Mount Kupé in Cameroon had weights of 938–1,858 g (mean 1,493 g) (Pimley *et al.*, 2005a), and three wild-caught adult females measured in Nigeria weighed 1,200–1,400 g (Jewell and Oates, 1969a).

The hair of the upper surfaces of Milne-Edwards's potto is a rich medium to dark brown color with a reddish hue, and with especially dark hair on the shoulders, but without a dorsal stripe. Long black bristles on the nape of the neck are particularly well developed in this taxon. The undersurfaces in Milne-Edwards's potto are yellowy gray.

Adult *P. edwardsi* measured in Gabon had a head and body length of 30–40 cm, a tail length of 4–7 cm (mean 5 cm), and a weight of 850–1,600 g (mean 1,100g) (Charles-Dominique, 1977). The smaller average size of animals in the Gabon population, compared to those in western Cameroon and Nigeria, is paralleled by the angwantibos of these two different regions. The angwantibos are now usually regarded as two distinct species; this suggests that there might be other differences between the potto populations that may eventually be considered to have taxonomic significance.

Similar species. The most likely species with which Milne Edwards's potto may be confused is the angwantibo (*Arctocebus calabarensis*). They occur together in Nigeria and Cameroon between the Niger and Cross rivers. Pottos are larger than angwantibos, which typically have a head and body length of less than 25 cm and a weight of less than 400 g. The angwantibo's tail is less than 1 cm long, even shorter than that of any of the pottos. The angwantibo has a more slender build and a more pointed snout, and typically occurs low down in secondary growth, rather than high in trees. There is also potential confusion, if animals are not clearly seen at night, with the galago species *Galagoides demidovii* and *G. thomasi*, *Euoticus elegantulus*, and *Sciurocheirus alleni*; all these galagos are smaller than *P. edwardsi*. They have long tails, and often jump, which pottos never do. The sympatric two-spotted palm civet (*Nandinia binotata*) is larger than the potto and has a long tail.

Fig. 8.25: Female and young Milne-Edwards's potto (*Perodicticus edwardsi*), Bashu, Cross River State, Nigeria (photo by A. P. Leventis).

Geographic Range

Perodicticus edwardsi occurs in the moist forest zone from the lower Niger in Nigeria east and south through Cameroon, Rio Muni, Gabon, the Central African Republic and the Republic of Congo to the Ubangi and Congo rivers.

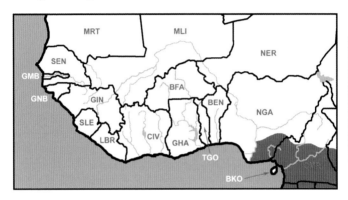

Fig. 8.26: Distribution of *Perodicticus edwardsi* in West Africa.

Natural History of *Perodicticus potto* and *P. edwardsi*

Field studies. The first thorough study of the behavior of wild pottos (along with other nocturnal prosimians) was conducted at Makokou in Gabon by Pierre Charles-Dominique in 1965–1973; this study was on *P. edwardsi*, referred to by Charles-Dominique (1971, 1977) as *P. potto edwardsi*. Further extended observations on *P. edwardsi* have been made on Mount Kupé, Cameroon, by Elizabeth Pimley (2002; Pimley *et al.*, 2005a, 2005b). Both Charles-Dominique and Pimley were able to use trapping, marking and radio-collaring to study wild pottos. In the course of more general survey work, observations on *P. edwardsi* were collected in Nigeria in 1966–1967 by Jewell and Oates (1969a, 1969b), in Rio Muni in 1968 by Jones (1969), and in Cameroon in 1992 by Bearder and Honess (1992). *Perodicticus potto* has been much less thoroughly investigated. Baudenon (1949) has a few notes about pottos in Togo (*P. p. juju*), but they mostly relate to captive animals. Rahm (1960) has notes on pottos in Côte d'Ivoire, again mostly based on captive animals, and Oates (1984) has published some brief observations on wild pottos in western Nigeria (*P. p. juju*) and Sierra Leone (*P. p. potto*).

Habitat. Pottos are found in the forest zone, in lowland forest and up to an altitude of at least 1,500 m in lower montane forest. They are typically associated with mature forest or older secondary moist forest, with relatively abundant large trees, but *P. p. juju* also occurs in gallery forest in the dry-forest zone of the Dahomey Gap in Togo (Baudenon, 1949).

Population. Pottos generally occur at low density. In Korup National Park, Cameroon, Bearder and Honess (1992) obtained 16 sightings of *P. edwardsi* along 168 km of forest trail. In mixed secondary forest and farmbush on Mt. Kupé, Cameroon, Pimley (2002) estimated a density of 4.7 animals/km². In the forests around Makokou, Gabon, Charles-Dominique (1977) estimated a density of 8–10 *P. edwardsi* per km².

Habitat use. Pottos are typically seen quite high up in the forest canopy using larger branches and lianas, but they also use smaller-diameter stems to climb from one tree crown to another. In eastern Nigeria, *P. edwardsi* has been observed at a mean height of 19 m (Bearder and Oates, 2009a), and in Korup, Cameroon, at 5–30 m (Bearder and Honess, 1992). At Mt. Kupé, Cameroon, Pimley (2002) obtained a majority of her observations at 6–15 m, but this was in an area of secondary forest containing considerable farmbush. At Makokou, Gabon, *P. edwardsi* was usually seen at heights of 5–30 m, using supports of 1–15 cm; the animals used greater heights in mature than in secondary forest (Charles-Dominique, 1977). In western Nigeria, individuals of *P. p. juju* were first observed in old secondary forest at heights of 9–24 m (mean 13 m) mostly using 5–15 cm supports (Oates, 1984).

Locomotion and posture. Potto locomotion is typically smooth, careful, relatively slow walking (with occasional running) along branches, typically using the upper surface of the branch but also going underneath branches and climbing vertical stems. Pottos usually keep a grip with three limbs, and move headfirst down trunks (Walker, 1969; Charles-Dominique, 1977). While foraging, pottos often keep their nose close to the substrate they are moving on, apparently using their sense of smell to locate food and detect signs of other pottos (Oates, 1984).

Special adaptations. In addition to their characteristic pattern of locomotion, pottos have broad, flat skulls with upwardly directed eyes and, in their neck region, vertebrae with elongated dorsal spines associated with a scapular shield of thickened skin bearing long bristles; the bristles, or vibrissae, have strong tactile sensitivity (Hill, 1953; Charles-Dominique, 1977; Oates, 1984). In its nose-down foraging posture the bristles on the potto's neck provide information on objects in front of it as it moves; the potto uses the scapular shield to thrust at predators, and it has also been suggested they use it in social contact with other pottos (Charles-Dominique, 1977; Oates, 1984).

Activity pattern. Pottos are nocturnal and only become active in full darkness. They are most active in the first half of the night (Pimley *et al.*, 2005a). Sleeping sites are typically in dense, leafy vegetation, where a potto grips a relatively thin branch, but they also sleep in tree hollows (Charles-Dominique, 1977; Ambrose, 2002).

Fig. 8.27: Milne-Edwards's potto (*Perodicticus edwardsi*), Bashu, Cross River State, Nigeria (photo by A. P. Leventis).

Vocalizations. Pottos are generally quiet animals, relying more on olfaction than calling for communication. For *P. edwardsi* in Gabon, Charles-Dominique (1977) has described a brief, high-pitched "tsic" call made before dawn by a mother and infant before they join up and move to a sleeping site; a two-phase (inhalation, exhalation) "groan" made by animals during aggressive encounters; and a high-pitched whistle (or "wheet") given by distressed animals.

Social organization and behavior. Pottos commonly forage alone, except in the cases of larger young accompanying their mother, and of adult males and females living as pairs that may sometimes join together when foraging. Small infants are "parked" while the mother forages (see below). Pimley *et al.* (2005a) found that some, but not all, Milne-Edwards's pottos in the Mount Kupé forest, Cameroon, lived as male-female pairs in home ranges that had a large degree of overlap. The members of a pair were seen within 5 m of each other about one-third of the time, and they engaged in affiliative interactions that included facial contact and grooming; members of a pair also slept in proximity to each other. At Makokou, Gabon, on the other hand, Charles-Dominique (1977) almost always saw adult pottos on their own, and found that the ranges of males overlapped the ranges of two or more females, but males visited the ranges of females most frequently—and slept close to them—when they were in estrus. Adult males show aggression to each other if they meet. Male and female pottos deposit urine marks on branches with the tip of the penis or clitoris; these marks can extend for one meter, and provide signals to other individuals; males show particular interest in the urine of estrous females.

Pimley *et al.* (2005a) describe pairs of *P. edwardsi* engaging in mutual marking with saliva and genital secretions. Such behavior is described in some detail in captive *P. potto* by Manley (1974); in addition to mutual licking and dental-comb raking, the pottos will scratch their fingers on the glandular surface of their scrotum or pseudoscrotum; the hand is then used to grasp the groomee's fur, transferring secretions from the genital glands to the other individual.

Reproduction. In Gabon, Charles-Dominique (1977) found that all potto births occurred between August and January, coinciding with the longer of two rainy seasons. On the other hand, births recorded in Ghana, Kenya, Côte d'Ivoire and Nigeria all occurred in February, a dry month at those locations (Jewell and Oates, 1969a). Females usually give birth to single young. The gestation period in *P. edwardsi* is about 190 days and infants are weaned at 120–180 days; interbirth interval is about one year (Charles-Dominique, 1977). Infants of *P. edwardsi* are born with pink skin, a white coat and blue eyes (JFO pers. obs.), but in *P. potto* the generally white coat has a light brown stripe in the middle of the back (Grand *et al.*, 1964), probably related to the dark coloration in the midline of the back in adult *P. potto*. Blackwell and Menzies (1968) describe the coat of a newborn potto in western Nigeria (therefore probably *P. p. juju*) as "almost white". The skin and coat start to darken within days and the full adult coloration is attained after about six months, by which time the young potto forages alone, but within the mother's range.

Infant parking. As in angwantibos, female pottos often "park" their infants during the night while they forage (Charles-Dominique, 1977). Mothers carry newborn infants clinging to their belly, but from about one week after birth the mother will sometimes leave the infant in an area of dense foliage and return to retrieve it before dawn. Larger infants travel clinging to the mother's back, or walking just behind her.

Ranging patterns. Charles-Dominique (1977) found that female *P. edwardsi* at Makokou in Gabon used home ranges of 6–9 ha, but that male ranges were often much larger, covering 9–40 ha. At Mount Kupé in Cameroon, Pimley *et al.* (2005b) found that all potto home ranges were larger than those reported from Makokou, and the ranges of males, as measured using a minimum convex polygon technique, were larger on average than those of females (♂♂ 45–289 ha, mean 180 ha; ♀♀ 27–164 ha, mean 118 ha); however, Pimley *et al.* say that this difference is not statistically significant.

Diet. Pottos feed on fruits, invertebrates and gummy tree exudates, with slow-moving invertebrates and gums discovered in the course of the potto's typical nose-to-branch foraging. Pimley (2002) found the diet of *P. edwardsi* at Mt. Kupé to be dominated by fruit (including that of *Musanga cecropioides*, the umbrella tree), with ants being the most frequently eaten invertebrates. In the stomachs of *P. edwardsi* in Gabon, Charles-Dominique (1971, 1977) recorded 65% fruits, 21% gums, and 10% invertebrates by weight of contents. Ants (particularly of the genus *Crematogaster*) were the most abundant of the insects in the pottos' stomachs, and snails were also a significant dietary item. Rahm (1960) noted *P. potto* in Côte d'Ivoire feeding on tree gum (as well as fruits and insects), and Oates (1984) observed *P. p. juju* is western Nigeria exploring the branches of gum-producing trees. Pottos also exploit flower nectar; Grünmeir (1990) describes *P. edwardsi* feeding on the nectar of *Parkia bicolor* (Mimosaceae) in Korup, Cameroon, thereby probably acting as a pollinator of this typically bat-pollinated tree.

Predators. Small carnivores are probably the main threat to pottos. At Makokou, Gabon, Charles-Dominique observed two unsuccessful attacks on *P. edwardsi* by immature palm civets (*Nandinia binotata*), and one unsuccessful attack on a young potto by a, normally terrestrial, black-legged mongoose (*Bdeogale nigripes*) that had climbed 15 m into the trees. Pottos defended against the palm civets by lunging at them with an open mouth, sometimes hitting them with their scapular shield. McGrew *et al.* (1978) report potto remains in two of 380 chimpanzee fecal samples from Niokolo Koba National Park, Senegal. Although pottos are highly arboreal, they occasionally come to the ground; this could explain why potto remains were found in one of 215 samples of leopard scat from the Taï forest, Côte d'Ivoire, examined by Hoppe-Dominik (1984). When touched or handled, pottos can produce a pungent "fear scent" from the genital glands (Manley, 1974).

Conservation Status

All the different forms of potto are recognized in the IUCN Red List under one species, *Perodicticus potto*, which is categorized as of Least Concern. Pottos are not major targets of human hunters (although they do sometimes get shot) and they survive in secondary forests, so they are still widespread and relatively common animals in the West African forest zone. They are almost certainly declining, however, because of a continuing conversion everywhere of forested land outside reserves into farmland.

Where to See It

Pottos can be seen in all the forest reserves and protected areas in the West African moist forest zone, but several hours of searching are often needed to ensure a sighting using a head-lamp. Among sites where *Perodicticus potto potto* occurs are Tiwai Island Wildlife Sanctuary (Sierra Leone), Taï National Park (Côte d'Ivoire), and Ankasa Conservation Area, Ghana. *Perodicticus p. juju* can be seen in the Okomu National Park and the Omo Forest Reserve in western Nigeria, and *P. edwardsi* can be seen in Cross River National Park (Nigeria), and in Korup and Takamanda national parks (Cameroon).

FAMILY CERCOPITHECIDAE
Old World monkeys

This family comprises all of the monkeys of Africa and Asia, and is the most species-rich of all the living primate families. Cercopithecids are all diurnal (day active) in their habits; most species are of medium size (by mammalian standards), with body weights in the range 5–25 kg; they typically have tails (although these are very short or vestigial in a few species), and these tails are not prehensile as they are in some tropical American monkeys; they have pads of thick, bare, leathery skin on either side of the tail base, known as ischial callosities, on which they sit; and they have characteristic molar teeth with four cusps in two pairs connected by ridges or lophs ("bilophodont molars"). Their arms and legs are either of roughly equal length, or their legs are longer than their arms.

Two subfamilies of Cercopithecidae are usually recognized, as in this book: the Cercopithecinae and the Colobinae. Groves (2001) and Grubb *et al.* (2003) follow that arrangement, but Groves (1989) treats these two groups as the Families Cercopithecidae and Colobidae.

SUBFAMILY CERCOPITHECINAE
Cheek-pouched monkeys

As their common name indicates, these monkeys have cheek pouches, expandable sacs with slitlike openings and a mucous membrane lining on the lower part of the cheeks which can be used to store small food items (such as fruits) that require further processing before thay can be chewed and swallowed. The cusps on their molar teeth are relatively low and rounded. Two major divisions within the cercopithecine monkeys are helpfully distinguished: the Tribes Papionini and Cercopithecini, which probably diverged from one another during a phase of drying climate in Africa about 11.5 million years ago (MYA) (see Section 4).

Tribe Papionini
Papionins

These are the macaques, baboons, geladas, mangabeys, and drills and their allies. The macaques occur in North Africa (one species only, the Barbary macaque, *Macaca sylvanus*) and in Asia, while all the other members of the group are restricted to Africa and the western part

Cercopithecinae

Sooty Mangabey
Cercocebus atys

White-naped Mangabey
Cercocebus lunulatus

Red-capped Mangabey
Cercocebus torquatus

Mainland Drill (male)
Mandrillus leucophaeus leucophaeus

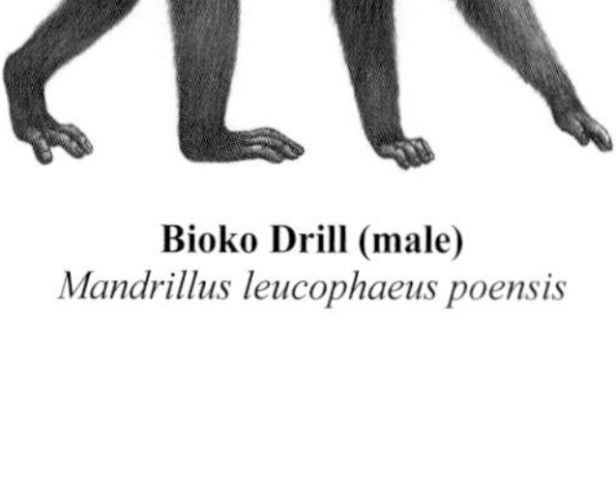

Bioko Drill (male)
Mandrillus leucophaeus poensis

Drill (female)
Mandrillus leucophaeus

Cercopithecinae

Fig. 8.28.

of the Arabian peninsula. Most papionins have relatively short tails compared to cercopithecins, and sometimes their tails are very short. They often have pronounced muzzles with strong jaws. Typically, their legs are not much longer than their arms, and their common mode of locomotion is quadrupedal walking. Many papionin species spend much of their time on the ground, and many occur in open woodland or grassland habitats, although some are restricted to rain forest and are highly arboreal. In most of the African species, adult females develop obvious perineal swelling around the time of ovulation.

Most classifications currently recognize seven genera of papionin: *Macaca*, *Lophocebus*, *Papio*, *Theropithecus*, *Cercocebus*, *Mandrillus*, and *Rungwecebus*. Four of these genera and seven species occur in West Africa. Although all the mangabey-like papionins were once grouped together in the genus *Cercocebus*, studies of the skeleton and DNA have demonstrated clearly that the two "groups" of mangabeys recognized by Schwarz (1928a) and Napier and Napier (1967)—the *albigena* group and the *torquatus* group—have phylogenetically distinct origins (Groves, 1978; Fleagle and McGraw, 1999; Disotell, 2000). The closest living relatives of the *albigena* group are the savanna and gelada baboons, while the closest relatives of the *torquatus* group are the drills and mandrills. This distinction is now widely recognized, so that the *torquatus* group is placed in the genus *Cercocebus* and the *albigena* group in the genus *Lophocebus* (Groves, 2001).

Cercocebus É. Geoffroy, 1812
White-eyelid mangabeys

Groves (2001) refers to *Cercocebus* as the white-eyelid mangabeys because of the color of their upper eyelids, while Kingdon (1997) calls them the drill-mangabeys. They are medium-sized to large, semi-terrestrial forest monkeys that typically travel on the ground but forage both on the ground and in trees. They occur in a very wide range of forest types, but seem to be especially associated with swamp and riverine habitats. Social groups are frequently large, and typically contain several adult males. Females exhibit conspicuous cyclical perineal swellings. Adult males make loud, staccato "cha-ku" calls. The tail is often held arched over the back, with the tip approaching the head.

The taxonomy of this group is in flux. Kingdon (1997) and Groves (2001) recognize six species: *Cercocebus torquatus*, *C. atys*, *C. agilis*, *C. galeritus*, *C. sanjei*, and *C. chrysogaster*. Grubb *et al.* (2003) place

Cercocebinae

agilis, *sanjei* and *chrysogaster* as subspecies of *galeritus* on the basis of vocal similarities. Kingdon, Groves and Grubb *et al.* all follow Booth (1958b) in regarding *lunulatus* of Côte d'Ivoire and Ghana as a subspecies of *Cercocebus atys*.

Cercocebus torquatus geospecies

Grubb (2006b) places all the white-eyelid mangabeys in the *C. torquatus* geospecies. No two species in the group occur in exactly the same place, although the ranges of *C. galeritus* and *C. torquatus* approach each other closely in parts of western equatorial Africa, with *C. torquatus* typically occurring in swampy coastal areas, and *C. galeritus* in inland forests.

Local Representatives

The taxa *atys*, *lunulatus* and *torquatus* inhabit the region covered by this guide. They are treated here as separate species on the basis of their distinctive coat patterns and the observation by Booth (1958b) that he observed examples of both *atys* and *lunulatus* between the Sassandra and Nzo rivers in western Côte d'Ivoire but never came across hybrids.

Cercopithecinae

Sooty mangabey
Cercocebus atys (Audebert, 1797)

Other English: Spectacled mangabey, smoky mangabey
French: Cercocèbe enfumé, mangabé fuligineux
Portuguese: Mangabei-cinzento
West African languages: Engendégorai, kalalu (Diola, Senegal);
Towei (Mende, Sierra Leone); Ka talaku (Temne, Sierra Leone);
Jacko (Liberian English); Du'ah (Bassa, Liberia); Kerbeh (Sapo,
Liberia)

Identification (see Fig. 8.28, p.152)

Like other members of this group, the sooty mangabey is a
medium-sized to large semi-terrestrial monkey. It has arms and legs
of about the same length and a relatively slender build. The sooty
mangabey has a coat of long hair that is predominantly ashy or smoky
gray in color, lighter ventrally and on the inner limb surfaces. The
back sometimes has an indistinct median stripe of darker hair. When
standing or walking, the sparsely-haired tail is often held at a raised
angle to the back, and sometimes held vertically or even curved over
towards the head. The skin around the eyes is pink and raised (giving
an impression of thick spectacle frames). The upper eyelids are white,
and the muzzle is pinkish-gray. The cheeks have tufts of gray hair
extending horizontally beyond the outline of the head. The outer
surfaces of the lower arms, and the hands and feet, are dark gray.

Cercocebus atys has a head and body length of about 65 cm in
males and 60 cm in females, and a tail length of about 80 cm in males,
70 cm in females. Adult males are heavier than adult females, weighing
about 11 kg, compared with an average female weight of about 6.5 kg
(Oates *et al.*, 1990b).

Similar species. Sooty mangabeys are not easily confused with
other monkeys with which they share their geographic range. Perhaps
the most similar monkey in this part of West Africa is the green monkey
(*Chlorocebus aethiops sabaeus*). The green monkey is also semi-
terrestrial and relatively drably and uniformly colored, but compared
with the ashy-gray colored mangabey, the green monkey is olivey-gray
or khaki on its dorsal surfaces, its face is black rather than pink, its
muzzle is less pronounced and its tail tip is yellow or pale orange. The
green monkey is typically a savanna primate that also occurs in farmed

areas of the forest zone and in mangroves. There is a degree of range overlap between green monkeys and sooty mangabeys, especially in the west of the *C. atys* range, where the mangabey occurs in dry forest and forest galleries. *Cercocebus atys* has been reported to overlap in range with its close relative *C. lunulatus* in a small area of western Côte d'Ivoire between the Nzo and Sassandra rivers (Booth, 1958b); *C. lunulatus* occurs east of the Sassandra, in Ghana and in southern Burkina Faso. *Cercocebus lunulatus* is brownish-gray rather than ashy-gray on its dorsal surfaces, with a distinct thin dark back stripe, and is white on its undersurfaces and inner limb surfaces. *Cercocebus lunulatus* has a very distinct half-moon shaped patch of white hair on the back of its crown.

Taxonomic Note

As explained above, this taxon is regarded here as a full species, but it is most commonly referred to in the literature as a subspecies: *C. atys atys* (sister to *C. atys lunulatus*) or *C. torquatus atys*.

Geographic Range

The sooty mangabey occurs in forest and forest-mosaic habitats from the southern edge of Senegal south through Guinea-Bissau, Guinea, Sierra Leone and Liberia to the western edge of Côte d'Ivoire. Its presence in Senegal was first recorded by Dupuy (1971) and Struhsaker (1971b). It appears to be uncommon and localized in Guinea-Bissau (Gippoliti and Dell'Omo, 2003).

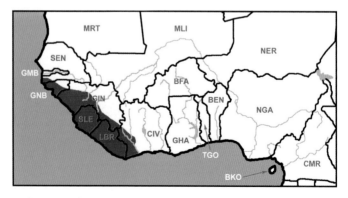

Fig. 8.29: Distribution of *Cercocebus atys*.

Natural History

Habitat. Sooty mangabeys occur in a variety of forested habitats, including high-canopy mature moist forest, secondary forest, farmbush, forest-palm mosaic, palm swamp, and dry deciduous forest with gallery forest.

Field studies. This monkey is typically wary of people and can be difficult to habituate. The only studies of habituated wild sooty mangabeys have been in the Taï Forest, Côte d'Ivoire (e.g., McGraw and Bshary, 2002; Range and Noë, 2002; Range and Fischer, 2004; McGraw and Zuberbühler, 2007; Range *et al.*, 2007). Less detailed information is available from observations in Sierra Leone, for instance in the Kilimi area (Harding, 1984), and at Tiwai Island (Whitesides *et al.*, 1988; Oates *et al.*, 1990b; Fimbel, 1994).

Population. Densities have been reported of 12 individuals/km² in the Taï Forest (McGraw and Zuberbühler, 2007), and about 1 group/km² in old forest on Tiwai Island, Sierra Leone, where an average group was estimated to contain about 35 monkeys (Whitesides *et al.*, 1988; Oates *et al.*, 1990b). In young secondary forest on Tiwai, density has been estimated at 2 groups/km² (Fimbel, 1994); the ranges of mangabey groups at Tiwai almost certainly include both young and old forest, with the higher density estimate in young forest indicating more frequent use of that habitat.

Habitat use. In the Taï Forest, sooty mangabeys were on the ground in 67% of observations during the day, and in lower parts of the forest canopy 30% of the time (McGraw and Zuberbühler, 2007). Sooty mangabeys sleep in trees but obtain much of their food on the ground; however, they will sometimes feed high up in large emergent trees (Harding, 1984).

Fig. 8.30: Sooty mangabey (*Cercocebus atys*), Taï Forest, Côte d'Ivoire (photo by W. S. McGraw).

Locomotion and posture. The typical locomotion of *Cercocebus atys* is quadrupedal walking on the ground, but climbing is also an important component of the locomotor repertoire, related to this species' frequent movement between the ground and the lower canopy; leaping is rare. McGraw (2007) describes sooty mangabey postural behavior as typically cercopithecine, with sitting being dominant and feeding frequently taking place while standing.

Activity pattern. In Taï, female sooty mangabeys have been found to rest relatively infrequently (about 9% of observations on average) and to spend much time feeding and foraging (72% of observations); 11% of observations were of monkeys travelling (Range *et al.*, 2007). In moving from one arboreal resting site to another, a mangabey group typically travels across the forest floor (with occasional excursions into the canopy) searching for food, frequently turning over debris with the hands while sitting or standing (McGraw and Zuberbühler, 2007).

Vocalizations. This is a noisy monkey. Range and Fischer (2004) describe 19 different vocalizations, of which the most frequently heard are grunts, twitters (produced only by females and young), screams and growls. The most striking sooty mangabey calls are a loud two-phase alarm call given by males (sounding something like "cha-ku" or "chalaku", with an initial staccato element or elements), and the male "whoop-gobble" call that is also made by other kinds of mangabeys. Whoop-gobbles consists of an initial low-pitched "whoop" followed after several seconds by a series of tonal syllables; the call is made early in the morning and when other groups are nearby. Females produce a call during copulation.

Social organization. Sooty mangabeys travel in multi-male, multi-female groups that are often very large. In the mosaic habitat in the dry forest zone of Kilimi in Sierra Leone, Harding (1984) counted groups of 3–37 individuals (mean 14.4) during surveys. Groups at Tiwai Island, Sierra Leone, were estimated to have a mean size of 35 (Oates *et al.*, 1990b). Grubb *et al.* (1998) report that groups of over 100 are not uncommon in Sierra Leone, but that 10–40 is normal. In the Taï Forest, Côte d'Ivoire, Galat and Galat-Luong (1985) reported groups of 20–48 individuals, but based on longer-term studies McGraw and Zuberbühler (2007) give a typical group size as approximately 100 individuals; a main study group in Taï is reported to contain 100–120 animals (Range and Noë, 2002; Range *et al.*, 2007). Groups of terrestrial forest monkeys are difficult to count, especially when not habituated, and many estimates of mangabey group size are probably underestimates; however, small groups are probably more common at sites such as Kilimi where closed forest is patchy. In Taï, large groups can split into subgroups when foraging. Females are philopatric, while males transfer between groups; all-male bands and solitary males are observed (McGraw and Zuberbühler, 2007; Range *et al.*, 2007). Range *et al.* (2007) describe some males as staying in a bi-sexual group for more than 6 months, some joining for a limited period of 1–4 months, and others visiting for hours or a few days and staying on the group periphery.

Social behavior. Both males and females in a sooty mangabey group form linear dominance hierarchies (Range *et al.*, 2007). Females tend to restrict their grooming to preferred partners (Range and Noë, 2002) and form coalitions with each other in agonistic interactions. Adult males tend to associate with a small number of other male partners and have not been seen to groom each other.

Interactions between groups. Patterns of intergroup interaction have not been specifically reported, but it is likely that sooty mangabeys have large overlapping home ranges. Males are known to move between groups (Range *et al.*, 2007).

Reproduction. Range *et al.* (2007) report that Taï sooty mangabeys have a mating season in June-October (a predominantly wet time of year), coinciding with a time when females exhibit perineal swellings. Adult males attempt to guard swollen females, but males from outside

Cercopithecinae

Fig. 8.31: Sooty mangabey (*Cercocebus atys*), Taï Forest, Côte d'Ivoire (photo by W. S. McGraw).

the group will visit and attempt to copulate with females. A subsequent birth season peaks in the December–February dry season, consistent with a 5.5 month gestation period observed in captivity (Gust *et al.*, 1990).

Ranging patterns. Little information has been published on sooty mangabey ranging behavior except for the Taï Forest, where Galat and Galat-Luong (1985) estimated group home range sizes of 4–6 km², and McGraw and Zuberbühler (2007) report a home range of just under 5 km².

Diet. McGraw and Zuberbühler (2007) note that the species has large jaws and strong teeth adapted for hard-object feeding. Fruits with hard seeds found on the forest floor are probably an important component of the diet, but a detailed study of sooty mangabey feeding has not been completed. In the Taï Forest, the overall diet is reported to consist of 68% fruits and seeds, and 26% invertebrates (R. Bergmüller cited in Range *et al.*, 2007). The largest proportion of feeding time (33%) is spent on the seeds of *Saccoglottis gabonensis* (Humiriaceae) (Range and Noë, 2002); *S. gabonensis* is a large tree that produces fruits with very large seeds in September–October (Poorter *et al.*, 2004). Many mangabey foods in Taï apparently occur in large patches, including patches of *Saccoglottis* fruits with a radius of up to 10 m, and patches of mushrooms or termites. Social groups will fragment into smaller foraging subgroups as food patchiness changes across the seasons (McGraw and Zuberbühler, 2007). Sooty mangabeys in Sierra Leone frequently raid farms (Grubb *et al.*, 1998).

Association with other species. During surveys in the Taï Forest, Galat-Luong and Galat (1978) and Galat and Galat-Luong (1985) saw *C. atys* in association with other monkeys less frequently than any of the other common species in the forest. However, McGraw and Bshary (2002) found in Taï that red colobus and Diana monkeys (both species that frequent the high canopy) use lower forest strata significantly more often when in association with sooty mangabeys; red colobus in particular used the ground and ate termite earth much more frequently when intermingled with a mangabey group. The sooty mangabeys evidently act as valuable sentinels for terrestrial predators. In experimental approaches to mixed-species monkey groups in Taï by a researcher wrapped in a leopard-skin cloth, McGraw and Bshary (2002) found that mangabeys gave alarm calls first more often than any other species.

Predators. In Taï Forest, sooty mangabeys are a preferred prey item for crowned eagles. They are also eaten by leopards, but are rarely preyed upon by chimpanzees (Shultz and Thomsett, 2007). Zuberbühler and Jenny (2007) report a successful capture of a mangabey by a Taï leopard after a prolonged period of hiding. Humans are the main predators on *C. atys* across most of their range, where natural predators are now rare.

Conservation Status

Cercocebus atys is listed as Near Threatened (under the name *C. atys atys*) in the IUCN Red List. Although sooty mangabeys are hunted for meat by humans across a major part of their range (for instance, in Liberia), and have declined in numbers as a result, their populations appear to have held up relatively well to this pressure, at least until recently. It may be that the mangabey's intelligence and its ability to move rapidly on the ground, and hide in thick growth, give it some chance to evade hunters despite its large size and often noisy behavior. However, sooty mangabeys were killed in greater numbers than any other monkey species during "monkey drives" against farm pests in southeastern and eastern Sierra Leone in 1948–1953 (Jones, 1998). Refisch and Koné (2005a, 2005b) calculated that the level of hunting on *C. atys* in and around Taï National Park in 1999-2000 was unsustainable in relation to estimated population numbers. In some of the more northerly parts of the sooty mangabey's range where the human population is predominantly Muslim (for instance in Sierra Leone and parts of Guinea), hunting of primates for meat has been less intense, but in central Guinea this pattern has been changing as traders have come from the south to purchase monkey meat (R. Kormos, pers. comm.).

Cercocebus atys is well protected in the primate research area of Taï National Park, Côte d'Ivoire, and at Tiwai Island Wildlife Sanctuary, Sierra Leone, but these are relatively small areas for such a widely-distributed species. It also occurs in the Gola Forest National Park and Loma Mountains proposed national park in Sierra Leone, and the Sapo National Park in Liberia.

Where to See It

The sooty mangabey can be seen most easily in the primate research area in the western part of Taï National Park, Côte d'Ivoire and at Tiwai Island Wildlife Sanctuary, Sierra Leone.

Cercopithecinae

White-naped mangabey
Cercocebus lunulatus (Temminck, 1853)

Other English: Crescent-naped sooty mangabey, white-crowned mangabey, crowned mangabey
French: Mangabé couronné, mangabé fuligineux à lunule
West African languages: Kpamin (Agni, Côte d'Ivoire); Krakuo, eku (Twi, Ghana)

Identification (see Fig. 8.28, p.152)

The white-naped mangabey closely resembles the sooty mangabey in build and habits. It is a medium-sized to large semi-terrestrial monkey, with arms and legs of similar length, a relatively slender body, and white upper eyelids. This species is grayish-brown on its back, tail and outer limb surfaces (including hands and feet). Most of the crown is dark gray tinged with brown, except that the posterior of the crown bears a very distinct half-moon shaped patch of white hair. There is also a distinct stripe of dark hair down the middle of the back. The throat, chest, belly and inner upper limb surfaces are white, with a sharp demarcation between the white chest and the dark color of the upper arm. The hair on the hands and feet is gray. The facial skin is grayish pink, darker on the muzzle than around the eyes. When standing or walking the tail is typically held straight or at a raised angle to the back, and is sometimes held vertically or recurved.

Cercocebus lunulatus has a head and body length of about 55 cm and a tail length of about 65 cm. Adult males are probably heavier than adult females, but body weight data are lacking.

Similar species. The white-naped mangabey is not very similar to any other monkey species in Côte d'Ivoire, Ghana or southern Burkina Faso with the exception of its very close relative, *Cercocebus atys*. At least in the past, the two species were found to overlap in their ranges in a small area of western Côte d'Ivoire between the Nzo and Sassandra rivers (Booth, 1958b). *Cercocebus atys* lacks the white patch on the back of the head present in *C. lunulatus*; *C. atys* is ashy gray rather than brownish on its dorsal surfaces, light gray rather than white ventrally, and also lacks a distinct dark back stripe. Potentially the white-naped mangabey can be confused with the green monkey (*Chlorocebus aethiops sabaeus*), especially where the two species co-occur in gallery forest in the savanna zone (as in southern Burkina Faso; Galat and Galat-Luong, 2006). The green monkey is also semi-terrestrial; it is

Cercopithecinae

smaller than the mangabey, with olive-khaki dorsal surfaces, a black face and ears, a less prominent muzzle, and a yellow or pale orange tail tip. The green monkey does not have a patch of white hair on the back of its head.

Taxonomic Note

The white-naped mangabey is regarded here as a full species. It is usually referred to in the literature as a subspecies of *Cercocebus atys* or *C. torquatus*. Its coat color pattern is very different from either of those other mangabey species. As already noted, Booth (1958b) reports observing examples of both *atys* and *lunulatus* between the Sassandra and Nzo rivers in western Côte d'Ivoire but did not see hybrids.

Geographic Range

The white-naped mangabey was once found from west of the Sassandra River in western Côte d'Ivoire eastward to the Volta River in Ghana. Its range extends north into the savanna woodland zone, where it is reported from the gallery forests of the Comoé River system in northeastern Côte d'Ivoire and southern Burkina Faso (Fischer *et al.*, 2000; Galat and Galat-Luong, 2006).

Natural History

Habitat. White-naped mangabeys have been reported from a wide range of forested habitats, including high-canopy mature moist and

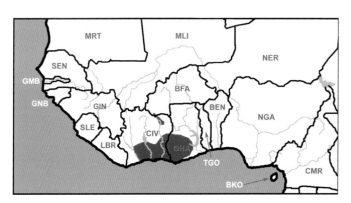

Fig. 8.32: Distribution of *Cercocebus lunulatus*.

semi-deciduous forest, secondary forest, palm swamp, farmland, and gallery forest in the savanna zone.

Field studies. Cercocebus lunulatus has been briefly observed during surveys in Ghana, Côte d'Ivoire and Burkina Faso, but has never been the subject of any long-term field study. Very little is known, therefore, about its social behavior, activity and ranging patterns, or its feeding habits in the wild. It probably shares many features of behavior and ecology with *C. atys* and *C. torquatus*.

Population. Cercocebus lunulatus is now a rare animal, apparently restricted to a small number of locations across its former range. There are no sites where it has not been hunted, and occasional sightings during surveys do not provide an adequate sample to estimate population density. During 14.5 hours of transect surveys in Ankasa River Forest Reserve, Ghana, in 1976, there were two observations of white-naped mangabeys (Martin, 1976); in 2006–2008, Gatti (2010) made seven direct sightings in Ankasa during 2,468 hours of surveys (0.07/hr) while walking 3,704 km (0.0019/km).

Fig. 8.33: White-naped mangabey (*Cercocebus lunulatus*) in the Endangered Primate Centre, Accra Zoo, Ghana (photo by J. Koegler, WAPCA).

Cercopithecinae

Habitat use. According to Booth (1956), the white-naped mangabey is highly terrestrial and only rarely ascends into the lower forest canopy.

Social organization. Galat and Galat-Luong (2006) observed a group containing at least nine individuals, including one adult male, in gallery forest on the Comoé River, Burkina Faso. Fischer *et al.* (2000) report seeing groups of up to 23 animals in Comoé National Park, Côte d'Ivoire; male loud calls were heard frequently at the beginning of the rainy season in March-May.

Diet. Galat and Galat-Luong (2006) saw these mangabeys eating fruit of *Saba* (= *Landolphia*) *senegalensis* (Apocynaceae) and *Dialium guineense* (Caesalpiniaceae) in gallery forest on the Comoé River, Burkina Faso. *Saba senegalensis* is a large, shrub-like liana with a large thick-walled fruit.

Conservation Status

Cercocebus lunulatus is listed as Endangered (under the name *C. atys lunulatus*) in the IUCN Red List. The white-naped mangabey has been in decline for 40 years and remaining populations appear to be small and fragmented. Its terrestrial habits make it vulnerable to hunters using dogs (Jeffrey, 1974) and to cable snares that are set to catch a variety of mammals (Fischer *et al.*, 2000).

In Ghana, Asibey (1978) reported it as present but rare in Bia National Park and common in Ankasa Game Production (now Resource) Reserve and the Nini-Suhien National Park adjacent to Ankasa. Asibey's report seems to have relied in part on the results from a 1976 survey of Ankasa by Martin who obtained two observations of white-naped mangabeys during 14.5 hours of surveys (Martin, 1976). In extensive surveys of western Ghanaian forests between 1993 and 1996, *C. lunulatus* was found still to be present at Ankasa, and at three other sites: Krokosua Hills Forest Reserve, Draw River Forest Reserve and Boi Tano Forest Reserve (Oates *et al.*, 2000a). Vocalizations were heard twice during surveys of Krokosua Hills Forest Reserve in August 1999 (White and Berry, 2000), but in 2005–2006 surveys of Boi-Tano, Krokosua Hills and Mamiri Forest Reserves, and of Bia National Park and Resource Reserve, no mangabeys were encountered and hunters in surrounding settlements reported no recent sightings. In 2001, Magnuson (2002) had one encounter with white-naped mangabeys in Ankasa, one in Dadieso Forest Reserve, and one in Yoyo Forest

Reserve. Surveys in 2006–2008 again encountered *C. lunulatus* in Ankasa, and a captive animal was found in a settlement close to Cape Three Points Forest Reserve (Gatti, 2010). These observations suggest that the Ankasa Conservation Area (made up of the Ankasa Resource

Cercopithecinae

Fig. 8.34: Female and young white-naped mangabeys (*Cercocebus lunulatus*), Endangered Primate Centre, Accra Zoo, Ghana (photo by S. Gatti, WAPCA).

Reserve and the Nini-Suhien National Park) is a key remaining stronghold for this species in Ghana.

In Côte d'Ivoire, McGraw carried out surveys in 1997 in forests in the east of the country (the classified forests of Bossematie, Mabi, Songan and Yaya) but encountered no white-naped mangabeys (McGraw, 1998a). During surveys in south-central Côte d'Ivoire in 2003–2004, local informants reported its presence in Marahoué National Park, and in the classified forests of Bolo West, Dassiéko and Niégré, but it was observed directly only in Dassiéko (Gonedelé Bi *et al.*, 2006, 2008). Marahoué National Park suffered a 93% reduction of its forest cover between 2002 and 2008 (Campbell *et al.*, 2008b). The white-naped mangabey was present in the Comoé National Park in northeastern Côte d'Ivoire in 1998–2001 but the park was then suffering serious hunting pressure (Fischer *et al.*, 2000); poaching apparently intensified with the civil conflict that began in 2002, and has been accompanied by burning and by overgrazing by herds of cattle. The mangabey has been confirmed as present in swamp forest lying between the Ehy Lagoon and Tano River in the southeastern corner of the country, an area referred to as the Tanoé Forest (McGraw and Oates, 2002; McGraw, 2005; Gonedelé Bi *et al.*, 2008).

In southern Burkina Faso, *Cercocebus lunulatus* has been found in the Comoé-Léraba Reserved Forest and Partial Wildlife Reserve, 50 km north of Comoé National Park in Côte d'Ivoire (Galat and Galat-Luong, 2006). The Comoé-Léraba Reserve is partly a safari hunting area, in which bushmeat hunting is considered to be an increasing threat.

Several European zoos have breeding groups of white-naped mangabeys. They have collaborated in establishing a program called West African Primate Conservation Action (WAPCA), located in the Achimota Forest Reserve in Accra, Ghana, with the aim of breeding white-naped mangabeys and roloway monkeys. WAPCA has been assisting with research and conservation activities in the Ankasa Conservation Area.

Where to See It

Cercocebus lunulatus is now a very difficult animal to observe in the wild. With considerable patience it might be seen in the Ankasa Conservation Area in Ghana.

Red-capped mangabey
Cercocebus torquatus (Kerr, 1792)

Other English: Collared mangabey, white-collared mangabey, red-crowned mangabey, cherry-capped mangabey
French: Cercocèbe à collier blanc
West African languages: Owe (Yoruba, Nigeria); Uhi, uhirhi (Bini, Nigeria); Opóú, apóú, okpe (Ijaw, Nigeria); Okato (Igala, Nigeria); Ikpok ebok (Ibibio, Nigeria); Ekpok (Korup, Cameroon and Nigeria); Mbi (Ejagham, Cameroon and Nigeria); Nkakoum (Bakossi, Cameroon); Musako (Banen, Cameroon); Kaki (Bassa, Cameroon)

Identification (see Fig. 8.28, p.152)

Cercopithecinae

Like the sooty and white-naped mangabeys, this is a medium-sized to large semi-terrestrial monkey, with arms and legs of similar length, a relatively slender body, a prominent muzzle and white upper eyelids. One of the most distinctive features of this species, from which it takes its common name, is the bright chestnut-red hair on the crown of its head—a color called "auburn" by Dandelot (1971). The skin above the eyes (as well as the eyelids) is white. The back, outer limb surfaces and proximal three-fifths of the tail are dark gray, tinged with brown, becoming black on the lower arms. The cheeks, nape of the neck, throat, chest and tail tip are pure white, and the flanks, belly and inner limb surfaces are light gray or light gray-brown. When the mangabey is standing, the tail is sometimes held in a recurved arch over the back, dangling above the head and shoulders (Jones and Sabater Pi, 1968).

Cercocebus torquatus exhibits considerable sexual dimorphism in size when adult. Males have a head and body length of about 60 cm, a tail length of about 65 cm and a body weight averaging about 11 kg, while females have a head and body length of about 55 cm, a tail length of about 60 cm and a body weight of around 6 kg.

Similar species. In the area covered by this guidebook, the red-capped mangabey shares parts of its range with two other semi-terrestrial monkeys, the tantalus and the drill; however, it has a markedly different appearance from both of them. Tantalus monkeys (*Chlorocebus aethiops tantalus*) occur in a few parts of southern Nigeria where farmland has significantly opened-up the forest. It is considerably smaller than the mangabey, and is predominantly a grayish-green khaki on all its upper surfaces, with no red crown, no white tail-tip and no white eyelids. In the moist forest zone between the Cross and Sanaga this mangabey sometimes co-occurs with the drill (*Mandrillus leucophaeus*). Drills are more baboon-like in appearance than mangabeys, with a very short tail, no red crown and an even more pronounced muzzle. Often, red-capped mangabeys are rare or absent where drills are present, suggesting that some competitive exclusion is at work.

Geographic Range

The red-capped mangabey occurs patchily through the forest zone of southern Nigeria from west to east, including the Niger Delta, and from the Nigerian border south through the coastal forests of Cameroon, Rio Muni and Gabon to the Republic of Congo (Happold, 1973; Maisels *et al.*, 2007b). There are unconfirmed reports of its presence in the south of the Republic of Bénin (Campbell *et al.*, 2008b). In Nigeria it once occurred in the forest-savanna mosaic zone of Igalaland, not far from the Benue River (Oates, 1982).

Natural History

Habitat. The red-capped mangabey inhabits moist high forest, semi-deciduous forest, marsh and swamp forest, mangrove forest and gallery forest. According to Gautier-Hion *et al.* (1999) this species is only rarely seen in primary dryland forest. Almost all known populations occur no more than 350 km inland from the coast (Maisels *et al.*, 2007b), and Jones and Sabater Pi (1968) observed them only below an elevation of 350 m.

Cercopithecinae

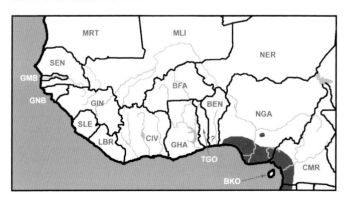

Fig. 8.35: Distribution of *Cercocebus torquatus* in West Africa.

Field studies. There has been no careful study of habituated groups of this species within the area covered by this field guide, and only a scattering of field records are available from forest surveys (Western Cameroon: Struhsaker, 1969; Gartlan and Struhsaker, 1972; Linder, 2008; Astaras *et al.*, 2011). There is a published report of a study conducted for a total of 15 months in 1983–1984 by Masazumi Mitani (1989) in the Campo Reserve of southern Cameroon, about 150 km south of the Sanaga River. Mitani's study involved both censuses and the tracking of two groups that were identifiable (but apparently not habituated). Additional notes are available from studies by Jones and Sabater Pi (1968) in Rio Muni, and by Maisels *et al.* (2007b) in southern Gabon and the Republic of Congo. At the time of writing, a long-term study was underway at Sette Cama, a coastal site in southwestern Gabon, by Catherine Cooke; only abstracted information from that study is yet available (Cooke, 2005; Cooke *et al.*, 2007, 2009).

Population. Human hunting appears to have heavily fragmented the distribution of *Cercocebus torquatus* and made it a rare primate across most of its former range. Precise density estimates have not been made in West Africa. In surveys along 352 km of transects in Korup National Park, Cameroon, in 2004–2005, Linder (2008) observed only three groups of this species; all encounters were in the southern section of the park. In 2006–2008, Astaras *et al.* (2011) encountered *C.*

Fig. 8.36: Red-capped mangabeys (*Cercocebus torquatus*) at CERCOPAN facility, Rhoko, Nigeria (photo courtesy of CERCOPAN).

Fig. 8.37: A juvenile red-capped mangabey (*Cercocebus torquatus*), Rhoko, Nigeria (photo courtesy of CERCOPAN).

torquatus on 51 occasions while covering 3,284 km of line transects in southern Korup (0.02/km).

Habitat use. On censuses in Korup, red-capped mangabeys were seen from ground level to 25 m in the forest canopy, but most observations were at heights of 3–10 m (Astaras *et al.*, 2011). In Campo, Cameroon, Mitani (1989) observed these monkeys to travel predominantly on the ground, but to feed most often at 20–30 m in the forest canopy; Mitani notes that there is a concentration of fruit production at that height in the canopy. Jones and Sabater Pi (1968) noted that in Rio Muni *C. torquatus* spends considerable time on the ground, and on mangrove roots. In Sette Cama, Gabon, a study group spent 70% of its time in dryland forest, 24% in mangrove, and 5% in beach forest (Cooke, 2005).

Vocalizations. Struhsaker (1969) noted that the whoop, rolling call and staccato bark of *C. torquatus* are some of the most commonly heard adult male loud calls in the forests of Cameroon, although he rarely observed the monkeys. These calls (which carry far) are also heard quite frequently in some western Nigerian forests, even though the mangabeys themselves are not often seen.

Social organization. Struhsaker (1969) was not able to collect reliable group size and composition data in five sightings of *C. torquatus* groups in Cameroon, but estimated that groups contained

Cercopithecinae

10–25 individuals. For Rio Muni, Jones and Sabater Pi (1968) report groups of 14–23 individuals, frequently with several adult males. Mitani (1989) records one Campo group as having 25 individuals, including several adult males; he notes that the group may be spread over an area 500 m in diameter when foraging and that it often splits into subgroups; group splitting is also reported by Jones and Sabater Pi. Mitani sometimes observed solitary males, but not all-male groups. By contrast, the long-term study by Cooke *et al.* (2009) at Sette Cama has found that a large group of about 60 individuals frequently splits into foraging subgroups.

Social behavior.   No details of red-capped mangabey social behavior in the wild have yet been published.

Interactions between groups.   In the Campo Reserve, four other groups showed overlap with the range of one focal study group (Mitani, 1989).

Reproduction.   Females exhibit large cyclical perineal swellings, but virtually nothing has been published on reproductive patterns of this species in the wild. Jones and Sabater Pi (1968) surmised that *C. torquatus* breeds throughout the year in Rio Muni.

Ranging patterns.   One Campo study group covered an area of 247 ha (2.5 km²) over a 15-month period, concentrating its time in half of this area in any three-month season, a pattern influenced by food availability (Mitani, 1989).

Diet.   In Campo, Mitani (1989) found fruits and seeds (the majority from canopy trees and lianas) to be the most commonly observed food items, making up 80% of the diet. The most frequently consumed species of fruit were *Grewia coriacea* (Tiliaceae), *Anthonotha* cf. *cladantha* (Caesalpiniaceae), and *Saccoglottis gabonensis* (Humiriaceae). The mangabeys also ate the shoots and leaves of terrestrial herbs, especially of *Haumannia danckelmaniana* (Marantaceae). Flowers, insects and mushrooms were seen to be eaten occasionally. Jones and Sabater Pi (1968) report *C. torquatus* in Rio Muni as mostly frugivorous, with several palms among a list of fruits eaten: *Raphia vinifera*, *Ancistrophyllum secundiflorum* and *Elaeis guineensis*. At Sette Cama, Cooke *et al.* (2009) have found red-capped mangabeys to commonly eat hard objects, including the seeds of *S. gabonensis* and crabs. The large seeds of *S. gabonensis* are a major food of sooty mangabeys in Taï Forest, Côte d'Ivoire.

Cercopithecinae

Association with other species. In nine out of 11 encounters with this species in western Cameroon the mangabeys were in association with monkeys of other species (Gartlan and Struhsaker, 1972). In Korup National Park, *C. torquatus* was in association with other species on 69% of encounters by Astaras *et al.* (2011); more than one third of these associations were with drills. On seven of 11 occasions when Jones and Sabater Pi (1968) encountered *C. torquatus* in Rio Muni, the mangabeys were in association with *Cercopithecus* species.

Predators. Humans are today the chief predator of the red-capped mangabeys across its range. Mitani (1989) lists the crowned eagle and leopard as potential predators in Campo Reserve; these are probably the main natural predators on this species, as they are of *C. atys* in Côte d'Ivoire.

Conservation Status

Cercocebus torquatus is listed as Vulnerable on the IUCN Red List. The species has been found to be relatively rare since the early days of primate field studies in its range in the 1960s. It has probably been in decline since then from a combination of habitat loss and hunting. As Maisels *et al.* (2007b) and Linder (2008) point out, this monkey's relatively large size, semi-terrestrial habits and loud far-carrying calls make it particularly vulnerable to hunters (especially hunters using dogs), and it may often get caught in wire snares set primarily to trap large rodents and small ungulates.

In the area covered by this guide, the red-capped mangabey occurs in the Okomu National Park and the Oban Division of Cross River National Park in Nigeria, and in the Korup National Park, the Banyang Mbo Wildlife Sanctuary and the proposed Ebo National Park in Cameroon. These sites do afford the mangabey some degree of protection, although not all of them have fully effective anti-poaching systems.

Where to See It

The rarity and wariness of this mangabey make it difficult to see readily at any West African site. Long searches with an experienced guide will usually be needed if the species is to be observed. The Okomu National Park in Nigeria and Cameroon's Korup National Park and Ebo Forest are probably the sites where a short-term visitor has the best chance of encountering red-capped mangabeys.

Cercopithecinae

Mandrillus Ritgen, 1824
Drills and mandrills

The drills and mandrills have a superficial resemblance to baboons, but differ in having a very short tail, paranasal ridges and, in males, a bright coloration on the perineum and face. They occur in moist forest rather than savanna habitats. It is now understood that their closest phylogenetic relatives are not the savanna baboons but the white-eyelid mangabeys (*Cercocebus*) (Groves, 1978; Fleagle and McGraw, 1999; Disotell, 2000; Groves, 2001). There are only two species in the genus: the mandrill (*M. sphinx*) and the drill (*M. leucophaeus*).

Mandrillus sphinx geospecies

Grubb (2006b) synonymizes the genus *Mandrillus* with the geospecies *Mandrillus sphinx*, the first named species in the group.

Local Representatives

Only the drill occurs in the region of this guide: *M. leucophaeus leucophaeus* on the mainland between the Cross and Sanaga rivers in eastern Nigeria and western Cameroon, and the very similar *M. l. poensis* on Bioko Island. *Mandrillus sphinx* occurs south of the Sanaga River in southern Cameroon, Rio Muni, Gabon and southern Republic of Congo.

Cercopithecinae

Drill
Mandrillus leucophaeus (F. Cuvier, 1807)

French: Drill
Spanish: Dril
West African languages: Keshuom (Boki, Nigeria); Mosum (Balegete and Becheve, Nigeria); Misaw, Mesor (Denya/Anyang, Cameroon and Nigeria); Nsim (Ejagham, Cameroon and Nigeria); Som (Bakossi, Cameroon); Somo (Banen, Cameroon); Ntin (Bassa, Cameroon); Mpoa, Tatapoa (Bubi, Bioko)

Identification (see Fig. 8.28, p.152)

The drill is a large, baboon-like and mostly terrestrial monkey, with arms and legs of similar length. It has a prominent, ridged muzzle, a black face (after the age of 6 months), and a very short stumpy tail. The coat is predominantly olivey gray-brown with lighter ventral surfaces; the hair in the mid-line of the belly is long and white, and in males forms a pronounced hanging fringe. The adult male is much larger than the female (typically more than twice as heavy), and is notable for the striking coloration on the rump, groin and face, contrasting strongly with the drab coloration of females; the male coloration (which is better portrayed in an illustration than with words) varies from individual to individual and is related to dominance rank (Marty *et al.*, 2009). In an adult male the skin of the sparsely-haired rump, base of the tail, and upper thighs displays shades of bright blue, mauve, pink and red. The penis and a band of skin anterior to it, and extending on to the inner thighs, are scarlet; the scrotum is pink to blue. Below the lower lip there is a narrow red band of skin, fringed below with white that continues around the sides of the face. Other features of the adult male's coat are: a prominent medial crest; long hair forming a "mane" on the nape of the neck and shoulders; darker coloration in the midline of the back, forming a distinct stripe; and patches of white hair behind the ears. Adult males also have very large canine teeth.

Subspecies. Although the mainland drill is commonly recognized as a subspecies (*M. l. leucophaeus*) distinct from that of Bioko (*M. l. poensis*), the differences between the two populations are relatively slight. The most pronounced difference is the smaller size of Bioko drills, especially males. According to Groves (2001), Bioko animals also have more grayish-toned bodies, more yellow-brown coloration on the sides of the crown, and more buffy coloration on the legs than

Cercopithecinae

Fig. 8.38: Wild Bioko drill (*Mandrillus leucophaeus poensis*) (photo by C. Santiestevan).

on the arms compared to mainland populations. In captivity, mainland adult males weigh 20–45 kg, with a median of 32 kg (the most dominant individuals are probably the heaviest), and females weigh 7–21 kg, with a median of 12 kg (Marty *et al.*, 2009). Head and body length in males is about 80 cm; in females about 65 cm. Wild adult males on Bioko weigh 14.5–27 kg (mean 20 kg) and females 6.5–12 kg (mean

8.5 kg). Adult head and body length in Bioko drills averages 67 cm in males and 54 cm in females (Butynski *et al.*, 2009).

Similar species. On Bioko Island there is no other primate similar to the drill. On the mainland, the drill can be confused with the olive baboon (*Papio anubis*) where the ranges of these species meet at the forest-savanna boundary (for instance, at the northern margin of the Okwangwo Division of Cross River National Park in Nigeria). Although drills have not been reported to use savanna, baboons will use forest fringes. Superficially, female drills and baboons are similar, but the baboon has a tail about 50 cm long with a distinct angle, compared to the short stub of a tail in the drill; the baboon's facial skin is dark gray, while that of the drill is black; and the baboon's muzzle does not have ridges. The bright color of the adult male drill's rump and the red mark beneath his lower lip are distinctive. In some forest areas the drill is sympatric with the red-capped mangabey (*Cercocebus torquatus*), which is semi-terrestrial; the mangabey can be readily distinguished from the drill by its long, white-tipped tail and red crown.

Geographic Range

On the mainland, the drill occurs in the coastal forest zone from the Cross River in southeast Nigeria (including forests of the Afi-Mbe-Okwangwo complex on northern tributaries of the Cross), east and south to the Sanaga River in Cameroon. It probably occurs (or once occurred) just south of the Sanaga, near its mouth, where *Cercopithecus*

Cercopithecinae

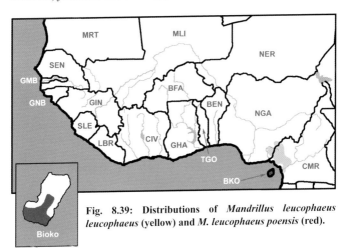

Fig. 8.39: Distributions of *Mandrillus leucophaeus leucophaeus* (yellow) and *M. leucophaeus poensis* (red).

erythrotis is also found (a species otherwise also restricted to north of the Sanaga) (Grubb, 1973). On Bioko, the drill occurs both on Pico Basilé and in the Southern Highlands (Butynski and Koster, 1994).

Natural History

Habitat. The drill inhabits lowland, submontane and montane forest, up to an altitude of around 2,000 m on Mount Kupé, Cameroon (Wild *et al.*, 2005) and probably to an altitude of 1,500 m on Bioko (Butynski and Koster, 1994). The drill is not reported from marsh and mangrove forests, where it seems to be replaced ecologically by the red-capped mangabey (*Cercocebus torquatus*). At Idenau, Cameroon, drills were observed to use older forest in preference to young secondary forest (Gartlan and Struhsaker, 1972); however, when drills in the past were more abundant they were often regarded as a farm pest.

Field studies. No groups have been fully habituated for behavioral studies, but a good deal of information on drill natural history has accumulated in the course of multiple encounters in western Cameroon forests, especially those of Stephen Gartlan in the Southern Bakundu Forest Reserve in 1967–1968 (Gartlan, 1970; Gartlan and Struhsaker, 1972). In Gartlan's study, drills were in view for 78 hours, in about half of which the animals were "in good view" (Gartlan, 1970). In 1966–1968, Thomas Struhsaker made some observations at Idenau and in other locations in Cameroon (Struhsaker, 1969; Gartlan and Struhsaker, 1972). More recently, those early observations have been supplemented by the work of Bethan Morgan and Chris Wild at Mount Kupé and other sites (Wild *et al.*, 2005), and by Christos Astaras *et al.* (2008, 2011) in Korup National Park. A population survey was conducted in Nigeria and Cameroon in 1989–1994 by Gadsby and Jenkins (1998). There are also reports from survey studies on Bioko (e.g., Butynski and Koster, 1994; Gonzales-Kirchner and de la Maza, 1996).

Population. Due to heavy human hunting pressure, this is now a relatively rare animal throughout most of its former range, although it is recovering in some areas where there is protection. Linder (2008), however, encountered only 0.01 groups/km on transects in southern Korup National Park in 2004–2005, similar to the frequency reported in the same area by Astaras *et al.* (2008) from surveys in 2006. Astaras *et al.* extrapolated their encounter rate to an estimated density of 1.7 drills/km^2 in areas of southern Korup, >5km from villages. In surveys in 1992 in southeastern Bioko, Maté and Colell (1995) encountered

0.03 groups/km, and in 2008 in the Gran Caldera de Luba, southwestern Bioko, Butynski and Owens (2008) encountered 0.05 groups/km.

Habitat use and locomotion. Drills sleep in trees and, although most of their travelling and much foraging takes place on the ground, as they walk quadrupedally over the forest floor, they do climb into the canopy to feed. In Southern Bakundu, 65% of feeding took place below a height of 3 m, and 90% of feeding occurred below 30 m; at Idenau, 74% of feeding observations were on the ground (Gartlan and Struhsaker, 1972).

Activity patterns. Due to the lack of systematic observations on habituated groups, published data are not available on time spent in different activities by wild drills.

Vocalizations. Gartlan (1970) reports two-syllable alarm barks made by males, a deep two-phase "grunt or roar" made by adult males, and a low-intensity two-phase "huffing grunt" made by subadult and adult males. Gartlan notes the roar as being made immediately before or during group progressions, facilitating group cohesion. Loud squeals occur during agonistic interactions (including chases) in the group, and a "crowing" call is made by members of subgroups (especially juveniles) when they are rejoining; loud crowing calls are made by agitated juveniles. Crowing calls begin as a series of discrete units but then merge into a continuous call (Gartlan, 1970).

Social organization and behavior. In his Southern Bakundu study, Gartlan (1970) obtained reliable counts of between 14 and 179 individuals in groups, and he interprets his observations as likely representing a fission-fusion form of social structure in which small social units join to form large aggregations. Gartlan refers to the large aggregations using the term "grandes hordes bruyantes" from Malbrant and Maclatchy (1949). The smaller units (of up to 22 individuals) typically have only a single fully adult male, but larger groups were seen to have 2–5 adult males, along with numerous adult females and young animals. Solitary adult males were also encountered in the forest. Gartlan reports relatively high rates of aggression in drill groups, including frequent chases involving adult and subadult males; Gartlan interprets this as possible enforced herding or "rounding-up" behavior by the males. Common threat gestures include head and shoulder jerking and branch shaking.

Cercopithecinae

In Cameroon, Struhsaker (1969) encountered groups of drills from 9 to about 65 individuals, with up to 6 or 7 adult males; he noted that groups of 20 or less had only one adult male. Astaras *et al.* (2008) counted four groups that ranged in size from 25 to at least 77 individuals in southern Korup, Cameroon; the smallest group had a single adult male, and there were multiple males in at least two of the larger groups; sub-grouping for a period of 30 minutes during foraging was observed.

During surveys in Bakossiland, Cameroon, in 1970–2002, Wild *et al.* (2005) obtained group size estimates of 5 to 400 animals, with a mean of 93; many of these counts are likely to have been from repeated sightings of the same group. Wild *et al.* had four observations of a group estimated to contain 400 drills; three of these were on Mt. Kupé (one in premontane forest at 900 m, one in submontane forest at 1,200 m, and one in submontane forest at 1,500 m) and one was in the Bakossi Forest Reserve (lowland forest at 500 m).

All these reports (and the reports of hunters in the Korup area to Steiner *et al.* [2003]) are consistent with mainland drill social structure typically consisting of one-male units of up to 25 individuals that will join together in "super-groups" or "hordes" of up to 400 animals, similar to the hordes of mandrills (*Mandrillus sphinx*) reported from Gabon, which, in Lopé National Park, can number more than 800 individuals (Abernethy *et al.*, 2002). It may be that the social structure of drills on Bioko is different, because Gonzales-Kirchner and de la Maza (1996) report that groups observed there never exceeded 20–25 individuals.

Reproduction. Female drills cyclically exhibit large perineal (or "sexual") swellings, and females mate most frequently during a period of maximum swelling (Böer, 1987). In a semi-free-ranging population in Nigeria, mean age at first swelling was 2.7 years, age at first birth was 4–5 years, and the gestation period was 176 days (Wood *et al.*, 2008). The large size of adult males and their striking coloration are almost certainly the result of intrasexual competition and selection among males related to mating (Gartlan, 1970), but details of such behavior in the wild have not yet been studied.

Ranging patterns. Ranging patterns have not been carefully studied. Gartlan (1970) observed members of what was likely one group using an area of 40 ha in Southern Bakundu reserve, but total range size is almost certainly much larger than this.

Cercopithecinae

Diet. In western Cameroon, Gartlan and Struhsaker (1972) recorded them eating a variety of fruits, along with insects and snails. Astaras *et al.* (2008) found seeds, other fruit remains, insects, leaves and mushrooms in drill fecal samples collected at Korup, and noted that the fleshy fruits of *Irvingia gabonensis* (Irvingiaceae) and *Musanga cecropioides* (Moraceae) were seasonally important in these samples. Bioko drills are reported to eat fruits, roots, invertebrates (including snails, termites and freshwater crustaceans) and marine turtle eggs, and are suspected to prey on other mammals (Schaaf *et al.*, 1990; Butynski and Koster, 1994). Where a drill group has passed in the forest there are

Cercopithecinae

Fig. 8.40: Mainland drills (*Mandrillus leucophaeus leucophaeus*) at Drill Ranch Afi Mountain, Cross River State, Nigeria (photo by A. Idoiaga). The adult male is behind, and below him an adult female and a juvenile.

usually abundant signs of the animals having searched the leaf litter for food items, turned over dead wood and broken open termite mounds).

Association with other species. In Korup National Park, Astaras *et al.* (2011) observed other monkey species being present during 50% of 44 encounters with drills (58%); most of these associations were with guenons, the most abundant monkeys in the forest. However, in relation to the relative abundance of other species, Astaras *et al.* most often saw drills in association with red-capped mangabeys (*Cercocebus torquatus*); in 25% of their encounters with *C. torquatus* in Korup, drills were also present. Seventy-three per cent of these drill-mangabey associations in Korup were in the rainy season when fruit is plentiful, and Astaras *et al.* suggest that at such times the potential cost of feeding competition between the two species is overridden by the potential advantages of increased predator detection during association.

Predators. Although it may be guessed that leopards were once a significant predator on mainland drills (there is no historical record of leopards from Bioko), they are now very rare or absent in most of the drill's range, and humans are by far the most significant predator on the species. Hunters commonly employ dogs to hunt drills, either using the dogs to drive the drills into trees where they are shot, or to prevent drills from descending to the ground from sleeping trees (Gartlan, 1970; Gadsby and Jenkins, 1998; Steiner *et al.*, 2003).

Conservation Status

Both the mainland and Bioko subspecies of drill are listed as Endangered on the IUCN Red List. Mainland drills suffer from intense hunting pressure from humans across most of their range and appear to have declined significantly in numbers since the 1970s (Gartlan, 1975; Gadsby and Jenkins, 1998). For instance, a 2004 survey in Southern Bakundu Forest Reserve in southwest Cameroon, where drills were studied by Gartlan (1970) in 1967–1968, encountered very few primates or other larger mammals and found no evidence of drills (Nku, 2004). Hunting in Cameroon, Equatorial Guinea and Nigeria is largely for the commercial bushmeat trade, but is also done for subsistence. Drills are typically hunted using dogs, and hunters report that, having forced a group of drills into trees by chasing them with dogs, they will target particularly the adult male with their shotguns both because of its large size and its danger to hunter and dog; 20 or more drills can be shot at one time using this hunting method (Gartlan, 1975; Steiner *et al.*, 2003). Drills also get caught in snare traps set on the ground.

Cercopithecinae

Populations have been both reduced and fragmented by hunting, and fragmentation has been exacerbated by forest loss to farms, plantations and the spread of settlements. Many forests have been opened up and degraded by logging. The fact that drills still manage to survive in many locations may be due both to their own high fecundity, and to the rugged nature of the terrain. Large hordes of drills may now be a very rare phenomenon.

Drill populations on Bioko Island were recovering in the early 1980s following a 1974 government ban on shotguns, but shotgun hunting has been increasing since then to supply the Malabo bushmeat market. Drills, like other monkeys, have been declining. Hearn *et al.* (2006) estimate that drill numbers fell by more than 30% between 1986 and 2006, to less than 2,000 individuals. Bioko hunters also use dogs to hunt drills (Butynski and Koster, 1994). A ban on shotgun hunting came into force again on Bioko in November 2007, but this has not stopped all hunting.

Drills are found in all the main protected areas within their range: in Nigeria in the Afi Mountain Wildlife Sanctuary and Cross River National Park; in Cameroon in the Korup, Takamanda and Mount Cameroon national parks, the proposed Ebo National Park, and the Banyang-Mbo Wildlife Sanctuary. On Bioko, they are found in the Pico Basilé National Park, and Gran Caldera and the Southern Highlands Scientific Reserve. In practice, anti-poaching measures have been weak in most of these areas, although in recent years law enforcement has improved both at Afi Mountain and in the southern part of Korup. At the base of Afi Mountain, the Drill Breeding and Rehabilitation Center (DBRC) of the Pandrillus organization has a facility where drills orphaned by the bushmeat trade have been rehabilitated. There they are breeding in large, electric-fenced forested enclosures, with the aim of ultimately releasing groups to the wild.

Where to See It

The drill is not easy to observe in the wild, but with sufficient effort can be seen (although often only fleetingly) in Afi Mountain Wildlife Sanctuary and in the Mbe Mountains in Cross River State, Nigeria; in Korup National Park and the Ebo Forest in Cameroon; and in the Gran Caldera and Southern Highlands Scientific Reserve, Bioko. Captive groups living in close-to-natural conditions can be readily observed in the Drill Breeding and Rehabilitation Center (DBRC) enclosures near Buanchor at the base of Afi Mountain.

Cercopithecinae

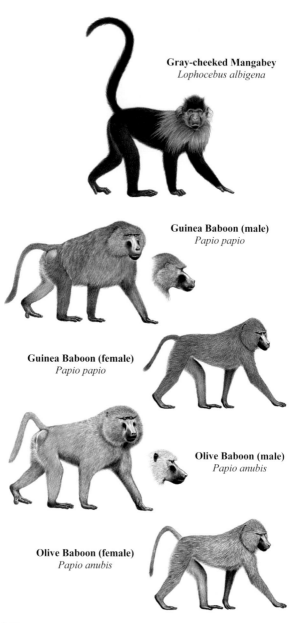

Gray-cheeked Mangabey
Lophocebus albigena

Guinea Baboon (male)
Papio papio

Guinea Baboon (female)
Papio papio

Olive Baboon (male)
Papio anubis

Olive Baboon (female)
Papio anubis

Fig. 8.41.

Lophocebus Palmer, 1903
Crested mangabeys

The *Lophocebus* mangabeys are medium-sized to large arboreal forest monkeys, with very long tails, and tufts of hair on the crowns of their heads or on their brows. They are generally associated with closed-canopy moist forest, but also range into semi-deciduous and gallery forest on the fringes of the moist forest zone. *Lophocebus* mangabeys share with *Cercocebus* mangabeys and with baboons a tendency to live in multi-male groups, and females have conspicuous cyclical perineal swellings. Like other mangabeys, adult males produce loud "whoop-gobble" calls. *Lophocebus* mangabeys differ from *Cercocebus* in lacking white eyelids.

The taxonomy of *Lophocebus* is confusing. Groves (1978) recognized just one species of *Lophocebus*: *L. albigena*, with five subspecies. Subsequently Groves (1989) separated the subspecies *aterrimus* of the south-central Congo Basin as a species from *albigena*, a course followed by Kingdon (1997) and by Grubb *et al.* (2003). Next, Groves (2001) separated *L. opdenboschi* from *L. aterrimus*, and most recently he has split *L. albigena* into four species (*albigena*, *johnstoni*, *osmani* and *ugandae* [Groves, 2007]), based on coat pattern and cranial measurements. Although the forms *albigena* and *johnstoni* occur, respectively, to the west and east of the Ubangui River, no obvious biogeographic barriers separate *johnstoni* from *ugandae*, or *albigena* from West African *osmani*. I do not consider that all the species listed in Groves's most recent treatments have yet been sufficiently well delineated, and therefore I follow Grubb *et al.* (2003) in recognizing only *L. albigena* and *L. aterrimus* until further research is completed. I also agree with Grubb *et al.* that there is insufficient evidence at this point to clearly identify different subspecies within *L. albigena*, although there is certainly considerable pelage variation within this taxon.

Lophocebus albigena geospecies

Grubb (2006b) places all the *Lophocebus* mangabeys in the geospecies *L. albigena*. He also included the recently-discovered "kipunji" of southern Tanzania in this group, but new studies have shown that this monkey deserves to be placed in its own genus, *Rungwecebus*, which is more closely related to *Papio* than to *Lophocebus* (Davenport *et al.*, 2006; Olson *et al.*, 2008).

Cercopithecinae

Local Representatives

Of the species recognized by Groves (2007a), only *L. osmani* is found in the area covered by the guide, in limited areas of western Cameroon and in Nigeria close to the Cameroon border. However, as explained above, the taxonomy of Grubb *et al.* (2003) is followed here, which recognizes only one species of gray-cheeked mangabey, *L. albigena*, with no subspecies, pending further research.

Cercopithecinae

Fig. 8.42: Gray-cheeked mangabey (*Lophocebus albigena*), Mbam & Djerem, Cameroon (photo by R. Fotso). The characteristic tufts of long black hair above the eyes of West African members of this species are just visible in this image.

Gray-cheeked mangabey
Lophocebus albigena (Gray, 1850)

Other English: Gray-cheeked crested mangabey, cloaked mangabey, black mangabey
French: Mangabé a joues blanches, mangabé a joues grises
West African languages: Kekekara, kekerere (Boki, Nigeria); Kebilika, gebilika (Okwa, Obonyi and Takamanda, Nigeria and Cameroon); Ambilika (Balegete, Nigeria); Shoen (Bamoun, Cameroon); Gobada (Gbaya, Cameroon); Nzirou (Mvouté, Cameroon)

Identification (see Fig. 8.41, p.184)

The gray-cheeked mangabey is a medium-sized to large arboreal forest monkey of relatively slender build with a very long, semi-prehensile tail. In West African populations, the hair on the back, crown of the head, arms and tail is predominantly blackish-brown, blacker on the lower back and tail. The thighs and belly are chocolaty-brown, and the chest and throat are lighter brown. The hands and feet are black. There is a cape or mantle of long gray-brown hairs on the shoulders and nape of the neck, extending to the upper arms—this mantle hair is slightly more russet between the shoulders. The cheek whiskers are gray. The hairs on the tail are particularly long, especially at the base; the tail hair becomes shorter and sparser towards the tip, giving the tail a tapered appearance. Above each eyebrow is a tuft of long black hairs. When the mangabey is standing, the tail is often held vertically, with the tip curved forwards. The skin of the face is entirely black, and the muzzle is prominent.

Lophocebus albigena has an average head and body length of 60–65 cm in adult males and 55 cm in females, and a tail length of about 90 cm in males and 80 cm in females. Adult males are heavier than adult females, weighing 8–9 kg on average, compared with an average female weight of about 6 kg (Delson *et al.*, 2000; Olupot, 2000).

Similar species. The gray-cheeked mangabey can be confused with the red-capped mangabey (*Cercocebus torquatus*) in the few parts of West Africa where these two species' ranges overlap (for instance, at least in the past both species occurred in, or close to, the Takamanda Forest Reserve, Cameroon [Sunderland-Groves and Maisels, 2003]). The two species are similar in size, proportions, and postural style, but

Cercopithecinae

the red-capped mangabey is distinguished by its red crown and gray back, and its white eyelids, chest and tail-tip. The red-capped mangabey is much more terrestrial than the gray-cheeked mangabey. In parts of Cameroon the gray-cheeked mangabey has sometimes been mistakenly identified as the black colobus monkey (*Colobus satanas*), which in our area occurs only south of the Sanaga River and on Bioko Island. The black colobus lacks a brown cape, has longer legs, a less hairy tail, and uses sitting, bounding and leaping more in its postural and locomotor repertoire, compared to more standing, climbing and walking by the gray-cheeked mangabey. The adult male colobus makes a "croaking" loud call, while male mangabeys produce a "whoop-gobble."

Taxonomic Note

Groves (1978) recognized three subspecies of *Lophocebus albigena*: *L. a. albigena* from western equatorial Africa including southern Cameroon; *L. a . osmani* from the Cross River region of Nigeria and northern Cameroon (including the Batouri District); and *L. a. johnstoni* from northern and eastern DRC, Burundi, Rwanda, Uganda and southern Sudan. Gautier-Hion *et al.* (1999) follows that arrangement. Napier (1981) was aware of Groves's 1978 treatment, but kept the earlier arrangement of Hill (1974), not recognizing "osmani" but instead placing the gray-cheeked mangabeys of western Cameroon south of the Sanaga River in the subspecies *L. albigena zenkeri*, whereas Groves (1978) had treated *zenkeri* as part of *L. a. albigena*. Debate has focused on the color of hair of the shoulder mantle in the different forms. According to Groves (1978), *osmani* has a rusty-brown or tobacco-brown mantle, while Hill (1974) describes *zenkeri* as having a brownish-gray mantle and Napier (1981) describes the *zenkeri* mantle as light-brown or tobacco-brown. Kingdon (1997) applied the name *L. a. osmani* to gray-cheeked mangabeys in the Cross River region, saying that they have a russet cape, and he retained the name *L. a. zenkeri* for the mangabeys of southern Cameroon, describing their cape as gray. Grubb *et al.* (2003) agreed that *L. albigena* exhibits pelage variation across its range, but could not agree on the validity of any of the described subspecies; they called for more research. Following a new multivariate analysis of the skull measurements used in his earlier paper, and applying the Phylogenetic Species Concept, Groves (2007a) elevated the three subspecies he had recognized in 1978 to full species, and added a fourth, *L. ugandae*. Groves's discriminant analysis used six cranial variables, which separated seven specimens allocated to *L. osmani* as a group distinct from other western and central African *Lophocebus*.

Cercopithecinae

Until more information is available, including the results of genetic research, it seems wise to follow the course taken by Grubb *et al.* (2003) which involves recognizing one species of gray-cheeked mangabeys, *Lophocebus albigena*, and reserving judgment on how many (and which) subspecies within it should be recognized. Images of gray-cheeked mangabeys from Mbam & Djerem in Cameroon (see Fig. 8.42, p.186) and Gashaka Gumti in Nigeria, show a brownish-gray rather than rusty-brown mantle coloration, and obvious horn-like brow tufts (which Groves, 1978, says are lacking in *osmani*).

Geographic Range

The gray-cheeked mangabeys (*Lophocebus albigena* in a broad sense) occur from the region of the Cameroon-Nigeria border eastward across the northern part of the Congo Basin to Uganda, and southward to the Congo Republic. The species is found in only in very limited, scattered areas within the region covered by this guidebook: the Okwangwo-Takamanda forests on the Nigeria-Cameroon border (where it may now be extinct) (Gartlan and Struhsaker, 1972; Groves, 1978; Oates *et al.*, 1990b; Sunderland-Groves and Maisels, 2003); the Gashaka Gumti National Park in Nigeria (K. Arnold, D. Inglis and V. Sommer, pers. comm.); and the Mbam & Djerem National Park, Cameroon, which straddles the Sanaga's major tributary, the River Djerem (R. Fotso and F. Maisels, pers. comm.). Immediately to the south of the Sanaga River, gray-cheeked mangabeys have been reported from Cameroon's coastal Douala-Edéa Reserve (Gartlan and Struhsaker, 1972).

Cercopithecinae

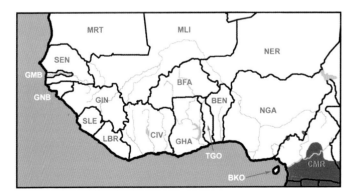

Fig. 8.43: Distribution of *Lophocebus albigena* in West Africa.

Natural History

Habitat. Through most of their range, gray-cheeked mangabeys seem to especially favor high-canopy mature moist forest (Jones and Sabater Pi, 1968; Gautier-Hion *et al.*, 1999), although they also occur in secondary forest and gallery forest.

Field Studies. Thomas Struhsaker made observations of *L. albigena* during surveys in Cameroon in the 1960s (Struhsaker, 1969; Gartlan and Struhsaker, 1972), but no in-depth studies have been conducted on this species in the region covered by this guide. Plentiful information is available, however, from other parts of Africa. The closest site to our region from which substantial information is available is the Dja Reserve in southern Cameroon, where a study of *L. albigena* feeding ecology was conducted in 1998 (Poulsen and Clark, 2001; Poulsen *et al.*, 2001a, 2001b). In western equatorial Africa, Rebecca Ham studied gray-cheeked mangabeys for her doctoral dissertation at Lopé, Gabon, in 1991–1992 (Ham, 1994; Tutin *et al.*, 1997), and Natasha Shah compared *L. albigena* and *Cercocebus galeritus* as a doctoral research project at Mondika in the Dzanga-Ndoki National Park of the Central African Republic in 1998–1999 (Shah, 2003). There is also published information from short-term observations in Rio Muni (Jones and Sabater Pi, 1968) and from surveys in Lopé and Makandé, Gabon (White, 1994; Brugière *et al.*, 2002). A great deal of behavioral data is available from East Africa, where Neil Chalmers (1968a, 1968b, 1968c) conducted some of the first-ever field studies of habituated wild African forest monkeys on this species in eastern Uganda. Subsequently, Peter Waser, William Freeland, Simon Wallis and William Olupot have studied gray-cheeked mangabeys in the Kibale Forest, western Uganda (e.g., Waser, 1975, 1976, 1977a, 1977b, 1980, 1982; Wallis, 1978, 1983; Freeland, 1979; Olupot, 1998, 2000; Olupot *et al.*, 1994, 1997, 1998; Olupot and Waser, 2001, 2005). This account will only briefly summarize some of the main features of the species' natural history revealed at sites outside the range of this guide because West African populations may well exhibit some differences in behavior from those living elsewhere.

Population. The gray-cheeked mangabey is now very rare in the forests of the Nigeria-Cameroon border region, but is widespread in the Mbam & Djerem National Park, Cameroon. Elsewhere, surveys have produced density estimates of 20 individual *L. albigena* per km² in the Dja Reserve, Cameroon (Poulsen *et al.*, 2001b); of 8 individuals/km² in Lopé, Gabon (White, 1994); of 3 individuals/km² at Makandé, Gabon

(Brugière *et al.*, 2002); and of 22 individuals/km² at Mondika, CAR (Shah, 2003). In the Kibale Forest, Uganda, Struhsaker (1997) reports densities of 10–19 individuals/km² in unlogged forest as against 1.7/km² in forest that had been heavily logged.

Habitat use. At most sites, gray-cheeked mangabeys predominantly use the upper forest canopy. At Lac Tisongo, Cameroon (in the Douala-Edéa Reserve) all 28 observations of gray-cheeked mangabeys were above a height of 31 ft (about 10 m) with 70% of observations above 75 ft (about 23 m) (Gartlan and Struhsaker, 1972). However, at Dja the mangabeys fed at lower heights during a fruit-lean period early in the year and fed higher when eating *Erythrophleum* seeds later in the year; they were occasionally seen to feed on the ground (Poulsen *et al.*, 2001a). At Mondika, CAR, 81% of scan samples of *L. albigena* came from 16 m or above, and the mangabeys were most frequently observed at 26–30 m (Shah, 2003). Most feeding in Kibale Forest, Uganda, occurs above 12 m (Waser, 1977a).

Locomotion and posture. Jones and Sabater Pi (1968) describe *L. albigena* as a deliberate and slow climber when compared to sympatric guenons. They also report that these mangabeys frequently adopt a sitting posture when at rest, with the limbs spread-eagled.

Activity pattern. In Dja, Cameroon, gray-cheeked mangabeys spent more than 50% of their time feeding and searching for food, more than 25% of their time traveling, and about 10% of their time resting (Poulsen *et al.*, 2001a). At Mondika, CAR, 49% of their time was spent in feeding and foraging, 28% in travel, and 14% in resting (Shah, 2003), while in the Kibale Forest, the mangabeys spent 44% of their time in feeding and foraging, 22% moving, and 21% of their time resting (Struhsaker and Leland, 1979).

Vocalizations. The gray-cheeked mangabey vocal repertoire has been well-studied and includes staccato barks (or "chuckles"), grunts, screams, soft growls, and a distinctive "whoop-gobble" call (Chalmers, 1968c; Struhsaker, 1969; Waser, 1977b). The loud whoop-gobble, given by adult males of both *Lophocebus* and *Cercocebus*, was first described from this species in Uganda (Chalmers, 1968c). The whoop-gobble consists of an initial low frequency "whoop" (or "hoot") about 3 sec long, whose energy is concentrated below 500 Hz, followed, after a 5 sec pause, by a longer, pulsed gobbling call pitched at 200–300 Hz. The whoop-gobble is typically given in a sequence of 2–3 calls and can carry for over 1 km through the forest canopy (Chalmers, 1968c;

Cercopithecinae

Waser, 1977b). Waser (1977b) has shown how the whoop-gobble mediates both cohesion within a mangabey group, and avoidance of other groups. Staccato barks are given by both males and females in a variety of alarming or disturbing situations, such as the appearance of potential predators, including unfamiliar humans (Struhsaker, 1969; Waser, 1977b). *Lophocebus albigena* females produce a special post-copulatory grunting call (Waser, 1977b).

Social organization and behavior. Gray-cheeked mangabey groups commonly contain 10–20 individuals, with several adult males, but the males are not stable group members. Struhsaker (1969) counted groups of 10 and 12 individuals in Cameroon, with 1–4 adult males, and observed another group with at least 12–13 individuals. A Dja study group contained 16–22 individuals, with two adult males (Poulsen *et al.*, 2001a); a main study group Lopé, Gabon, contained 18–23 individuals, with 1–3 adult males, and a second group had 18–20 members, two of which were adult males (Ham, 1994); and at Mondika, CAR, a study group contained 12–14 individuals, with 3–4 adult males (Shah, 2003). These observations in western Africa are consistent with data from East Africa; in the Lwamunda forest, Uganda, a study group contained 19 individuals, with 4 adult males (Chalmers, 1968a), while in Kibale Forest, Uganda, seven well-known groups ranged in size from 5–26 with a median size of 12; the Kibale groups contained a median of 3 adult males (range 1–10) and 7 adult females (Olupot and Waser, 2005). Studies in Kibale reveal that groups have a resident core of females, and a much less stable complement of males. Males leave their natal groups as they mature and, after a solitary period, attempt to join bisexual groups; some become long-term residents, some spend long periods as peripheral group members, and some remain solitary for long periods. Resident males may migrate and become resident in new groups, or may visit other groups for less than two weeks. Dispersal into, or visits to, other groups by males are related to the number of estrous females (those with swollen sexual skin) in these groups. One adult male in a group typically has a "rapid approach" role in interactions with other groups; this male is also the most frequent recipient of female grooming and the one most frequently observed to copulate (Olupot and Waser, 2001, 2005).

Interactions between groups. In Kibale, Uganda, groups have very large ranges that overlap extensively with the ranges of other groups; groups show a tendency to avoid each other, typically withdrawing if they detect another group with 500 m. This behavior is mediated by adult male monitoring behavior and "whoop-gobble" vocalizations (Waser, 1976).

Cercopithecinae

Reproduction. Females develop deep pink, rounded perineal swellings around the time of ovulation. Two or three days before the time of peak swelling, males begin to follow swollen females at a distance of about 20 m, and almost all copulations occur within two days of the time of peak swelling (Chalmers, 1968b; Wallis, 1983). Gestation period in the Kibale Forest is 185–189 days (Wallis, 1983). There is no distinct breeding season, at least not in East African populations.

Ranging patterns. Gray-cheeked mangabey range size and use is probably highly contingent on forest structure and the presence of competitors, but groups usually range widely. In Gabon, the annual range of a group of 18–23 individuals was 215 ha, while a group of 18–20 ranged over 156 ha (Ham, 1994). At Mondika, CAR, a study group travelled an average of 1,137 m per day and used 167 one-hectare cells in the course of a year (Shah, 2003); when fruit was least abundant, the mangabeys travelled less and ate more leaves. By contrast, in the small Lwamunda forest in eastern Uganda (where the only other monkey was *Cercopithecus ascanius*), the study group of Chalmers (1968a) had a range of only 13 ha. In Kibale Forest, western Uganda (home to six sympatric monkey species and chimpanzees), a group had a home range of over 410 ha (Waser, 1977a). The Kibale group used about 7–8 ha of this range each day, travelling on average about 1 km. While foraging, the group can be spread over a linear distance of more than 500 m. A group will reside in an area with abundant food resources for a week or so, and then move on to another area in a seminomadic fashion, so exploiting food patches that are widely scattered in time and space (Waser, 1977a; Olupot *et al.*, 1997).

Diet. Seeds are a major component of this mangabey's diet in western Africa. In Dja, Cameroon, the observed diet of *L. albigena* was made up of 62% fruit (about half of which was seeds extracted from fruit mesocarp) and 27% insects, with the remainder being leaves, flowers, buds and bark (Poulsen *et al.*, 2001a). The most frequently eaten food items were the seeds of the large emergent tree *Erythrophleum sauveolens* (Leguminosae, Caesalpiniodeae). At Dja, mangabeys were also seen to eat a squirrel and a galago (Poulsen and Clark, 2001). More leaves and flowers were eaten by Dja mangabeys at the beginning of the year when fruit was less abundant. Fruit and seeds made up 76% of the diet of gray-cheeked mangabeys at Mondika, CAR, with insects forming 13% of feeding records, and leaves 7% (Shah, 2003); the seeds of *Erythrophleum ivorense* were the most frequently-eaten item at Mondika. In Lopé, Gabon, the diet consisted of 24% fruit flesh, 41% seeds and 25% animals (Tutin *et al.*, 1997). At Makandé, Gabon, diet is reported to be 57% seeds, 26% fruit pulp and aril, and 11% leaves, with 58% of the feeding records coming from the leguminous Caesalpinioideae family (Brugière *et al.*, 2002). In forest of very different composition at Kibale, Uganda, the recorded diet is nearly 60% fruits (with fewer seeds than in western Africa); 8–9% young leaves, flowers and buds; 3–5% bark; and 25–30% arthropods (Waser 1977a; Freeland, 1979; Olupot, 1998). Large fig trees are an important food resource in Kibale, and some figs are probably exploited more for the wasp larvae they contain than for the fruits themselves; stripping tree bark to reach cambial layers is facilitated by the mangabey's powerful jaws and teeth.

Association with other species. In western Africa, *L. albigena* is often seen in association with guenons, and most frequently with the crowned guenon (*Cercopithecus pogonias*), which typically follows the mangabeys (Gartlan and Struhsaker, 1972; Waser, 1980, 1982). In Kibale, Uganda, gray-cheeked mangabeys are often seen in association with other canopy monkeys, but these associations are generally transient; only association with redtail monkeys (*Cercopithecus ascanius*) occurs more frequently than would be expected by chance or through meeting at common food resources. The redtails probably follow the mangabeys to increase their access to food and to reduce their risk from predators (Waser, 1980, 1982).

Predators. In West Africa, hunters are the most serious predator today on gray-cheeked mangabeys. Crowned eagles are probably the major predator on this species in pristine ecosystems. At Mondika, CAR, Shah (2003) observed a crowned eagle eating a subadult male mangabey, and an analysis of prey remains beneath crowned eagle nests in Kibale Forest, Uganda, found that *L. albigena* remains were more abundant in relation to the abundance of this species in the forest than those of any other monkey (Struhsaker and Leakey, 1990). Henschel *et al.* (2005) have recorded *L. albigena* remains in leopard scat at Lopé, Gabon.

Conservation Status

Although *Lophocebus albigena* is listed as a species of Least Concern in the IUCN Red List, it is rare and highly localized in the region covered in this guide. It was seen near the Maku and Makweli rivers in the area of the Takamanda Forest Reserve in South West Cameroon in 1966 (Gartlan and Struhsaker, 1972), but it was not

Cercopithecinae

encountered during recent surveys of Takamanda, even though local hunters have a name for this species and give an accurate description of it (Sunderland-Groves and Maisels, 2003). In 1990, hunters across the border in the Okwangwo region of Nigeria also had a name for this monkey, and described it well, but surveys in that part of Nigeria have also failed to produce a sighting (Oates *et al.*, 1990a). Gray-cheeked mangabeys are, therefore, guessed to be extinct or verging on extinction the Okwangwo-Takamanda forests. However, a population was recently discovered surviving in Nigeria's Gashaka Gumti National Park, north of Okwangwo (K. Arnold, D. Inglis and V. Sommer, pers. comm.). It is not known whether the rarity of this species in our area is the result of ecological factors (such as a low abundance of preferred food), or of hunting; a combination of the two may be responsible.

In West Africa, a viable population of *L. albigena* occurs in Cameroon's Mbam & Djerem National Park (about 5,000 km^2), where it occurs both in closed-canopy forest in the south of the park and in forest galleries in the north (F. Maisels, pers. comm.).

Where to See It

The only site within the region of this guide where a visitor has a good chance of seeing this species is in the Mbam & Djerem National Park, Cameroon.

Cercopithecinae

Papio Erxleben, 1777
Baboons

The baboons are large terrestrial monkeys that occur in savanna, woodland, dry forest and semi-desert habitats throughout sub-Saharan Africa (and in two mountainous areas in the Sahara), as well as on the western edge of the Arabian Peninsula. Their arms and legs are of similar length, their tails are relatively short, and they have very elongated dog-like muzzles with terminal nostrils. Baboon social groups are typically large, with several adult males, and often exhibit a multi-layered structure. Adult males are considerably larger than females and have very long canine teeth. Adult females have large ovulatory genital swellings.

Genetic studies (e.g., Disotell, 2000) have confirmed that baboons are close evolutionary relatives of the gelada (*Theropithecus*) of the Ethiopian plateau, and that these two groups share a common ancestry with *Lophocebus* mangabeys. The recently-discovered mangabey-like "kipunji" (*Rungwecebus*) of the southern highlands of Tanzania is genetically closely related to *Papio* (Olson *et al.*, 2008).

The species-level taxonomy of baboons has long been a matter of considerable debate; there are regional baboon populations that have distinctive features, but hybridization and intergradation occur between some of these populations. Napier and Napier (1967) recognized two species groups, *Papio hamadryas* and *Papio cynocephalus*, the second including four species: *P. papio*, *P. anubis*, *P. cynocephalus* and *P. ursinus*. Thorington and Groves (1970) made these two species groups into two individual species, although Groves put forward his personal view in this joint publication that all baboons should be considered as belonging to one biological species, *Papio hamadryas*. Jolly (1993) also considered it best to regard all the baboons as a single species (pointing out that the species is not an absolute concept), and he suggested that nine subspecies could be recognized. Hill (1970), on the other hand, made a thorough analysis of baboon taxonomy and settled on a five-species arrangement (*P. hamadryas*, *P. papio*, *P. anubis*, *P. cynocephalus* and *P. ursinus*), one that has been followed by Dandelot (1971), Kingdon (1997), Groves (2001) and Grubb *et al.* (2003). Mainly because of its familiarity and widespread use, that is the taxonomy adopted in this guide. The most recent phylogeographic analysis based on mitochondrial genetic research has found, however, that DNA data are not consistent with this taxonomy (Zinner *et al.*, 2010). For instance, the olive baboons of West Africa appear to have had a complex evolutionary history and may be derived in part from a lineage that separated long ago from East African olive baboons.

Papio cynocephalus geospecies

Grubb (2006b) places all of the baboons into the single geospecies *P. cynocephalus*, containing the five species listed above.

Local Representatives

Of the five species listed by Grubb *et al.* (2003), two occur in West Africa: *Papio papio* in the far west, and *Papio anubis* in the remaining part of the savanna zone together with the Aïr Mountains of Niger.

Cercopithecinae

Fig. 8.44: Two adult female olive baboons (*Papio anubis*), Gashaka, Nigeria (photo by D. M. Inglis).

Guinea baboon
Papio papio (Desmarest, 1820)

Other English: Western baboon
French: Babouin de Guineé
Portuguese: Macaco-cão
West African languages: Kongo (Sossé, Senegal); Gon (Fula,
Senegal); Gbon (Dioula, Senegal); Tchom (Balanta, Guinea-Bissau)

Identification (see Fig. 8.41, p.184)

Like the other species of *Papio*, the Guinea baboon is a large
terrestrial monkey, with arms and legs of similar length, a relatively
short tail and an elongated muzzle. The Guinea baboon carries its
tail in a gentle curve, rather than with the distinct angle seen in the
olive baboon (*P. anubis*). The general coloration of the coat is a warm
brownish-fawn (or light reddish-brown), the facial skin is gray or
pinkish-gray, and the ischial callosities are also pinkish-gray. Guinea
baboons are strongly sexually dimorphic; males are much larger than
females, have a well-developed cape or mane on the shoulders, and a
ruff of hair on the sides of the face. Adult females develop large sexual
swellings.

Papio papio is of medium size for a baboon. Kingdon (1997) gives
a head and body length of 75 cm in males and 55 cm in females, and a
tail length for both sexes of 35–60 cm. Adult males weigh about 19 kg
and females 12–13 kg (Dunbar, 1988; Kingdon, 1997).

Similar species. Baboons are not easily confused with other
monkeys, but different kinds of baboon cannot always be readily
distinguished from one another; this is especially the case with females
and young. *Papio anubis* is larger than *P. papio*, with a speckled,
olivaceous khaki-brown and gray coat, a distinct angle in its tail, and a
darker gray face and callosities. The olive baboon's nostrils protrude
strongly, overhanging the front of the muzzle more than in the Guinea
baboon. Published maps suggest that the ranges of *Papio papio* and *P.
anubis* meet in Mali, Guinea, Sierra Leone and perhaps southeastern
Mauretania, but little field work has been done in this region. Other
terrestrial or semi-terrestrial monkeys within the range of the Guinea
baboon (the green monkey, patas and sooty mangabey) are smaller in
size and have longer tails.

Cercopithecinae

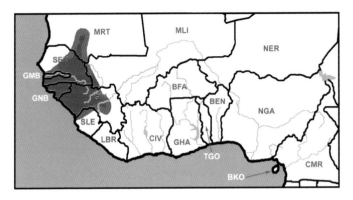

Fig. 8.45: Distribution of *Papio papio*.

Taxonomic Note

This is one of the most distinctive geographical forms of baboon, and all recent taxonomies place it in its own species. Some older treatments list the Guinea baboon as a subspecies of *Papio hamadryas* (e.g., Thorington and Groves, 1970; Smuts *et al.*, 1987).

Geographic Range

Papio papio is known from southern Mauritania, Senegal, the Gambia, Guinea-Bissau, western Guinea, the western edges of Mali, and northwestern Sierra Leone, but is becoming rare in parts of its former range. Decreased rainfall is affecting its northern range limits (Galat *et al.*, 2000).

Natural History

Habitat. The habitats of the Guinea baboon range from coastal mangrove to Sahelian steppe, including shrub and woodland savanna, and secondary forest (Galat-Luong *et al.*, 2006). The important population in the Niokolo Koba National Park in Senegal inhabits an area transitional between the Guinean and Sudanian savanna woodland zones. Niokolo Koba has large areas of quite dense shrubland, with forest along watercourses and in ravines. Where *P. papio* has been observed at Kilimi in Sierra Leone the vegetation is predominantly Guinea savanna woodland with gallery forests and patches of dry forest. Gallery forest is reported to be where they like to sleep in Senegal (Dunbar and Nathan, 1972).

Cercopithecinae

Field studies. This is the least studied of the five commonly recognized baboon species. There have been several studies in and around the Niokolo Koba National Park in Senegal, but most of these have been short-term (e.g., Dunbar and Nathan, 1972; Byrne, 1981; Anderson and McGrew, 1984; Galat-Luong *et al.*, 2006). Sharman (1981) conducted a doctoral study on *P. papio* ecology and behavior at this site, but most of the findings of this study have not been published (although some summary statistics are available in Dunbar, 1988). Observations have also been collected in the Kilimi area of Sierra Leone as part of a general primate survey (Harding, 1984).

Population. In the early 1980s, Harding (1984) estimated that there were 700–1,350 Guinea baboons in the 240 km² Kilimi area of what later became the Outamba-Kilimi National Park, Sierra Leone. In 1998, Galat-Luong *et al.* estimated a population size of about 230,000 in the 9,130-km² Niokolo Koba National Park, Senegal, compared with less than 150,000 individuals in 1990–1993.

Habitat use. In Niokolo Koba, Guinea baboons spend 45–50% of their time in shrub savanna, 30–35% in tree savanna, 10–20% in forest, and the rest of their time in grassland (Galat-Luong *et al.*, 2006).

Cercopithecinae

Fig. 8.46: Guinea baboons (*Papio papio*), Haut Niger National Park, Guinea (photo by C. Colin).

Activity pattern. Sharman (in Dunbar, 1988) found that baboons at Niokolo Koba spent a relatively large amount of their time (about 20%) in social activities and, compared to many other primates, a relatively small amount of time resting (also about 20%). Niokolo Koba baboons move most and socialize least at the end of the dry season, but as grasses become more widely available in the wet season, the baboons fed and socialized more, and moved less (Galat-Luong *et al.*, 2006).

Vocalizations. Byrne (1981) describes the Guinea baboon as highly vocal, recognizing 12 distinct call types, besides coughing and sneezing. These calls include loud two-phased "wahoo" barks and "roargrunts" given by adult males, and a variety of barks and grunts given by all age-sex classes except infants. Single and double-phased barks enable foraging subgroups to maintain contact in thick vegetation, and then to rejoin before crossing open areas. Adult males characteristically produce sequences, or volleys, of loud calls from sleeping sites; these volleys are typically provoked by the calls of predators or by volleys from other baboons (which may be 2–3 km away).

Social organization. Wild and captive observations have shown that a multi-level structure is typical of Guinea baboon society. Guinea baboons commonly travel in large multi-male troops. Dunbar and Nathan (1972) studied a group in Senegal that contained 83 individuals with 12 adult males, and Dunbar (1988) gives a mean group size as 184 animals. Galat-Luong *et al.* (2006) observed troops in Niokolo Koba ranging from 22 to 249 with a mean of 62. Mean troop size in Kilimi, Sierra Leone, was estimated at 100–150 by Harding (1984). These large groups contain small subgroups, or parties, whose basic unit consists of 8–10 individuals with only a single adult male. These one-male units separate during foraging and resting during the day, and for sleeping, at which time the troop may be dispersed in trees over a wide area (Dunbar and Nathan, 1972; Galat-Luong *et al.*, 2006). Subgroups come together as a column when moving to or from sleeping sites or across open ground (Boese, 1975; Byrne, 1981). Galat-Luong *et al.* (2006) identified spatially-distinct second-level groups between the one-male units and the large troop; at Niokolo Koba these second-level subgroups are spatially distinct and averaged 19 individuals.

Social behavior. Galat-Luong *et al.* (2006) observed that adult males lead and control group movements, running to speed progression, and displaying to change the direction of travel. Adult males receive the most submissive behavior (both from other males and from females) and perform the most agonistic acts. In captive Guinea

Cercopithecinae

baboons, Maestripieri *et al.* (2007) found that mating and affiliative behaviors are concentrated in the one-male units.

Reproduction. Females copulate most frequently when their perineal swellings are of maximum size. At the end of copulation, females commonly make a low-pitched rhythmic call (Maestripieri *et al.*, 2005).

Ranging patterns. Dunbar (1988) gives a typical day range length for a group of Guinea baboons as 7.9 km, and mean home range area as 29 km².

Diet. The diet of Guinea baboons in Niokolo Koba is reported to consist of 74% fruits, 9% flowers, 8% leaves, 4% roots and 3% animals (Sharman, 1981, as quoted by Dunbar, 1988). Among animals eaten, McGrew *et al.* (1978) saw these baboons catching and eating a hare and a young antelope. Guinea baboons have been reported to be a serious pest as crop raiders in Sierra Leone (Harding, 1984).

Predators. Lions, leopards, wild dogs and spotted hyenas are predators on the baboons of Niokolo Koba (Byrne, 1981; Anderson and McGrew, 1984; Galat-Luong *et al.*, 2006). The high predation risk and relatively thick vegetation of Niokolo Koba in Senegal may be related to the high frequency of calling by baboons at that site (Byrne, 1981).

Conservation Status

Papio papio is listed as Near Threatened on the IUCN Red List. Although still abundant in some places (such as Niokolo Koba in Senegal), Guinea baboon populations are reported to be in general decline because of habitat loss caused by agriculture, grazing, tree-cutting and fire (G. K. Boese quoted in Wolfheim, 1983; Galat *et al.*, 2000; Gippoliti and Dell'Omo, 2003). Galat *et al.* (2000) report that their northern distribution in Senegal has contracted because of decreased rainfall. They are hunted in parts of Senegal and Guinea (Wolfheim, 1983; Galat-Luong and Galat, 2003).

Where to See It

Papio papio can be readily observed in Niokolo Koba National Park, Senegal, and it is present in the River Gambia National Park in the Gambia. The baboons in Haut Niger National Park, Guinea, may be a hybrid *P. papio-P. anubis* population (Zinner *et al.*, 2010).

Olive baboon
Papio anubis (Lesson, 1827)

Other English: Anubis baboon, doguera baboon
French: Babouin doguera
West African languages: Kongongulai (Mende, Sierra Leone); Oturno (Baoulé, Côte d'Ivoire); Gbon (Sénoufo, Côte d'Ivoire); Botimo (Agni, Côte d'Ivoire); Kontromfi (Twi, Ghana); Kessé (Ewe, Togo); Han (Fon, Bénin); Adaka (Igbo, Nigeria); Akato (Yoruba, Nigeria); Akharo (Bini, Nigeria); Gogo (Hausa, Nigeria); Nkepac (Bamileke, Cameroon); Ndoro (Foufoulbe, Cameroon)

Identification (see Fig. 8.41, p.184)

The olive baboon is a very large terrestrial monkey, with arms and legs of similar length, a relatively short tail and an elongated muzzle. The tail has a distinct kink; at first it rises steeply from the rump (for about one-fourth of its length), then falls away sharply. The rather shaggy coat has a grayish-tan, "pepper and salt" (or speckled) appearance, with a slight olivaceous tinge. The speckling is produced by gray and yellow banding on the hairs. The facial skin is dark gray to black, and the ischial callosities dark purplish gray. The nostrils at the end of the prominent muzzle protrude beyond the plane of the upper lip. Olive baboons have pronounced sexual dimorphism, with adult males being much larger than females. Adult males have a mane on the shoulders, but this is less strongly developed than in some other baboon species, such as *P. papio*. Adult females develop large peri-ovulatory genital swellings.

Adult olive baboons have a head and body length of 75 cm in males and 60 cm in females, and a tail length of about 50 cm in males and 45 cm in females (Napier, 1981). Adult males average about 23 kg (but can reach weights of up to 37 kg) and adult females average 14 kg (with maximum weights of 18 kg) (Delson *et al.*, 2000).

Similar species. The species most similar to the olive baboon in West Africa is the Guinea baboon, found in the far west of this region. Guinea baboons (*Papio papio*) are not as large as olive baboons, have a more reddish-brown coat, lighter gray facial skin, and a tail carried in a curve without an acute angle. The nostrils of the Guinea baboon do not protrude as far as those of the olive baboon. The mane of adult male Guinea baboons is more pronounced than that in olive baboons.

Cercopithecinae

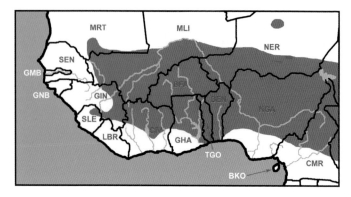

Fig. 8.47: Distribution of *Papio anubis* in West Africa.

Where the savanna zone meets the forest in the Nigeria-Cameroon border region, the range of the olive baboon adjoins that of the drill (*Mandrillus leucophaeus*). Superficially, female drills and baboons are similar, but drills have only a short stub of a tail, and their faces are intensely black; adult male drills have a striking blue and pink rump, and a red mark beneath the lower lip. Other terrestrial or semi-terrestrial monkeys within the range of the Guinea baboon (the green monkey, patas, and white-naped mangabey) are smaller in size and have much longer tails.

Taxonomic Note

The olive baboon is sometimes treated as a subspecies of *Papio hamadryas* (e.g., Thorington and Groves, 1970; Smuts *et al.*, 1987; Gautier-Hion *et al.*, 1999). Several subspecies have been recognized, but, as noted by Dandelot (1971), these are poorly defined. The subspecies name *P. anubis anubis* has been applied to the population in West Africa that extends from Mali to western Sudan. The olive baboons in the very small population that occurs at almost 2,000 m in the Tamgak Massif of Niger's Aïr Mountains have a darker coat than those found further south and are sometimes considered members of a distinct subspecies.

Geographic Range

In West Africa, *Papio anubis* occurs in savanna and grassland zones from western Mali and west-central Guinea, east to northern and central Cameroon and western Chad. Beyond West Africa, *P. anubis* extends east to Sudan and Ethiopia (where its range meets that of *P. hamadryas*, and where hybridization occurs) and south through eastern DRC, Uganda and western Kenya to northwestern Tanzania (where its range meets that of *P. cynocephalus*, and where there is also hybridization). Isolated populations of olive baboons occur in the Sahara, in the Aïr Mountains of central Niger and in the southern Tibesti Mountains of northern Chad.

Natural History

Habitat. Olive baboons occupy a very wide range of habitats, including semi-desert scrub, grassland, savanna woodland, thickets, dry and gallery forests, and montane vegetation. In eastern DRC and in Uganda they penetrate the edges of moist forest. When able to, olive baboons use farmland and raid agricultural crops.

Cercopithecinae

Fig. 8.48: Olive baboon (*Papio anubis*), Parc National de la Pendjari, Bénin (photo by J. Van de Voorde).

Field studies. The olive baboon is one of the most thoroughly studied of African primates. In many of the habitats in which *Papio anubis* is found, observation conditions are good and habituation is relatively easy (probably in part because hunting is at a low level, or absent). One of the earliest primate field studies of the modern era was on the olive baboons of Nairobi National Park in Kenya, where Irven DeVore began a study in 1959 (DeVore and Hall, 1965; Hall and DeVore, 1965); not long afterwards, Thelma Rowell studied a population living in gallery forest and savanna in Queen Elizabeth National Park, Uganda (Rowell, 1966). In the early 1970s, Robert Harding and Shirley Strum initiated long-running studies near Gilgil in Kenya (Harding, 1976, 1977; Strum, 1987), and in 1978 Robert Sapolsky began studies in Masai Mara National Park, also in Kenya (Sapolsky, 2001). West African olive baboons have been less studied than those in East Africa, but field research has been conducted at Gashaka Gumti National Park in Nigeria (Warren, 2003; Higham *et al.*, 2008a, 2008b; Ross *et al.*, 2010) and in the Comoé National Park in Côte d'Ivoire (Kunz and Linsenmair, 2007, 2008a, 2008b). Studies in the Shai Hills in Ghana have included a master's thesis project (Depew, 1983) and research on baboons as seed dispersers (Lieberman *et al.*, 1979). This account will focus on findings from studies in West Africa.

Cercopithecinae

Fig. 8.49: Olive baboon (*Papio anubis*), Parc National de la Pendjari, Bénin (photo by J. Van de Voorde).

Population. Olive baboons can be one of the most abundant larger mammals, and certainly the most abundant large primate in localities where they are not heavily trapped or hunted (such as Gashaka Gumti National Park in Nigeria and the Shai Hills Reserve in Ghana). However, their density is very variable. On transects in four forest sites at Gashaka Gumti, Dunn (1993) sighted 0.04–0.28 groups/km compared with 0.17 groups/km in savanna; these baboon groups were almost certainly moving between the forest and savanna habitats. Based on the forest encounters, Dunn estimated *P. anubis* density in that habitat to be 0.2–1.4 groups/km². In the more open habitat of Comoé National Park, Côte d'Ivoire, density is 1.2 individuals/km² (Kunz and Linsenmair, 2008a).

Habitat use. Olive baboons are great generalists and use gallery forest, dry forest, woodland and open grassland in the typically mosaic habitats in which they occur. Two groups in Comoé, Côte d'Ivoire, spent 52–55% of their active time in savanna woodland, 26–33% of their time in forest, and 15–20% of their time in open grassland (Kunz and Linsenmair, 2008a). In habitats in which trees are abundant, much of olive baboon food comes from trees. They sleep in trees, or on rocky cliffs or inselbergs.

Activity pattern. At Gashaka in Nigeria, a study group not exploiting agricultural crops divided its time into 31% feeding (including searching for invertebrates), 30% moving, 28% resting and 9% socializing, while a crop-raiding group's activity budget was 27% feeding, 25% moving, 35% resting and 11% socializing. Both groups spent more time feeding and travelling in the dry season and more time resting in the wet season (Warren, 2003). Two groups in Comoé, Côte d'Ivoire, spent 41–42% of their time feeding and foraging, 25–26% moving, 18–20% resting and 14% socializing (Kunz and Linsenmair, 2008a).

Vocalizations. Hall and DeVore (1965) describe 12 different vocalizations among East African olive baboons, including: loud two-phase barks and roars produced only by adult males; grunts, made frequently by most individuals except infants and often heard in chorus when a group congregates in sleeping trees; shrill barks made on the appearance of potential predators; and a female copulation call.

Social organization. The multi-level social structure found in Guinea baboons is not evident in olive baboons. While groups of over 100 individuals can be seen in eastern Africa, olive baboons studied

Cercopithecinae

to date in West Africa typically live in relatively small multi-male groups. Two study groups at Gashaka in Nigeria contained 14 and 28 individuals, with 4 and 6 adult males respectively (Warren, 2003). Ten groups counted in Comoé National Park, Côte d'Ivoire contained 4–44 individuals, and the average size of eight completely-counted groups was 15 (Kunz and Linsenmair, 2008a). Groups in Comoé contained from 1 to 6 adult males, with larger groups tending to be multi-male; one group of 26 individuals with 4 adult males split temporarily into two subgroups, one with only a single adult male.

Social behavior. Olive baboon social behavior has not been the subject of in-depth study in West Africa. In East Africa, female olive baboons remain in the group in which they are born, while males move between groups after they reach puberty. Both males and females exhibit within-sex dominance hierarchies, with more overt and frequent agonism displayed among males than among females. Female dominance is based on matrilines, and high-ranking mothers pass on high rank to their offspring (a system buttressed by the ability of high-ranking mothers to come to the aid of their daughters during conflicts). Female relatives are the most frequent exchangers of grooming. Individual males and females establish long-lasting special relationships, or "friendships", in which they associate preferentially with each other; a female's male friend reduces the vulnerability of females and their young to aggression from other males, and the female often favors the male as a mate (Smuts, 1985). Outside of contest situations, olive baboon males reinforce their rank relationships with ritualized greeting gestures, which involve approach, staring, ear retraction and presenting.

Interactions between groups. Home ranges of olive baboons overlap, without territorial defence.

Reproduction. Around the time of ovulation, female olive baboons develop large, purplish-pink swellings of their perineal tissue ("sexual swellings"). Males are attracted to swollen females and attempt to establish consortships with them, copulating frequently and attempting to exclude other males from proximity to their consort. Hormonal analysis of the feces of Gashaka females has shown that ovulation typically occurs a few days before the swelling starts to subside (detumesce). The swelling is at its largest within 2–3 days of ovulation, and in this baboon population, the largest swellings were observed in females who had not given birth or who had cycled several times without conceiving (Higham *et al.*, 2008a, 2008b). East African olive

Cercopithecinae

baboons do not have breeding seasons. The young are born after a six-month gestation period. At birth they have black coats and pink skin, and from the age of one month they will sometimes ride on the mother's back, often riding jockey-style when 4–6 months old.

Ranging patterns. Groups of 14 and 28 individuals at Gashaka in a mosaic habitat in Nigeria that includes woodland, gallery forest and dry forest used home ranges of about 1.5 km²—considerably smaller than the ranges of olive baboons using savanna woodland in East Africa (Warren, 2003). A crop-raiding group had an average day journey length of 3.1 km, and a non-crop-raiding group travelled on average 2.4 km. In Comoé, Côte d'Ivoire, in a predominantly savanna habitat with forest galleries and patches of dry forest, a group of 12 baboons used a range of 414 ha, while a group of 40 used a range of about 1.7 km² (Kunz and Linsenmair, 2008a).

Diet. Olive baboons have an eclectic diet, of which seeds are a significant component. Baboons at Gashaka in Nigeria consumed parts from at least 111 wild plant species (including 76 trees) and eight crop species. The diet of a group that did not exploit crops was made up of 63% fruits and seeds, 8% animals, 6% leaves, 5% flowers and 18% other items; among the most frequently eaten foods by the non-crop-raiding group were the fruits and seeds of the oil palm, *Elaeis guineensis* (Palmae), the nectar of the tree *Daniellia oliveri* (Leguminosae, Caesalpinioideae), and the fruits of the trees *Uapaca togoensis* (Euphorbiaceae) and *Parkia biglobosa* (Leguminosae, Mimosoideae) (Warren, 2003). Two groups in Comoé National Park, Côte d'Ivoire, were seen to eat 84 plant species; the diet consisted of 40–54% fruits and seeds, <2% animals, 4–6% leaves, 4–8% flowers and 25–33% grass; the most frequently eaten plant species were the trees *Daniellia oliveri*, *Parkia biglobosa*, *Diospyros mespiliformis* (Ebenaceae), and *Ficus* spp. (Moraceae) (Kunz and Linsenmair, 2008a, 2008b). In the Shai Hills, Ghana, Depew (1983) found a diet consisting of 59% fruits, 17% roots, 8% leaves, and 5% flowers (quoted in Dunbar, 1988). Olive baboons will catch and eat vertebrates, including young antelopes and other mammals (DeVore and Hall, 1965; Grubb *et al.*, 1998). Wherever olive baboons occur near to farmland they are serious crop pests; at Gashaka in Nigeria, major crops exploited by baboons include maize, cassava and sweet potato (Warren, 2003).

Predators. Many species of terrestrial carnivore are potential predators on baboons, but many them are now rare or absent across much of the range of West African *P. anubis*. In Faro National Park,

Cercopithecinae

Cameroon, *P. anubis* remains were found in 7% of lion fecal samples and in 2.5% of spotted hyena feces (Breuer, 2005). In Comoé National Park, Côte d'Ivoire, 3% of leopard scats contained baboon remains (M. Gross, quoted in Kunz and Linsenmair, 2008a).

Conservation Status

Papio anubis is listed as of Least Concern in the IUCN Red List. Because of the olive baboon's very wide distribution, its behavioral and ecological flexibility, and the fact that much of its range is in regions where humans do not eat monkey flesh, this species is presently one of the least threatened of African primates. It is often regarded as vermin because of the damage it causes to agricultural crops.

Where to See It

Papio anubis is one of the most readily observed West African monkeys. A particularly accessible site where they can be seen is the Shai Hills Resource Reserve, 17 km from Accra, Ghana. Among many other protected areas where they occur in West Africa are the Loma Mountains proposed national park (Sierra Leone), Comoé National Park (Côte d'Ivoire), Mole National Park (Ghana), Pendjari National Park (Bénin), W National Park (Niger, Bénin, Burkina Faso), Yankari and Gashaka Gumti national parks (Nigeria), and Faro and Waza national parks (Cameroon).

Cercopithecinae

Tribe Cercopithecini
Guenons

In their general form, members of this group of primates typify what many people think of when the word "monkey" is used. Apart from the very small talapoin, they are of small to medium size, and almost all of them have long tails and rounded heads, without prominent muzzles. Although a few writers (e.g., Rowe, 1996) restrict the term "guenon" to members of the genus *Cercopithecus*, the term is more commonly applied to all members of this tribe. The origin and meaning of "guenon" are obscure; the word appears to be French in origin, referring to any female monkey or to an ugly woman, but in natural history writing it has come to be used much more widely in English than in French accounts.

Although a few guenon species are semi-terrestrial and travel and forage extensively on the ground, the majority spend most of their time in trees. Most species occur in moist forests, but they are also found in dry forest and wooded savanna habitats. Apart from an isolated population of patas monkeys in the Aïr Mountains of Niger, all the cercopithecins are restricted to sub-Saharan Africa. Many species, especially arboreal forest-living members of the genus *Cercopithecus* ("typical guenons"), have brightly-colored coat markings. Compared to papionins, the social interactions of guenons tend to be low-key; there are relatively infrequent within-group interactions, but more frequent interactions between groups (often with territorial defence) (Rowell, 1988). Female sexual swellings occur in Allen's swamp monkeys (*Allenopithecus*) and talapoins (*Miopithecus*), but not in other members of this tribe.

The generic-level classification of the Cercopithecini has not been stable. Hill (1966) recognized four genera: *Cercopithecus*, *Miopithecus*, *Allenopithecus* and *Erythrocebus*. Napier and Napier (1967) reduced this to just two, *Cercopithecus* (with subgenera *Miopithecus* and *Allenopithecus*) and *Erythrocebus* (the patas monkey). Groves (2001) follows Hill, but separates the green and vervet monkeys out into a fifth genus, *Chlorocebus*. Grubb *et al.* (2003) use the generic taxonomy of Hill.

This book recognizes six genera of Cercopithecini, adding the genus *Allochrocebus* (Preuss's monkey and allies) to the five listed by Groves (2001). This course is taken based particularly on a consideration of the results of a study of DNA sequences in X and

Y chromosomes by Tosi *et al.* (2004). Their study shows that the Preuss's monkeys form an evolutionary grouping with the green monkeys (*Chlorocebus*) and the patas monkey (*Erythrocebus*), and that these three terrestrial and semi-terrestrial cercopithecins form a sister group to the arboreal guenons (*Cercopithecus*). The implication of these findings is that, taxonomically, either all of the terrestrial cercopithecins should be grouped together in the genus *Chlorocebus* or, if the genera *Chlorocebus* and *Erythrocebus* are used respectively for the green and patas monkeys, then the Preuss's monkeys must be placed in their own genus, *Allochrocebus* (a name introduced by Elliot [1913]). After a morphological analysis of the postcranial skeleton of the green, patas and Preuss's monkeys, and a comparison with the arboreal guenons, Sargis *et al.* (2008) agree that the terrestrial forms have all evolved from one common ancestor, and they also find that *Allochrocebus*, *Chlorocebus* and *Erythrocebus* are very different from each other; however, Sargis *et al.* prefer to recognize them as subgenera within the genus *Chlorocebus* because they feel that giving each of them generic rank does not adequately recognize their common ancestry. I prefer to recognize three separate genera, to highlight their individual distinctiveness.

Miopithecus I. Geoffroy, 1842
Talapoins

The talapoins are the smallest of all the Old World monkeys. They have long been regarded as related to, but distinct from, the arboreal forest guenons. Like the swamp monkeys (*Allenopithecus*), they retain the ancestral condition for the subfamily Cercopithecinae of adult females displaying sexual swellings. Studies of sex chromosome genetics, especially of the X-chromosome, suggest that the talapoins represent an early evolutionary branch that differentiated after the separation of all the other guenons from *Allenopithecus* (Tosi *et al.*, 2004).

Historically the talapoin monkeys were considered to belong to a single species, *Miopithecus* (or *Cercopithecus*) *talapoin* with a geographical range from southern Cameroon to northern Angola (e.g., Napier & Napier, 1967). In his account of the mammals of Angola, Machado (1969) showed that the talapoins to the north and south of the Congo River were best regarded as belonging to two different species: a "typical" form south of the river [to which he applied the name *Cercopithecus* (*Miopithecus*) *talapoin*] and another form centered on the forests of Gabon (which he called the *Miopithecus* of Gabon). In

1997, Kingdon applied the name *Miopithecus ogouensis* to the northern form, noting that the Ogooué River formed the center of its distribution.

Miopithecus talapoin geospecies

Grubb (2006a) regards the two members of the genus *Miopithecus* (*M. talapoin* and *M. ogouensis*) as belonging to one geospecies, *M. talapoin*.

Local Representative

Only *M. ogouensis* (the northern talapoin) occurs in the region covered by this book. The talapoin has been known for quite some time to occur on both banks of the lower Sanaga River in Cameroon (Gartlan and Struhsaker, 1972; J. S. Gartlan in Wolfheim, 1983), but quite recently these monkeys were reported from further north in Cameroon. During surveys in the Mbam & Djerem National Park in 2003–2006, Maisels *et al.* (2006) observed talapoins along the Djerem River and one of its tributaries at around 6°N; the Djerem is itself a major tributary of the Sanaga. Thus the northern talapoin is one of several primates characteristic of the forests of Central Africa that occur on the Upper Sanaga River on the edge of the region covered by this field guide, in an area that is transitional between the moist forest and savanna zones. Only a short description of the talapoin and the other primarily Central African forms (*Cercopithecus neglectus* and *C. cephus*) are included in this book (along with illustrations), particularly to aid visitors to the region of Cameroon's Mbam & Djerem National Park.

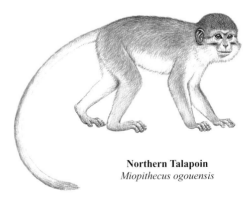

Northern Talapoin
Miopithecus ogouensis

Fig. 8.50.

Northern talapoin
Miopithecus ogouensis Kingdon, 1997

Other English: Gabon talapoin
French: Talapoin du nord
West African languages: Dikiti (Gbaya, Cameroon); Djane (Mvouté, Cameroon)

Identification (see Fig. 8.50, p.213)

The most obvious characteristic of this monkey is its small size; these are the smallest monkeys in Africa. On average, adult males are slightly larger than females. Gautier-Hion *et al.* (1999) give a mean head and body length of 34 cm in males, 28 cm in females; a tail length of 43 cm in males, 37 cm in females; and mean body weights of 1.4 kg in males and just 1.1 kg in females. In comparison to the body, the head of the talapoin is relatively large, so that the adults have a juvenile appearance. The northern talapoin is drably colored compared to the other forest guenons, with yellowish olive-green dorsal surfaces speckled with gray; the yellow tinge is especially marked on the limbs. The undersurfaces are creamy white. The tail is grayish khaki, darkening towards the tip. The face has obvious golden-yellow whiskers; naked skin on the muzzle and ears is pinkish, while the nose is gray. Fingers and toes are grayish-pink. The male scrotum is large and azure colored; females have cyclical pink perineal swellings.

Cercopithecinae

Geographic Range

The population occurring along tributaries of the upper Sanaga River in Cameroon is an outlier (Maisels *et al.*, 2006). The main range of the northern talapoin is from the Sanaga south through Cameroon and Rio Muni to southern Gabon and the northern part of coastal Congo Republic, and east to upper tributaries of the Sangha River in northern Congo Republic. The southern talapoin (*M. talapoin*) is found in Angola and parts of southwestern Democratic Republic of Congo.

Natural History

Because the talapoin occurs only on the extreme edge of the region covered by this book, and has not been studied in this region, aspects of its natural history will be only briefly summarized here.

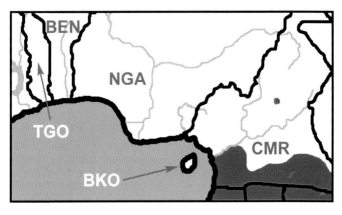

Fig. 8.51: Distribution of *Miopithecus ogouensis* in West Africa.

Fig. 8.52: Wild-caught northern talapoins (*Miopithecus ogouensis*) in captivity at Makokou, northeastern Gabon (photo by A. Gautier-Hion).

Cercopithecinae

The most important field studies of the northern talapoin have been by Annie Gautier-Hion in north-eastern Gabon, conducted in the 1960s along the Ivindo River (Gautier-Hion, 1966, 1968, 1971, 1973, 1978), and their natural history is summarized by Gautier-Hion *et al.* (1999). The talapoin is especially associated with dense and often flooded forest along rivers in the rain-forest zone, often close to human settlements. Social groups are large, averaging over 60 and sometimes exceeding 100 individuals. Groups typically contain multiple adult males, with twice as many adult females as males. Talapoins form small sleeping groups, choosing narrow supports, such as lianas, overhanging water. If disturbed they plunge into the water and swim below the surface to escape. During the day a group will range away from riverbanks to feed; a group in Gabon was found to travel an average of 2.3 km a day and range over an area of 1.2 km². Gautier-Hion found 36% insects in a sample of stomachs, along with 43% fruits and seeds. Groups living near human settlements feed on cassava and other crops (such groups are referred to by Gautier-Hion as "parasitic" on humans). Females have a 5.5-month pregnancy and in Gabon there is a November–April birth season (centered on a short dry season). Large snakes may be significant predators on talapoins.

Conservation Status

Miopithecus ogouensis is listed as of Least Concern in the IUCN Red List. Its small size and dense and often swampy habitat probably make it a less common target of human hunters than many other forest monkeys, and its habitat generally escapes conversion by logging and farming. Because of the talapoin's habit of exploiting human foods their numbers, at least in the past, were probably increased by human activity.

Where to See It

Although the northern talapoin can be seen in many places in western equatorial Africa, the only place where there is probably a good chance of observing this species in the region covered by this guide is along forested rivers in the Mbam & Djerem National Park in Cameroon.

Cercopithecinae

Patas Monkey
Erythrocebus patas

Tantalus Monkey
*Chlorocebus aethiops
tantalus*

Green Monkey
*Chlorocebus aethiops
sabaeus*

**Bioko Preuss's
Monkey**
*Allochrocebus preussi
insularis*

Preuss's Monkey
*Allochrocebus preussi
preussi*

Cercopithecinae

Fig. 8.53.

Erythrocebus Trouessart, 1897
Patas monkeys

The patas are highly distinctive, slender, long-legged, red-haired monkeys of open country that travel long distances on the ground, often at high speed. Females do not have sexual swellings. Genetic studies show the close evolutionary relationship of patas to the green monkeys (*Chlorocebus*) and the Preuss's monkey group (*Allochrocebus*); all of these monkeys are terrestrial or semi-terrestrial in their habits and together form a sister group to the arboreal guenons (*Cercopithecus*) (Tosi *et al.*, 2004; Sargis *et al.*, 2008). Most classifications over the last 100 years have recognized only a single species of *Erythrocebus*, *E. patas*.

Erythrocebus patas geospecies

Erythrocebus patas is the sole member of this geospecies (Grubb, 2006b). It occurs through most of the savanna zone of West Africa.

Cercopithecinae

Fig. 8.54: Patas monkeys (*Erythrocebus patas*), Abuko Nature Reserve, The Gambia (photo by E. D. Starin).

Patas monkey
Erythrocebus patas (Schreber, 1774)

Other English: Hussar monkey, red patas monkey, military monkey
French: Patas, singe rouge, singe pleureur
Portuguese: Macaco-fula
West African languages: Enaréniémai (Diola, Senegal); Tugd-haal (Balanta, Guinea-Bissau); Silaouleng (Foula, Sossé; Senegal); Soula oulé (Malinké, Mali); Kodiô (Baoulé, Côte d'Ivoire); Kotuno (Sénoufo, Côte d'Ivoire); Botimo (Agni, Côte d'Ivoire); Asabara (Twi, Ghana); Ablavidgé (Ewe, Togo); Klan vovo (Fon, Bénin); Ijimere (Yoruba, Nigeria); Otobo (Igbo, Nigeria); Jambiri (Hausa, Nigeria); Wandou wadérou (Foufoulbe, Cameroon)

Identification (see Fig. 8.53, p.217)

The patas is a relatively large, highly terrestrial monkey of slim build with exceptionally long arms and legs (that are of similar length), and a moderately long and slender tail. Its hair is relatively coarse, with a distinctive light foxy red-brown color on the crown, back, shoulders, outer thighs and upper surface of the tail; the red is most intense on the crown. The arms, lower legs and undersurfaces vary from light fawn to white. The pelage of the adult male patas is brighter and more contrasting than that of the female, with whiter lower limbs and grayer upper arms. Adults have white hair above and below the lips, forming a mustache and short beard. The eyebrows are black, and black hair extends laterally to the temples. The skin of the face is gray and, particularly around the eyes, pink. In West African populations the nose is typically dark gray or black. Males have a turquoise blue scrotum. In the second half of pregnancy, the female's coat lightens; in late pregnancy the female's nose becomes white, the black temporal lines disappear, and the facial skin turns to a light gray (Loy, 1974). In East African patas the nose of females remains white throughout adulthood (Isbell *et al.*, 2009). Females do not develop sexual swellings. Infants are born with a dark brown coat, which changes gradually to light gray-brown in the first three months of life.

Male patas are considerably larger than females. Adults have a head and body length of 60–65 cm in males and 50 cm in females, and a tail length of about 60 cm in males and 50 cm in females (Napier, 1981). In a Senegalese population, adult males average 12.4 kg and adult females average 6.5 kg (Galat-Luong *et al.*, 1996), while in

Cercopithecinae

northern Cameroon mean body weight of two adult males was 11.2 kg and of five females 5.9 kg (Nakagawa, 1999).

Similar species. The distinctive patas is not easily confused with other species. In the open country in which it typically lives, the most similar species are the green monkey (*Chlorocebus aethiops sabaeus*)—found west of the Volta River in Ghana—and the tantalus monkey (*Chlorocebus aethiops tantalus*)—found east of the Volta. The green and tantalus monkeys are smaller than the patas, with relatively shorter limbs and longer tails, and the dorsal surfaces of their coats are grayish khaki with an olivey tinge. They have dark facial skin with no white mustache. West African red colobus monkeys have a variety of reddish hues on their limbs flanks and tail, but their backs are generally gray or black. The red colobus are forest monkeys that only occasionally travel on the ground, while the patas is highly terrestrial.

Taxonomic Note

Several subspecies of patas have been recognized, but Dandelot (1971) notes that the pelage of this species varies greatly (including age and sex differences within a population), and that some subspecies have been described based on very little material. Hill (1966), Dandelot (1971) and Kingdon (1997) list four subspecies: *E. p. patas* from Senegal to Nigeria; *E. p. pyrrhonotus* from Cameroon east to Ethiopia and Kenya; *E. p. villiersi* from the Aïr Mountains, Niger; and *E. p. baumstarki* in northwestern Tanzania. Grubb *et al.* (2003) say that these subspecies "do not appear well founded."

Geographic Range

In West Africa, *Erythrocebus* has a huge geographic range, the most extensive of any West African primate. It occurs from the southern edge of the Sahara to the northern edge of the moist forest zone, and from western Senegal to the northern half of Cameroon. There is an isolated population in the central massifs and plateaux of the Aïr Mountains in central Niger.

Natural History

Habitat. Patas are found in a wide range of open habitats, including semi-desert scrub, grassland with scattered trees ("wooded steppe"),

Cercopithecinae

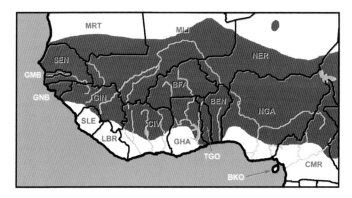

Fig. 8.55: Distribution of *Erythrocebus patas* in West Africa.

wooded savanna and agricultural land. In the Aïr Mountains they live in rocky areas (Hall, 1965).

Field studies. The earliest major field study of patas monkeys was by Ronald Hall in 1963–1964 in the Murchison Falls National Park in Uganda (Hall, 1965). The first West African field observations were by Thomas Struhsaker and Stephen Gartlan in the Waza Reserve (now National Park) in northern Cameroon in 1966–1968 (Struhsaker and Gartlan, 1970). In 1978, Thelma Rowell and her graduate students made observations in northern Ghana; these studies shifted to the Laikipia District in Kenya in 1979, where they were continued by Dana Olson and Janice Chism in 1979–1983, by Olson and Robert Harding in 1984, and by Lynne Isbell in 1992–2004 (Harding and Olson, 1986; Chism and Rowell, 1988; Isbell, 1998; Enstam and Isbell, 2002; Isbell and Chism, 2007; Isbell *et al.*, 2009). Back in West Africa, Hideyuki Ohsawa and Naofumi Nakagawa conducted a long-term, intermittent study from 1984 to 1997 of the patas population in the small Kalamaloué National Park in northern Cameroon, close to Lake Chad (Ohsawa *et al.*, 1993; Nakagawa, 1989, 1992, 1999, 2000a, 2000b; Nakagawa *et al.*, 2003). A few observations from W National Park in Niger have been reported by Poché (1976) and Koster (1985).

Population. Although the patas has a very extensive geographic range, much of it is in relatively low-productivity habitats, and many patas populations therefore occur at low densities. Pavy (1993) estimates a density of 1.7 individuals/km² in the Bafing Faunal Reserve, Mali, and Fischer *et al.* (2000) report a 1991 estimate of 1,150 individuals in the 11,500 km² Comoé National Park, northern

Cercopithecinae

Côte d'Ivoire (i.e., 1 per km²). Densities of 0.2–1.5 individuals/km² are reported for East Africa (Isbell and Chism, 2007).

Locomotion and habitat use. Patas can cover long distances on the ground rapidly and efficiently, aided by their very long limbs and slender build (the effective length of their limbs is increased by the habit of walking on their fingers and having elongated ankles); in this way they can efficiently exploit the small scattered food sources of dry savannas (Chism and Rowell, 1988; Isbell, 1998). In Laikipia, Kenya, patas are said to strongly prefer open acacia woodland and woodland margins (Chism and Rowell, 1988), crossing open grassland cautiously after long periods of scanning from a woodland edge, in a "leap-frog" fashion: one or two animals go ahead to a tree in the grassland, the bulk of the group then follow and sit in the tree, scanning, while a few animals move ahead to the next tree, with this pattern repeated until woodland is regained (Booth, 1960). Hall (1965) describes the patas as the fastest of all primates, able to run at 55 km/h (with a "grayhound-like" stride). Both in short pauses when running, and for longer periods, patas will scan for danger by rising upright on their hind legs, often using their tail as a third support (Hall, 1965; Dunn, 1999).

Special adaptations to a hot, dry habitat. In addition to their adaptations for efficient terrestrial movement, patas have especially

Fig. 8.56: Patas monkey (*Erythrocebus patas*), Parc National de la Pendjari, Bénin (photo by J. Van de Voorde).

abundant eccrine sweat glands in their skin, giving them the ability to sweat at 2–6 times the rate of a rhesus monkey (Gisolfi *et al.*, 1982). The use of sweating as a significant thermoregulatory device in hot weather probably explains the importance to patas of finding drinking water at the height of the dry season, as reported by Struhsaker and Gartlan (1970) in northern Cameroon. Abundant eccrine glands and high sweating ability are typical of *Homo sapiens*, another African primate that probably has a long evolutionary history in savanna habitats.

Activity pattern. Patas in northern Cameroon have peaks of activity in the mid-morning and late afternoon, with a long rest period in the (hot) middle of the day. About 30% of their activity period is spent in feeding, 20% in moving, and 40–50% resting (Nakagawa, 1989). In Laikipia, Kenya, 39% of patas time was taken up in moving and only 11% in feeding (Isbell, 1998).

Vocalizations. Hall (1965) describes patas as quiet monkeys, demonstrating "adaptive silence" (at least in the presence of humans). Descriptions of call types in the literature are confusing. Struhsaker and Gartlan (1970) have noted "chutter", "scream", "squawk" and "roar" calls from patas in Cameroon, with the roars made by adult males. Enstam and Isbell (2002) describe "coughs", "chutters", "nyows" and "geckers" as alarm calls given by female and young patas in East Africa on detecting potential predators. Chism and Rowell (1988) and Enstam and Isbell (2002) note that resident adult males give a two-phase "bark grunt" as a predator alarm, a call that is also produced when extragroup males are detected; this call is probably the same as the "roar" of Struhsaker and Gartlan (1970), and the "barking" described by Hall (1965). Hall describes males as typically barking from trees, producing volleys of up to 35 calls.

Social organization. Patas monkeys typically live in small to medium-sized groups with just one fully adult male. Occasionally, groups have two or more adult males. Groups enumerated in Waza, Cameroon, ranged in size from 7 to 34 (Struhsaker and Gartlan, 1970). A primary study group in Kalamaloué ranged in size from 16–45, and a secondary group from 12–44; the numbers in each group crashed following a major drought in 1984 (Nakagawa *et al.*, 2003). Groups of 3–17 are reported from Comoé National Park, Côte d'Ivoire (Fischer *et al.*, 2000), and of 3–38 in W National Park, Niger (Poché, 1976). All-male groups containing several adult males, or a mixture of adult and subadult males, have been seen in Waza. Males leave their natal group

Cercopithecinae

between the ages of 2.5 and 4.5 years (Struhsaker and Gartlan, 1970; Nakagawa *et al.*, 2003).

Social behavior. In his studies of wild patas in Uganda, Hall (1965) observed that aggression within a group was rare, and when it did occur it was brief and silent; grooming was by far the most common friendly behavior, and was performed most frequently by adult females. Hall describes group progressions after rest periods as typically led by adult females, with males often following after most other group members have descended from trees. In the non-mating, non-birth season at Kalamaloué, Cameroon, high-ranking females form a group core that frequently exchanges affiliative behaviors such as grooming; low-ranking females are peripheral to this core, and the group male is distantly peripheral and rarely involved in grooming (Nakagawa, 1992). Describing male behavior in heterosexual groups during the mating season in Laikipia, Kenya, Harding and Olson (1986) note that adult males show a marked degree of vigilance from high vantage points, monitoring female solicitation behaviors and intrusions by extra-group males, and frequently descending from a tree and rushing 50 m or more to mate with a soliciting female or to disrupt a copulation. In the mating season at Laikipia, adult males and females may form consort pairs.

Interactions between groups. Patas groups show extensive range overlap (Nakagawa, 1999). Conflicts between groups increase towards the end of the dry season in habitats such as the Sahelian savanna of Waza, Cameroon, when the patas concentrate near waterholes. At these times there are frequent vocalizations, yawns, head-bobbing gestures, and chases (Struhsaker and Gartlan, 1970).

Reproduction and life history. The patas gestation period is 163–168 days (Harding and Olson, 1986). Patas females in northern Cameroon give birth for the first time at three years of age on average, and commonly have a one-year inter-birth interval (Nakagawa *et al.*, 2003). A similar pattern holds in East Africa, giving female patas the highest intrinsic population growth rate of any haplorhine primate (Isbell *et al.*, 2009). In the strongly seasonal environments where they have been studied in West and East Africa, patas are seasonal breeders, with a short breeding season. In northern Cameroon, the birth season is from late December to the middle of February, in the middle of the dry season (Nakagawa *et al.*, 2003).

Cercopithecinae

Male influxes. With many females becoming sexually receptive at the same time, nontroop males may enter groups and mate, giving groups a temporary multi-male structure (Harding and Olson, 1986). During this mating season there is a high turnover in male residency in a group. Ohsawa *et al.* (1993) describe the invasion of a one-male group in Kalamaloué, Cameroon, by several males following the take-over of the group by an outsider male during a mating season; in this situation, only 31% of copulations were performed by the resident male.

Ranging patterns. A patas group in Kalamaloué, Cameroon, moved an average distance of between 4.35 km/day (in the early dry season) and 6.20 km/day (in the mid dry season). In total, the group used 266 ha in the early dry season and 440 ha in the mid dry season (based on occupancy of 100×100 m quadrats), and covered an annual range of about 9.6 km². This is a considerably smaller range than that reported for patas groups in East Africa. The annual home ranges of two groups at Laikipia, Kenya, were calculated at 23 and 32 km², based on occupancy of 10.1 ha quadrats (Chism and Rowell, 1988), and a group watched for over 200 hours by Hall (1965) at Murchison Falls, Uganda, covered 52 km².

Diet. Although patas travel on the ground between feeding sites, much of their food typically comes from trees. In Laikipia, Kenya, 85% of observed patas diet over a 17-month period came from three species of *Acacia* tree, and included gums, swollen thorns, flowers and seeds; most of the swollen thorns of these trees contained social ants (Isbell, 1998). Major food species in the patas diet in Kalamaloué, Cameroon, were the trees *Acacia sieberiana* (Mimosaceae), *Crateva religiosa* (Capparidaceae), *Diospyros mespiliformis* (Ebenaceae) and *Acacia seyal* (Mimosaceae) (Nakagawa, 1999). In W National Park, Niger, Poché (1976) saw feeding on fruits and gum (especially of *Combretum*), seeds, grasshoppers and termites. In the same park, Koster (1985) found that the main food items consumed by a tame but free-ranging young female patas were the fruits of trees and shrubs (especially *Tamarindus*, *Diospyros* and *Lannea*), grass seeds, and insects.

Predators. Jackals (*Canis aureus* and *C. adustus*), spotted hyenas and domestic dogs are reported as patas predators in Kalamaloué, northern Cameroon (Nakagawa *et al.*, 2003). Additional carnivores that are likely predators of patas (at least in East Africa) are lions, leopards, cheetahs, wildcats, wild dogs and eagles (Isbell, 1998;

Cercopithecinae

Enstam and Isbell, 2002; Isbell *et al.*, 2009). Humans sometimes kill patas involved in crop raiding. Patas are thought to suffer especially high predation as a result of their use of such open habitat and this factor has been proposed to have contributed to the evolution of the high reproductive potential of females (Isbell *et al.*, 2009).

Conservation Status

Erythrocebus patas is listed as of Least Concern in the IUCN Red List. Although the natural range of the patas monkey in West Africa is very large, much patas habitat within this range is being degraded by grazing, burning and desertification. On the other hand, agriculture has also made some forest areas more suitable as patas habitat, and it is often a farm pest. A large part of the patas range is in areas where people do not eat monkey meat, and the elusiveness and speed of the patas make it a difficult animal to hunt. Currently, this species is not seriously threatened, and occurs in many protected areas in the savanna zone.

Where to See It

Protected areas where patas can be observed in West Africa include Niokolo Koba National Park (Senegal), Boucle du Baoulé National Park (Mali), Comoé National Park (Côte d'Ivoire), Mole National Park (Ghana), Pendjari National Park (Bénin), W National Park (Niger, Bénin, Burkina Faso), Yankari and Gashaka Gumti national parks (Nigeria), and Kalamaloué and Waza national parks (Cameroon).

Cercopithecinae

Chlorocebus Gray, 1870
Green and vervet monkeys

Members of this group of relatively small, rather drably colored, long-tailed monkeys of the savanna zone are probably the most common and widespread of African primates. Apart from a blue scrotum in males, the vervet and green monkeys lack striking color patterns. A description often given of these monkeys to Booth (1960) was "just an ordinary monkey…sort of grayish." Females do not have sexual swellings.

Chlorocebus is part of an evolutionary branch that includes the other terrestrial and semi-terrestrial guenons: *Allochrocebus* (Preuss's monkey and relatives) and *Erythrocebus* (the patas) (Tosi *et al.*, 2004; Sargis *et al.*, 2008). Until recently, many authors placed the green and vervet monkeys in the genus *Cercopithecus*; here they are put in *Chlorocebus* based on the rationale laid out in the earlier section introducing the tribe Cercopithecini.

The species-taxonomy of *Chlorocebus* is not well settled. Dandelot (1971) recognized four species (*Cercopithecus sabaeus*, *C. aethiops*, *C. tantalus* and *C. pygerythrus*). Kingdon (1997) recognizes five species, adding *C. djamdjamensis* of the Bale Mountains, Ethiopia, to Dandelot's four. Groves (2001)—using *Chlorocebus*—lists six species, adding *C. cynosurus* of southern central Africa to the five species recognized by Kingdon. Groves notes, however, that the group is in need of a taxonomic revision. Hybrid zones occur between several of the geographic forms, which cannot readily be distinguished by their vocalizations; the reason cited by Grubb *et al.* (2003) to treat all of them as members of one highly polytypic species, with six subspecies; a course followed in this guide.

Cercopithecinae

Chlorocebus aethiops geospecies

Grubb (2006b) regards *Chlorocebus aethiops* as the only member of the *C. aethiops* geospecies. The first long-term studies of members of the *C. aethiops* geospecies were of the East African vervet monkey, *C. aethiops pygerythrus*, by Thomas Struhsaker at Amboseli, Kenya, in 1963–1964 (e.g., Struhsaker, 1967a, 1967b, 1967c, 1971a), and by Stephen Gartlan on Lolui Island and at Chobi in Uganda, also in 1963–1964 (e.g., Gartlan and Brain, 1968). These were some of the earliest long-term field studies on any African primates.

Local Representatives

Two forms of *Chlorocebus aethiops* occur in West Africa, *C. aethiops sabaeus* from Senegal east to the Volta River in Ghana, and *C. aethiops tantalus* from the Volta east to western Kenya. Some Ghanaian individuals show a combination of *sabaeus* and *tantalus* features, but there has not been a careful study of populations in the vicinity of the Volta.

Cercopithecinae

Fig. 8.57: A juvenile green monkey (*Chlorocebus aethiops sabaeus*), Bijilo Forest Park, The Gambia (photo by R. A. Mittermeier).

Green monkey
Chlorocebus aethiops sabaeus (Linnaeus, 1766)

Other English: Callithrix monkey, mangrove monkey
French: Singe vert, singe callitriche
Portuguese: Macaco-verde
West African languages: Conié (Foula, Senegal); Bambiudo (Sossé; Senegal); Mancoyo (Mandingo, Guinea-Bissau); Soula fin (Malinké, Mali); Ka sangata (Temne, Sierra Leone); Njaguaa (Mende, Sierra Leone); Pépéufwé (Baoulé, Côte d'Ivoire); Kolo (Sénoufo, Côte d'Ivoire); Botimo (Agni, Côte d'Ivoire); Akakawa (Twi, Ghana)

Identification (see Fig. 8.53, p.217)

A medium-sized, long-tailed monkey, with long limbs, that may be seen either on the ground or in trees. The predominant color of the green monkey's upper surfaces is a speckled grayish-golden or khaki brown with an olive tinge. The undersurfaces are creamy white or off-white. The skin of the face is dark gray to black, contrasting strongly with long creamy-yellow side whiskers, and the fingers and toes are gray. There are long dark guard hairs above the brow, and a narrow gray brow-band. The ears are large, prominent and blackish-gray. The tail tip is light orange-brown. The scrotum is pale blue.

Males are somewhat larger than females. Adult males have a head and body length of 50–55 cm and a tail length of about 65–70 cm, while in adult females the head and body is about 40 cm and the tail 55 cm. Average adult body weight in a Senegal population is 6.3 kg in males and 4.4 kg in females (Galat-Luong *et al.*, 1996).

Similar species. The green monkey can be confused with several other species because its habitat overlaps with those of both forest and savanna monkeys. In some places it occurs in the same riverine forests as Campbell's and spot-nosed monkeys, and the olive colobus, all of which are of similar size. However, these other species travel on the ground much less frequently than does the green monkey. Campbell's monkey has pink lips and dark gray limbs and tail; the spot-nosed monkey has a distinctive white nose-spot, white-fringed ears and a prominent ruff of white hair under the chin; the olive colobus has a reddish-brown back, gray undersurfaces and a distinct crest on the crown of the head. In savanna habitats the green monkey co-occurs extensively with the patas monkey, but the patas has even longer limbs,

Cercopithecinae

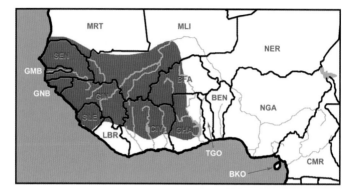

Fig. 8.58: Distribution of *Chlorocebus aethiops sabaeus*.

a bright red-brown back, a white mustache and grayish-white arms and legs. The patas is more strongly terrestrial than the green monkey. The closely-related tantalus monkey, found east of the Volta, is described in detail in the following profile.

Taxonomic Note

The green monkey is regarded by Dandelot (1971), Kingdon (1997) and Groves (2001) as a distinct species, *Cercopithecus* (or *Chlorocebus*) *sabaeus*.

Geographic Range

The green monkey occurs from western Senegal eastward to the vicinity of the Volta River in Ghana, where it is replaced by *C. a. tantalus*. It is found in most vegetation types, except for closed-canopy high forest, between the coast and the southern Sahel. The boundary between the ranges of green monkeys and tantalus monkeys in Mali and Burkina Faso is unclear. Booth (1956) notes that *tantalus* rather than *sabaeus* occurs on the Accra Plain to the west of the lower Volta in Ghana. *Chlorocebus a. sabaeus* has been introduced to the islands of Barbados, St. Kitts, Nevis and St. Maarten in the Caribbean, and also to Cape Verde; these introductions are probably a result of this monkey's long history as a human pet.

Natural History

Habitat. *Chlorocebus a. sabaeus* has a very broad habitat range, including savanna woodland, dry forest, coastal scrub, mangrove swamp and agricultural landscapes. It is particularly common in riparian forest (including forest galleries in the Sahel), and also occurs in parts of the moist-forest zone where there is extensive farming activity. In drier habitats, green monkeys usually sleep in gallery forests even if they range beyond that forest during the day.

Field studies. Robin Dunbar made a three-month study of *C. aethiops sabaeus* at Badi on the northern border of Niokolo Koba National Park, southeastern Senegal, in 1969 (Dunbar, 1974), and Michael Harrison carried out studies of this monkey for his PhD at Mount Assirik in the same park from October 1978 to December 1979 (Harrison, 1982; 1983a, 1983b, 1983c; 1984; 1985). In 1975–1976, Gérard Galat and Anh Galat-Luong made observations of green monkeys in mangrove forest at the mouth of the Saloum River, Senegal, and on the island of Morfil in the Senegal River in the Sahelian zone of far northern Senegal (Galat and Galat-Luong, 1976, 1977, 1978).

Cercopithecinae

Figs. 8.59: Green monkeys (*Chlorocebus aethiops sabaeus*), Bijilo Forest Park, The Gambia (photo by R. A. Mittermeier).

Population. The population density of green monkeys is highly variable across its wide habitat range, but they can be very common in localized areas. Harrison (1983a) estimates an overall population density of 4.4 individuals/km² at Mt. Assirik, while in the Bafing Faunal Reserve, Mali, the estimated density is only 1.2/km² (Pavy, 1993).

Habitat use. Like other members of the *C. aethiops* geospecies, green monkeys are agile in trees, but also come to the ground frequently. At Mt. Assirik, Harrison (1983c) found that a study group spent 33% of the day on the ground. Green monkeys travel across mud flats in mangrove swamp. They swim, probably more readily than any other West African monkey.

Activity pattern. The time budget of green monkeys is strongly influenced by their environment. Galat and Galat-Luong (1976) recorded green monkeys in mangrove spending about 64% of their time resting, 20% moving, 8% feeding and 8% socializing. By contrast, in northern Senegal resting occupied only 25% of the monkeys' time, moving 40%, feeding 28% and socializing 7%. At Mt. Assirik, Harrison (1985) found an intermediate value for resting, which took up about 47% of a study group's time, while 45% of the monkeys' time was spent in feeding and searching for food, and 9% in socializing (Harrison did not score "moving" as a separate activity).

Vocalizations. A careful study of calling behavior in *C. aethiops sabaeus* has not been conducted, but the repertoire is probably similar to that of the East African vervet, *C. a. pygerythrus.* Struhsaker (1967b) distinguished over 30 different vervet call types, along with lip-smacking and teeth-chattering; adult and subadult males give barks during agonistic intragroup and intergroup encounters; different alarm calls are given to different classes or predators: carnivores such as leopards, eagles, and snakes.

Social organization. Great variation in group size has been reported in this species, but groups normally contain two or more adult males. Within the tribe Cercopithecini to which *Chlorocebus* belongs, such a multi-male pattern of social organization is otherwise found only in Allen's swamp monkey (*Allenopithecus*) and the talapoins (*Miopithecus*). Dunbar (1974) counted groups of 8 to 16 green monkeys in Niokolo Koba, with 2–4 adult males. Elsewhere in the same park, the group studied by Harrison (1984) varied in size over a one-year study from 18 to 28, with 3–6 adult males. The Senegalese mangrove study group of Galat and Galat-Luong (1976) contained 33 individuals, including 7 adult males, while the two groups that Galat and Galat-Luong (1977) studied in northern Senegal varied in size across a two-year study from 33 to 47, and 140 to 174. In East Africa, *C. aethiops* females remain in their natal groups and males disperse (Isbell *et al.*, 2002).

Social behavior. *Chlorocebus a. sabaeus* has not been the subject of an in-depth study of social behavior. During his short study in Senegal, Dunbar (1974) noticed that adult males often rested higher up in trees than other group members, and reacted with attention responses to disturbances. Adult females received and gave more grooming than other age-sex classes in relation to their representation in a group, and they directed grooming particularly to a "central male." Little overt aggressive behavior was observed, and most of it involved males attacking or displacing other males. Departures from sleeping trees were led by both adult females and males, but in group progressions males were often in the rear.

Interactions between groups. In Niokolo Koba in Senegal, Dunbar (1974) found that the ranges of two groups overlapped extensively. When groups met in this overlap zone, an adult male in each group jumped around in trees. Harrison (1983c) describes these male displays at Niokolo Koba as ritualized "leaping and crashing." They are accompanied by displays of their white chests, canines and by jerking penile erections. Throughout the encounter females and young produce a chorus of "chuttering." Harrison found that when groups met in an area where a food resource was more important to one group than the other, the former group would aggressively supplant the latter, whereas members of each group would give intense displays when they met in an area where there were resources important to both.

Reproduction and life history. In Niokolo Koba, southeastern Senegal, green monkeys have a distinct birth season at the height of the dry season in January–March (Dunbar, 1974; Harrison, 1982). By contrast, in the drier habitat of northern Senegal births are reported to be concentrated in the June–September wet season; food is very scarce in the dry season there (Galat and Galat-Luong, 1977). *Chlorocebus aethiops* is an "*r* strategist" in its life-history characteristics; populations can grow rapidly in favorable conditions and recover quickly from the high mortality that these monkeys frequently suffer in the marginal habitats in which they often occur. Females of *C. aethiops* can have a first birth at the age of 2.5 years and a one-year interbirth interval, although first reproduction at an age of 4–5 years may be more typical.

Cercopithecinae

The gestation period is six months and weaning may begin at 12 weeks (Harvey *et al.*, 1987; Fedigan and Fedigan, 1988; Isbell *et al.*, 2009). The average age at sexual maturity of female *C. a. sabaeus* in the population introduced to Barbados is estimated at 34 months by Horrocks (1986), with male sexual maturity estimated to occur at 60 months. Infants of East African vervets are born with a coat of dark, silky hair, and with pink ears and faces; the face is black by 3 months of age and the coat is close to the adult appearance after 6 months (Struhsaker, 1971a).

Ranging patterns. The group of 33 green monkeys observed by Galat and Galat-Luong (1976) for 72 hrs over an 8-month period in a mangrove habitat in Senegal covered a minimum of 138 ha. The group of 18–28 studied by Harrison (1983a) in Niokolo Koba travelled between 665 and 2,670 m each day, and used a home range of 100 ha in the course of a year, calculated from their occupancy of 25×25 m quadrats. Ninety percent of the quadrats used by the Niokolo-Koba group were in gallery forest, and the group spent 50% of its time in only 9% of the quadrats; group members spread out most when foraging in open woodland away from the gallery forest where their activities were based.

Diet. Green monkeys are eclectic in their choice of food, selecting from a variety of fruits, leaves and animals depending upon availability. In the main study group of Galat and Galat-Luong (1977) in northern Senegal, leaves comprised 37% of the monkeys' diet (ranging from 14–67%, depending on the season), fruits 27% (8–44%), gum 11% (6–17%), and animal matter (especially insects) 13% (4–16%); leaves, fruits and the gum of *Acacia nilotica* (a tree which dominates the riparian forest vegetation) were important food items. In a group inhabiting mangrove, animal matter (especially fiddler crabs) made up 41% of the diet, and the flowers, fruits, young leaves and embryos of the mangroves *Avicennia* and *Rhizophora* were also eaten (Galat and Galat-Luong, 1976, 1978). At Mt. Assirik, the group studied by Harrison (1984) had a diet comprising 63% fruits and seeds, 13% invertebrates, 13% flowers, and 7% leaves. The diet encompassed 65 plant species, and there was great month-to-month variation in their dietary composition.

Predators. Many potential predators (such as larger carnivores and eagles) have been eliminated or reduced to small numbers across the range of the green monkey. At Mt. Assirik in Senegal, green monkeys flee from chimpanzees (Harrison, 1983a), and a chimpanzee at Fongoli,

Cercopithecinae

to the east of the park, has been seen eating a green monkey (Pruetz and Bertolani, 2007). Because the people living in much of the range of this primate are Muslims who do not eat the meat of monkeys, *C. aethiops sabaeus* does not suffer high levels of human predation, but it is harassed and killed as a crop pest; domestic dogs are probably a threat to young monkeys.

Conservation Status

Chlorocebus aethiops sabaeus is listed (as *Chlorocebus sabaeus*) as of Least Concern in the IUCN Red List. This monkey and its relatives in the *C. aethiops* group are probably the least threatened of Africa's monkeys. Many of their populations live in areas where people do not eat primate flesh. They are ecologically extremely flexible—in many ways a classic "weed" species. Clearing of rain forest by humans has increased the area of habitat available to green monkeys, which are often a serious pest of farm crops.

Where to See It

The green monkey occurs in all the savanna-zone protected areas between Senegal and central Ghana and is frequently encountered outside protected areas.

Cercopithecinae

Tantalus monkey
Chlorocebus aethiops tantalus (Ogilby, 1841)

French: Cercopithèque tantale
West African languages: Efio (Ewe, Togo); Zin ahiwé (Fon, Bénin);
Kirikaa (Hausa, Nigeria); Ngangage (Bakossi, Cameroon); Puera
(Bamoun, Cameroon); Banguil laendé (Foufoulbe, Cameroon)

Identification (see Fig. 8.53, p.217)

Like the green monkey, the tantalus is a medium-sized, long-tailed
monkey, with long limbs, and can be seen both in trees and on the
ground. The crown of the head is speckled yellow and dark gray; the
back, most of the tail, and outer upper limb surfaces are a speckled
grayish khaki with a golden-olive tinge; the lower limbs are light
gray, and the ventral surfaces are silvery cream. The tantalus has a
conspicuous white brow band (with scattered long guard hairs), and a
thin black line extends from the corner of each eye to the temples. The
skin of the face is intensely black, contrasting with long creamy-white
side whiskers that partly obscure the ears. The fingers and toes are
gray. The ears are large and gray. The tantalus has tufts of white hair
at the base of the tail, and the tail tip is pale khaki or creamy yellow. In
males, a sky-blue scrotum is surrounded by rusty brown hair. Infants
are born with reddish skin and sparse black hair, and gradually attain
the coloration typical of adults over a period of 4–5 months.

Adult males are larger than females, but not greatly so. However,
few data are available on the specific body dimensions of tantalus
monkeys. In museum specimens, adult males have head and body
lengths of 40–50 cm and tails of about 60 cm.

Similar species. Like its close relative the green monkey, the
tantalus can be confused with several other monkey species which
share its extensive geographical range. In forest galleries in the Guinea
savanna, and on forest edges, it co-occurs in many places with the mona
monkey (*Cercopithecus mona*). The mona is smaller than the tantalus,
has pink lips, a reddish-brown back, white underparts and a distinctive
patch of white hair on each hip. Mona monkeys sometimes travel on
the ground, but do so less frequently than the tantalus. In savannas
the tantalus commonly co-occurs with the patas monkey, but the patas
has longer limbs, a bright red-brown back and a white mustache. The
patas is even more strongly terrestrial than the tantalus and favors more
open country.

Cercopithecinae

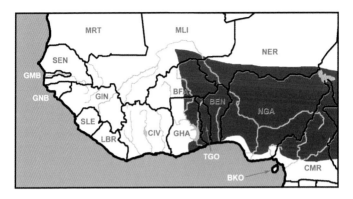

Fig. 8.60: Distribution of *Chlorocebus aethiops tantalus* in West Africa.

The tantalus differs from the green monkey (*C. a. sabaeus*) in its paler coloration and its obvious white browband. The green monkey's tail tip is orangey-yellow, rather than creamy-white.

Taxonomic Note

The tantalus monkey is regarded by Dandelot (1971), Kingdon (1997) and Groves (2001) as a distinct species, *Cercopithecus* (or *Chlorocebus*) *tantalus*.

Geographic Range

The tantalus monkey occurs from eastern Ghana through Togo, Bénin, Nigeria and Cameroon to western Sudan and Uganda, both in the savanna zone and along the northern edge of the moist forest zone. Although the western boundary of its range is generally regarded as the Volta River, it is found on the Accra Plain, immediately to the west of the lower Volta, and may hybridize with *C. a. sabaeus* there. *Chlorocebus a. tantalus* hybridizes with *C. a. pygerythrus* in Uganda (Groves, 2001).

Natural History

Habitat. Like the green monkey, the tantalus occupies a broad range of habitats, including the Guinean, Sudanian and Sahelian savannas, and areas of moist forest that have been opened up by farming. It is particularly associated with riparian gallery forest.

Cercopithecinae

Field studies. For such a widespread, common monkey, surprisingly little systematic field work has been done on the tantalus monkey, particularly in West Africa. The only long-term studies in West Africa with published results are those undertaken in Cameroon by Michael Kavanagh in 1974–1975 (Kavanagh, 1977, 1978, 1980, 1981), and by Naofumi Nakagawa in 1987–1989 (Nakagawa, 1999, 2000a, 2000b). Kavanagh compared the behavioral ecology of tantalus monkeys at three sites: one in open Sahelo-Sudanian woodland in the Kalamaloué National Park; one in gallery forest and Guinea savanna woodland at Buffle Noir immediately west of the upper Benue River in the Bénoué National Park; and one in a farm and secondary forest mosaic habitat in the moist forest zone in southern Bakossi. Nakagawa also worked in Kalamaloué, comparing the ecology of the tantalus with patas monkeys.

Population. The population density of tantalus monkeys varies greatly across their wide range; they are often very common. Based only on the home ranges of study groups, Kavanagh (1977, 1981) estimated a density of 149/km² at Kalamaloué (Sahel), 113/km² at Bakossi (forest), and 18/km² at Buffle Noir (Guinea savanna).

Habitat use. Although tantalus monkeys sleep high up in trees, much of their feeding occurs low down, or on the ground; tantalus

Cercopithecinae

Fig. 8.61: Tantalus monkey (*Chlorocebus aethiops tantalus*), Parc National de la Pendjari, Bénin (photo by J. Van de Voorde).

frequently travel on the ground between feeding sites and to reach water sources. If disturbed when on the ground they often gallop to the nearest tree to take refuge. In savanna sites in Cameroon, Kavanagh (1978) found that 30% of feeding took place on the ground, and 90% of feeding occurred below a height of 10 m. In the farm-forest mosaic of Bakossiland, the tantalus were first seen on the ground (rather than in trees) on 9% of occasions.

Activity pattern. At savanna sites in Cameroon where they were studied, tantalus monkeys spent on average 20–25% of their day feeding, but there was considerable monthly variation, with more than 35% of time devoted to feeding in the dry season month of February at Buffle Noir. At Buffle Noir there was a marked reduction in feeding activity around midday in dry months, but at Kalamaloué feeding was spread more evenly across the day (Kavanagh, 1977, 1978).

Vocalizations. The general call repertoire is probably similar to that of the East African vervet, *C. a. pygerythrus*, studied by Struhsaker (1967b). Because the crop-raiding monkeys studied by Kavanagh (1977, 1980) in the forest zone at Bakossi were harassed by farmers, and hunted with dogs, they were extremely quiet when foraging in cultivated areas; their most frequent call (57% of all vocalizations) was a soft, low frequency "!kock" that seemed to act both as a contact call and as a low-intensity alarm call. These "!kock" calls were rarely heard in savanna populations, and their equivalence to a call in the repertoire of *C. a. pygerythrus* is unclear; it may be equivalent to the vervet "uh!".

Social organization. As in other forms of *Chlorocebus aethiops*, group size in *C. a tantalus* varies greatly, but groups typically contain two or more adult males. At the Sahelian site of Kalamaloué, Kavanagh (1978) observed a group of 76 individuals, including 10 adult males. At Buffle Noir in Guinea savanna a study group contained 18 individuals with three adult males, while in the forest zone at Bakossi, one group had 18 monkeys with 4 adult males and another group had at least 11 monkeys with one adult male. The group studied at Kalamaloué by Nakagawa (1999) varied in size from 16 to 21 with 4–8 adult males. Groups of up to 35 individuals are reported from Kainji National Park, Nigeria (Howell, 1968).

Interactions between groups. Kavanagh (1981) found that patterns of intergroup interaction varied among tantalus populations in different habitats. In the forest-farmland habitat of Bakossi, groups appeared to display rigid territoriality, defending their small ranges

Cercopithecinae

against other groups and having almost no range overlap; during territorial encounters, males occupied high vantage points and gave loud bark calls, as reported in similar encounters in *C. a. sabaeus* and *C. a. pygerythrus*. Intergroup relationships were more relaxed in the savanna populations studied by Kavanagh, and the ranges of tantalus groups overlapped, especially at the Sahelian site of Kalamaloué. Even at Kalamaloué, however, there were aggressive interactions in areas of overlap.

Reproduction and life history. The reproductive characteristics of tantalus monkeys are probably similar to those of green monkeys and vervets. *Chlorocebus a. tantalus* in Kalamaloué have a mating season in the middle of the dry season, and give birth in the wet season (Nakagawa, 2000a).

Ranging patterns. As with all primates, the use of space by tantalus monkeys is heavily influenced by the nature of the habitat and the distribution and abundance of food. At Kalamaloué, Kavanagh (1981) found that a group of 76 tantalus travelled between 683 and 3,720 m per day, and used a total range of 56 ha. At Buffle Noir, on the other hand, a group of 18 travelled only 220 to 1,365 m each day, but covered a range of 103 ha. The group studied by Nakagawa (1999, 2000a) at Kalamaloué travelled 1,300–2,540 m per day, depending on the season, and used a 90-ha home range. In the forest zone at Bakossi, Kavanagh (1981) estimated that two study groups of 11 and 18 individuals had very small ranges of only 12 and 15 ha, respectively.

Fig. 8.62: Tantalus monkey (*Chlorocebus aethiops tantalus*), Yankari, Nigeria (photo by A. P. Leventis).

Diet. Like other kinds of *Chlorocebus aethiops*, tantalus monkeys are dietary generalists, eating fruit, flowers, leaves, gum and invertebrates, but the actual composition of their diet varies very greatly from place to place. At the Sahelian site of Kalamaloué, Kavanagh (1978) found that the monkeys spent 63% of their time eating fruits and seeds, 17% of their time eating leaves and shoots, 11% eating flowers and 7% invertebrates. In the gallery forest and wooded savanna site of Buffle Noir, on the other hand, 28% of food intake was fruits and seeds, 5% leaves and shoots, 34% flowers and 29% invertebrates. Focusing on the feeding behavior of particular individual monkeys in Kalamaloué, Nakagawa (2000) found strong seasonal variation in tantalus diet. The most important foods in the dry season were the fruits of the shrubby trees *Ziziphus spina-christi* (Rhamnaceae) and *Morelia senegalensis* (Rubiaceae). In the wet season, the most important food was the fruits of the tree *Celtis integrifolia* (Ulmaceae). In many parts of their range, tantalus monkeys feed on agricultural crops, and at Bakossi in Cameroon they include cocoa, banana, avocado, pineapple, maize, groundnuts, yam and cocoyam (Kavanagh, 1978, 1980).

Predators. Few firm data are available about predation on tantalus monkeys. In Cameroon, Kavanagh (1980) found that the monkeys gave loud alarm calls (and, if they were on the ground, ascended into trees) at the approach of jackals and hunting dogs at savanna sites. Breuer (2005) examined the scats of lions, leopards and spotted hyenas in Faro National Park, Cameroon, and found just one sample, from a hyena, that contained the remains of a tantalus monkey. Eagles are likely predators of these monkeys. Tantalus are harassed and sometimes killed by people because of their crop-raiding, but their meat is not usually eaten in the savanna zone.

Conservation Status

Chlorocebus aethiops tantalus is listed (as *Chlorocebus tantalus*) as of Least Concern in the IUCN Red List. Like the green monkey and other members of the *C. aethiops* group, the tantalus is one of the least threatened of Africa's monkeys. Not only do many tantalus populations live in areas inhabited by Muslim people who do not eat primate flesh, but the conversion of rain forest to agricultural land has increased the area of habitat available to them.

Where to See It

The tantalus occurs in all the savanna-zone protected areas of Togo, Bénin, Nigeria and Cameroon, and in W National Park in Niger, and it is often encountered outside protected areas.

Cercopithecinae

Allochrocebus Elliot, 1913
Mountain monkeys

These relatively large forest-living monkeys are semi-terrestrial. Although they sleep, and to some extent forage, in trees, they do much of their travelling on the ground, where they obtain some of their food. Their color patterns vary, but all are dark with gray limbs, some degree of brown or reddish-brown pelage on the back, a dark gray or black face, and a white or whitish throat. When standing, these monkeys typically hold their tail tip in the shape of a question mark. Males have bright blue scrotums. As discussed above, *Allochrocebus* shares a common evolutionary ancestor with the patas monkey (*Erythrocebus*) and the green monkeys (*Chlorocebus*).

Most recent classifications recognize three species of *Allochrocebus*, which have a disjunct distribution across equatorial Africa: *A. preussi* (Preuss's monkey) in West Africa, *A. solatus* (the sun-tailed monkey) in Gabon, and *A. lhoesti* (l'Hoest's monkey) of the Albertine Rift region of East Africa (Gautier *et al.*, 2002). The sun-tailed monkey only became known to science in 1988 (Harrison, 1988), but genetic analysis suggests it represents the most ancient evolutionary branch of this group, from which the other two species diverged about 0.5 MYA (Tosi, 2008).

Allochrocebus preussi geospecies

Grubb (2006b) places the three species of this genus in the geospecies *Allochrocebus preussi*. *Allochrocebus preussi* and *A. lhoesti* are especially associated with highland forest, whereas *A. solatus* occurs in both hilly and lower-lying areas.

Local Representatives

The species in our region is *Allochrocebus preussi*, a secretive forest monkey that is mostly restricted to hills and mountains both on Bioko and on the mainland between the Nigeria-Cameroon border and the Sanaga River. The mainland form belongs to the subspecies *A. p. preussi*, and the Bioko form to the subspecies *A. p. insularis*.

Cercopithecinae

Preuss's monkey
Allochrocebus preussi (Matschie, 1898)

Other English: Preuss's guenon, black monkey
French: Le cercopithèque de Preuss
Spanish: Cercopiteco de Preuss
West African languages: Nka'mbok (Ejagham, Nigeria and
Cameroon); Ipeya (Boki, Nigeria); Kepemsi, gepémese (Denya/
Anyang, Cameroon and Nigeria); Konowok (Korup, Cameroon and
Nigeria); Ngotto kem (Bakossi, Cameroon); Nten (Banen and Bassa,
Cameroon); Nyumbú (Bubi, Bioko)

Identification (see Fig. 8.53, p.217)

This monkey uses the ground more frequently than any of the
other forest guenons in our region. Seen at a distance in poor light,
Preuss's monkey appears to be generally dark gray or black (indeed, it
is called "black monkey" in parts of its range). The crown of the head,
upper arms, shoulders, flanks, thighs and mid-tail are dark gray (with
silvery speckles apparent at close range, caused by hair banding). The
throat is silvery-white, and the tail tip and arms (except for the outer
surfaces of the upper arms) are black. The middle back and dorsal
part of the tail base are reddish brown mixed with gray; the extent of
red coloration apparent varies with the lighting conditions when the
monkey is viewed. The belly and inner surfaces of the legs are gray,
and the undersurface of the tail, except at the tip, is light gray. The face
is dark gray and the hair of the hands and feet is black.

Like other members of the *A. preussi* geospecies, adult males have
an intensely powder-blue scrotum, and display this by standing on low
tree branches with their tail raised. The tail of Preuss's monkey is only
slightly longer than the head and body, and is therefore relatively short
compared to that in other, more arboreal guenons. A characteristic
feature of Preuss's monkey is the way in which it holds its tail high
with a backward hook or loop at the tip, like a question mark.

Subspecies. The Bioko subspecies, *A. p. insularis*, differs from
the mainland form, *A. p. preussi*, in having longer hair and a less red
dorsal patch; the dorsal patch in the island form is olive red-brown.
The island form is considerably smaller than the mainland form. Adult
males from Mt. Cameroon and the Rumpi Hills have a head and body
length averaging 57 cm, with a 68-cm tail, and adult females a head and
body of about 50 cm with a 56-cm tail (Eisentraut, 1973). By contrast,

Fig. 8.63: Mainland Preuss's monkey (*Allochrocebus preussi preussi*) in CERCOPAN facility, Calabar, Nigeria (photo courtesy of CERCOPAN).

Bioko adult males have an average head and body length of 48 cm and a tail of 55 cm, while females have a head and body of 40 cm and a tail of 48 cm (Butynski *et al.*, 2009). Bioko adult males average 5.5 kg, and females 3.5 kg (Butynski *et al.*, 2009).

Similar species. Preuss's monkeys can be distinguished from most of the other forest guenons in their geographical range by their dark appearance, lacking very distinct light markings other than their whitish throat. For instance, the similarly-sized and dark-gray colored putty-nosed monkey has an obvious white nose spot; and while the putty-nose typically feeds and moves in the upper canopy of the forest, Preuss's monkey moves and forages extensively on the ground. In the northern parts of its range in the Bamenda Highlands and Obudu Plateau, and in areas along the Jide valley in Bakossiland, Preuss's monkey overlaps geographically with the semi-terrestrial tantalus monkey, *Chlorocebus aethiops tantalus*. While Preuss's monkey mostly uses forest, the tantalus mostly uses open woodland, grassland and farmland. Preuss's monkey will, however, cross grassland between forest patches. Like Preuss's monkey, the male tantalus has a bright blue scrotum, but unlike *A. preussi* the tantalus has a light olive-khaki back, creamy undersurfaces, and a white brow band that contrasts strongly with its black face; the tantalus tail is relatively longer, and the tip is not held in a question-mark configuration.

Taxonomic Note

Although *A. preussi* has sometimes been regarded as a subspecies of *A. lhoesti* (as *Cercopithecus lhoesti preussi*; e.g., Dandelot, 1971) it is now generally recognized as a distinct allopatric species.

Geographic Range

The geographical distribution of Preuss's monkey is centered on Mount Cameroon and the Cameroon Highlands (including the Rumpi Hills, Bakossiland and Mt. Oku), and it also occurs in the highlands of Bioko. It extends west into Nigeria, where it occurs on the Obudu Plateau and adjacent hills (including the Okwangwo Division of Cross River National Park), and south to the Ebo Forest of Cameroon's Nkam Division (Littoral Region).

Natural History

Habitat and population. Although Preuss's monkey is often described as a montane or highland species, and is most abundant in montane habitats, it is also to be found in areas of lowland forest

Cercopithecinae

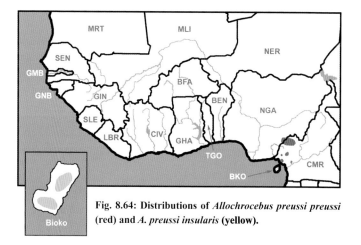

Fig. 8.64: Distributions of *Allochrocebus preussi preussi* (red) and *A. preussi insularis* (yellow).

Bioko

adjacent to hill areas. For instance, Gartlan and Struhsaker (1972) observed this monkey in the forests at Idenau, which lie at altitudes between 100 and 300 m on the western edge of Mount Cameroon, but above 1,000 m on Mt. Cameroon, where the only anthropoid primates observed were Preuss's monkey and the chimpanzee. On Bioko, *A. preussi* is most abundant at an altitude of 1,700–2,250 m on Pico Basilé in open-canopy forest with a thick understorey dominated by the medium-sized tree *Schefflera abyssinica* (Araliaceae), but it occurs as high as 3,000 m (Butynski and Koster, 1994; Gonzalez-Kirchner, 2004). On Kilum Mountain, Cameroon, *A. preussi* is the most common monkey in the higher-altitude montane forest, occurring there also up to 3,000 m (Beeson *et al.*, 1996).

Field studies. This is a relatively poorly-known species. There is one published study of its ecology carried out by Mark Beeson in the Kilum-Ijim Forest, Mt. Oku, Cameroon in 1992–1994 (Beeson *et al.*, 1996). Otherwise, information has been gathered from surveys that were looking at a range of species, either in Cameroon (e.g., Struhsaker, 1969; Dowsett-Lemaire and Dowsett, 2001) or on Bioko Island (e.g., Butynski and Koster, 1994; Gonzalez-Kirchner, 2004). *Allochrocebus lhoesti* and *A. solatus*, close relatives of *A. preussi*, have been studied in, Rwanda (Kaplin, 2001, 2002) and Gabon (Gautier *et al.*, 1992; Brugière and Gautier, 1999) respectively,

Habitat use and locomotion. Preuss's monkeys restrict their activities to the lower levels of the forest and the ground. For instance, at Idenau in Cameroon, Gartlan and Struhsaker (1972) almost always saw *A. preussi* below a height of 9 m in the canopy. On Pico Basilé, Bioko, more than 60% of observations were of monkeys on the ground or in the shrub layer, also below 10 m (Gonzalez-Kirchner, 2004). At Kilum in Cameroon, Beeson *et al.* (1996) found that Preuss's monkeys spent most of their time in trees, but travelled on the ground especially to cross open areas.

Vocalizations. Especially at dusk, adult males give a very distinctive two-phase cooing loud call, rendered by Struhsaker (1969) as "oop-uuh" and by Dowsett-Lemaire and Dowsett (2001) as "ouou-owe"; each male usually calls once only, and the call is answered by males in other groups, so that a "spreading wave" of calls moves through the forest. This loud call is not heard in either *A. lhoesti* or *A. solatus* (Gautier *et al.*, 2002). In alarming situations, adult females and young give one-unit chirps, while adult males give hacks (Struhsaker, 1970a).

Cercopithecinae

Social organization and behavior. Struhsaker (1969) estimated that groups he encountered in Cameroon were small, containing 2–9 individuals, including a single adult male (though once two males were heard calling in the same group). Beeson *et al.* (1996) point out that poor visibility at low levels of the forest make it difficult to count groups of Preuss's monkey, and note that the most accurate counts can be made when the monkeys travel between forest areas on more open ground. In those situations they often observed groups at Kilum of "well under 10," and their maximum count was a group of 19. They report that there was often more than one adult male in a group, and they speculate that groups may be flexible in their make-up. Butynski and Koster (1994) note that Bioko hunters describe *A. preussi* as living in groups of 4–5, but they suggest that most groups may be larger. In contrast to these observations of *A. preussi*, a study group of the related *A. lhoesti* in Rwanda comprised 29 individuals (Kaplin, 2001).

Cercopithecinae

Fig. 8.65: Bioko Preuss's monkey (*Allochrocebus preussi insularis*) in the Gran Caldera de Luba (photo by R. A. Bergl).

Reproduction and life history. No data are available on reproduction in wild *A. preussi*. In a semi-free-ranging group of *A. solatus* in Gabon, females first reproduced at around four years of age, and the interbirth interval was about 18 months (Peignot *et al.*, 1999).

Ranging patterns. Range size in *A. preussi* is not known. The group of *A. lhoesti* studied in the Nyungwe Forest, Rwanda, by Kaplin (2001) used 28-81 ha in a month, and a total area of 117 ha; they travelled an average of 2,092 m per day.

Diet. At Kilum, Beeson *et al.* (1996) found that fruit and seeds made up 52% of feeding observations, tree shoots 26%, and stems and leaves of herbs 14%. Shoots were eaten most in the early rainy season in March and April. Beeson *et al.* also saw the Kilum monkeys catching small aquatic animals (possibly frogs and crabs) in streams. In Ebo, Cameroon, these monkeys eat termites (B. Morgan, pers. comm.). Kaplin (2002) reports a similar diet for the related *A. lhoesti* of the Albertine Rift, with significant quantities of terrestrial herbs being eaten in addition to fruit (Kaplin, 2002).

Association with other species. Unlike other forest guenons in West Africa that are frequently seen moving in association with other monkey species, groups of Preuss's monkey very often move alone. Gartlan and Struhsaker (1972) observed this species in Cameroon in monospecific groups on 16 of 19 times occasions (84% of the time) when they encountered them. On Bioko, Butynski and Koster (1994) never saw *A. preussi* in association with other species. However, B. Morgan (pers. comm.) reports that *A. preussi* is often seen in polyspecific associations in the Ebo Forest.

Predators. On the mainland, leopards are a potential predator of Preuss's monkey, but these cats are now very rare or exterminated in most of the habitats still occupied by the monkey. Humans must be the most serious predator on *A. preussi* today.

Conservation Status

Allochrocebus preussi is listed (as *Cercopithecus preussi*) as Endangered on the IUCN Red List. Although Endangered, this species is possibly not as threatened as some other primates inhabiting the same region. Its secretive habits make it more difficult both to observe and to hunt than monkeys that are more arboreal. Its actual status is poorly known as a result, and no firm data are available on its rate

Cercopithecinae

of decline in the wild. Dowsett-Lemaire and Dowsett (2001) point out that its terrestrial habits make it susceptible not only to shotgun hunting, but also to hunting with dogs and to being caught in snares set for a variety of ground-living animals. In the Kilum-Ijum Forest on Mt. Oku, Cameroon, Maisels *et al.* (2001) report the numbers of Preuss's monkeys fell during the 1990s, as the densities of all larger mammals were reduced by hunting. In the Malabo bushmeat market on Bioko, the number of Preuss's monkey carcasses is reckoned to have increased greatly in the years 2001–2005, although some confusion with putty-nosed monkeys may have occurred (Hearn *et al.*, 2006). Much of the montane habitat of this species in Cameroon is poorly protected and is being severely degraded by cultivation and the spread of pasture (Oates *et al.*, 2004).

Allochrocebus preussi occurs in a number of protected areas, including the Okwangwo Division of Cross River National Park in Nigeria; the Takamanda National Park, Mount Cameroon National Park, and the proposed Ebo National Park in Cameroon; and in both the Pico Basilé and the Gran Caldera and Southern Highlands Scientific Reserve on Bioko (Equatorial Guinea).

Where to See It

Because of the cryptic appearance and behavior of this monkey it is difficult to see even in habitats where it is still common. It is easier to hear its calls (especially the male loud call at dusk) than to catch sight of the animal. It is most readily encountered on the upper elevations of Pico Basilé on the island of Bioko, but there is also a chance of seeing it on the Obudu Plateau at the edge of the Okwangwo Division of Cross River National Park in Nigeria, as well as on Mount Cameroon and in the Ebo Forest in Cameroon.

Cercopithecinae

Cercopithecus Linnaeus, 1758
Forest guenons

This is the most species-rich group of African monkeys. According to the classification followed in this book, there are currently 15 named species of *Cercopithecus*, belonging to seven geospecies. New species may be named in the future (such as a recently-discovered form of owl-faced monkey in eastern Democratic Republic of Congo).

With the exception of *Miopithecus*, the forest guenons are, on average, the smallest of African monkeys. Most *Cercopithecus* are highly arboreal and have very long tails, but the owl-faced monkey (*C. hamlyni*) spends much time on the ground and its tail is not quite as long as its head and body. Many of the arboreal species have brightly-patterned coats; their facial markings are particularly colorful, and are often emphasized in head-flagging displays (Kingdon, 1980); social groups of these arboreal species typically have only a single fully adult male, and adult males produce distinctive loud calls.

The geospecies in this genus are *C. diana*, *C. dryas*, *C. neglectus*, *C. mona*, *C. hamylni*, *C. cephus* and *C. nictitans* (Grubb, 2006b). These guenons share the same arrangement of chromosomes, and the genetics of their X-chromosomes indicate that they have evolved from a common ancestor (Dutrillaux *et al.*, 1988; Tosi *et al.*, 2005; however, these analyses did not include *C. dryas*).

Cercopithecus diana geospecies

Grubb (2006b) includes the single species *Cercopithecus diana* in this geospecies. This geospecies is restricted entirely to the Upper Guinea rain forest region of West Africa—the only African primate geospecies with such a pattern of distribution. According to the classification followed in this book, *Cercopithecus diana* has two subspecies: *Cercopithecus diana diana*, the Diana monkey, and *C. diana roloway*, the roloway monkey. Groves (2001) regards these two forms as separate species, but individuals have been found near the Sassandra River with features that are intermediate (Oates, 1988a).

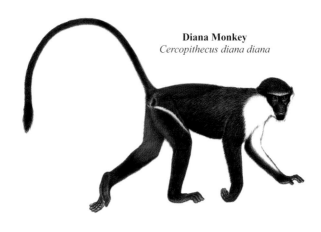

Diana Monkey
Cercopithecus diana diana

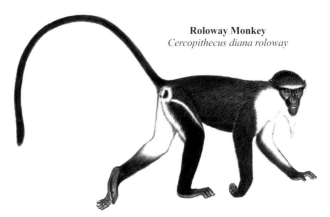

Roloway Monkey
Cercopithecus diana roloway

Cercopithecinae

De Brazza's Monkey
Cercopithecus neglectus

Fig. 8.66.

Cercopithecus diana (Linnaeus, 1758)
Diana and roloway monkeys

Identification (see Fig. 8.66, p.251)

The Diana and the roloway are two of Africa's most beautiful monkeys; they have a strikingly-patterned coat, conspicuous white brow hairs, a white beard, an oblique white thigh-stripe and a long tail. Adult male head and body length is 50–60 cm, with an 85-cm tail; adult female head and body length is about 45 cm, with a 70-cm tail; adult males average 5.2 kg in weight, adult females 3.9 kg (Napier, 1981; Oates *et al.*, 1990a). The skin of the face, hands and feet is black, as is the hair of the lower legs, belly and tail. The coat of the upper back, flanks and outer thighs is dark speckled gray, and the lower back is dark chestnut. The throat, chest and anterior surfaces of the upper arms are white, sharply demarcated from the dark color of the other surfaces. When moving, Diana monkeys commonly hold their tail in a high arching curve.

In *C. d. diana* the inner thighs and pubic region are bright rust-red; particularly conspicuous when an animal is sitting facing an observer. *Cercopithecus d. roloway* closely resembles *C. d. diana* in its appearance and behavior, but its inner thighs and pubic region are orange-yellow or creamy-white rather than red, and its white beard is much longer (75 mm versus 25 mm) and more pointed. The roloway has a more prominent band of white hair across the brow that extends further to the sides of the brow than that of Diana, and the white thigh stripe is narrower in *C. d. roloway* than in *C. d. diana*.

Similar species: In the field, the visually striking appearance of Diana monkeys makes them hard to confuse with any other primate if they are seen clearly. If they are only glimpsed, then they might sometimes be confused with two other guenons (*C. campbelli* and *C. petaurista*) with which they are widely sympatric, or with *C. nictitans stampflii* which overlaps the range of *C. diana diana* in a few forests in Liberia and Côte d'Ivoire. *Cercopithecus campbelli* and *C. petaurista* typically forage lower in the forest canopy than *C. diana*; they are smaller, and they lack the black coloration of the Diana's upper back, shoulders and crown. *Cercopithecus nictitans stampflii* is similar in size to *C. diana* and also forages in the upper canopy, but it lacks the pure white and sharply demarcated pelage of Diana's chest, throat and inner arms. None of these other species have red inner thighs, and *C. petaurista* and *C. nictitans* have obvious white nose spots. Red colobus

Cercopithecinae

monkeys (*Procolobus badius*) of West Africa might be confused with Diana monkeys because they occur in many of the same habitats and also have a combination of black and red in their coats, but they lack white markings and have many differences in body build, posture, locomotion and vocalizations. The loud croaking call of male black-and-white colobus (*Colobus polykomos* and *C. vellerosus*) is similar to that of the male Diana monkey, but the individual "croaks" in the Diana call are shorter, higher pitched, of lower volume, and are usually delivered in shorter sequences.

Geographic Range

Cercopithecus diana diana occurs from the Forécariah Province of Guinea eastward to the Sassandra River in Côte d'Ivoire. *Cercopithecus d. roloway* once occurred from the Sassandra eastward to south-western Ghana, and perhaps as far east as western Togo (Booth, 1958b; Oates, 1988a; Barnett *et al.*, 1994). A partial skin in the Berlin Museum (collected in 1895) is labeled as originating from Misahöhe in Togo, close to the present Ghana border; however, since the coloration of the thighs on this specimen resembles *C. diana diana* there is a possibility that this specimen is mislabeled. *Cercopithecus d. roloway* is also listed as present in Togo by Roure (1966), but this monkey has not been found in that country in any recent surveys (e.g., Campbell *et al.*, 2008b). Although roloway monkeys (like Diana monkeys) seem to occur predominantly in the moist forest zone near the coast, they are also reported to occur in gallery forests along large rivers in Côte d'Ivoire (Tahiri-Zagrët, 1976), including the gallery forests of Comoé National Park at around 9°N in the savanna zone, where they were last seen in 1993 (Fischer *et al.*, 2002).

Cercopithecus d. diana has been more thoroughly studied than *C. d. roloway*, and while *C. d. diana* is still relatively common in some places, *C. d. roloway* is almost extinct in the wild. Given these disparities, the natural history of each subspecies will be treated separately in this account.

Cercopithecinae

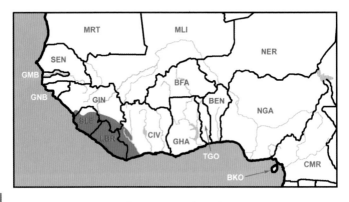

Fig. 8.67: Distribution of *Cercopithecus diana diana*.

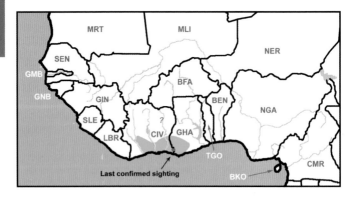

Fig. 8.68: The historical distribution of *Cercopithecus diana roloway* (pink). The arrow points to the Tanoé Forest, Côte d'Ivoire (red); the last confirmed sighting of a population of this monkey.

Diana Monkey
Cercopithecus diana diana (Linnaeus, 1758)

Other English: Diana Guenon
French: Cercopithèque diane
West African languages: Keli (Mende, Sierra Leone); Ka sakari
(Temne, Sierra Leone); Guod (Bassa, Liberia); Klay (Sapo, Libera);
Glé (Guéré, Côte d'Ivoire); Tchiè (Agni, Côte d'Ivoire)

Natural History

Habitat. Diana monkeys occur predominantly in high-canopy
mature forest and are rare or absent in farmbush and degraded forest.
They are able to persist in quite small forest patches, so long as tall
trees remain (Oates, 1988a).

Field studies. Extended studies of habituated groups have been
made in the Tiwai Island Wildlife Sanctuary, Sierra Leone (Oates and
Whitesides, 1990; Hill, 1991; Whitesides, 1991), and in the Taï National
Park, Côte d'Ivoire (e.g., Galat and Galat-Luong, 1985; Holenweg *et
al.*, 1996; Buzzard, 2004, 2006a, 2006b; Buzzard and Eckardt, 2007).
The Taï studies have included a series of careful investigations of
alarm-calling behavior by Klaus Zuberbühler and associates (e.g.,
Zuberbühler, 2000, 2007; Zuberbühler *et al.*, 1997).

Population. Diana monkeys can be abundant in suitable habitat,
and when they are not hunted. Their density has been estimated at 48–
75 individuals/km^2 in parts of the Taï Forest (Holenweg *et al.*, 1996;
McGraw and Zuberbühler, 2007), 46–66/km^2 at Tiwai Island (Oates
et al., 1990), and 71/km^2 in the Gola Forest, Sierra Leone (Klop *et
al.*, 2008). The Diana was encountered much more frequently than
any other monkey during surveys of Gola Forest in 2005–2007 (Klop
et al., 2008). In the rain forest of Liberia's Sapo National Park they
have been estimated to be the second most abundant monkey, after red
colobus (Agoramoorthy, 1989).

Habitat use. Although Diana monkeys use all forest strata and
occasionally move on the ground, they spend most of their time in the
middle and upper canopy of the forest. At Tiwai Island they were most
often seen at 10–25 m above the ground (Whitesides, 1991) and in
the Taï Forest they spent over 50% of their time above 15 m in the
canopy and emergent layers of the forest; this compares with 22% for
C. petaurista and 5% for *C. campbelli* (McGraw, 2000).

Locomotion and posture. Dianas are active monkeys that walk, run and climb quadrupedally through the forest canopy and leap between canopy gaps. They use large boughs (large branches) more than do the smaller forest guenons, especially for travelling (McGraw, 2000, 2007).

Activity pattern. At Tiwai and in the Taï Forest they have been found to spend 40–45% of their time feeding and foraging, and about 25% of their time moving, though there is considerable variation across groups, seasons and years in time allocation (Hill, 1991; Whitesides, 1991; Buzzard, 2004).

Vocalizations. Diana monkeys are very vocal animals, with females and young using at least five common types of call to maintain contact and provide alerts to danger (Zuberbühler *et al.*, 1997; Zuberbühler, 2000). The most commonly heard of these calls is a whistle-like "wheeo" contact call. A more tonal, higher-intensity version of this whistle call may be given when the monkeys are disturbed, and may be considered an alarm or "alerting" call. Other variants are given if leopards or eagles are detected (Zuberbühler *et al.*, 1997). Adult males

Fig. 8.69: Diana monkey (*Cercopithecus diana diana*), Taï Forest, Côte d'Ivoire (photo by W. S. McGraw).

have a characteristic loud "croaking" (or "honking") call. This loud call, produced in multi-syllable trains, carries over long distances in the forest and is responded to by males in other groups. The careful studies by Zuberbühler *et al.* (1997) in the Taï Forest have shown that there are three acoustic variants of this male loud call: one given in response to crowned eagles, one to leopards, and one in other situations, such as at the sound of breaking branches and during territorial interactions.

Social organization. Diana monkeys live in relatively large social groups of 15–30 individuals that typically contain one adult male, 5–13 adult females, and young. Males that have not managed to join a group will move on their own, sometimes traveling with groups of other species.

Social behavior. Compared to other guenons studied in the Taï Forest, Diana monkeys show relatively low levels of affiliative interactions within their group, but high levels of agonistic behavior (Buzzard and Eckardt, 2007). Buzzard and Eckardt ascribe this pattern to high levels of feeding competition in groups of a highly frugivorous monkey that contain many females. Buzzard and Eckardt also note that male Dianas are less closely integrated into their social group than are males in other Taï guenon species; adult females were seen to groom other females and young monkeys, but did not groom adult males.

Interactions between groups. Dianas defend territories. During interactions between groups at territorial boundaries, females and young chase animals in the opposing group, while adult males display and give loud calls. In these situations male calls are often preceded by a quieter "chatter-scream" vocalization produced only by females. These female calls appear to incite male calling in support of territorial defence (Hill, 1991).

Reproduction. Reproductive patterns in this species have not been carefully studied. The usually lone adult males in social groups probably attempt to limit the access of other males to females in the group. At Tiwai Island in Sierra Leone, young infants have been seen most frequently in the dry months of January and February, suggesting that Diana monkeys have a December–February birth peak as is found in many other guenons.

Ranging patterns. The distance traveled each day and the area that a Diana monkey group uses in the course of a year are highly variable. They depend on such factors as social group size, habitat features and

Cercopithecinae

resource availability. An average daily travel distance is between one and 1.5 km, while group home ranges of 58 to 93 ha have been reported in the Taï Forest, and of 29 to 41 ha at Tiwai Island (Galat and Galat-Luong, 1985; Holenweg *et al.*, 1996; Hill, 1991; Whitesides, 1991; Buzzard, 2004, 2006b).

Diet. Fruit, insects and leaves are the major food items in the diet of Diana monkeys, and flowers are seasonally important. Leaves become seasonally important as a standby when fruits, flowers and insects are scarce in the forest. Dianas spend long periods carefully searching the foliage of canopy trees for insect prey. In Taï, the Diana was found to be the most frugivorous of the guenons, with fruit making up 59% of scan records of feeding (Buzzard, 2006a). Among commonly-eaten fruits in Taï are those of the canopy trees *Sacoglottis gabonensis* (Humiriaceae) and *Dialium aubrevillei* (Caesalpiniaceae), while at Tiwai Island commonly-eaten fruits are those of the liana *Landolphia hirsuta* (Apocynaceae) and the stilt-rooted tree *Uapaca guineensis* (Euphorbiaceae) (Hill, 1999; Whitesides, 1999; Buzzard, 2004). In the Taï Forest, Diana monkeys have high overlap in the fruit component of their diet with Campbell's monkeys, but Campbell's monkeys feed lower in the canopy and eat more insects than Dianas (Buzzard, 2004).

Association with other species. Groups of Dianas are often seen in close association with groups of other monkey species. They appear to be a "nuclear" species to which other "satellite" species attach, in part because of their vivid coloration and noisy behavior (Buzzard, 2004). In the Taï Forest, red colobus monkeys maintain especially close associations with Diana monkeys, probably because the Dianas can provide early warning about the approach of chimpanzees, which are significant red colobus predators in Taï; the red colobus, that tend to feed high in the canopy, can warn Dianas of the presence of eagles (Holenweg *et al.*, 1996; Noë and Bshary, 1997). On Tiwai Island, some groups of Diana monkeys are followed on a semi-permanent basis by olive colobus monkeys (*Procolobus verus*). Olive colobus travel in very small groups, and probably gain benefits from the extra eyes and ears provided by Diana monkeys to detect predators (Oates and Whitesides, 1990). Because colobus monkeys and guenons have low dietary overlap, these associations carry a low cost to members of each species in terms of interspecific food competition. When semi-terrestrial sooty mangabeys are foraging nearby, Diana monkeys in Taï will use lower levels of the forest canopy, probably because the mangabeys can act as sentinels for ground predators (McGraw and Bshary, 2002).

Cercopithecinae

Predators. The main predators of Diana monkeys are crowned eagles (*Stephanoaetus coronatus*), leopards, and humans. Today, leopards and eagles are rare or absent in many West African forests, so that humans are probably now the chief predator of these monkeys. The main natural predators still occur in Côte d'Ivoire's Taï Forest, where the hair of Diana monkeys was the most frequent primate hair found in one study of leopard scats, occurring in 8% of the samples (Hoppe-Dominik, 1984). It is not clear how many of these Diana remains might be the result of leopards scavenging the carcasses of monkeys killed by eagles. In a later study by Zuberbühler and Jenny (2007), only 3% of scats contained Diana remains. One variant of the male Diana loud call has been shown to be produced specifically as an alarm call in response to leopards, while another variant is a specific response to crowned eagles (Zuberbühler *et al.*, 1997; Zuberbühler, 2007). Shultz and Thomsett (2007) found crowned eagles to be the main predator on the Diana and other *Cercopithecus* species in Taï;

Cercopithecinae

Fig. 8.70: Diana monkey (*Cercopithecus diana diana*), Taï Forest, Côte d'Ivoire (photo by W. S. McGraw).

the eagles hunt in pairs, flying through the canopy or lying in wait in the path of foraging monkey groups (Shultz, 2002). Diana monkeys maintain high levels of vigilance; their frequent visual scanning of their surroundings probably helps them to detect the proximity of potential predators and other Diana groups.

Conservation Status

Cercopithecus diana diana is listed as Vulnerable on the IUCN Red List. Because Diana monkeys are dependent on high forest their distribution has become fragmented, as mature forest habitat has been logged and cleared for agriculture in the Upper Guinea rain-forest region. And because of their relatively large size, bright coloration, and noisy calling behavior they are more vulnerable than the other guenons of these forests to hunters. Therefore, although they are still abundant in a few areas of old-growth forest where hunting pressure is low, across most of their range they are becoming rare.

The Diana monkey occurs in a number of protected areas in the region, including the Tiwai Island Wildlife Sanctuary and the Gola National Park, and Loma Mountains proposed national park in Sierra Leone; the Sapo National Park in Liberia; and Taï National Park in Côte d'Ivoire. Substantial areas of the Gola National Park have been degraded by logging, but hunting does not seem to be occurring at high levels. Sapo is threatened by widespread illegal mining and by hunting, but Diana monkeys do not appear to have been heavily targeted by hunters (M. Abedi-Lartey, pers. comm., 2008). Taï National Park and surrounding forests suffer from high levels of commercial hunting, despite the protected status of Taï and the official prohibition of hunting through Côte d'Ivoire. The human population in the area around Taï increased fourfold between 1975 and 1989, largely because of immigration, and research by Refisch and Koné (2005a, 2005b) indicates that Dianas, like other large forest monkeys, are being harvested at unsustainable levels; only areas regularly visited by researchers are free from poaching.

Where to See It

Diana monkeys can still be observed relatively easily in the Tiwai Island Wildlife Sanctuary and in the Gola Forest, Sierra Leone (especially in the Gola North and West Forest Reserves); in Sapo National Park, Liberia; and in primate research areas on the western edge of the Taï National Park, Côte d'Ivoire.

Cercopithecinae

Roloway monkey
Cercopithecus diana roloway (Schreber, 1774)

Other English: Roloway Guenon
French: Palatine
West African languages: Boapea, buapia (Twi, Ghana); Monkia (Attie, IVC); Kakahua (Agni, Baoulé, Côte d'Ivoire); Glê (Godie, Côte d'Ivoire); Guêlé (Gouro, Côte d'Ivoire); Soula mansa (Dioula, Côte d'Ivoire)

Natural History

Field studies. Cercopithecus d. roloway has been much less intensively studied than *C. diana diana*, so that fewer details of its behavior and ecology are known. Sheila H. Curtin conducted a study in Ghana's Bia National Park in 1976–1977 and habituated a group (Curtin and Olson, 1984; Curtin, 2002); the roloway is almost certainly extinct now in Bia (Oates *et al.*, 2000a; Gatti, 2010).

Habitat. The roloway is assumed to be similar to the Diana monkey in the essentials of its ecology and behavior, but its reported distribution suggests that it may have the ability to occupy drier and more seasonal forest habitats, although it may still require mature forest with tall trees.

Population. Magnuson (2002) estimated a density of only 1.5 groups per km^2 in a few areas of mature but logged forest in southwestern Ghana where she encountered roloway monkeys, but this would be a population affected by intense human hunting.

Habitat use. Curtin (2002) notes that the roloway, like the Diana, is a high-canopy specialist which gets much of its food from the terminal branches of large emergent trees, and from large woody climbers infesting these trees.

Locomotion. Curtin (2002) describes *C. d. roloway* as displaying almost feline agility in the search for insect prey, including making acrobatic leaps to catch orthopterans.

Vocalizations. Adult male roloways produce a croaking loud call, similar to that of the *C. diana diana* male.

Cercopithecinae

Social organization. A typical group of roloway monkeys is probably similar to a Diana group, containing one fully adult male, several adult females, and young. The only social group studied carefully initially contained two adult males and six adult females, until one adult male was driven out; this group, in Bia National Park, Ghana, had a total of 14–15 individuals (Curtin, 2002). Groups probably defend territories.

Reproduction. No information is available on the reproductive patterns of roloway monkeys in the wild.

Ranging patterns. In the Bia study, a group of roloway monkeys travelled 1 to 3 km per day, on average moving further in the dry season than the wet, and covered a total range of 190 ha (Curtin and Olson, 1984), substantially larger than found for groups of Diana monkeys at Taï and Tiwai.

Cercopithecinae

Fig. 8.71: Roloway monkey (*Cercopithecus diana roloway*), Endangered Primate Centre, Accra Zoo, Ghana (photo by S. Wolters, WAPCA).

Diet. While fruit, insects and young leaves were observed to be the major food items in the diet of a roloway group in Bia—and in that way resembled *C. d. diana*—the roloways differed from Dianas in their more frequent consumption of the seeds of mature fruits (22% of recorded feeding events); these seeds, particularly the oil-rich seeds of *Pycnanthus angolensis*, are especially important dry-season foods. Roloway monkeys in Bia spent much time throughout the year carefully searching the branches and foliage of canopy trees for insects, especially hunting insects in terminal branches of the large leguminous tree *Piptadeniastrum africanum* (Curtin, 2002).

Association with other species. Roloways have been observed moving in close association with other monkey species, particularly the smaller guenons (*C. campbelli* and *C. petaurista*).

Predators. In the past, Roloway monkeys likely faced a similar range of predators to Diana monkeys. Today, by far their most significant predators are human hunters.

Conservation Status

Cercopithecus diana roloway is listed as Endangered on the IUCN Red List. This rating needs to be updated to Critically Endangered. The roloway monkey is one of Africa's most endangered primates. Not only was its original geographical range small, but this monkey appears to have been rare within this range even before bushmeat hunting reached its present levels. In 1956, Angus Booth described it as undoubtedly the rarest monkey in the Gold Coast (Ghana) (Booth, 1956). Roloways are threatened by the loss of tall, mature forest (their preferred habitat) to logging and agriculture, and by commercial hunting for bushmeat. The part of West Africa where they lived has a high human population density and has suffered one of the highest recent rates of deforestation in the world. Where forest does remain it has often been degraded by logging, and logging operations have opened the forest up to hunters.

In the 1970s roloway monkeys were present in the Ghana's 300-km^2 Bia National Park but, in 1977, 75% of Bia was downgraded to a "Game Production Reserve" in which logging concessions were assigned. The small remaining park area did not receive adequate protection. Recent surveys have found no roloways present in Bia National Park (Oates, 1999; Oates *et al.*, 2000a; Gatti, 2010). In surveys in western Ghana and eastern Côte d'Ivoire in 1993–1997, roloway monkeys were encountered at only five sites in Ghana (the

Cercopithecinae

Ankasa Resource Reserve, and the forest reserves of Krokosua Hills, Yoyo, Boin River and Draw River) and one in Côte d'Ivoire (the Forêt Classée de Yaya). In later surveys, Magnuson (2002) added Ghana's Dadieso Forest Reserve to this list, and McGraw and Oates (2002) added the forest near the Ehi lagoon (also known as the Tanoé Forest) in far south-eastern Côte d'Ivoire. Interviews conducted by Koné and Akpatou (2004) near the Parc National des Îles Ehotilé and the Forêt Classée de Dassioko suggested that roloways might also be present at those sites. However, the most recent surveys in both countries (Gonedelé Bi *et al.*, 2008; Gatti, 2010) were able to confirm the presence of *C. d. roloway* at only one site, the Tanoé Forest in Côte d'Ivoire, although unconfirmed reports suggest that it might still hang on in very small numbers at Ankasa in Ghana.

Where to See It

Only in the Tanoé Forest in southeastern Côte d'Ivoire, close to the border with Ghana, is it still possible to see this monkey in the wild. Most of the Tanoé is swamp forest that is difficult of reach, so observing monkeys there is not easy.

Cercopithecus neglectus geospecies

This geospecies contains only de Brazza's monkey, *Cercopithecus neglectus* (following Grubb, 2006b). Evolutionarily, *C. neglectus* seems to represent an independent early branch of the arboreal guenon group, most closely related to members of the Diana, mona and Hamlyn's geospecies (Disotell and Raaum, 2002; Gautier *et al.*, 2002; Tosi *et al.*, 2004).

De Brazza's monkey has a vast geographical distribution. It occurs throughout the Congo Basin, west from that basin to the Atlantic coasts of southern Cameroon and Rio Muni, and east to central Kenya and southwestern Ethiopia. Until recently, however, this species was not known from north of the Sanaga River in the region covered by this book. In the early 2000's, however, it was encountered during surveys of the Mbam & Djerem National Park in Cameroon, on tributaries of the upper Sanaga River (Maisels *et al.*, 2007a), and therefore on the edge of the region covered by this guide. Because of this monkey's peripheral occurrence in West Africa its natural history will be only briefly described here.

De Brazza's monkey
Cercopithecus neglectus Schlegel, 1876

Other English: De Brazza's guenon, Brazza's monkey
French: Cercopithèque de Brazza, le singe de Brazza
West African languages: Founga (Gbaya, Cameroon); Dongbi
(Mvouté, Cameroon)

Identification (see Fig. 8.66, p.251)

Viewed close up, and especially head on, this is a strikingly patterned monkey. Because it is very secretive in nature and favors thick riparian forest, however, it is not often clearly seen. De Brazza's monkey is one of the largest guenons. It has a chunky appearance and, compared with many other species of *Cercopithecus*, has relatively short arms and legs and a relatively short, thick tail. In a large sample described by Gautier-Hion *et al.* (1999), adult males averaged 6.4 kg in weight (ranging up to 8 kg), with a 55-cm head and body and a 70-cm tail, while the considerably smaller females averaged 3.6 kg, with a 45-cm head and body and a 56-cm tail. The back, flanks, posterior crown and tail base are a speckled olivey gray (the speckles resulting from black and white bands on the hairs). The tail, the arms and a broad band across the middle of the crown are black. The anterior crown above the eyebrows has a diadem of orange-brown hair edged with white. This narrow band of white hair extends laterally as tassles, which fringe the sides of a dark mask around the monkey's eyes and across its upper nose. The muzzle and upper lip are white, and pure white hair continues on the lower jaw as a well-developed beard. A white stripe runs obliquely across the thigh. The rump and inner thighs are white, and the chest, belly and hands and feet are black. The male's scrotum is blue.

Cercopithecinae

Geographic Range

In our region, De Brazza's monkey has been recorded only along the Djerem River and its tributaries in the Mbam & Djerem National Park of Cameroon. The Djerem is a major tributary of the Sanaga River, and it may be that future surveys will reveal that *Cercopithecus neglectus* has a wider distribution on the Sanaga system. Beyond the region covered by this guide, *C. neglectus* occurs from the Atlantic coast of southern Cameroon, Rio Muni and Gabon eastward to the Ubangi and Congo rivers and then across most of the Congo Basin to

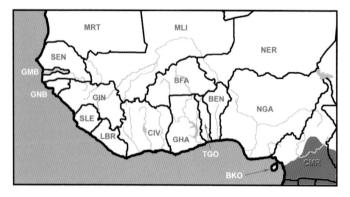

Fig. 8.72: Distribution of *Cercopithecus neglectus* in West Africa.

the Western Rift Valley. Scattered populations occur in eastern Africa, in Uganda, western Kenya, southern Sudan and southwestern Ethiopia.

Natural History

Because de Brazza's monkey (like the talapoin and the mustached monkey), occurs only on the edge of the region covered by this book, and has not been studied in our region, its natural history is only briefly summarized here.

Although the geographical range of de Brazza's monkey is huge, within this range it has a restricted distribution, being particularly associated with river-fringing and swamp forests, including gallery forests on East African mountains up to an elevation of 2,200 m. Information has been collected on its natural history during several survey studies in eastern Africa, but there have been few extended studies of its behavior in the wild. The study conducted most proximate to West Africa was by Gautier-Hion and Gautier (1978) along the Ivindo River in north-east Gabon; this study was aided by placing a radio-transmitter on an adult male. De Brazza's monkeys move slowly and cautiously, call infrequently and, if disturbed, may hide in "freezing" positions for several hours.

In Central Africa, social groups of *Cercopithecus neglectus* are typically very small, commonly consisting of just an adult male, an adult female, and young. In eastern Africa, larger groups are commonly reported (Mwenja, 2007). Adult males make loud, low-frequency double "boom" calls, especially in the early morning, with the two

Cercopithecinae

booms interrupted by a branch-shaking display (Gautier-Hion *et al.*, 1999; Maisels *et al.*, 2007); these boom calls are often the only way by which the species' presence can be detected. The monkeys move in the lower levels of the forest and on the ground. The group focused on by Gautier-Hion and Gautier (1978) travelled 500–550 m each day and had a home range of 6 ha; other groups had ranges of up to 10 ha. The de Brazza's monkeys avoided groups of other species, rather than forming polyspecific associations. An analysis of the contents of nine stomachs found 74% fruits and seeds, 9% leaves, 5% mushrooms, and 5% animal material. In captivity, de Brazza's monkeys have been observed to mark trunks and branches with secretions from a specialized chest gland, most commonly after the monkeys were introduced to new surroundings, or after new objects were introduced to their environment (Loireau and Gautier-Hion, 1988). Similar marking behavior has been observed in the semi-terrestrial *Allenopithecus*, *Chlorocebus* and *Cercopithecus hamlyni*.

Conservation Status

Cercopithecus neglectus is listed as of Least Concern on the IUCN Red List. Like all forest monkeys in Central Africa, de Brazza's monkey is hunted for its meat; however, its riparian habitat and cryptic behavior probably reduce its risk of being shot. Habitat conversion is threatening its survival in eastern Africa.

Where to See It

De Brazza's monkey is quite difficult to see wherever it occurs, and in West Africa it can only be observed in Cameroon's Mbam & Djerem National Park.

Fig. 8.73: DeBrazza's monkey (*Cercopithecus neglectus*), Bristol Zoo, England (photo by R. A. Mittermeier).

Cercopithecinae

Cercopithecus mona geospecies

Grubb (2006b) includes *C. mona*, *C. campbelli* and *C. pogonias* in this geospecies. They are relatively small, long-tailed, predominantly arboreal monkeys found in moist and dry forests from Senegal and The Gambia east to the Western Rift Valley. There has been great disagreement as to the number of species best recognized in this group. In an early review, Schwarz (1928b) recognized three "sections" within one species (*C. mona*), and 10 subspecies. In a thorough later review, Booth (1955) split the group into five species (*C. mona*, *C. campbelli*, *C. pogonias*, *C. wolfi* and *C. denti*) with two monotypic species and 10 subspecies. Gautier-Hion *et al.* (1999) regard *denti* as a subspecies of *C. wolfi*, while Grubb *et al.* (2003) treat both *denti* and *wolfi* as subspecies of *C. pogonias* based on the similarity of their calls.

Local Representatives

Cercopithecus mona, *C. campbelli* and *C. pogonias* occur in West Africa and can be distinguished from each other by their coat patterns and male loud calls; all have distinctive pink lips. *Cercopithecus campbelli* (with a gray or blackish lower back and white underparts) is found from The Gambia to the Volta River in Ghana. *Cercopithecus mona* (with a reddish-brown back, white underparts, and a white patch either side of the tail) occurs from the Volta River east through Nigeria to the lower Sanaga River in Cameroon. *Cercopithecus pogonias* (of which the local forms have a sagittal crest of black hair on the crown of the head and a golden-yellow belly) is found east and south of the Nigeria-Cameroon border region into western equatorial Africa and the forests of the northern Congo Basin, as well as on the island of Bioko. *Cercopithecus mona* was once sympatric with *C. campbelli* on the western bank of the Volta and Afram rivers in Ghana (Booth, 1955), in areas that are mostly now inundated by the Volta Lake. *Cercopithecus mona* is also broadly sympatric with *C. pogonias* in the moist forest from the Nigeria-Cameroon border to the Sanaga River.

Cercopithecinae

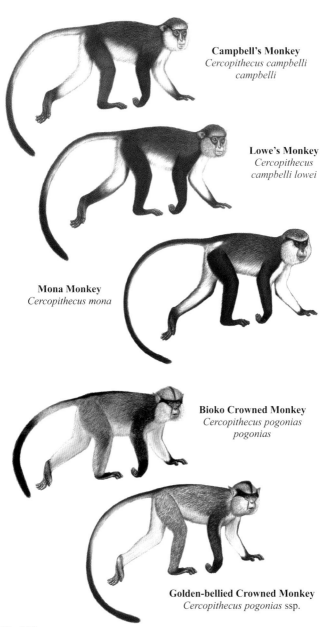

Campbell's Monkey
*Cercopithecus campbelli
campbelli*

Lowe's Monkey
*Cercopithecus
campbelli lowei*

Mona Monkey
Cercopithecus mona

Bioko Crowned Monkey
*Cercopithecus pogonias
pogonias*

Cercopithecinae

Golden-bellied Crowned Monkey
Cercopithecus pogonias ssp.

Fig. 8.74.

Campbell's monkey
Cercopithecus campbelli Waterhouse, 1838

Other English: Campbell's guenon, Campbell's mona monkey, Lowe's monkey (*C. campbelli lowei*)
French: Mone de Campbell
Portuguese: Macaco-mona
West African languages: Balbu, ekakumbé (Diola, Senegal); Conhê (Fula, Guinea-Bissau); Logboi (Mende, Sierra Leone); Doga'ah (Bassa, Liberia); Van-j'lay (Sapo, Liberia); Yrohié (Guere, Côte d'Ivoire); Sramblé (Agni, Côte d'Ivoire); Komou (Appolo, Côte d'Ivoire); Okwakuo (Akan, Ghana)

Identification (see Fig. 8.74, p.269)

This monkey is not immediately identifiable by one particular striking feature of its coat, and is best distinguished from other sympatric forest guenons by its lack of a white nose spot or of white spots on the rump. The upper back is speckled gray-yellow and the lower back gray or blackish. The outer surfaces of the arms and legs, and dorsal surface of the tail, are dark gray or black. The underparts are white and the skin of the scrotum is blue. As in other members of the mona group, the lips and muzzle skin are pink. Adult males have head and body lengths averaging about 50 cm, with a 70–80 cm tail; the body length of adult females averages 40 cm, with a 60–70 cm tail; the body weight of adults varies considerably, but averages about 4.0 kg in males and 2.5–3.0 kg in females (Napier, 1981; Delson *et al.*, 2000).

Subspecies. Two subspecies are recognized: *C. campbelli campbelli* from The Gambia to the Cavally River of Côte d'Ivoire, and *C. campbelli lowei* from the Sassandra River in Côte d'Ivoire to the Volta River in Ghana. Between the Cavally and Sassandra is a mixed region where both subspecies are present, as well as some individuals with intermediate features (Oates, 1988a). In *C. c. campbelli* the upper back is fawn-yellow, while the back of *C. c. lowei* has a warmer, more golden tinge. The lower back, outer limb surfaces and dorsal surface of the tail are dark gray in *C. c. campbelli* and dark gray or black in *C. c. lowei*. *Cercopithecus c. campbelli* has a speckled white brow, while the upper brow hairs of *C. c. lowei* are usually yellow. The undersurfaces in *C. c. campbelli* are silvery grayish-white, compared to a purer white in *C. c. lowei*. The entire lower third of the tail in *C. c. lowei* is dark gray or black, while the upper ventral surface of the tail is light gray.

Cercopithecinae

Fig. 8.75: Lowe's monkeys (*Cercopithecus campbelli lowei*), in the Boabeng-Fiema Monkey Sanctuary, Ghana (photo by F. Campos).

In general, then, *C. c. lowei* is a more brightly colored monkey than *C. c. campbelli*, but there is a good deal of intra-populational variation in the intensity of coloration.

Similar species. Most similar to Campbell's monkey is its close relative, *Cercopithecus mona*, which differs from *C. c. lowei* in having a reddish-brown rather black lower back, and in having a white patch on the upper thigh, near the base of the tail either side of its rump. *Cercopithecus c. lowei* and *C. mona* once occurred sympatrically on the west bank of the lower Volta River and on the west bank of the Volta's tributary, the Afram, but most of these areas are now under water (Grubb *et al.*, 1998) and it is not known whether these two monkeys still occur together near the edge of Lake Volta. Across the rest of its range, *C. campbelli* is broadly sympatric with the spot-nosed monkey, *C. petaurista*, to which it is similar in size, body proportions and locomotion. Campbell's monkey differs from the spot-nose in having a pink rather than black muzzle, and in lacking a white nose. In Campbell's monkey the lower back and dorsal surface of the tail are dark gray or black, whereas in the spot-nose they are olive-brown. Stampfli's putty-nosed monkey (*Cercopithecus nictitans stampflii*) is sympatric with *C. campbelli* in a limited region on the northern edge of the moist forest zone in Liberia and Côte d'Ivoire. *Cercopithecus n. stampflii* is larger than *C. campbelli*, uses higher levels of the forest canopy, and has a prominent white nose-spot.

Geographic Range

Campbell's monkey is widespread in the West African forest and forest-savanna mosaic zones from southern Gambia to the Volta River in Ghana. The western subspecies, *C. c. campbelli*, meets the eastern subspecies, *C. c. lowei*, between the Cavally and Sassandra-Nzo rivers in eastern Côte d'Ivoire, where some individuals with features intermediate between the two subspecies have been found (Booth, 1955; Oates, 1988a).

Natural History

Habitat. Campbell's monkeys occur in a broad range of habitats in the moist forest zone and in the forest-savanna mosaic zone north of the rain-forest. They are also found in coastal mangrove forest. In the forest-savanna mosaic zone they have been seen not only in riparian forest galleries but also in savanna woodland (for instance, in the Comoé National Park in northern Côte d'Ivoire [Fischer *et al.* 2000]).

Cercopithecinae

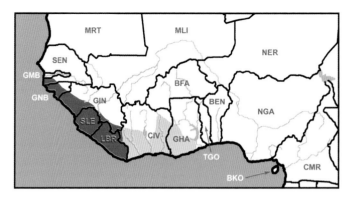

Fig. 8.76: Distributions of *Cercopithecus campbelli campbelli* **(red) and** *C. campbelli lowei* **(yellow).**

Field studies. Careful, long-term behavioral studies of *C. campbelli campbelli* have only been conducted in the Taï Forest, Côte d'Ivoire (Galat and Galat-Luong, 1985; McGraw, 1998b, 1998c, 2007; Buzzard, 2004, 2006a, 2006b; Buzzard and Eckardt, 2007; McGraw and Zuberbühler, 2007; Zuberbühler, 2001), but some observations are also available from Sierra Leone, collected in the course of primate community studies (Harding, 1984; Fimbel, 1994). Limited observations on *C. campbelli lowei* have been made at Adiopodoumé, Côte d'Ivoire (Bourlière *et al.*, 1970).

Population. Campbell's monkeys are especially abundant in disturbed habitats where there is a mosaic of secondary forest, farmbush and farms. *Cercopithecus campbelli* is said to be the most common monkey in Sierra Leone, a country with highly mosaic vegetation, most of it heavily modified by human activity (Grubb *et al.*, 1998). Apart from baboons, it was found to be the most numerous monkey in Kilimi, Sierra Leone (Harding, 1984). *Cercopithecus campbelli* and *C. petaurista* were the most frequently encountered monkeys in surveys in Ghana's Kakum National Park (Oates *et al.*, 2000a), and in reserved forests in eastern Côte d'Ivoire (McGraw, 1998a). *Cercopithecus campbelli* densities of 15 and 24 per km^2 are reported in mature forest in the Taï National Park, Côte d'Ivoire (Galat and Galat-Luong, 1985; Buzzard, 2004; McGraw and Zuberbühler, 2007), and of 39–44 per km^2 in old secondary forest in the Tiwai Island Wildlife Sanctuary, Sierra Leone (Oates *et al.*, 1990b).

Cercopithecinae

Habitat use. Although Campbell's monkey is predominantly arboreal, it spends more time in the lowest parts of the forest canopy than the other guenons with which it shares its habitat, and quite often it travels on the ground. In a study in the Taï Forest in Ivory Coast, McGraw (2000) found that *C. campbelli* used the ground for 15% of its time. *Cercopithecus diana* and *C. petaurista*, by comparison, used the ground less than 2% of the time. *Cercopithecus campbelli* used the shrub layer of the forest 22% of the time, compared to 9% for *C. petaurista* and 4% for *C. diana*. In the same forest, Buzzard (2004, 2006a) recorded that 58% of Campbell's monkey feeding occurred in the shrub layer (below 5 m) and on the ground. Campbell's monkey uses small lianas and twigs for support less often than does the spot-nosed monkey (McGraw, 2000). It is also reported to be a good swimmer, allowing it to forage on small islands (Grubb *et al.*, 1998).

Locomotion and posture. Of the predominantly arboreal monkeys in the Taï Forest, *C. campbelli* was found to walk more and leap less than any other species, and sat when resting and stood when feeding more than any other monkey (McGraw, 2007).

Fig. 8.77: Lowe's monkey (*Cercopithecus campbelli campbelli*), Taï Forest, Côte d'Ivoire (photo by W. S. McGraw).

Activity pattern. Two studies in the Taï Forest report different activity profiles for Campbell's monkey. McGraw (1998b) reports that the monkeys spend 70% of their time feeding and foraging, 20% resting, and 7% travelling, while Buzzard (2004) reports 50% feeding and foraging, 18% resting and 28% travelling. These differences probably result from different definitions of foraging, because McGraw (1998c) defines "foraging" as travel while feeding.

Vocalizations. The adult male loud calls of Campbell's monkey, like those of the related mona, are some of the more commonly heard primate vocalizations in West Africa. One set of these calls is given the name "hack" by Struhsaker (1970a) and "bark" by Booth (1955); it is a variable vocalization, sometimes given as a two-syllable call (sounding like "wa-hu" or "ah-uh" with the first syllable of higher frequency), and sometimes as a single syllable with the first part of the call dropped. These hacks are often made when the monkeys are disturbed, including instances when they are alarmed by humans, by other potential predators, and when other species have made loud calls. Zuberbühler (2001) has shown that Campbell's monkeys in the Taï Forest give different versions of the call to crowned eagles and to leopards; the eagle call is shorter and starts at a lower frequency than the leopard call. The other distinctive male loud call is a very low frequency "oom" (referred to as a "boom" by Struhsaker, 1970), and this call often precedes a sequence of hacks. Females and young produce a pulsed "chirruping" or "chinking" alarm call.

Social organization. Social groups of 5–33 individuals have been reported, with average group sizes of 9–14 (Galat and Galat-Luong, 1985; Oates *et al.*, 1990b; Buzzard, 2004; Buzzard and Eckardt, 2007). Typical groups contain a single adult male and several adult females. Aggressive male takeovers of one-male groups occur. They are accompanied by infanticide (Galat-Luong and Galat, 1979). As reported in other members of the *mona* geospecies, but rarely in other forest guenons, subadult and adult male Campbell's monkeys that are not part of heterosexual groups associate together in small but persistent all-male groups (Bourlière *et al.*, 1970; Buzzard, 2004; Buzzard and Eckardt, 2007).

Social behavior. Buzzard and Eckardt (2007) report a a relatively high rate of affiliative interactions and a lower rate of agonistic interactions in Campbell's monkey groups in the Taï Forest than in sympatric guenons. They suggest that the low rate of agonism is related to a small group size and dispersed feeding pattern compared to,

Cercopithecinae

especially, Diana monkeys. Most affiliative interactions involved adult females grooming other adult females.

Interactions between groups. When social groups of Campbell's monkeys meet they interact aggressively, with males more involved in aggressive displays (threats and loud calling) than females (Buzzard, 2004). However, encounters between groups of *C. campbelli* in the Taï Forest were relatively infrequent (Buzzard and Eckardt, 2007).

Reproduction. Bourlière *et al.* (1970) estimate that female *C. campbelli lowei* become sexually mature at three to four years of age. They saw mating taking place in June–September in central southern Côte d'Ivoire, and all births occurred in the November–January period, at the end of the long rainy season and early dry season.

Ranging patterns. Daily group travel distance is between 1,000 m and 1,200 m (Buzzard, 2004, 2006b), and estimates of annual home range size in Taï are between 40 and 80 ha (Galat and Galat-Luong, 1985; Buzzard, 2004, 2006b).

Diet. Fruit dominates the diet of this species, but the diet is eclectic and many leaves and insects are also eaten. In the Taï study by Buzzard (2004, 2006a), 46% of feeding records were of fruit, 33% of animals, and 8% foliage, making the Campbell's monkey the most faunivorous of Taï guenons. Bourlière *et al.* (1970) describe Campbell's monkeys carefully searching through foliage and dead wood for insect larvae, and Buzzard (2004) notes that 20% of insect foraging comprises searches of rolled leaves. In Taï, the main fruits in the diet are from *Sacoglottis gabonensis* (Humiriacae), *Dialium aubrevillei* (Caesalpiniaceae) and *Memecylon lateriflorum* (Melastomataceae), which were also the top fruits in the diet of sympatric Diana monkeys (Buzzard, 2004, 2006a). In mangrove habitats, mangrove leaves and seeds, crabs, shrimps and mudskippers are eaten (Grubb *et al.*, 1998). It can be a serious farm pest.

Association with other species. Campbell's monkeys are very often seen in close association with other monkey species, especially other guenons. In scans of habituated groups in Taï Forest, Campbell's monkeys were associated with Diana monkeys in 89% of scans, with spot-nosed monkeys in 51–68% of scans, and with olive colobus monkeys in 80% of scans; they were alone only 4.5% of the time (Buzzard, 2004). *Cercopithecus campbelli* was responsible for initiating and terminating all associations with *C. diana* groups, and

Cercopithecinae

probably gained anti-predator benefits from the association; *C. diana* most often called first in the presence of aerial and terrestrial predators.

Predators.   Natural predators of Campbell's monkeys include crowned eagles, leopards and chimpanzees, but today human hunters are usually their main predator.   In relation to their abundance, Campbell's monkeys are the most heavily-hunted by humans of the five monkey species studied in the Taï region of Côte d'Ivoire (Refisch and Koné, 2005b).   Hoppe-Dominik (1984) found *C. campbelli* remains in 1.9% of leopard scats in the Taï Forest, and Zuberbühler and Jenny (2007) found remains in 1.8% of scats; surprisingly low frequencies given the tendency of this guenon to forage on the ground and in low levels of the forest.   Chimpanzees in Taï only occasionally capture this guenon (Boesch and Boesch-Achermann, 2000).

Conservation Status

Cercopithecus campbelli is listed as a species of Least Concern on the IUCN Red List.   Despite heavy hunting pressure, it is still one of the most abundant primates in the Upper Guinea forest zone, along with the spot-nosed monkey.   These two species are often seen together, especially in forest regrowth.

Where to See It

This is probably the most readily observed monkey in the forests of Upper Guinea and in gallery and coastal forests outside the moist high forest zone.   It is common in all the protected forests of Upper Guinea.   *Cercopithecus campbelli campbelli* can be seen in Tiwai Island Wildlife Sanctuary (Sierra Leone), Sapo National Park (Liberia) and Taï National Park (Côte d'Ivoire).   *Cercopithecus campbelli lowei* can be seen in Ghana in Kakum National Park and Boabeng-Fiema Monkey Sanctuary.

Cercopithecinae

Mona monkey
Cercopithecus mona (Schreber, 1774)

Other English: Mona guenon, mona
French: Mone
West African languages: Alokpaya (Éwé, Togo); Zin houi, zin houm, zin ho (Fon, Bénin); Edun (Yoruba, Nigeria); Ogi (Bini, Nigeria); Kémé bugo (Ijaw, Nigeria); Okpoucha (Igbo, Nigeria); Ikpok ebok (Ibibio, Nigeria); Efu (Boki, Nigeria); Muka-msi (Okwa, Nigeria); Mesése (Denya/Anyang, Cameroon); Mba'mbok (Ejagham, Nigeria and Cameroon); Enkei (Korup, Cameroon and Nigeria); Atoneekem (Bakossi, Cameroon); Hikam (Banen, Cameroon); Hikem (Bassa, Cameroon)

Identification (see Fig. 8.74, p.269)

Like other members of the mona group in West Africa, this species has pink skin on its lips and muzzle, but it is readily distinguished from them by elongated patches of white hair on its rump. The coat of the chest, belly, and inner limb surfaces is pure white, contrasting strongly with black hair on the outer surfaces of the lower arms and legs. The back is speckled reddish-brown, the crown of the head is dark gray speckled with yellow-gold, and there is a white browband. Dark skin on the upper nose and around the eyes, along with dark hair on the temples, gives this monkey a "masked" appearance. The adult male's scrotum is blue. Newborn infants have a very dark coat. *Cercopithecus mona* has similar body dimensions to *C. campbelli*. No subspecies of mona monkey are recognized and there is little variation in the appearance of populations across its range.

Similar species. Compared to *C. mona*, *C. campbelli* lacks white hip patches and has a gray or black lower back. While *C. campbelli* has a narrow area of sympatry with *C. mona* in Ghana, there is broad sympatry between the mona and its other close relative, *C. pogonias*. In this region of sympatry from the far southeastern corner of Nigeria east and south to the Sanaga River in Cameroon, *C. pogonias* is best distinguished from *C. mona* by its bright golden-yellow ventral surfaces, its dark sagittal crest on the crown, and its lack of white hip patches. In Cameroon, Struhsaker (1970a) has observed wild hybrids of *C. mona* and *C. pogonias*; these individuals exhibited a variety of intermediate coat-pattern features. Compared to the single-unit "boom" vocalizations of male *campbelli* and *pogonias*, *mona* males emit a two-unit call. *Cercopithecus mona* is sympatric across its range

Cercopithecinae

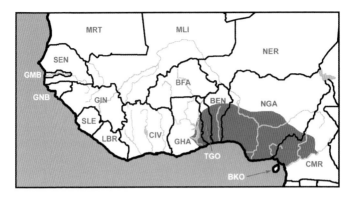

Fig. 8.78: Distribution of *Cercopithecus mona*.

with a variety of other guenons, including *C. petaurista*, *C. nictitans*, *C. erythrogaster*, *C. sclateri* and *A. preussi*. Unlike the mona monkey, *C. petaurista*, *C. nictitans* and *C. sclateri* all have white noses; *C. erythrogaster* and *A. preussi* have no white hair on their ventral surfaces; and none of these species has white thigh patches.

Geographic Range

The mona monkey occurs in the forest and forest-savanna mosaic zones from the vicinity of the Volta River (and Lake) in eastern Ghana to the Sanaga River in Cameroon. At least in the 1950's, *C. mona* was sympatric on the right bank of the lower Volta with *C. campbelli*, and in the south of its range there is a population in a limited area on the left bank of the Sanaga River (Booth, 1955; Oates, 1988a). Introduced populations are found on the Gulf of Guinea islands of São Tomé and Príncipe, and on the Caribbean island of Grenada (Dutton, 1994; Glenn *et al.*, 2002). However, mona monkeys are absent from Bioko Island, suggesting that they were not present on the immediate mainland at the time of Bioko's isolation 10,000 years ago.

Natural History

Habitat. The mona monkey is an ecological generalist. Indeed, it might be considered a "weed" species. It occurs in mature rain forest, secondary and logged forest, including regenerating farmland, agricultural plantations, gallery forest in the savanna zone (as far north as the Sudanian woodland zone), and freshwater and mangrove swamp

Cercopithecinae

forest (Oates, 1988a). In parts of eastern Nigeria, where little forest remains and most forest anthropoid primates are extinct, *C. mona* is often the only forest monkey still present.

Field studies. Despite the ubiquity of mona monkeys in parts of West Africa, there are relatively few published accounts of field studies in this region. Thomas Struhsaker and J. Stephen Gartlan made some observations on unhabituated *C. mona* in Cameroon during wide-ranging studies of forest primate community ecology and behavior in 1966–1968, with their observations concentrated in rain-forest habitats near Mount Cameroon, at Idenau and in the Southern Bakundu Forest Reserve (Struhsaker, 1969, 1970a; Gartlan and Struhsaker, 1972). Richard Howard made a study of relationships among three species of forest *Cercopithecus*, with a focus on *C. mona*, in the Mungo Forest Reserve, Cameroon, in 1972–1973, and presented his results in a doctoral dissertation (Howard, 1977). Reiko Matsuda Goodwin focused a doctoral study on this species in the Lama Forest of Bénin in 1995–1997, but was not able to fully habituate the monkeys (Goodwin, 2007). Lama is a dry-forest habitat where there is typically a November–February dry season and a shorter July–August dry interval, and the forest canopy is made up of a relatively small number of tree species of low stature. Some further popular density information has been derived from survey projects (e.g., Edwards, 1992; Dunn, 1993; Linder, 2008). Introduced island populations of monas have been studied by Mary Glenn on the Caribbean island of Grenada in 1992–1995 (including habituated groups), and on the Gulf of Guinea islands of São Tomé and Príncipe in 1998 (Glenn, 1997, 1998; Glenn *et al.*, 2002).

Population. Although mona monkeys are often abundant in marginal habitats, such as mangrove and gallery forests, where other forest monkeys are rare or absent, they may themselves be uncommon in mature lowland rain forest, especially in the presence of other *Cercopithecus* monkeys. In a study at Idenau, Cameroon, the mona monkey was the only guenon present in young secondary forest, it occurred at moderate density in older secondary forest, and was very rare in mature forest, where *Cercopithecus nictitans* and *C. pogonias* were much more common (Gartlan and Struhsaker, 1972). In the mature rain forest of Ikenge in Korup National Park, Cameroon, Edwards (1992) estimated a density of 0.86–0.96 groups per km² (equivalent to about 9 individuals per km² if group size at Korup averages 10). In 2004–2005, Linder (2008) encountered between 0.03 and 0.12 groups per km of mona monkeys on census walks at three different sites in and near Korup National Park, with the most frequent encounters occurring

Cercopithecinae

Fig. 8.79: Mona monkey (*Cercopithecus mona*), Cross River State, Nigeria (photo courtesy of CERCOPAN).

at the most disturbed site, Bajo, which also has the lowest monkey species richness of the three sites, and where the related *C. pogonias* is very rare. At three sites in gallery forest in savanna regions of Gashaka Gumti National Park, Nigeria, Dunn (1993) estimated densities of between 16.5 and 50 individual monas per km², while in montane forest in the park densities were about 60/km². In the dry forest of

Lama, Bénin, Goodwin (2007) reports mona densities ranging from 30 individuals per km² in farmbush to 50 per km² in old forest; the only other forest *Cercopithecus* at Lama is *C. erythrogaster*, which was encountered at less than one third of the frequency of *C. mona*. Among the introduced island populations, where monas face no competition from other monkeys, Glenn (1998) estimated an average density of 42 individuals/km² in the mountain forests of central Grenada in the West Indies (assuming a group size of 18), while Glenn *et al.* (2002) estimated densities of 19 and 21 individuals/km² respectively on São Tomé and Príncipe in the Gulf of Guinea.

Habitat use and locomotion. In high forest, mona monkeys concentrate their activities in the lower layers of the forest, and quite frequently they also move on the ground, like their close relative *C. campbelli*. For instance, in the Southern Bakundu Forest Reserve, Cameroon, 60% of *C. mona* activity was below a height of 50 feet (15.2 m) (Gartlan and Struhsaker, 1972); in the Mungo Forest Reserve, Cameroon, monas were most often seen at heights of 4–10 m and foraged on the ground more than other *Cercopithecus* species (Howard, 1977); in the Lama Forest, Bénin, 29% of *C. mona* sightings were on the ground (Goodwin, 2007). No studies have made a systematic investigation of mona locomotor behavior, however. Like Campbell's monkeys (McGraw, 2007), much of mona movement when in the forest canopy consists of relatively slow and deliberate quadrupedal walking, with infrequent leaping. Gartlan and Struhsaker (1972) observed a

Fig. 8.80: Mona monkey (*Cercopithecus mona*), Cross River State, Nigeria (photo courtesy of CERCOPAN).

Cercopithecinae

group swimming across a 4-m-wide creek in a Cameroon mangrove swamp.

Activity pattern. In all-male groups on Grenada, resting occupied 48% of the activity budget, feeding and foraging 26%, grooming 12%, and moving 8% (M. Glenn, pers. comm.).

Vocalizations. Mona monkeys have a range of distinctive vocalizations. Adult males produce a deep two-unit "oom-oom" (or "boom") call, with a frequency of 0.1–0.2 kHz (Struhsaker, 1970a). These booms often precede a chain of loud low-frequency "hack" calls ("ah-uh"), but booms or hacks may be given alone. A train of hacks can extend to over 100 calls, with the spacing between them decreasing and then increasing during the sequence (Struhsaker, 1970a). Soft contact calls are given by foraging females and young, sounding like "wheee" or "whee-ow." Adult females and young also produce a one-unit "chink" (or "sneeze") call in alarming situations. The mona monkey also appears to be unique among guenons in producing special calls during copulation. Two types of copulation call have been recognized, "warbles" and "grunts." As described by Glenn *et al.* (2002), "warbles are characterized by a continuous whining, which rises and falls erratically in pitch. Grunts are choppy, low-toned calls that are rapidly repeated. Warbles and grunts are given simultaneously, alternately, or singly during call series." These calls have only been heard by Glenn *et al.* (2002) and Goodwin (2007) when adult males mount females in mixed-sex groups; these observers could not determine which sex makes which call, but Howard (1977) states that copulation calls are made by males.

Social organization and behavior. Social groups of 3–35 have been reported in southwestern Cameroon, with an average size of 9–10 (Struhsaker, 1969), or 19 (Howard, 1977). In Bénin's Lama Forest, Goodwin (2007) reports an average size of 13.5 for mixed-sex groups. Although most mixed-sex groups contain a single adult male and several adult females, almost 20% of Lama groups have more than one adult male. Howard (1977) reports that the three mixed-sexed groups he observed in Mungo, Cameroon, all contained more than one adult male. As in *C. campbelli*, all-male groups of *C. mona* also occur, containing adults, subadults and juveniles. Pairs are the most commonly seen all-male grouping in Lama, but up to five males have been seen travelling together (Goodwin, 2007). All-male groups have also been seen on Grenada (Glenn *et al.*, 2002). The social behavior of wild *C. mona* has not been well studied. Among the unhabituated monas in Lama, adult females were the individuals most often seen to groom others, and adult males were the most frequent recipients of grooming (Goodwin, 2007).

Interactions between groups. Howard (1977) recorded extensive overlap of group ranges in the Mungo forest, but aggressive interactions were seen between groups when they met. Goodwin (2007) also noted aggressive group interactions at Lama, with males producing loud calls, giving head-bobbing and branch-shaking displays, chasing each other, and showing aggressive contact, including biting and wrestling. These intergroup encounters were accompanied by a characteristic call, the "chortle."

Reproduction. Mona monkeys appear to be seasonal breeders. In Mungo, Cameroon, Howard (1977) heard copulation calls mostly in September–December, and small dark infants were most often seen in April–June. In Lama, Bénin, copulation calls were heard only between September and March, and all but two copulations were seen in that same period. Small clinging infants were seen between April and September (Goodwin, 2007).

Ranging patterns. Ranging behavior has not been carefully studied in *C. mona*.

Diet. Fruit is the most common item in the diet of mona monkeys. The most careful study of diet was carried out by Goodwin (2007) at Lama in Bénin. There, monas were found to spend about 60% of their time feeding on ripe fruits and unripe seeds, especially of *Dialium guineense* and *Diospyros mespiliformis*. Seeds were most commonly eaten in the dry season, when ripe fruits were scarce in the forest. Other seasonally important foods were insects (up to 18% of feeding time in the wet season), and flowers and nectar (up to 37% of feeding time in one dry season).

Association with other species. Like other West African forest guenons, groups of mona monkeys frequently associate with groups of other monkey species where these occur sympatrically. In southern Bakundu, Cameroon, *C. mona* was encountered on 62 occasions; on four of these occasions monas were alone, but on the other 58 (94%) they were in the company of other monkey species; the most common monkey polyspecific association observed in southern Bakundu was between *Cercopithecus erythrotis*, *C. mona* and *C. nictitans* (Gartlan and Struhsaker, 1972). In the Lama Forest, *C. mona* was most often seen alone (85% of encounters), but was also observed in association with the much rarer *C. erythrogaster* and with very rare *Procolobus verus* (Goodwin, 2007).

Predators. At Mungo, Cameroon, monas gave alarm calls to crowned eagles (Howard, 1977), but over the majority of *C. mona*'s geographic range its chief potential predators (crowned eagles and leopards) are now rare or absent, and humans are today the main predator on this species.

Conservation Status

Cercopithecus mona is listed as of Least Concern on the IUCN Red List. Although high forest on dry land is now highly fragmented and degraded across much of the geographical range of the mona monkey, *C. mona* remains a relatively common species in many areas because of its ability to thrive in swamp forests, young secondary forest and savanna gallery forest. This is the most frequently encountered monkey in the heart of its range in southern Nigeria, where other forest monkeys are now rare or absent. The mona is especially numerous where hunting pressure is light, such as in Muslim areas in the north of its range.

The mona is present in many protected areas, including the Tafi Atome Monkey Sanctuary in Ghana; the Fazao-Malfakassa National Park in Togo; the Okomu, Cross River and Gashaka Gumti national parks, and the Afi Mountain Wildlife Sanctuary in Nigeria; and in the Korup, Mount Cameroon and Takamanda national parks, the proposed Ebo National Park, and the Banyang-Mbo Wildlife Sanctuary in Cameroon.

Where to See It

This is a very readily observed species. It can be seen in the Tafi Atome Monkey Sanctuary in the Volta Region of Ghana, in the Lama Forest of Bénin, in Nigeria's Okomu and Gashaka Gumti national parks, and at many sites in Cameroon including Korup National Park. Monas are quite often encountered in small patches of forest near human habitation, such as the Lekki Conservation Centre of the Nigerian Conservation Foundation on the edge of Lagos, Nigeria, in several sacred grove forests in southern Nigeria, and next to tourist beaches in south-western Cameroon.

Cercopithecinae

Crowned monkey
Cercopithecus pogonias Bennett, 1833

Other English: Crowned guenon, golden-bellied crowned monkey,
crested mona
French: La mone couronnée
Spanish: Cercopiteco coronado
West African languages: Mbie (Boki, Nigeria); Oko'mbok (Ejagham,
Nigeria and Cameroon); Ékábógé (Denya/Anyang, Cameroon);
Konfang (Korup, Cameroon and Nigeria); Mbetekem (Bakossi,
Cameroon); Mboiit (Banen, Cameroon); Issuni (Bassa, Cameroon);
Momá (Bubi, Bioko)

Identification (see Fig. 8.74, p.269)

The most striking feature of the subspecies of crowned monkey
in our part of West Africa is the bright orange-gold hair of the chest,
belly and inner limb surfaces. No other monkey in the region has
this feature. As its common name suggests, this monkey is also
distinguished by a crest of black hair on the crown of its head. Either
side of this crest the crown is speckled yellow-black; the temples are
also black. The outer surfaces of the arms are variably fawn, gray or
black, and the flanks and outer leg surfaces are speckled gray-fawn. A
dorsal band of dark hair begins at the shoulders and extends to the tail
root, broadening posteriorly. The tail is dark above and golden-brown
below for about two-thirds of its length, becoming entirely black at the
tip. *Cercopithecus pogonias* has pink skin on its lips and muzzle, like
C. campbelli and *C. mona*. The ear margins have a small tuft of long
golden hairs. Body dimensions of *C. pogonias* are similar to other
members of the geospecies, but the population living on Bioko Island
is smaller, as described in the next section.

Subspecies. Usually, only one subspecies of crowned guenon, *C.
pogonias pogonias*, is recognized from our region, but Gautier-Hion *et
al.* (1999) have noted that the mainland form differs from the nominate
form on Bioko Island. According to Grubb *et al.* (2003), the mainland
form has black or dark gray outer arms, whereas Bioko monkeys have
fawn arms; however, photographs of Bioko animals show that the outer
surfaces of their lower arms are frequently gray. Bioko *C. pogonias*
certainly have longer hair than those on the mainland and generally
less intense coloration, including a less bright belly. The island form
is also smaller than the mainland populations. Butynski *et al.* (2009)

Cercopithecinae

reports on a large sample of adult females from Bioko having a head and body length of 34–41 cm (mean 37 cm) and a tail length of 48–61 cm (mean 56), whereas one adult female from Cameroon's Rumpi Hills had a head and body of 42.5 cm and a tail of 64 cm (Eisentraut, 1973). Adult males from Bioko average 3.7 kg in weight and adult females 2.8 kg (Butynski *et al.*, 2009). Gautier-Hion *et al.* (1999) give average weights for mainland *C. pogonias* as 4.4 kg for adult males and 2.9 kg for adult females. Other subspecies of *C. pogonias* are *C. p. grayi* in southern Cameroon, northern Gabon, Central African Republic, Republic of Congo and northwestern Democratic Republic of Congo, and *C. p. nigripes* in Gabon south of the Ogooué River.

Similar Species. Except on Bioko, *C. pogonias* is broadly sympatric with its close relative *C. mona*, but the mona monkey's range extends west beyond that of *C. pogonias* and north into the forest-savanna mosaic zone where the crowned monkey is absent. The crowned monkey is easily distinguished from the mona monkey by its golden rather than white undersurfaces, and by the dark median crest on the head. The lower back of the crowned monkey is black, while

Cercopithecinae

Fig. 8.81: Male Bioko crowned monkey (*Cercopithecus pogonias pogonias*) in the upper Gran Caldera de Luba (photo by Tim Laman, ILCP Bioko RAVE).

that of the mona is reddish-brown, and the mona has distinctive white patches on its upper thighs. Adult male crowned monkeys produce a single-unit "boom" vocalization, while the mona male makes a two-unit call. *Cercopithecus pogonias* is also sympatric with *C. erythrotis*, *C. nictitans*, and *A. preussi*. *Cercopithecus erythrotis* is slightly smaller than *C. pogonias* and has a bright red tail, while *C. nictitans* is slightly larger and has a prominent white nose spot absent in *C. pogonias*. *Allochrocebus preussi* is largely restricted to hill forest, is semi-terrestrial, and predominantly gray, without a white, gold belly or red belly, or white nose. In western Cameroon, Struhsaker (1970a) observed several hybrids between *C. pogonias* and *C. mona* that had a variety of intermediate coat patterns.

Geographic Range

The crowned monkey occurs from the far southeastern edge of Nigeria eastwards and southwards into Cameroon and Central Africa. If the forms *denti* and *wolfi* are regarded as subspecies of *C. pogonias*, then the species extends right across the Congo Basin to the western Rift Valley. If *denti* and *wolfi* are not included in *C. pogonias*, then *pogonias* is absent from the central Congo Basin but occurs in the northern Basin extending to about 26°E. If two subspecies are recognized in our region, *C. pogonias pogonias* is limited to Bioko Island, while an as yet unnamed mainland form is restricted to the moist forest region from Cross River State, Nigeria, to the Sanaga River in Cameroon.

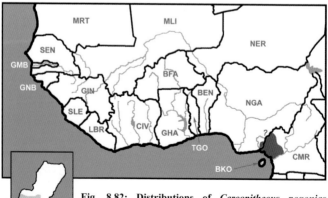

Fig. 8.82: Distributions of *Cercopithecus pogonias pogonias* (yellow) and *C. pogonias* ssp. (red).

Cercopithecinae

Natural History

Habitat. While its relative the mona monkey is an ecological generalist, the crowned monkey appears to be a rain-forest specialist. In studies at Idenau on the edge of Mount Cameroon, Gartlan and Struhsaker (1972) found *C. pogonias* absent in young secondary forest, moderately abundant in older secondary forest and most abundant in mature forest.

Field studies. Rather little is known about the behavior of wild crowned monkeys. No observational studies on habituated monkeys, with published results, appear to have focused on this species. Rather, observations have been collected during general surveys and multi-species community studies, such as the work of Gartlan and Struhsaker (1972) in Cameroon, and of Gautier-Hion and Gautier (1974), Gautier - Hion (1980) and Tutin *et al.* (1997) in Gabon. Observations in Gabon refer to the subspecies *C. pogonias grayi* and *C. p. nigripes*.

Population. The abundance of *C. pogonias* varies greatly from place to place within its West African range; usually it is not common. In Korup National Park, Cameroon, Edwards (1992) encountered *C. pogonias* at a rate of only 0.05 groups per km of line-transect census walk, from which a density of 0.5 groups per km² was estimated. In the same Ikenge area in 2004–2005, Linder (2008) encountered 0.04 groups/km. On the other hand, in surveys of a small area of primary forest in the southeast of Bioko in 1992, Maté and Colell (1995) encountered this monkey at a rate of 0.64 groups/km, more frequently than any other (the closely-related *C. mona* is absent on Bioko). In the Gran Caldera de Luba in southwestern Bioko, Butynski and Owens (2008) encountered 0.34 groups of *C. pogonias* per km surveyed.

Habitat use. In their study at Idenau, Cameroon, Gartlan and Struhsaker (1972) observed *C. pogonias* using canopy levels higher than is found in any other species. Fifty per cent of observations of crowned monkeys were above a height of 55 ft (16.8 m), and feeding occurred on average at higher levels than travelling. In Southern Bakundu Forest Reserve, Cameroon, Gartlan and Struhsaker also found that 50% of *C. pogonias* feeding heights were, as at Idenau, above 70 ft (21.3 m); this again represents a higher average feeding height than other monkey species. In surveys in southeastern Bioko, where the monkey community is similar to that found at Idenau, *C. pogonias* was most frequently sighted at heights of between 10 and 24 m in the forest canopy (Maté and Colell, 1995).

Activity pattern. There is no published information on the activity budget of *C. pogonias* in West Africa.

Vocalizations. Adult male *C. pogonias* give deep, resonant one-unit "boom" calls like those of *C. campbelli* males (Struhsaker, 1970a). As in *C. campbelli* and *C. mona* these booms often precede a series of low-frequency "hack" calls that are often two-phrased ("ah-uh"), and are sometimes given without booms. In alarming situations, adult females and young give two-unit "staccato-chirps", and their contact call is an "ooo" that has several variants (Struhsaker, 1970a).

Social organization. Social groups of 9–19 have been reported from southwestern Cameroon, with an average size of 13 to 14 (Struhsaker, 1969). Typical groups contain a single adult male and several adult females.

Reproduction. A small sample from northeastern Gabon suggests that *C. pogonias grayi* in that region gives birth between November and April, coinciding with the driest time of the year (Gautier-Hion *et al.*, quoted in Butynski, 1988).

Ranging patterns. There has been no careful study of *C. pogonias* ranging behavior and diet in West Africa, but at Idenau in Cameroon, Gartlan and Struhsaker (1972) found that groups of crowned monkeys moved, in half a day, over an area 2-3 times as large as groups of *C. nictitans* in the same forest. Patterns of movement were strongly seasonal and apparently influenced by fruit abundance. In Central African forests, Gautier-Hion *et al.* (1999) report ranges of at least 100 ha for *C. pogonias* and a daily travel distance of 1.5 km. This is consistent with the Cameroon observations that suggest that this monkey ranges over a wide area.

Diet. In the Idenau study, Gartlan and Struhsaker observed crowned monkeys eating fruits, fruit arils and flowers. In a sample of 77 feeding observations made on *C. pogonias nigripes* in Lopé National Park, Gabon, 78% were of fruits and seeds, 9% of flowers, 6.5% of leaves and 6.5% of animal matter (Tutin *et al.*, 1997). Stomach contents of *C. p. grayi* animals killed by hunters near Makokou, Gabon, contained an average of 78% (by dry weight) fruits and seeds, 12% animal remains and 6% leaves (Gautier-Hion 1980).

Association with other species. In the Idenau forest, crowned monkeys were always seen moving in association with groups of other monkey species, although the associations were often short-lived (Gartlan and Struhsaker, 1972). In northeast Gabon, *C. pogonias grayi* is often seen with *C. nictitans* and *C. cephus*, and these associations can have great stability (Gautier-Hion and Gautier, 1974).

Predators. In Cameroon, crowned monkeys reacted strongly to the presence of humans and crowned eagles, suggesting that these species are common predators of the monkey (Gartlan and Struhsaker, 1972).

Conservation Status

Cercopithecus pogonias is listed as of Least Concern on the IUCN Red List, but the subspecies *C. p. pogonias* (described as occurring on Bioko and the mainland) is rated as Vulnerable. The crowned monkeys in our region appear to be habitat specialists with restricted ranges that are uncommon or absent outside mature forest. Conversion of closed-canopy high forest by the spread of agriculture and by logging are therefore a serious threat to this monkey, and it is hunted throughout its range. Although hunters report that it once occurred in the Okwangwo Division of Cross River National Park, Nigeria, recent surveys have failed to locate the species, but it is still present in the adjacent Takamanda National Park in Cameroon. Other protected areas where it occurs in our region are the Oban Division of Cross River National Park in Nigeria (but where it is now very rare); Korup National Park, Mount Cameroon National Park, Banyang-Mbo Wildlife Sanctuary and the proposed Ebo National Park in Cameroon; and the Gran Caldera and Southern Highlands Scientific Reserve on Bioko (Equatorial Guinea). Although it occurred until recently in the southern part of the Pico Basilé National Park on Bioko it may now have been eliminated from that area, or very greatly reduced in numbers, by hunting.

Where to See It

Because of its restricted range and habitat specialization, this is not an easy monkey to observe in West Africa. The most accessible site where it can be seen with reasonable reliability is the southern portion of Korup National Park, Cameroon. It is relatively abundant in parts of southern Bioko, where it can be observed in the vicinity of Moka. Although crowned monkeys occur in Nigeria (in the Oban Division of Cross River National Park, adjacent to Korup), they are uncommon and very hard to see.

Cercopithecinae

Cercopithecus cephus geospecies

Grubb (2006b) includes the species *C. cephus*, *C. ascanius*, *C. erythrogaster*, *C. erythrotis*, *C. petaurista* and *C. sclateri* in this diverse geospecies which is found in the moist forest zone from Guinea-Bissau east to the Great Lakes region of East Africa. These are small, agile, long-tailed, brightly-patterned and highly-arboreal rain-forest monkeys that spend much of their time in the forest understorey. With the exception of the Bioko red-eared monkey, adult males have a head and body length averaging 45–50 cm, with a 70–80 cm tail; the body length of adult females is 40–45 cm, with a 65–70 cm tail. Adult males average 4.0–5.0 kg in weight, adult females 2.5–3.0 kg.

Local Representatives

Five of the six species in this group occur in West Africa; they can be quite readily distinguished from each other by the coloration and patterning of hair on their heads, bellies and tails. *Cercopithecus petaurista* (with a white nose, chest and belly) is found from the Guinea-Senegal border region to western Togo; *C. erythrogaster* (with no distinct nose-spot and a red or gray belly) is found from eastern Togo to the Niger Delta; *C. sclateri* (white on the nose, and red on the ventral surface of the upper part of the tail) is found only in Nigeria from the eastern side of the Niger Delta to the Cross River; *C. erythrotis* (nose and entire tail rusty-red) occurs in the southeastern corner of Nigeria, western Cameroon and Bioko Island; and *C. cephus* (white mustache and red lower tail) occurs mostly to the south of the Sanaga River in Cameroon, although there are populations found just to the north of the upper Sanaga. A small area of hybridization between *C. erythrogaster* and *C. sclateri* has been discovered in Bayelsa State on the eastern edge of the Niger Delta in Nigeria (Baker, 2004), and another small area of hybridization occurs between *C. erythrotis* and *C. cephus* just south of the lower Sanaga, below Edéa (Struhsaker, 1970a). *Cercopithecus petaurista*, *C. erythrogaster* and *C. erythrotis* each have two subspecies; only one of the three recognized subspecies of *C. cephus* occurs in our area.

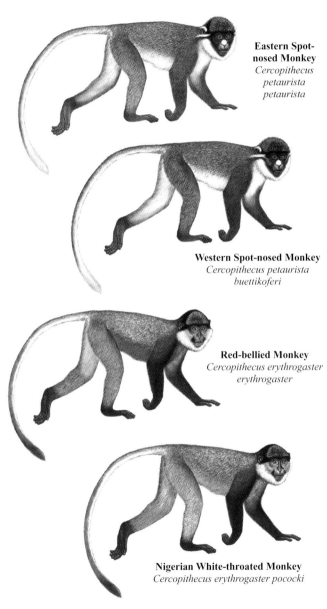

Eastern Spot-nosed Monkey
Cercopithecus petaurista petaurista

Western Spot-nosed Monkey
Cercopithecus petaurista buettikoferi

Red-bellied Monkey
Cercopithecus erythrogaster erythrogaster

Nigerian White-throated Monkey
Cercopithecus erythrogaster pococki

Cercopithecinae

Fig. 8.83.

Spot-nosed monkey
Cercopithecus petaurista (von Schreber, 1774)

Other English: Lesser spot-nosed guenon (or monkey), lesser white-nosed monkey (or guenon), spot-nose
French: Pétauriste
Portuguese: Nariz-branco
West African languages: Hokpalakui (Mende, Sierra Leone); Tardo way' (Bassa, Liberia); Nomo-jueh (Sapo, Liberia); Êlilêh (Agni, Côte d'Ivoire); Ahenhema, krawa (Twi, Ghana)

Identification (see Fig. 8.83, p.293)

This guenon has a very obvious triangular patch of pure white hair on its nose, contrasting strongly with a generally dark face; the patch is broad across the bridge of the nose and tapers towards the inter-nostril area. The spot-nosed monkey's prominent ears have a conspicuous fringe of white hair, and on each side of the head a linear tuft or "flash" of white hair extends laterally below the ear. The throat has a ruff of white hair, and the hair of the chest and belly is also white. The monkey's back, flanks, and outer upper limb surfaces are speckled golden olive-brown, coloration resulting from the golden banding of dark hairs. The dorsal surface of the tail is also a speckled golden-brown, becoming darker towards the tip, while the undersurface is grayish-white. Spot-nosed monkeys are often difficult to see, given their tendency to forage and hide in thick growth, but when glimpsed they can often be identified by their white nose-spot (accentuated by bobbing motions of the head) and the white flashes below their ears, along with their characteristic alarm calls (see below).

Subspecies. Two subspecies are recognized: *C. petaurista petaurista* from the Sassandra River of Côte d'Ivoire to the western edge of Togo, and *C. petaurista buettikoferi* from Guinea-Bissau and Senegal east to the Sassandra. These two subspecies are very similar in appearance, but *C. p. petaurista* has a band of black hair across the nape of the neck that is lacking in *C. p. buettikoferi*. Some *C. p. buettikoferi* individuals have a patch of creamy-speckled hairs on the cheek, under the eye, but this seems to be a variable characteristic; in some individuals the cheek patch is not obvious, or is silvery.

Similar species. *Cercopithecus erythrogaster*, which occurs to the east of *C. petaurista*, and is probably a close evolutionary relative, differs in having a red or gray belly, and it lacks the white nose-spot, the white ear fringes and the white lateral facial flashes of *C. petaurista*. Of broadly sympatric monkeys, the most similar to *C. petaurista* in size, body proportions and locomotion is Campbell's monkey, *Cercopithecus campbelli*. Campbell's monkey differs from *C. petaurista* in having a pink muzzle and no white nose-spot. In Campbell's monkey the lower back and dorsal surface of the tail are dark gray or black, depending on the subspecies. East of the Volta River in Ghana, *C. p. petaurista* has a small area of sympatry with *Cercopithecus mona*, a close relative of *C. campbelli*. The mona monkey is characterized by having a white spot on either side of its rump. On the northern edge of the moist forest zone in Liberia and western Côte d'Ivoire, *C. petaurista buettikoferi* is sympatric with another white-nosed monkey, Stampfli's putty-nosed monkey (*Cercopithecus nictitans stampflii*). *Cercopithecus n. stampflii* appears to be a rare monkey that uses higher levels of the forest canopy than the spot-nose. It is larger than *C. petaurista*, lacks white ear fringes and the white lateral tufts below the ears, and is generally darker in color, with black or dark gray arms and legs.

Geographic Range

The spot-nosed monkey occurs in the forest zone and forest-savanna mosaic from the Boké Province of western Guinea to the western edge of Togo; north of Boké it has been recorded from Guinea-Bissau's Bijagos Archipelago (but those records await full confirmation) and from the Guinea-Senegal border region (Oates, 1988a; Grubb *et al.*, 1998; R. Kormos, pers. comm.). In 2005, a solitary young male *C.*

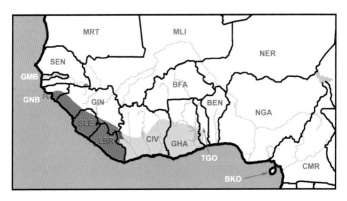

Fig. 8.84: **Distributions of** *Cercopithecus petaurista buettikoferi* **(red),** *C. p.* *petaurista* **(yellow), and where they overlap (purple).**

Cercopithecinae

petaurista was observed in the Fongoli region of southeastern Senegal, possibly an "accidental migrant" from northern Guinea, 35 km to the south (Pruetz *et al.*, 2010).

The boundary between the subspecies *C. p. buettikoferi* and *C. p. petaurista* appears to coincide approximately with the Cavally River on the Liberia-Côte d'Ivoire border, but *C. p. buettikoferi* does occur west of the upper Cavally, meeting *C. p. petaurista* between the Cavally and Nzo rivers, where intermediate individuals have been recorded (Oates, 1988a).

Natural History

Habitat. Spot-nosed monkeys occur both in the coastal moist forest zone of Upper Guinea and in forest patches and riparian forest in the forest-savanna mosaic zone north of coastal zone. They flourish in disturbed forest, including young farmbush, where they are often

Fig. 8.85: **Eastern spot-nosed monkey (*Cercopithecus petaurista **petaurista***), Taï Forest, Côte d'Ivoire (photo by W. S. McGraw).**

more abundant than in mature high forest (Oates, 1988a; Grubb *et al.*, 1998).

Population. Densities of 25–29 per km² are reported in mature forest in the Taï National Park, Côte d'Ivoire (Galat and Galat-Luong, 1985; Buzzard, 2004; McGraw and Zuberbühler, 2007) and 58 per km² in the more disturbed secondary forest of the Tiwai Island Wildlife Sanctuary in Sierra Leone (Oates *et al.*, 1990b). They were the most frequently encountered monkey, along with *C. campbelli*, in surveys in the Kakum and Bia national parks in Ghana, and in reserved forests in eastern Côte d'Ivoire (Oates *et al.*, 2000a; McGraw, 1998a).

Fig. 8.86: A captive eastern spot-nosed monkey (*Cercopithecus petaurista petaurista*) at Klouto, Togo (photo by J. F. Oates).

Field Studies. The only behavioral studies of habituated groups have been conducted in the Taï Forest, Côte d'Ivoire (Galat and Galat-Luong, 1985; McGraw, 1998b, 1998c, 2007; Buzzard, 2004, 2006a, 2006b; Buzzard and Eckardt, 2007; McGraw and Zuberbühler, 2007). Some less intensive observations are available from Sierra Leone, collected in the course of community studies (Harding, 1984; Fimbel, 1994). Spot-noses are difficult animals to study; they can quickly vanish when being followed by observers (McGraw and Zuberbühler, 2007).

Habitat use. Spot-nosed monkeys are highly arboreal and rarely travel on the ground. However, they also use the upper part of the main forest canopy infrequently and very rarely enter the crowns of tall emergent trees. In Taï Forest, nearly 70% of their time is spent in the forest understorey, though they tend to use higher levels of the understorey than sympatric Campbell's monkeys (Galat and Galat-Luong 1985; McGraw, 2000). They commonly frequent tangles of climbers around the trunks of large forest trees.

Cercopithecinae

Locomotion and posture. Spot-noses move through their habitat in a quiet, skulking fashion, climbing quadrupedally on branches, twigs and climber stems, and avoiding large boughs (Oates and Whitesides, 1990; McGraw, 2000; Buzzard, 2004).

Activity pattern. In the Taï Forest they have been found to spend 45% of their time feeding and foraging, about 26% of their time moving, and 24% resting (Buzzard, 2004).

Vocalizations. Spot-nosed monkeys forage quietly. Males produce a soft, low-frequency throaty pulsed "growling" call when alarmed, while females make bird-like "squeak" or "tweet" calls. In response to the loud calls of other species, or to a major disturbance, adult males make a characteristic low-frequency "k-urrr" call; the first brief syllable possibly being an inhalation, and the subsequent pulsed "urrr" component resembling the deep croak of a frog; commonly, a pair of these relatively loud calls is delivered. This male loud call is referred to as a "hack" or "klunk" by Struhsaker (1970a), but those terms do not capture well the quality of the sound.

Social organization. Social groups of 4–24 individuals have been reported from Taï Forest, Côte d'Ivoire, but most groups are relatively small, with an average size of 11 (Galat and Galat-Luong, 1985;

Fig. 8.87: Carcass of a western spot-nosed monkey (*Cercopithecus petaurista buettikoferi*) being offered for sale in a village near Sapo National Park, Liberia (photo by E. J. Greengrass).

Buzzard, 2004).   Carefully-counted groups usually contain a single
adult male, together with adult females and young, but a second adult
male has been seen associating with a group in Taï.

Social behavior.   Spot-nosed monkeys in the Taï Forest show
relatively low levels of within-group social interaction; the most
common interaction is grooming by adult females of other females,
males and young (Buzzard and Eckardt, 2007).

Interaction between groups.   In Taï Forest, *C. petaurista* groups
have been found to have a high-level of range overlap, but aggressive
encounters occur between groups, especially at feeding trees. Adult
males and females participate in these aggressive interactions between
groups (Buzzard, 2004).

Reproduction.   No   published   information   is   available   on
reproductive patterns in *C. petaurista*.

Ranging patterns.   Daily group travel distance is between about
500 m and 1,800 m, with an average of about 1 km (Buzzard, 2004).
The annual home range of a social group is 40–100 ha (Galat and
Galat-Luong 1985; Buzzard, 2006b).

Diet.   Major foods of spot-nosed monkeys are leaves, ripe fruits,
insects and flowers. In the Taï Forest, foliage was the most frequently
eaten food item (40% of scan observations of feeding), followed by fruit
(34% of observations).   By contrast, sympatric Diana and Campbell's
monkeys eat more fruit (Buzzard, 2006a).   Young leaves and new
stems from lianas were the most frequently eaten foliage items, while
the single most important food item was the fruit of the canopy tree
Dialium aubrevillei (Caesalpiniaceae), an item also important in the
diet of Diana monkeys (Buzzard, 2004).

Association with other species. Like other guenons in West African
forests, spot-nosed monkeys are frequently seen in close association
with other monkey species. During census walks on Tiwai Island,
Sierra Leone, spot-noses were in association with other monkey
species in 48% of encounters (Oates and Whitesides, 1990). At Taï
(where there are more natural monkey predators than at Tiwai), spot-
nose groups were seen alone less than 5% of the time, while they were
with *Cercopithecus campbelli* and *C. diana* almost 80% of their time
(Buzzard, 2004).   In the presence of eagles and potential mammalian
predators (chimpanzees and leopards), adult males of the other guenon

Cercopithecinae

species almost always made loud calls before *C. petaurista*, but *petaurista* males were often the first to call at the sound of a treefall or other environmental disturbance. Spot-nosed monkeys were most often alone when foraging in the understorey. *Cercopithecus petaurista* appears to follow other guenons (especially Diana monkeys when foraging in upper levels of the forest canopy), and by doing this the spot-noses probably reduce their risk of predation, particularly by eagles.

Predators. Despite their cryptic behavior and habit of associating with other monkeys, spot-noses are not immune to predation. In one study of leopard scat in the Taï Forest, 2.3% contained *C. petaurista* remains (Hoppe-Dominik, 1984), but in a second study only one of 165 samples (0.6%) had remains of this species (Zuberbühler and Jenny, 2007). In Taï they are also occasionally (but rarely) eaten by chimpanzees, which preferentially hunt red and black-and-white colobus monkeys (Boesch and Boesch-Achermann, 2000). Today, their main predators in most places are almost certainly humans, especially where larger and less cryptic monkeys have been eliminated or greatly reduced by hunting and habitat modification.

Conservation Status

Cercopithecus petaurista is listed as of Least Concern on the IUCN Red List. The spot-nosed monkey has held up quite well in the face of human pressure across its range, and it is one of the last monkeys in the Upper Guinea forest to go locally extinct. It is usually more abundant in regrowth forest than in mature high forest, and it is not a prime target for hunters because of its small size and habit of hiding in thick undergrowth, where it is difficult to shoot. It has high visual acuity, and is adept at detecting approaching humans before they detect it. *Cercopithecus petaurista* can also survive in quite small forest patches and extends into the savanna zone from gallery forests.

Where to See It

Although this is one of the most common of primates in the forests of Upper Guinea it often takes patience to get a clear view of it because of its habit of lurking in thick growth and its quiet movements. It can be seen relatively easily in all the main protected areas in Upper Guinea, including Tiwai Island Wildlife Sanctuary (Sierra Leone), Sapo National Park (Liberia), Taï National Park (Liberia), and Kakum National Park (Ghana).

Cercopithecinae

White-throated monkey
Cercopithecus erythrogaster Gray, 1866

Other English: Red-bellied monkey (or guenon), Nigerian white-throated monkey (or guenon)
French: Cercopithèque à ventre rouge, singe à ventre rouge
West African languages: Agbé (Yoruba, Bénin); Iware, ughare (Yoruba, Nigeria); Ekhoko (Bini, Nigeria); Ekéké, akéké (Ijaw, Nigeria)

Identification (see Fig. 8.83, p.293)

As its name implies, a characteristic feature of the white-throated monkey is the prominent ruff of white hair under its lower jaw that extends onto the sides of the neck. Another distinguishing feature is a black-edged diadem of gold-flecked black hairs on the anterior crown of the head. The cheeks have tufts of light yellow-and-black banded hairs. The white-throated monkey's back, its flanks, the outer surfaces of its legs and upper arms, and the dorsal surface of its upper tail are gray with olivaceous golden-brown speckling (a result of the banding pattern of individual hairs). The outer surfaces of the forearms are black or dark brown. The tail has a pale grayish-white ventral surface and a dark tip. *Cercopithecus erythrogaster* is cryptic and not easily observed. The predominant impression an observer has when glimpsing it in the forest understorey is of a dark monkey, though its white throat, gold crown patch and light tail undersurface can be discerned on careful inspection.

Subspecies. Two subspecies are recognized. The red-bellied monkey *C. erythrogaster erythrogaster* of Bénin and Togo has a bright rust-red chest and belly; the Nigerian white-throated monkey *C. erythrogaster pococki* of southwestern Nigeria has a brownish-gray chest and belly, sometimes with a slight reddish tinge.

Similar species. *Cercopithecus petaurista*, which occurs to the west of *C. erythrogaster*, differs in having a white nose-spot, a white belly, white ears, and a white stripe below the ear. *Cercopithecus sclateri*, which occurs immediately to the east of *C. erythrogaster*, has a white nose-spot, white ears, a paler muzzle and a red ventral surface on the distal part of its tail. Of sympatric monkeys, the most similar to *C. erythrogaster* in size, body proportions and locomotion is the mona monkey, *C. mona.* The mona is readily distinguished from the white-

Cercopithecinae

throated monkey by the white hair of its chest, belly and inner limb
surfaces, its whitish browband, the pink skin of its muzzle, and by its
possession of two prominent white spots on the rump, either side of the
base of the tail.

Geographic Range

The white-throated monkey occurs in the coastal forest zone from
far eastern Togo to the eastern edge of the Niger Delta in Nigeria
(Oates, 1985; Oates, 1996a; Sinsin *et al.*, 2002; Campbell *et al.*,
2008b; Nobimè *et al.*, 2009).   In Bénin, its original habitat is highly
fragmented, and *C. erythrogaster* mostly occurs in small isolated forest
fragments (several of them sacred groves) in the valley of the lower
Ouémé River.   In Nigeria it was until recently quite widespread in the
extensive, but heavily exploited, forest reserves of the southwest, and
its distribution extends as far east as the Orashi River in Rivers State,
east of the Niger's main tributaries in the Niger Delta.   In a small area
to the west of the Orashi there is a zone of overlap and hybridization
between *C. erythrogaster* and *C. sclateri*.

Natural History

Habitat.   White-throated monkeys occur in lowland moist and
semi-deciduous forest, including riverine gallery and swamp forest.
Most of the forests in which they live have been heavily modified by
human activities (Oates, 1985; Nobimè *et al.*, 2009).

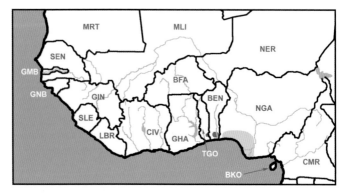

**Fig. 8.88: Distributions of *Cercopithecus erythrogaster erythrogaster* (red)
and *C. erythrogaster pococki* (yellow).**

Cercopithecinae

Fig. 8.89: Nigerian white-throated monkey (*Cercopithecus erythrogaster pococki*), Okomu, Nigeria (photo by N. Rowe).

Population. *Cercopithecus erythrogaster* can be a relatively common species in suitable habitat where hunting pressure is low, but throughout its range it is now generally rare due to intense hunting by humans on all large and medium-sized mammals. In the course of walking 176 km of census transects in the Lama Forest, Bénin, Goodwin (2007) had 16 encounters with *C. erythrogaster* (0.09/km), and in the central part of Okomu Forest Reserve (now a national park) Oates (1985) had 0.15 encounters per km walked.

Field studies. There has not been a study of habituated white-throated monkeys. Such information as is available on their natural history has either been collected in the course of relatively short-term surveys in Nigeria (e.g., Oates, 1985; Robinson, 1994) and in Bénin and Togo (Oates, 1996a; Sinsin *et al.*, 2002; Campbell *et al.*, 2008a; Nobimè *et al.*, 2009), or through observations on unhabituated monkeys in Bénin's Lama Forest (Nobimè and Sinsin, 2003; Goodwin, 2007).

Habitat use, locomotion and activity. *Cercopithecus erythrogaster* typically frequents the lower levels of the forest canopy and dense tangled growth in canopy gaps and along rivers. Like other members of the *C. cephus* group, it is an agile quadruped, walking, running and climbing quietly through the forest on small and medium-sized supports. Watchful, and with acute vision, white-throated monkeys quickly drop out of sight on detecting approaching humans, and creep away silently through the lower canopy (Robinson, 1994).

Vocalizations. Adult males make a distinctive low-frequency, guttural, "croaking" (or "growling") loud call, similar to that of *C. petaurista* but typically delivered in multiple units, while the male *petaurista* loud call is a single "croak."

Social organization. Although *C. erythrogaster* lives in social groups, it has not been the subject of careful behavioral studies, and accurate data on group composition are not available. Most groups probably range in size from 10–20, with a single fully adult male (Mason, 1940; Oates, 1985). Groups counted on census walks in Lama, Bénin, by Goodwin (2007) had a mean size of 9.6, but it is usual not to see all group members during surveys of this type. Solitary adult males have also been observed.

Reproduction. No information is available on reproductive patterns in *C. erythrogaster*.

Fig. 8.90: Red-bellied monkey (*Cercopithecus erythrogaster erythrogaster*) at Drabo Gbo, Bénin (photo by P. Neuenschwander).

Diet and ranging. The diet and foraging behavior of white-throated monkeys are poorly known, but groups appear to forage in a dispersed fashion, carefully searching their habitat for fruits and insects. In the Lama Forest, Bénin, ripe tree fruits are reported to be the main items of the diet, with immature fruit eaten in the dry season (Nobimè and Sinsin, 2003).

Association with other species. White-throated monkeys are often seen moving in close association with groups of other monkeys, especially *C. mona.*

Predators. Humans are almost certainly the most important predator of this species at the present time. Although crowned eagles are known to prey on other members of this geospecies elsewhere in the African forest zone, these eagles are now rare in the range of *C. erythrogaster.*

Conservation Status

Cercopithecus erythrogaster is listed as Vulnerable on the IUCN Red List. However, the subspecies with the more restricted range, *C. erythrogaster erythrogaster,* is listed as Endangered. The dense human population that occurs throughout most of the range of *C. erythrogaster* has led to its forests being heavily fragmented by agriculture and human settlement. Like most of the larger mammals in this area, white-throated monkeys are also hunted for their meat. On the other hand, the vigilance and cryptic behavior of white-throated monkeys makes them difficult to hunt, and groups do not require very large areas of forest to survive.

Although most of the original semi-deciduous forest vegetation of southern Bénin and southeastern Togo has been lost to cultivation, small populations of the red-bellied subspecies (*C. e. erythrogaster*) persist in patches of seasonally-flooded forest that are not readily cultivated, in some sacred tree groves (where they are not hunted), and in gallery forests (Sinsin *et al.,* 2002; Nobimè *et al.,* 2009). The largest remaining population of *C. e. erythrogaster* is probably in the Lama Forest of Bénin where there is a protected central refuge of semi-deciduous forest, about 20 km^2 in area. The only confirmed population in Togo is in the mountains of the Réserve Nationale de Togodo, close to the Bénin border.

Cercopithecinae

In Nigeria, where *C. erythrogaster pococki* is found, the largest population is probably that in the central part of the Okomu Forest Reserve, Edo State. This central forest area became a Wildlife Sanctuary in 1985 and a National Park in 1999. The Nigerian subspecies also occurs in the Omo Forest Reserve of Ogun State, which contains a Biosphere Reserve and where a larger wildlife conservation area is planned. The largest area of continuous forest remaining within the range of *C. e. pococki* is in the Niger Delta, but this forest contains no protected area and most of it has been seriously degraded. Hunting pressure, on the other hand, is lower here than in most other parts of southern Nigeria.

Where to See It

The best sites to observe *C. e. erythrogaster* are in the Noyau Central of the Fôret de la Lama, south of Bohicon (Lama is administered by the Office National du Bois), and in the sacred grove forest of Togbota near Adjohoun on the flood plain of the Ouémé River.

In Nigeria, Okomu National Park in Edo State (30 km west of Benin City) was originally established as a wildlife sanctuary specifically to protect white-throated monkeys. Simple tourist infrastructure has been established at Okomu, and *C. e. pococki* can be observed there relatively easily.

Fig. 8.91: Red-bellied monkeys (*Cercopithecus erythrogaster erythrogaster*) at Togbota in the Ouémé valley, Bénin (photo by M. L. Pirot).

Fig. 8.92: Illustration of *Cercopithecus erythrogaster erythrogaster* by J. Smit, accompanying the first published description of the species by J. E. Gray (*Proceedings of the Zoological Society of London*, 1866, pl. XVI).

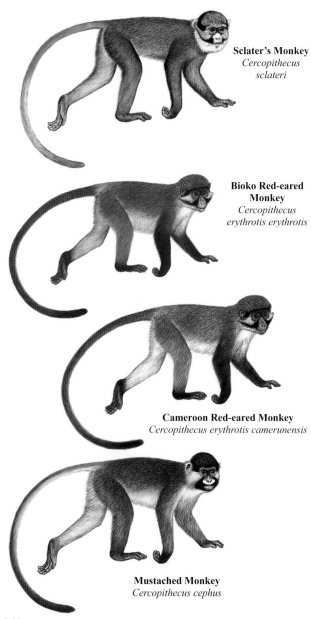

Sclater's Monkey
Cercopithecus sclateri

Bioko Red-eared Monkey
Cercopithecus erythrotis erythrotis

Cameroon Red-eared Monkey
Cercopithecus erythrotis camerunensis

Mustached Monkey
Cercopithecus cephus

Cercopithecinae

Fig. 8.93.

Sclater's monkey
Cercopithecus sclateri Pocock, 1904

Other English: Sclater's guenon, Sclater's white-nosed monkey
French: No established common name
West African languages: Amina (Igbo, Oguta region, Nigeria); Nsim
ebok, ubet ebok (Ibibio, Nigeria); Egoro (Biyase, Nigeria)

Identification (see Fig. 8.93, p.308)

The ears of this guenon have a prominent fringe of white hairs,
and the hairs on the upper part of the nose are white or light rusty-red,
forming a distinctive triangular nose spot. The skin of the muzzle,
including the tip of the nose, is pale and pinkish. The anterior crown of
the head has a diadem of gold-flecked hair, bordered posteriorly with
a black band that is broadest behind the ears. The cheeks have tufts
of lemon-yellow hairs. The hair under the throat is white, but does
not form the distinctive dense "ruff" seen in *C. erythrogaster*. The
belly is gray. The coat of the back, flanks, outer limb surfaces, and
dorsal proximal surface are a speckled golden olive-brown ("agouti"
coloration). The undersurface of the upper part of the tail is rust-red.
The lower half of the tail is typically grayish-white with a charcoal
tip, although there is considerable individual variation in this feature.
There are no recognized subspecies of *C. sclateri*.

Similar species. The coloration of this monkey's tail and its white
ear tufts are distinctive features, readily separating it from its close
relatives *C. erythrogaster* and *C. erythrotis*, and from the sympatric
C. mona. *Cercopithecus erythrogaster* has no white hairs on the ears
and no red coloration on the tail; *C. erythrotis* has red hairs on the ears,
and a tail that is red on both surfaces for most of its length. The mona
monkey is distinguished from Sclater's monkey by the white hair of its
chest, belly and inner limb surfaces, its whitish browband, and by its
prominent white rump spots.

Geographic Range

Sclater's monkey has a very restricted distribution, occurring only
in the forest and derived savanna zone of southeastern Nigeria between
the Niger and Cross rivers, as far north as the eastern Aboine River in
Ebonyi State at 6°17'N (Oates and Anadu, 1989; Tooze, 1995; Baker
and Olubode, 2008). Although the type specimen of the species was

Cercopithecinae

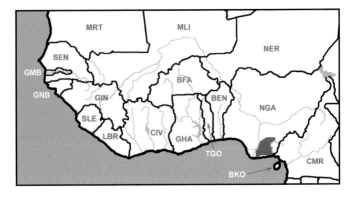

Fig. 8.94: Distribution of *Cercopithecus sclateri*.

reported as coming from Benin (almost certainly referring to Nigeria's Benin City, west of the Niger River, or the region of that city), no wild population of this animal has been found west of the Niger, where *C. erythrogaster* occurs. This type specimen (a pet that ended up in London Zoo) was probably brought to Benin, a major regional trade center, from east of the Niger. There is a small area of hybridization between *C. erythrogaster* and *C. sclateri* on the eastern edge of the Niger Delta, in Bayelsa State (Baker, 2005).

Natural History

Habitat. Sclater's monkey occurs in the lowland moist forest zone and in the forest-savanna mosaic zone to the north of the forest. In these zones it inhabits remnant patches of high forest, as well as swamp forests, riparian forests and sacred groves; all the sites from which it is known are below an elevation of 130 m. The monkey even occurs in some villages where only scattered trees remain, but where the monkeys are regarded as sacred (Oates *et al.*, 1992; Baker, 2005; Baker and Olubode, 2008).

Population. In walking surveys at three sites, Baker and Olubode (2008) had rates of encounter with *C. sclateri* of between 0.02 and 0.27/km. Density in the Edumanom Forest Reserve, Bayelsa State, has been estimated at 3.1–3.7 groups/km² (Baker *et al.*, 2011).

Field studies. Information on the natural history of *Cercopithecus sclateri* derives from survey work in southeastern Nigeria organized by

Oates, Zena Tooze and Lynne Baker (Oates and Anadu, 1989; Oates *et al.*, 1992; Tooze, 1995; Baker and Olubode, 2008; Baker *et al.*, 2009). There have been no extended field studies on the behavior of habituated groups.

Habitat use and locomotion. These small monkeys are typically arboreal and can be seen at all levels of the forest canopy. In areas where they are hunted, they spend much of their time in thick, low growth.

Vocalizations. Sclater's monkeys do not vocalize frequently, but adult males have a low-pitched loud call, described as a nasal honking or snorting.

Social organization. Short-term observations have found groups ranging in size from 3 to 30 individuals (Oates *et al.*, 1992; Baker *et al.*, 2009). Loud calls usually come from only one location in a group, suggesting that these guenons typically move in one-male groups.

Reproduction. The reproductive characteristics of *C. sclateri* have not been studied.

Cercopithecinae

Fig. 8.95: Sclater's monkey (*Cercopithecus sclateri*), Lagwa, Nigeria (photo by L. R. Baker).

Diet and ranging. Their feeding behavior is probably similar to that of other members of the *C. cephus* group; the diet, as such, includes fruits, insects, young foliage and flowers. In villages where Sclater's monkeys are considered sacred, they commonly move on the ground and their diet includes agricultural crop plants. They steal food from houses.

Association with other species. Sclater's monkeys have been seen moving in association with groups of putty-nosed monkeys (*C. nictitans*), mona monkeys (*C. mona*) and red-capped mangabeys (*Cercocebus torquatus*).

Predators. Most of the potential natural predators of *C. sclateri* are now very rare or extinct across its range, and humans are the main threat that these monkeys face.

Conservation Status

Cercopithecus sclateri is listed as Vulnerable on the IUCN Red List. Until the 1980's this species was believed to be on the verge of extinction and no wild populations had been located by scientists. Extensive surveys since 1987 have found it to still survive at more than 30 sites, but most of these sites are widely separated from one another and most support only limited areas of forest and small populations of monkeys (Oates *et al.*, 1992; Baker, 2005; Baker *et al.*, 2009). The area across which it occurs has one of the densest human populations in all of Africa. Although *Cercopithecus sclateri* is protected by traditional beliefs in a few Igbo and Ibibio villages, it does not occur in any area formally protected by government for wildlife conservation. It is found in the Edumanom Forest Reserve in Bayelsa State (87 km²), the Upper Orashi Forest Reserve in Rivers State (90 km²), and the Stubbs Creek Forest Reserve, Akwa Ibom State (310 km²). The forest in each of these reserves has been fragmented and degraded by farming and logging, and wildlife suffers from unregulated hunting (Baker, 2005).

Where to See It

Sclater's monkey can be observed most readily in the villages where it is protected as a sacred animal. These include Lagwa in Imo State and Akpugoeze in Enugu State, in each of which about 200 monkeys survive, and Ikot Uso Akpan in Akwa Ibom State. Akpugoeze is the most scenic location as the village also protects several sacred groves of large trees, associated with shrines to traditional deities.

Red-eared monkey
Cercopithecus erythrotis Waterhouse, 1838

Other English: Red-eared guenon, russet-eared guenon (or monkey)
French: Moustac à oreilles rousses
Spanish: Cercopiteco de nariz roja, cercopiteco de orejas rojas
West African languages: Ekwa, unklo (Boki, Nigeria); Onkot (Korup, Nigeria); Mbi'mbok (Ejagham, Nigeria and Cameroon); Nkwémese (Denya/Anyang, Cameroon and Nigeria); Nsop-nkem (Bakossi, Cameroon); Ntet (Bassa, Cameroon); Neesok (Banen, Cameroon); Nkoncha (Bubi, Bioko)

Identification (see Fig. 8.93, p.308)

This guenon has more red hair on its coat than any other member of the *cephus* geospecies. It takes its name from a fringe of rusty-red hairs on the outer margin of its ears, but this feature is hard to see on wild animals at a distance. In the wild, the most obvious feature of this monkey is its rusty-red (or russet) colored tail; ventrally, the tail is red for most of its length, although the dorsal surface is brownish red and the tip blackish. The bridge of the nose has a diamond-shaped patch of red hair. Bare skin around the eyes is bluish-gray, the lower cheeks have black hair, and the upper cheeks have tufts of white and lemon-yellow hair. The lips are pinkish. The crown of the head, the back, the dorsal tail base and upper outer leg surfaces are grayish with orange-brown speckles (resulting from dark gray and orange-brown banding on the hairs), with this coloration becoming grayer on the flanks. The throat is whitish. The lower arms are dark gray, and the belly is gray.

Subspecies. Two subspecies of *C. erythrotis* are recognized. The type form, *C. erythrotis erythrotis*, occurs only on the island of Bioko, and *C. erythrotis camerunensis* lives on the mainland in Nigeria and Cameroon. The coat of the Bioko form is markedly longer and softer than that of the mainland subspecies and generally darker. The tail is more uniformly red throughout its length.

Similar species. No monkey living sympatrically with *C. erythrotis camerunensis* in Nigeria has a red tail, but in Cameroon the related *Cercopithecus cephus cephus* occurs south of the Sanaga River, and in limited areas north of the upper Sanaga. *Cercopithecus c. cephus* also has a red tail, but differs from *C. erythrotis* in having a white mustache of hair below its nose, it lacks red hair on its nose, and has white rather than red ear tufts. *Cercopithecus mona* is sympatric with

C. erythrotis in Nigeria and Cameroon and is of similar size, but can be readily distinguished by its white undersurfaces, distinctive white rump spots and different male loud call. West of the Cross River in Nigeria, *C. erythrotis* is replaced by *C. sclateri*; these two species share several features and for some time Sclater's monkey was considered as a third subspecies of *C. erythrotis*. Sclater's guenon has white rather than red hairs fringing its ears, its nose spot is usually white (though sometimes tinged with red), and the lower half of its tail is grayish-white rather than red. Sclater's guenon also has a black band of hair extending across the back of the head (occipitally), between the ears; a feature lacking in *erythrotis*.

Geographic Range

Cercopithecus erythrotis occurs in the moist forest zone between the lower Cross River in Nigeria and the lower Sanaga River in Cameroon (*C. e. camerunensis*), as well as on the island of Bioko (*C. e. erythrotis*). It is found in forest on the northern tributaries of the Cross River up to about 6°20'N on the edge of the Obudu Plateau. Unlike *C. mona* and *C. nictitans* (or its close relative *C. petaurista* in Upper Guinea), it does not extend into the forest-savanna mosaic zone in gallery forest. The distribution of *C. erythrotis* extends just south of the Sanaga River near the river's mouth, between Tinaso and Lake Tisongo, and hybrids have been observed here between *C. erythrotis* and the closely-related *C. cephus* (Struhsaker, 1970a; Gartlan and Struhsaker, 1972).

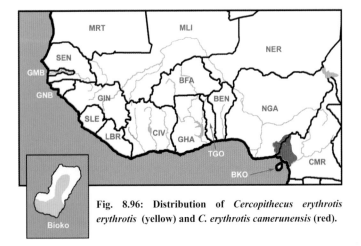

Fig. 8.96: Distribution of *Cercopithecus erythrotis erythrotis* (yellow) and *C. erythrotis camerunensis* (red).

Cercopithecinae

Natural History

Field studies. The behavior and ecology of this species remain relatively poorly known. No field study has yet been conducted on habituated individuals, and most information on its natural history has been obtained from surveys.

Habitat and population. On the mainland, the red-eared monkey appears to be more common in mature forest than in young secondary forest, perhaps due to competition with the mona monkey, which flourishes in disturbed and edge habitats. It also seems to be more abundant in the wetter forests in the south of its range than in more northerly semi-deciduous forests. Density in mature forest in the Ikenge area of Korup National Park, Cameroon, was estimated by Edwards (1992) to be 0.3 groups per km². Linder (2008) sighted *C. erythrotis* at a rate of 0.05–0.17/km at different sites in Korup. *Cercopithecus erythrotis* is the most abundant monkey on Bioko Island, where the

Cercopithecinae

Fig. 8.97: Cameroon red-eared monkey (*Cercopithecus erythrotis camerunensis*) in the collection of CERCOPAN, Calabar, Cross River State, Nigeria (photo courtesy of CERCOPAN).

Fig. 8.98: Bioko red-eared monkeys (*Cercopithecus erythrotis erythrotis*) in the Gran Caldera de Luba (photo by R. A. Bergl).

mona is absent. It occurs in mature and secondary lowland forest, in overgrown cacao plantations, and above an elevation of 2,000 m on Pico Basilé in montane forest and grassland (Butynski and Koster, 1994; Gonzalez-Kirchner, 1996). Gonzalez-Kirchner (1996) found it to be most common in mature lowland forest. Butynski and Koster (1994) sighted *C. erythrotis* at a rate of 0.13/km in surveys across Bioko. Maté and Colell (1995) had a sighting rate of 0.14/km in a limited forest area in the southeast of the island, while Butynski and Owens (2008) encountered 0.57 groups/km in the Gran Caldera de Luba in the southwest.

Habitat use. In Cameroon, Gartlan and Struhsaker (1972) observed *C. erythrotis* feeding and travelling lower in the forest canopy than other arboreal guenons. On Bioko, Gonzalez-Kirchner (1996) saw these monkeys at all heights in the canopy, and sometimes above 45 m, but most sightings were between 5 and 25 m; the species was also seen moving on the ground in montane grassland, and on the beaches of southern Bioko.

Vocalizations. Struhsaker (1970a) describes the adult male loud call as a "hack" given in single or multiple units. Adult females and juveniles give "chirp" alarm calls and "grunts" that may facilitate group cohesion.

Social organization. Struhsaker (1969) reports groups of "about 4 to more than 29" in southwestern Cameroon, with a single adult male, and Butynski and Koster (1994) report similar group sizes on Bioko. Maté and Colell (1995) observed groups of 8–12 in southeastern Bioko.

Reproduction. There is no published information on reproduction in wild *C. erythrotis*.

Diet and ranging. The limited information available on the feeding behavior of red-eared monkeys indicates that fruit is a major component of the diet (Gartlan and Struhsaker, 1972). Ranging patterns have not been studied.

Association with other species. In Cameroon, *C. erythrotis* groups are frequently seen moving in association with groups of other monkey species, especially other species of *Cercopithecus* (Gartlan and Struhsaker, 1972).

Predators. The main predator of red-eared monkeys today is *Homo sapiens*. Where crowned eagles (*Stephanoaetus coronatus*) and leopards still occur these are likely predators on *C. erythrotis*. Struhsaker (2000) has suggested that the relatively high frequency with which he observed red-eared monkeys on Bioko Island in 1992 that were moving alone and moving on the ground is related to the absence of crowned eagles and leopards there. Hunting of monkeys on Bioko occurred at very low levels in 1992, but has subsequently greatly increased.

Conservation Status

Cercopithecus erythrotis erythrotis and *C. erythrotis camerunensis* are each rated as Vulnerable on the IUCN Red List. Human hunting activity is intense across most of the range of the red-eared monkey, and monkeys are among the species hunted for the bushmeat trade. Hunting is often as severe inside protected areas as outside. Linder (2008) estimated that 1,025 *C. erythrotis* carcasses were sold annually at three markets in and around Cameroon's Korup National Park. This is the most common monkey species in the bushmeat market at Malabo on Bioko; in March-October 1991, Fa *et al.* (2000) recorded 622 *C. erythrotis* carcasses, while in the same period in 1996, following a great increase in shotgun hunting, only 279 carcasses were noted. Despite such hunting pressure, the red-eared monkey remains relatively common in some areas; like other members of the *C. cephus* group it is small, and adept at detecting hunters and hiding from them.

In addition to Korup National Park, *C. erythrotis* is present in Cameroon in the Takamanda and Mount Cameroon national parks, the proposed Ebo National Park, and the Banyang-Mbo Wildlife Sanctuary; in Nigeria in the Cross River National Park and the Afi Mountain Wildlife Sanctuary in Cross River State; and on Bioko, Equatorial Guinea, in the Pico Basilé National Park and Gran Caldera and Southern Highlands Scientific Reserve.

Where to See It

On the mainland, the red-eared monkey can be most readily observed in the Mundemba area of Cameroon's Korup National Park. This is the most widespread monkey on Bioko Island, where it is most easily seen in the Moka area on the edge of the Gran Caldera and Southern Highlands Scientific Reserve.

Fig. 8.99: Bioko red-eared monkey (*Cercopithecus erythrotis erythrotis*) in the Gran Caldera de Luba (photo by R. A. Bergl).

Cercopithecinae

Mustached monkey
Cercopithecus cephus (Linnaeus, 1758)

Other English: Mustached guenon, moustached monkey (British English)
French: Moustac à oreilles rousses

The mustached monkey is one of several primates characteristic of the forests of Central Africa that have a limited range extension in Cameroon to the north of the upper Sanaga River and to the east of the Mbam River, a region that has a mosaic of moist forest and derived savanna. Others are the talapoin, the De Brazza's monkey, and the Central African chimpanzee (*Pan troglodytes troglodytes*). The behavior of these primates has not been studied in this area, and they are thoroughly treated in the account by Gautier-Hion *et al.* (1999) of the natural history of the primates of Central Africa. Only a short description of the natural history of *C. cephus* is therefore given here.

Identification (see Fig. 8.93, p.308)

The most distinctive feature of this monkey is a chevron-shaped white mustache just below its nose. Of the three currently recognized subspecies of *C. cephus*, the one that intrudes into the south of our area is *C. cephus cephus*. This monkey is similar to *C. erythrotis* in its body size and proportions, but its dorsal surfaces are a slightly brighter orangey gray-brown (with a speckled appearance from hair banding) and its belly is a lighter gray color. Unlike *C. erythrotis*, the tail of *C. cephus cephus* is not almost entirely red; although the lower three-quarters of the tail are red, the proximal one-quarter is olive above and gray below. The cheek whiskers of *C. cephus* are more distinctly yellow than in *C. erythrotis*, there is black hair on the upper lip and on the sides of the muzzle, and blue rather than bluish-gray skin around the eyes.

Geographic Range and Subspecies

The distribution of *C. cephus* extends from the Upper Sanaga south and east through the moist forest zone to the Congo and Oubangui rivers. *Cercopithecus c. cephus* is the most widespread of the three subspecies, and is the only form occurring in Cameroon; *C. c. cephodes* is found in Gabon south of the Ogooué River, and *C. c. ngottoensis* in the Congo Republic and Central African Republic between the Sangha and

Cercopithecinae

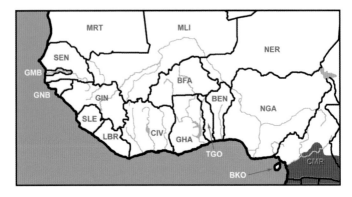

Fig. 8.100: Distribution of *Cercopithecus cephus cephus* in West Africa.

Oubangui rivers (Gautier-Hion *et al.*, 1999). On the south bank of the Lower Sanaga, between Tinaso and Lac Tisongo, Struhsaker (1970a) reports seeing monkeys with facial patterns intermediate between *C. erythrotis* and *C. cephus*, suggesting the presence of a hybrid zone in this area, and that the Sanaga River does not form a complete isolating barrier between these taxa.

Natural History

The mustached monkey has not been the subject of any careful studies in the small part of West Africa in which it occurs, but it has been studied in Gabon (Gautier-Hion *et al.*, 1981), and a good summary of its natural history is given in Gautier-Hion *et al.* (1999). Social groups range in size from 5 to 22 individuals, typically with one adult male. The monkeys spend much of their time in the lower forest strata (60% of observations were below 15 m in the canopy) and prefer to use areas with a dense understorey. Pulpy fruit makes up about 80% of the diet, and most of the remainder of this monkey's food is insects, which are consumed more frequently by females than by males. Struhsaker (1970a) describes the calls of *C. erythrotis* and *C. cephus* as being very similar, with a "hack" adult male loud call in both species. "Twitters" (often given as alarm calls by females and immature animals) are reported by Struhsaker to be more common in *C. cephus* than in *C. erythrotis*.

Conservation Status

Cercopithecus cephus (and the subspecies *C. cephus cephus*) are listed as of Least Concern in the IUCN Red List. Although like all forest monkeys in Central Africa it is subject to hunting for the bushmeat trade, its small size and habit of hiding in thick growth make it less vulnerable than many other monkey species. It is still widely spread and relatively common in many areas, and can thrive in disturbed forests.

Where to See It

The mustached monkey occurs only in the far southeast of the region covered by this guide, where it may be observed in the gallery forests of the 5,000-km² Mbam & Djerem National Park in Cameroon.

Fig. 8.101: A captive mustached monkey (*Cercopithecus cephus cephus*) in the research collection of Paimpont Biological Station, France (photo by J. F. Oates).

Cercopithecus nictitans geospecies

In addition to *Cercopithecus nictitans* (the putty-nosed monkey), Grubb (2006b) includes *C. mitis* (the blue monkey) in this geospecies. These are relatively large, long-tailed, arboreal guenons, widespread in African forests. *Cercopithecus nictitans* occurs in western Africa, and *C. mitis* in the central Congo Basin and the forests of eastern and southern Africa. Eastern and southern African forms in this group are sometimes separated from *C. mitis* as the species *C. albogularis*.

Local Representatives

Only the species *C. nictitans* occurs in West Africa. In this region there is a great deal of variation in the coloration of these monkeys, which has resulted in some confusion as to the number of subspecies that may sensibly be recognized. The type form, *C. n. nictitans*, is found throughout the forests of western equatorial Africa but also extends north of the Sanaga River into parts of the Cameroon Highlands. Following Oates (1988a) and Grubb *et al.* (2000), this book recognizes four other subspecies in our region: *C. n. martini* on Bioko Island, *C. n. ludio* in eastern Nigeria and southwestern Cameroon (including Mount Cameroon), *C. n. insolitus* in central and western Nigeria, and *C. n. stampflii* in Côte d'Ivoire and Liberia. Other publications have grouped *martini*, *ludio*, *insolitus* and *stampflii* together as one subspecies, *C. n. martini* (Dandelot, 1971; Grubb *et al.*, 2003), or as two, *C. n. martini* and *C. n. stampflii* (see Lernould, 1988).

Cercopithecinae

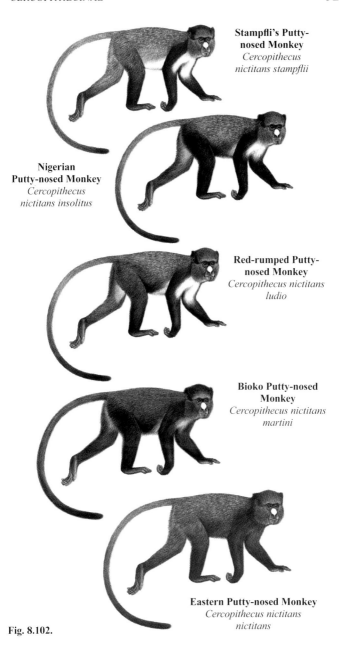

Stampfli's Putty-nosed Monkey
Cercopithecus nictitans stampflii

Nigerian Putty-nosed Monkey
Cercopithecus nictitans insolitus

Red-rumped Putty-nosed Monkey
Cercopithecus nictitans ludio

Bioko Putty-nosed Monkey
Cercopithecus nictitans martini

Eastern Putty-nosed Monkey
Cercopithecus nictitans nictitans

Fig. 8.102.

Cercopithecinae

Putty-nosed monkey
Cercopithecus nictitans Linnaeus, 1766

Other English: Putty-nosed guenon, putty-nose, greater white-nosed monkey (or guenon), greater spot-nosed monkey (or guenon)
French: Le pain à cacheter, hocheur
Spanish: Cercopiteco de nariz blanca
West African languages: Okin (Yoruba, Nigeria); Oken (Bini, Nigeria); Aka, akan (Ijaw, Nigeria); Ubit ebok (Ibibio, Nigeria); Eji (Boki, Nigeria); Nya'mbok (Ejagham, Nigeria and Cameroon); Obin (Korup, Cameroon and Nigeria); Lambili (Okwa, Nigeria); Dambele (Denya/Anyang, Cameroon); Ahendé (Bakossi, Cameroon); Nko (Bamileke, Cameroon); Nihinde (Banen, Cameroon); Binda (Bassa, Cameroon); Ñilá (Bubi, Bioko)

Identification (see Fig. 8.102, p.323)

As its name suggests, the most characteristic feature of this monkey is its bulbous nose bearing an oval patch of white hair (resembling, to some eyes, a blob of putty). The crown, shoulders, and back of putty-nosed monkeys are dark gray speckled with olive-yellow (due to the banding patterns on the hairs). The outer legs are also dark gray, with some light speckling, and the outer arms, distal part of the tail, and hands and feet are black.

The putty-nosed monkey is highly arboreal, and has the longest tail in relation to its body length of any of the forest guenons in our region. Among mainland populations, adult male head and body length averages 55 cm, with a 90-cm tail, and adult female head and body length averages about 48 cm, with an 80-cm tail (Gautier-Hion *et al.*, 1999; Napier, 1981). Adult males average about 6.7 kg in weight, and adult females 4.2 kg (Gautier-Hion *et al.*, 1999; Delson *et al.*, 2000; Bitty and McGraw, 2007). The Bioko population, *C. n. martini*, is typically smaller, with adult males having an average head and body length of 48 cm and tails of 74 cm, and females having an average head and body of 44 cm and tail of 65 cm. Average weight of Bioko adult males is 5.1 kg and of females 4.1 kg (Butynski *et al.*, 2009).

Subspecies. The subspecies vary in their coat patterns as follows.

Cercopithecus n. stampflii (Liberia and Côte d'Ivoire). Creamy white hair on the chest extends down to the groin. The back and tail are lighter than in the other subspecies. The tail is speckled gray for more than half its length, with only the tip completely black. There is no red hair in the perineal region.

Cercopithecus n. insolitus (Nigeria). These monkeys have a creamy-white chest and throat, and the white hair extends on the inner surface of the arms to the elbows. There are no red hairs at the base of the tail. The lower legs are dark gray to black, and the abdomen is gray.

Cercopithecus n. ludio (far eastern Nigeria and western Cameroon). The chest is pure white, with the white hair extending down the inner arms to the elbows. There is a distinct area of reddish-brown hairs on the inner thighs and below the base of the tail (the perineum). The lower legs are gray. Some individuals have a reddish or gold-speckled forehead, but this is a variable feature.

Cercopithecus n. martini (Bioko Island). The hair is longer than in mainland populations and the coat has a generally darker appearance. The upper back has fewer lighter speckles than other forms, and the fore-chest is dirty white or grayish-white. There are few or no reddish hairs on the perineum.

Fig. 8.103: A male Bioko putty-nosed guenon (*Cercopithecus nictitans martini*) feeding on the fruits of a fig (*Ficus* sp.) (photo by Tim Laman, ILCP Bioko RAVE).

Cercopithecinae

Cercopithecus n. nictitans (Central Africa). All underparts are gray. In some individuals, a few reddish hairs are present in the perineal region. The lower legs are gray.

Similar species. Putty-nosed monkeys can be distinguished from most of the other long-tailed forest guenons with which they share West African forest habitats by their conspicuous white nose-spots and drab olivey-gray dorsal surfaces. In two areas they overlap with other white-nosed guenons: *Cercopithecus petaurista* in parts of Liberia and Côte d'Ivoire, and *C. sclateri* in eastern Nigeria. Each of these other species (and their close relative *C. erythrogaster*) is smaller than *C. nictitans*, and they tend to forage in thick, low growth, whereas putty-noses more typically feed and move in the upper canopy. Unlike *C. nictitans*, *C. petaurista* and *C. sclateri* have fringes of white hairs around their ears. *Cercopithecus petaurista* can also be recognized by its prominent white throat ruff and the flashes of white hair below its ears, and *C. sclateri* by its red and light-gray tail. The similarly-sized *C. diana diana*, also an upper-canopy feeder, lacks a white nose, has a white thigh-stripe and white beard, red inner thighs and a chestnut lower back. *Cercopithecus campbelli*, *mona* and *pogonias* have pink lips.

Geographic Range

The species *C. nictitans* occurs in dry and moist forests from western Nigeria to the northern part of the Congo Basin, on Bioko Island, and in a limited area of Liberia and Côte d'Ivoire.

Cercopithecus n. stampflii is the subspecies found in northern Liberia and western Côte d'Ivoire. *Cercopithecus n. insolitus* is found in central-southern Nigeria, including the Niger Delta, with its range extending into the forest-savanna mosaic zone, especially in gallery forests along the Niger and Benue rivers and their tributaries. *Cercopithecus n. ludio* occurs east of the Cross River in Nigeria and in the forests of the Nigeria-Cameroon border region including Mount Cameroon; it is limited in the south by the Sanaga River. *Cercopithecus n. martini* is restricted to Bioko Island where today it may be limited to the south of the island. *Cercopithecus n. nictitans* has most of its distribution in the moist forests of western equatorial Africa and in the northern Congo Basin (where it reaches to the right bank of the Congo River and east to the River Itimbiri), but in the west of its range it crosses the upper Sanaga River and extends to the northern Cameroon Highlands. *Cercopithecus n. nictitans* appears to meet *C. n. ludio* in the vicinity of the Mambilla Plateau in Nigeria (Grubb *et al.*, 2000).

Cercopithecinae

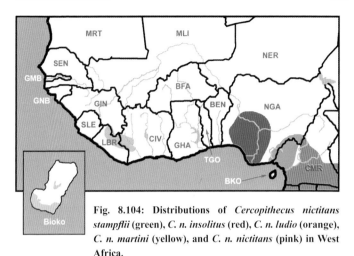

Fig. 8.104: Distributions of *Cercopithecus nictitans stampflii* **(green),** *C. n. insolitus* **(red),** *C. n. ludio* **(orange),** *C. n. martini* **(yellow), and** *C. n. nictitans* **(pink) in West Africa.**

Fischer *et al.* (2000) report that *C. nictitans* was observed in Comoé National Park in north-eastern Côte d'Ivoire in the past but that "it has not been seen within the last nine years" and might now be extinct there. Given the long-standing confusion in West Africa between *C. nictitans* and *C. petaurista*, and the lack of other reliable records from this area, this locality should be considered uncertain. Past records of this species from southern Bénin (Sayer and Green, 1984) appear to be spurious. Campbell *et al.* (2008) did not find any evidence for the presence of putty-nosed monkeys during a careful survey of southern Bénin and Togo in 2003.

Natural History

Habitat. Putty-nosed monkeys in Liberia and Côte d'Ivoire are particularly associated with the dry semi-deciduous forest to the north of the coastal moist forest zone. This may be the result of competitive exclusion by Diana monkeys in moister habitats (Oates, 1988a; Eckardt and Zuberbühler, 2004). In Nigeria and Cameroon putty-nosed monkeys have a widespread distribution, occurring in moist and semi-deciduous forests, in gallery forests in the forest-savanna mosaic zone north of the forest zone, and in sub-montane forests.

Field studies. The behavior of putty-nosed monkeys remains relatively poorly known. In West Africa, Winnie Eckardt has made a study in Taï Forest of competition between *C. nictitans stampflii* and

Cercopithecinae

C. diana (see, for example, Eckardt and Zuberbühler, 2004; Buzzard and Eckardt, 2007). Also in Taï, Anderson Bitty and Scott McGraw have studied putty-nose locomotion (Bitty and McGraw, 2007), and there have been some observations by J. Adanu and K. Arnold in Gashaka Gumti National Park in Nigeria (Arnold and Zuberbühler, 2006). Outside our area, in Gabon, Gautier-Hion (e.g., 1968, 1978, 1980; Gautier-Hion and Gautier, 1974) collected observations on the ecology of *C. nictitans nictitans* in the course of extended studies of primate community ecology.

Population. In the Lofa forests of northwestern Liberia, Dunn (1991) reports densities of 0.6–1.9 groups/km². These are considerably higher densities than those of Diana monkeys in the same forests, but lower than the densities of *C. campbelli* and *C. petaurista*. On the other hand, in the study area of the Taï Forest Monkey Project in Côte d'Ivoire, Buzzard and Eckardt (2007) report a density of only 0.05 groups/km² (or 0.45 individuals/km²). In Nigeria and Cameroon, *C. nictitans* densities also seem to vary greatly from place to place. Although reasons for this variation are not well understood, in general *C. nictitans* appears to be most abundant in the more mature closed-canopy forest habitats. For instance, Gartlan and Struhsaker (1972) found that it was the most frequently sighted monkey species in old secondary and mature forest at Idenau in Cameroon. In the lowland high forest of Cameroon's Korup National Park, *C. nictitans* was the monkey most frequently encountered by Edwards (1992), who reports densities of 1.0–1.5 groups/km² in the Ikenge area. Linder (2008) encountered *C. nictitans* in Korup at rates of 0.15, 0.18 and 0.22 groups/km in the Mundemba, Bajo and Ikenge areas respectively, and he estimated a density of 1.1–2.6 groups/km² in the Mundemba area. Maté and Colell (1995) obtained a sighting rate of 0.24 groups per km of *C. n. martini* in a small area of southeastern Bioko. In northeast Gabon, Gautier-Hion (1978) reports that the population density of *C. n. nictitans* is 20–40 individuals/km².

Habitat use. Putty-nosed monkeys predominantly use the middle and upper canopy of the forest rather than the lower canopy and understorey. At several sites where Gartlan and Struhsaker (1972) studied forest monkeys in western Cameroon, *C. nictitans ludio* consistently used higher average levels of the forest for traveling and feeding than all other sympatric guenons. In northeastern Gabon, almost all observations of *C. n. nictitans* by Gautier-Hion (1978) were made above 10 m in the canopy, and a majority came from above 20 m. A majority of sightings of *C. n. martini* in southeastern Bioko forests were made between 10 and 30 m in the canopy, and this was the most frequently seen monkey above a height of 20 m (Maté and Colell, 1995). In the Taï Forest, *C. n. stampflii* spent 75% of their time in the main canopy and in emergents (i.e., above a height of 15 m), compared to 51% for *C. diana*, 22% for *C. petaurista* and only 7% for *C. campbelli* (Bitty and McGraw, 2007).

Locomotion and posture. During travel and foraging, *C. nictitans* in the Taï Forest predominantly uses quadrupedal walking, along with climbing, leaping and running. This species was found to walk a little more frequently and to climb less frequently than *C. diana*. In general, the Taï putty-nosed monkeys had a similar locomotor repertoire to other sympatric forest guenons, but they moved on large branches much more often, and used twigs much less often, than the other species (Bitty and McGraw, 2007). Bitty and McGraw hypothesize that putty-nosed monkeys in Taï use upper canopy levels more than other *Cercopithecus* species in the forest because of direct competition from Diana monkeys.

Activity pattern. Data are not available on the activity budgets of West African *C. nictitans*.

Vocalizations. Adult male putty-nosed guenons produce two characteristic loud calls, the "pow" (or "pyow") and "hack" (Struhsaker, 1970a) and, much more rarely, a low frequency "boom" (Gautier, 1973). The "pow" is an explosive call, falling in pitch and, although short in duration (less than 0.5 sec), longer than the even shorter, sharper "hack" call. Commonly, "pows" precede "hacks", but the calls can also grade into one another. Females and young make "chirp" calls and grunts (Struhsaker, 1970a). The boom call of *C. nictitans* is less often heard than the similar call of *C. mitis* and members of the *C. mona* geospecies. The call may be made relatively rarely because of the common use of booms by sympatric forms of the mona group, and may be less easy for humans to hear because of its low pitch (around 110 Hz) (J.-P. Gautier, 1973, and pers. comm.). In the Taï Forest, *C. nictitans* males have also been found to give distinctive "tock" alarm calls to playbacks of crowned eagle calls, and "zeck" calls to playbacks of leopard calls (Eckardt and Zuberbühler, 2004).

Social organization and behavior. The average size of 13 groups of *C. nictitans ludio* counted by Struhsaker (1969) in Cameroon was 10.5, while eight counted groups of *C. n. nictitans* averaged 9.3. In both cases only a single adult male was seen in social groups. The

Cercopithecinae

C. n. stampflii study group of Eckardt and Zuberbühler (2004) in the Taï Forest, Côte d'Ivoire, contained 12 individuals, with one adult male and four adult females. This Taï group showed a higher rate of within-group affiliative interactions (mostly grooming among females) than any other *Cercopithecus* species in that area, while agonistic interactions were less frequent than in Diana monkeys (Eckardt and Zuberbühler, 2004). According to Gautier-Hion (1978), groups of *C. n. nictitans* in northeast Gabon contain an average of 20 individuals.

Reproduction. Butynski (1988, taken from Gautier-Hion, 1968) indicates a birth season for *C. n. nictitans* in notheast Gabon of December–April. Linder (2008, using unpublished records from captives at CERCOPAN in Nigeria) estimated the average age of first reproduction in putty-nose females as 4.7 years, with an annual birth rate of 0.41 young per year.

Ranging patterns. In Taï Forest, a *C. nictitans stampflii* study group covered a range of 93 ha over a seven-month period (Buzzard and Eckardt, 2007). In western Cameroon, Gartlan and Struhsaker (1972) report that putty-nosed guenons have considerably smaller home ranges than do sympatric groups of *C. pogonias*. In northeast Gabon, Gautier-Hion (1978) reports that *C. nictitans nictitans* groups have ranges of between 55 and 80 ha, with an average day range length of about 1,500 m.

Fig. 8.105: Red-rumped putty-nosed monkey (*Cercopithecus nictitans ludio*), Gashaka, Nigeria (photo by K. Arnold).

Cercopithecinae

Diet. Opportunistic observations in western Cameroon recorded a wide variety of fruits and flowers in the diet of *C. n. ludio*, as well as young leaves and bark (Gartlan and Struhsaker, 1972). More systematic data collected on a habituated group of *C. n. stampflii* in Taï Forest found that fruits made up 59% of the diet and invertebrates 31%, with the remainder of food intake being leaves, flowers and other items (Eckardt and Zuberbühler, 2004). The most frequently eaten fruits were those of *Dialium aubrevillei* (Leguminosae, Caesalpinioidae) and *Sacoglottis gabonensis* (Humiriaceae). Stomach contents of *C. nictitans nictitans* killed by hunters in northeastern Gabon contained an average of 81% fruits and seeds (by dry weight), 28% leaves and 8% animal matter (especially caterpillars) (Gautier-Hion, 1978). Leaf consumption increases in the May–August dry period in Gabon (Gautier-Hion, 1980)—this ability to use leaves as a major food source may explain how *C. nictitans* can exploit relatively dry forest habitats where fruits and insects may be seasonally scarce.

Association with other species. Like other West African forest guenons, groups of putty-nosed monkeys are very commonly seen in temporary associations with groups of other monkey species, and particularly with other species of *Cercopithecus*. In western Cameroon, Gartlan and Struhsaker (1972) found that *C. nictitans ludio* has a particularly strong tendency to associate with *C. erythrotis*. Such a pattern was considered probably related to the relative lack of competition between these species, given the much smaller size of *C. erythrotis* and its habit of foraging in thick growth in lower layers of the forest canopy. Alternatively, one or both species in such a foraging relationship can gain the anti-predator benefits of associating with other animals, without significantly increasing competition for food. In Taï Forest, Côte d'Ivoire, a *C. nictitans stampflii* group was found to have a near permanent association with a group of *C. diana*. The two species had similar diets, but Diana monkeys aggressively excluded putty-noses from favored food trees. Despite their high degree of competition, the two species apparently associate because of the benefits they gain in predator defence (Eckardt and Zuberbühler, 2004). In northeast Gabon, Gautier-Hion (1978) reports *C. nictitans nictitans* frequently associating with *C. pogonias* and *C. cephus*, with one group of *C. nictitans* and *C. pogonias* spending 97% of their time together over two three-month observation periods.

Predators. Gartlan and Struhsaker (1972) observed a successful attack of a crowned eagle (*Stephanoaetus coronatus*) on an adult female putty-nosed monkey in Southern Bakundu Forest Reserve,

Cercopithecinae

Cameroon. No putty-nosed monkey hair has been found in studies of leopard scat in Taï Forest, Côte d'Ivoire, but *C. nictitans* is rare in Taï, and the distinct responses of Taï putty-noses to playbacks of crowned eagles and leopards strongly suggests that these are predators on this species (Eckardt and Zuberbühler, 2004; Zuberbühler and Jenny, 2007). Today, humans are probably the chief predator of these monkeys where they occur in West Africa.

Conservation Status

The IUCN Red List rates *Cercopithecus nictitans* as a species of Least Concern. The Red List follows Grubb *et al.* (2003) in provisionally recognizing just two subspecies: *C. n. nictitans* and *C. n. martini*, with the latter including all the West African populations. *Cercopithecus n. nictitans* is listed as of Least Concern, but *C. n. martini* as Vulnerable.

The health of putty-nosed monkey populations varies very much from place to place. At some sites, such as Korup National Park in Cameroon, their populations seem to hold up in the face of heavy hunting pressure better than those of other forest monkeys, but they are less resistant to forest disturbance than species in the *C. mona* and *C. cephus* groups and are now a rare animal in many Nigerian forest reserves that have been subjected to heavy logging, farming and hunting. In Liberia and western Côte d'Ivoire competition with *C. diana* combines with habitat conversion and hunting to make them scarce. Thus, *C. n. stampflii* and *C. n. insolitus* each probably justify the status of Endangered subspecies. On Bioko, *C. n. martini* seems to be a naturally rare animal, possibly now restricted to the south of the island; given this very small range and increasing hunting pressure, this subspecies also merits Endangered status.

Cercopithecus n. stampflii is present in low densities in the northern part of Taï National Park in Côte d'Ivoire. Although reported by Agoramoorthy (1989) from Sapo National Park in Liberia, this may be a case of confusion with *C. petaurista*, because the species has not been documented in more recent surveys (Waitkuwait, 2001). *Cercopithecus n. insolitus* is found in Okomu National Park in western Nigeria, but is rare there. *Cercopithecus n. ludio* occurs in Nigeria's Cross River and Gashaka Gumti national parks, and in the Afi Mountain Wildlife Sanctuary. In Cameroon, it is found in Korup, Mount Cameroon and Takamanda national parks, the Banyang-Mbo Wildlife Sanctuary and the proposed Ebo National Park. In our area, *C. n. nictitans* occurs in

Cercopithecinae

the Mbam & Djerem National Park of Cameroon, while *C. n. martini* is found at low densities in Bioko's Gran Caldera and Southern Highlands Scientific Reserve.

Where to See It

In West Africa, *Cercopithecus nictitans* is probably most readily observed in Cameroon's Korup National Park and Nigeria's Gashaka Gumti National Park; each of these populations is best considered to belong to *C. n. ludio*, although the monkeys in Gashaka do not appear to have as conspicuously red coloration at the tail base as do those in Korup. *Cercopithecus n. stampflii* may be observed in the northern part of Taï National Park in Côte d'Ivoire. *Cercopithecus n. insolitus* may be glimpsed, or at least heard, by visitors to the Omo Forest Reserve in Ogun State Nigeria and, with luck, by visitors to the Okomu National Park in Edo State. *Cercopithecus n. nictitans* can be observed in gallery forests in the Mbam & Djerem National Park, Cameroon.

Cercopithecinae

Fig. 8.106: Eastern putty-nosed monkeys (*Cercopithecus nictitans nictitans*), Mbam & Djerem National Park, Cameroon (photo by R. Fotso).

Subfamily Colobinae
Colobine monkeys

The colobines include the colobus monkeys of Africa and the langurs, leaf monkeys and snub-nosed monkeys of Asia. The African colobus have very reduced or absent thumbs, from which their name is derived (from the Greek *kolobos*, meaning mutilated). The most significant way in which colobines differ from cercopithecines is in the anatomy and physiology of their digestive systems. Unlike the cercopithecines, which have simple stomachs, colobines have large, multi-chambered stomachs. The first part of this stomach (the forestomach) is especially enlarged and supports a population of bacteria that have the ability to digest plant cellulose and break down certain plant toxins. This digestive mechanism, combined with enlarged salivary glands and high-cusped molar teeth, allows colobines to subsist mainly or entirely on plant foods that include leaves and unripe fruits and seeds (see chapters in Davies and Oates, 1994).

Although some fossil colobines appear to have been terrestrial and lived in open habitats (Delson, 1994), the African colobus monkeys of today are highly arboreal and are restricted to forests (including gallery forests in the savanna zone). There are relatively few living species of colobus, and no more than three species ever co-occur in the same habitat; it is not unusual, by contrast, to find at least five cercopithecine species in the same African forest. Parts of the Ituri Forest in eastern Democratic Republic of Congo support three colobine species but 10 cercopithecines (Hart *et al.*, 1986).

The living African colobus species have hindlimbs that are relatively long compared to their arms, correlated with the importance of leaping in their locomotor repertoire. Their heads are relatively small, and their abdomens have a swollen ("pot-bellied") appearance as a consequence of the large size of their multi-chambered stomachs.

There are three main kinds of colobus monkeys, commonly known as the olive, red and black-and-white colobus. It has for long been appreciated that the olive and red species are more closely related to one another than either is to the black-and-white colobus, but there continues to be disagreement about how this pattern of relationships is best reflected in a taxonomy. Kingdon (1997) and Groves (2001) place each kind of colobus in its own genus: *Procolobus* for the olive, *Piliocolobus* for the red, and *Colobus* for the black-and-white. Oates *et al.* (1994) and Grubb *et al.* (2003), on the other hand, follow Kuhn

Colobinae

(1967) in treating *Procolobus* and *Piliocolobus* as subgenera of the genus *Procolobus*, to reflect the affinity of these two forms. The latter arrangement was also used by Ting (2008), whose analysis of mitochondrial DNA sequences suggest that that the *Colobus* line separated from the other living colobus around 7.5 MYA, and that *Procolobus* and *Piliocolobus* subsequently diverged around 6.4 MYA. This book also follows the two-genus arrangement of Kuhn.

Procolobus Rochebrune, 1887
Olive and red colobus monkeys

The olive and red colobus monkeys have a small but distinct extra stomach compartment, the praesaccus, at the mouth of the main forestomach sac (the saccus or fundus); this pouch, of uncertain function, is lacking in black-and-white colobus (Kuhn, 1964; Groves, 2007b). Female olive and red colobus display obvious sexual swellings, which are absent or very small in black-and-white colobus females. Adult males differ from those of black-and-white colobus in not having an enlarged larynx, and in not producing an associated loud call.

Subgenus *Procolobus* Rochebrune, 1887
Olive colobus

Procolobus verus geospecies

The species *Procolobus verus*, the olive colobus monkey, is the only member of this subgenus, and it is treated by Grubb (2006b) as the only member of a geospecies of the same name. The olive colobus is restricted to West Africa and in many ways is the most unusual of all the monkeys of the region. Among the special features that distinguish it from the red colobus monkeys are its small size (it is the smallest member of the subfamily Colobinae), and several features of its reproductive biology. For instance, the male's testes are very large in relation to body size, and are contained in a pendulous scrotum; the glans of the penis is unique among anthropoids in being adorned with small horny spicules; and uniquely among monkeys and apes, infant olive colobus do not travel clinging to their mother's coat, but are carried in her mouth. Hill (1952) has provided a very detailed anatomical description of this monkey. There are no recognized subspecies.

Colobinae

Olive Colobus
Procolobus verus

Temminck's Red Colobus
Procolobus badius temminckii

Bay Colobus
Procolobus badius badius

Miss Waldron's Red Colobus
Procolobus waldroni

Colobinae

Fig. 8.107.

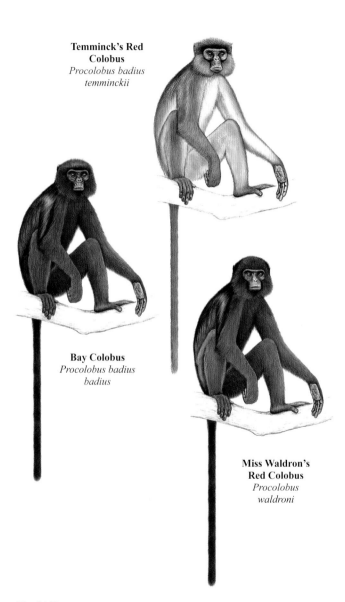

Temminck's Red Colobus
Procolobus badius temminckii

Bay Colobus
Procolobus badius badius

Miss Waldron's Red Colobus
Procolobus waldroni

Colobinae

Fig. 8.108.

Olive Colobus
Procolobus verus (Van Beneden, 1838)

Other English: Van Beneden's Colobus
French: Colobe de Van Beneden
West African languages: Kpengbai (Mende, Sierra Leone); Dorh-j'lay
(Sapo, Liberia); Esiè (Agni, Côte d'Ivoire); Asibe (Twi, Ghana); Zin
gbo (Fon, Bénin); Osiso, Osiko-siko, Osiosio (Ijaw, Nigeria)

Identification (see Fig. 8.107, p.336)

In addition to being the smallest of the living colobine monkeys, the
olive colobus is slender, but has a relatively large abdomen. Its short
hair is drably colored, with no striking pattern. The back and crown are
brown, ranging from light reddish-brown to dark grayish-brown, with
an olive-green tinge; in certain lighting conditions the back can appear
quite reddish-orange. There is considerable inter-individual variation
in this dorsal coloration, even in the same social group. The flanks,
outer limb surfaces and the dorsal surface of the tail are typically a
lighter olivey gray-brown, and the cheek whiskers and ventral surfaces
are a silvery gray. The crown of the head has a median crest of reddish
hair, most obvious in adult males, with grayish frontal whorls either
side of the crest. Infants are similar to adults in color, but darker, with
black-tipped hairs on dorsal surfaces.

The head of *Procolobus verus* is small and rounded; the facial
skin is hairless and dark gray; the ears are relatively large, rounded
and prominent, and have short, sparse hairs on their surfaces; there are
scattered long, black whisker-like hairs on the brow. The hands are
long, with extremely reduced thumbs, and the feet are especially long,
longer than either the thigh or the lower leg.

Olive colobus monkeys exhibit little sexual dimorphism in body
and tail length, with males and females having an average head and
body length of 45–50 cm, and a tail of 55–60cm. Adult males, however,
are slightly heavier than females, averaging 4.7 kg in weight, compared
to 4.2 kg in adult females (Oates *et al.*, 1990b). Adult females develop
large perineal swellings that can reach a length of >6 cm. Small
perineal swellings are also seen in juvenile males. Because of the habit
of females carrying their babies in their mouths, a mother carrying an
infant can, when glimpsed briefly at a distance, look like a monkey
with a very large head.

Colobinae

Fig. 8.109: Adult female olive colobus (*Procolobus verus*) in the Taï Forest, Côte d'Ivoire, displaying a large perineal swelling (photo W. S. McGraw).

Similar species. When seen clearly in the field it is difficult to confuse this monkey with any other, but its secretive nature means that it is often only glimpsed in thick vegetation. In these cases it may be confused with some of the smaller guenons with which it often associates; for instance, there are similarities between the olive colobus and spot-nosed monkey (*Cercopithecus petaurista*) in the color of hair on the back. However, when good views are available, the spot-nosed monkey is readily distinguished by its white nose spot, white flashes below the ears, and white throat ruff. The similarly-sized Campbell's monkey (*Cercopithecus campbelli*) has a pinkish rather than gray muzzle. In poor light the olive colobus can also be confused with a young western red colobus monkey, given similarities in the body shape and proportions of these species, but in good light the black back and red limbs and undersurfaces of the red colobus are distinctive. Red colobus typically use the upper canopy of the forest more than does the olive colobus. None of these species carry their young in their mouths.

Geographic Range

The olive colobus occurs in the moist forest zone from southeastern Sierra Leone east through Liberia, south-western Guinea and southern Côte d'Ivoire to the Ghana-Togo border (Oates, 1981). It has also been observed in isolated dry forest patches in southern Bénin, and hunters' reports given to Campbell *et al.* (2008b) suggest that it may also occur in part of eastern Togo. There are two known populations in Nigeria: in the central Niger Delta and the Ayangba area of Benue State (Menzies, 1970; Anadu and Oates, 1988). It is possible that the olive colobus has (or once had) a wider distribution in Nigeria and has been overlooked because of its secretive habits. So far, no obvious differences have been observed in the appearance of populations across this wide range, and subspecies are not recognized. Average body weights of individuals collected in Ghana are, however, lower than those collected in Liberia. Almost all known populations occur south of 8.5°N, with the exception of a record from the Comoé National Park in northeastern Côte d'Ivoire (Fischer *et al.*, 2000).

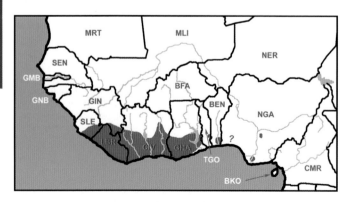

Fig. 8.110: Distribution of *Procolobus verus*.

Natural History

Habitat. The olive colobus inhabits moist forests, swamp forests, and forest galleries in the dry forest zone It is most often encountered in dense woody vegetation near water, and occurs in heavily disturbed as well as more mature forests (Booth, 1957; Grubb *et al.*, 1998; Kuhn, 1964; Oates 1981). It has not been reported at high elevations.

Field studies. This was one of the first African monkeys to have its natural history described, based on extensive observations of unhabituated animals by Angus Booth in the Gold Coast (now Ghana) in the 1950s (Booth, 1957). Subsequently, Anh Galat-Luong made pilot studies in Côte d'Ivoire in the late 1970s, and followed these with systematic data collection of habituated animals in the Taï Forest in 1979–1982, as part of a study of three sympatric colobus species (Galat-Luong, 1983; Galat and Galat-Luong, 1985). Soon after Galat-Luong's observations began, JFO made pilot studies in Sierra Leone, and then collected data on a habituated group on Tiwai Island in 1982–1985 (Oates, 1988b, 1994a; Oates and Whitesides, 1990). Amanda Korstjens studied several groups in the Taï Forest in 1994–1999, and—like Galat-Luong before her—comparing olive colobus with red and black-and-white species (Korstjens, 2001; Korstjens and Noë, 2004; Korstjens and Schippers, 2003).

Population. Where the olive colobus does occur, it is rarely common. Densities of 14–21 individuals/km² have been reported from Taï National Park, Côte d'Ivoire (Galat and Galat-Luong, 1985; Korstjens, 2001), and of 7/km² from Tiwai Island Wildlife Sanctuary in Sierra Leone (Oates *et al.*, 1990b). In Kakum National Park, Ghana, 0.06–0.19 groups were encountered per km of transect walked (Oates *et al.*, 2000a).

Habitat use. Booth (1957) noted that olive colobus normally feed and travel in the lower layers of the forest. At Tiwai Island, 75% of observations of this species were from below a height of 20 m (Oates and Whitesides, 1990) and in the Taï forest 77% of records came from below that height (McGraw, 1998b). Both at Taï and at Tiwai, olive colobus used lower heights in the canopy for foraging than for travelling; as Booth (1957) reported long ago, much of their feeding takes place in dense low growth and liana tangles. When foraging, olive colobus at Taï were observed to use twigs as supports 44% of the time. This compares with 38% of the time in red colobus monkeys and 34% in black-and-white colobus (McGraw, 1998b).

Colobinae

Locomotion and posture. Olive colobus typically intersperse spells of resting or feeding, when they are relatively static, with periods of rapid movement when they run and leap through the forest canopy. In the Taï Forest, McGraw (1996, 2007) found *P. verus* to leap more often than was observed in two sympatric colobus species and four cercopithecines. When they are not moving, olive colobus, like other colobines, spend the great majority of their time sitting rather than standing.

Activity pattern. The activity and ranging patterns of an olive colobus group are strongly influenced by the behavior of the other species with which they typically associate. Groups observed in the Taï forest and at Tiwai spent between 13 and 28% of their day feeding, 30–59% resting, 19–30% moving and 4–7% socializing (McGraw, 1998b; Oates and Korstjens, 2012).

Vocalizations. Olive colobus are quiet monkeys, producing infrequent high-pitched "whee" and lower-pitched "ooo" calls. The most distinctive call is the adult male's "laugh", which typically consists of a series of three or four "ooo-er" units that rise in pitch to a penultimate "whee", before dying away to an "ooo" (Hill and Booth, 1957; JFO pers. obs.). These laughing calls often follow calling by male guenons (Oates and Whitesides, 1990).

Social organization. Social groups of olive colobus are typically small, but very variable in size. Group composition is fluid. Across the species' range in West Africa, group sizes have been seen to range from 2–15 individuals, but most groups have less than ten monkeys. Mean reported group size in Taï is seven, and a typical Tiwai group is reported to have six monkeys; one to three adult males can be found in a single group (Galat and Galat-Luong, 1985; Oates *et al.*, 1990b; Oates, 1994a; Korstjens and Schippers, 2003; Korstjens and Noë, 2004). Young olive colobus of both sexes disperse from their natal groups and adult females often move between groups; adult males are a more stable element of groups (Oates, 1994a; Korstjens and Schippers, 2003).

Social behavior. Olive colobus show relatively weak levels of intra-group cohesion, and overt social interactions in groups are relatively rare. Grooming is the most frequently observed interaction, and is most common when they congregate at sleeping sites and between males and females (especially when in consortships) (Oates, 1994a).

Interactions between groups. Given the fluid nature of their social system and their cryptic behavior, it is not clear that olive colobus groups defend territories, but adult males may defend the areas they are using against other males. When adult male olive colobus accompanying different Diana monkey groups approach each other, the males exchange laughing calls, and may make open-mouth threats, moving their heads from side to side, while the females remain hidden (Oates, 1994a; Korstjens and Noë, 2004).

Reproduction. The studies at Tiwai Island and the Taï Forest indicate that olive colobus are at least to some extent seasonal breeders, with most mating concentrated in the wet season, and most births in the dry season. Females display periodic perineal swellings that can persist for up to 20 days (median swollen period in Taï is 17 days) and reoccur over several months; these swellings are sometimes seen in pregnant females (Korstjens, 2001; Korstjens and Noë, 2004). At Tiwai, females with large swellings were seen only in the middle of the wet season in June through August. Swollen females are often followed closely by adult males for long periods, and during these consortships mating is frequent (sometimes occurring >40 times/day). If there is more than one adult male in the group, both may mate with the same female within a few minutes of each other (Oates, 1994a; Korstjens and Noë, 2004). Solitary swollen females may visit a group briefly and mate before leaving again (Korstjens and Schippers, 2003). The length of the gestation period is not known with any precision, but based on the timing of most mating and births observed at Tiwai is estimated to be 160–170 days, similar to other colobines (Harvey *et al.*, 1987). Very young infants have been observed in olive colobus study groups at Tiwai and Taï in the October–April period, which straddles the main December–February dry season. Weaning takes place at about 12 months (Korstjens, 2001).

Mouth carriage of infants. The mother's habit of carrying small infants in her mouth was first noted by Booth (1957). The mother grasps the infant by the skin of its flank, and the infant tucks itself against the mother's neck with its tail wrapped around her neck and upper back (Oates, 1994a). This behavior continues until infants are at least 10 months old. Booth notes an infant of 400 g that was sometimes carried in the mother's mouth and sometimes clinging to her belly. Booth has suggested that this behavior occurs because the infant olive colobus would have difficulty clinging to its mother because of its rudimentary thumb and her short coat, and would therefore be in danger of being dislodged as the mother moves through dense vegetation.

Colobinae

Ranging patterns. Average daily path lengths of two Taï groups travelling with Diana monkeys were 1,202 and 1,222 m (Korstjens, 2001). Annual home range sizes of groups associating with Diana monkeys were between 29 and 58 ha in size in the Taï forest, and 28 ha at Tiwai Island (Galat and Galat-Luong, 1985; Oates, 1994a; Korstjens, 2001).

Diet. The olive colobus diet consists predominantly of young leaves from trees and climbing plants, with liana leaves as a year-round staple. Seeds can be important, especially in the dry season. Of 521 identified food items eaten by a group at Tiwai Island, 59% were young leaves, 15% other leaves or leaf parts, 14% seeds, and 7% flowers (Oates 1988b). During feeding, members of a social group are often highly dispersed. The four most common food items recorded at Tiwai during scan sampling were the young leaves of the trees *Terminalia ivorensis* (Combretaceae) and *Sapium aubrevillei* (Euphorbiaceae), the young leaves of the climber *Acacia pennata* (Mimosoideae, Leguminosae), and the petioles of mature leaves from *S. aubrevillei* (Oates, 1988b). Tree species most heavily fed on in the Taï forest were *Dialium aubrevillei* (Caesalpinioideae, Leguminosae), *Scytopetalum tieghemii* (Scytopetalaceae) and *Napoleona leonensis* (Lecythidaceae) (Korstjens, 2001).

Association with other species. One of the several peculiarities of olive colobus is that they almost always move in close association with groups of other species, particularly guenons (*Cercopithecus* spp.). For instance, during observations of one olive colobus group at Tiwai Island (on 33 days) and one Diana monkey group (on 36 days), members of one species were seen within 50 m of members of the other on more than 80% of observational samples (Oates and Whitesides, 1990). In Taï National Park, two olive colobus study groups were within 50 m of members of Diana groups 90–100% of the time (Korstjens and Schippers, 2003). Olive colobus can also be seen attached to groups of *Cercopithecus campbelli*, *C. mona*, *C. nictitans* and/or *C. petaurista* (Booth, 1957; Oates, 1982; Oates and Whitesides, 1990). Association is the result of orientation of the olive colobus towards the guenons, which mostly appear to ignore them. This behavior probably provides advantages to the colobus in terms of the early detection of potential predators, while at the same time not appreciably increasing costs from interspecific competition because of the relatively low overlap between the diets of the colobus and the guenons.

Predators. Crowned eagles (*Stephanoaetus coronatus*), leopards (*Panthera pardus*) and chimpanzees (*Pan troglodytes*) have all been reported to prey on olive colobus in the Taï forest (Boesch and Boesch, 1989; Shultz *et al.*, 2004). Chimpanzees prey on olive colobus much less frequently, however, than they do on red colobus monkeys, even when the lower density of olive colobus is taken into account (Boesch and Boesch, 1989). Schultz *et al.* (2004) have calculated that 1.0% of the olive colobus population are preyed on each year by leopards, and 4.8% by crowned eagles.

Conservation Status

On the IUCN Red List the olive colobus is listed as Near Threatened. Because this species flourishes in disturbed forest, swamps and riverine growth it is less negatively affected than some other forest anthropoids by logging, but like all West African forest mammals its overall population must be in decline from the ever-increasing conversion of forest habitat to farmland. Olive colobus do not seem to be primary targets for human hunters, probably in part because of their relatively small size and their cryptic appearance and behavior. But they may also be actively avoided as prey by some hunters; in Sierra Leone some people report that they will not eat olive colobus because they have a bad taste, or because you get sick if you eat them. The olive colobus skin does have a pungent smell and this may be another facet of their many adaptations to reduce the threat of predation.

Procolobus verus occurs in several protected areas in the Upper Guinea forest zone, including Tiwai Island Wildlife Sanctuary and the Gola Forest National Park in Sierra Leone, Sapo National Park in Liberia, Taï National Park in Côte d'Ivoire, and the Ankasa and Bia conservation areas and Kakum National Park in Ghana.

Where to See It

Even in habitats where this species is not uncommon it can be difficult to see because of its cryptic behavior. Among accessible sites where it can be relatively easily observed are Tiwai Island Wildlife Sanctuary in Sierra Leone, Taï National Park in Côte d'Ivoire, and Kakum National Park in Ghana. One group can often be seen quite readily in the degraded 10 ha forest surrounding the Oklu Lodge on Monkey Hill in the coastal city of Sekondi-Takoradi, Ghana, where the monkeys sometimes sleep in the same large cotton trees (*Ceiba pentandra*) as a number of vultures and kites.

Colobinae

Subgenus *Piliocolobus* Rochebrune, 1887
Red colobus

The red colobus are relatively large, highly-arboreal forest monkeys that generally prefer the canopy of old-growth forest. All of these monkeys have some red or reddish hair somewhere on their coat, but the shade, extent and patterning of this coloration varies greatly. Around the time of ovulation, red colobus females develop obvious perineal swellings that vary in size across populations but which are especially large in West African populations (Struhsaker, 2010). At least in young males of *P. badius badius* there is also a raised area (supported by subcutaneous adipose tissue) between the ischial callosities and the anus that resembles a female ovulatory swelling; this can result in these individuals being mistaken for adult females (Kuhn, 1972).

Many geographically distinct forms of red colobus occur across Africa from Senegal in the west to Kenya and Tanzania in the east, and there has been very great disagreement as to the classification of these forms. Rahm (1970) lists one species and 14 subspecies; Dandelot (1971) lists five species, three "potential" species and an additional six subspecies (a total of 14 forms); and Kingdon (1997) has eight species and an additional 11 subspecies. In a recent revision, employing the phylogenetic species concept, Groves (2007b) lists 16 species, one of which has two subspecies. Ting (2008), using evidence from mitochondrial DNA, recognizes five species and an additional 13 subspecies. As discussed in Section 3, this book follows Groves (2007b).

Procolobus badius geospecies

All the different geographic forms of red colobus are allopatric, leading Grubb (2006b) to place them all in one geospecies, *Procolobus badius*.

Local Representatives

In recent studies there has been general agreement that there are six different forms of red colobus in the area covered by this guide, each occupying a different geographical area, but there is not agreement as to the number of distinct species into which these forms may best be grouped. Groves (2007b), who is followed here, recognizes five species in West Africa: *Procolobus badius*, with two subspecies (*P. b. temminckii* in Senegal, the Gambia and Guinea-Bissau, and *P. b. badius* in Guinea, Sierra Leone, Liberia and western Côte d'Ivoire); *P. waldroni* in eastern Côte d'Ivoire and western Ghana; *P. epieni* in the Niger Delta; *P. pennantii* on Bioko Island; and *P. preussi* in eastern Nigeria and Cameroon.

Most West African red colobus populations exhibit relatively low levels of sexual dimorphism, but there is much variation within and between populations. In adults, head and body lengths are typically 50–60 cm, and tail lengths 55–70 cm. Adult males weigh slightly more than females; for instance adult males of *P. b. badius* average 8.4 kg in weight while females average 7.8 kg (Delson *et al.*, 2000). East African forms show greater sexual dimorphism (Struhsaker, 2010).

Colobinae

Fig. 8.111: Temminck's red colobus (*Procolobus badius temminckii*), Abuko Nature Reserve, The Gambia (photo by E. D. Starin).

Western red colobus
Procolobus badius (Kerr, 1792)

The two subspecies of western red colobus, *P. badius badius* and *P. badius temminckii*, are each given an individual account in this book. Each form has been the subject of several field studies, and there are considerable differences in the habitats of each form in the core parts of their ranges: The Gambia and adjacent parts of Senegal in the case of *P. b. temminckii*, and Liberia and adjacent parts of Sierra Leone and Côte d'Ivoire in the case of *P. b. badius*. In southern Senegal and Guinea-Bissau, red colobus occur that are intermediate in coloration between the "typical" ashy gray and orange pattern of *P. b. temminckii* in the north of its range, and the much darker coloration of typical *P. b. badius* to the south. Harding (1984) reports red colobus monkeys in the Kilimi area of Sierra Leone that are dark gray above and reddish-orange on the sides and flanks, similar to those in Guinea-Bissau. It is apparently this gradation that leads Groves (2007b) to group *temminckii* and *badius* in the same species, while separating all other forms of red colobus into different species.

Temminck's red colobus
Procolobus badius temminckii (Kuhl, 1820)

French: Colobe bai de Temminck
West African languages: Ironkukai (Diola, Senegal); Fatafaré, pataparé (Fula, Guinea-Bissau, Senegal; Sossé, Senegal); As (Balante, Guinea-Bissau); Sera (Papel, Guinea-Bissau)

Identification (see Figs. 8.107 & 108, pp.336 –37)

Temminck's red colobus monkeys are typically an orangey rust red color on the outer surfaces of the forearms and lower legs, and on the cheeks; the tail is also red, but of a slightly darker hue than the limbs. The back is dark ashy gray, tinged with brown, and this gray color extends to the outer surfaces of the upper thighs and posterior part of the upper arms; the anterior of the upper arms is rust-red. The shoulders and crown of the head are also gray (and somewhat darker than the back). The back of the crown is tinged with red, and there is a black band of hair on the brow. The flanks are light red-brown and the chest is creamy-white; the white coloration extends to the midline of the abdomen and inner surfaces of the limbs, and there is also white

Colobinae

hair in the perineal region. There is considerable variation between individuals in coloration (see also "Geographic Range").

Similar species. There is little possibility of confusing other species with Temminck's red colobus. There is no other very similar monkey in its range. The patas monkey (*Erythrocebus patas*) is of somewhat similar size and parts of its coat are a similar shade of red to Temminck's colobus. Patas, however, are highly terrestrial monkeys, sometimes using trees, whereas Temminck's colobus is highly arboreal, sometimes using the ground. The back and crown of Temminck's colobus are gray, while in patas the back and crown are foxy red-brown. In the south of its range Temminck's colobus co-occurs with black-and-white colobus monkeys (*Colobus polykomos*), but these black-and-white colobus have no red hair and a white tail.

Geographic Range

Temminck's red colobus occurs from around 13°40'N in the Saloum Delta in Senegal, south through The Gambia to the Casamance region of southern Senegal and then south again across Guinea-Bissau to the Cacine basin near the border with the Republic of Guinea; they may extend as far south as northern Sierra Leone (see below) (Gatinot, 1974; Gippoliti and Dell'Omo, 1996, 2003; Diouck, 2001; Galat-Luong and Galat, 2005). To the east, the distribution extends to around 13°W along the Gambia River in Niokolo Koba National Park, Senegal, and along the Koulountou River on the border of Senegal and Guinea; however, Temminck's colobus has disappeared in recent years from east of the Niokolo Koba National Park (Galat *et al.*, 2009). In

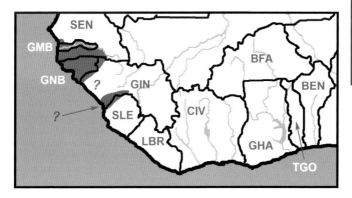

Fig. 8.112: Distribution of *Procolobus badius temminckii*.

Colobinae

Fig. 8.113: Temminck's red colobus (*Procolobus badius temmincki*), Abuko Nature Reserve, The Gambia (photo by R. A. Mittermeier).

the southern part of its range the coloration of these monkeys becomes darker, with a darker gray back and richer red arms and tail (Monard, 1938; Groves, 2007b).

Natural History

Habitat. Temminck's red colobus inhabits gallery forests and relic forest patches in the savanna woodland landscape of the Sudanian vegetation zone in Senegal, where important large trees are *Khaya senegalensis* and *Daniellia oliveri* (Gatinot, 1976), and it occurs in similar habitats in the coastal region of the Guinean forest-savanna mosaic zone to the south of Senegal.

Field studies. Studies of Temminck's red colobus began in 1969, when Thomas Struhsaker made observations in the Casamance province of Senegal and in The Gambia for 26 days in December 1969–January 1970. Those pioneering studies were followed by more intensive observations in the small Abuko Nature Reserve, The Gambia, by Virginia Gunderson in 1973–1974 (Gunderson, 1977) and in the Fathala Forest within the Saloum Delta National Park, Senegal, by Bernard Gatinot in 1973–1974 and 1975–1976 (Gatinot, 1976, 1977). In 1978, Dawn Starin began a long-term study at Abuko, which extended to 1983, with later follow-up visits (Starin, 1981, 1988, 1991, 2009). In 1986–2002, Anh Galat-Luong and Gérard Galat made further observations at Fathala, Senegal, and in The Gambia, and conducted surveys over a wide area of Senegal (Galat-Luong, 1988; Galat-Luong and Galat, 2005; Galat *et al.*, 2009). Other information on this monkey's natural history has come from surveys in 1981–1982 in the Kilimi region of Sierra Leone (Harding, 1984), and in 1994 in the Cantanhez Forest region of Guinea Bissau (Gippoliti and Dell'Omo, 1996, 2003).

Population. Extrapolating from the home range sizes of a small number of studied groups, population densities of 81–480/km^2 have been estimated (Galat-Luong, 1988), but larger landscapes with unoccupied habitat would have lower densities.

Habitat use. In relatively undisturbed gallery forest, Temminck's red colobus spend much of their time in the upper levels of the canopy (although in these forests in Fathala, Senegal, mean tree height is only 12 m). In more degraded habitats, lower levels are used for feeding and moving, and the monkeys will come to the ground to travel from one group of trees to another and, occasionally, to feed (Galat-Luong, 1988; Galat-Luong and Galat, 2005).

Colobinae

Activity pattern. Procolobus b. temminckii resembles other forms of red colobus in its activity budget. Starin (1991) found Abuko monkeys spent 51% of their time resting, 32% feeding, and 8% moving.

Vocalizations. Struhsaker (1975, 2010) reports that *P. b. temminckii* is similar in its vocal repertoire to *P. b. badius*, each form commonly producing "chirp" and "nyow" (or "bark") calls. *Procolobus b. temminckii* however, makes "whine," "whimper" and "coo" calls not yet heard in other red colobus. Like *P. b. badius*, Temminck's red colobus females also make quavering calls during copulation (Starin, 1991).

Social organization. Group sizes of 12–28 individuals have been reported from several sites in The Gambia and Senegal by Struhsaker (1975), Gatinot (1977), Starin (1981, 1991), and Galat-Luong (1988); all these groups contained two or more adult males. One exceptional group observed by Gatinot (1977) in the Fathala forest, Senegal, contained 62 individuals, including 13 adult males. Starin (1981, 1991) records group structure as being relatively fluid in Abuko (especially during a mating season), with both adult females and males transferring between groups.

Social behavior. In the study group at Abuko, females performed the majority of grooming, directing 42% of grooming to adult females, 26% to two adult males, and 26% to their own offspring (Starin, 1991). Adult males groomed others infrequently, and never groomed each other. Among Abuko females there was a dominance order, with some consistently winning aggressive interactions, and others losing.

Interactions between groups. The Abuko focal study group shared about 60% of its range with two other groups (Starin, 1991). When they met, groups would supplant each other based on apparent dominance relationships rather than on location. Males and females both took part in aggressive interactions during encounters, directing their aggression towards males in the opposing group.

Reproduction. Female Temminck's red colobus display large periodic perineal swellings (up to 10 cm in length), presumably related to ovulation (Starin, 1991). In Abuko, adult females solicited copulations with courtship displays, as well as making quaver calls. The gestation period is 173–174 days (Starin, 1988).

Colobinae

Ranging patterns. Two groups with known home ranges at Abuko used 34 and 11 ha respectively over a four-year period (Starin, 1991).

Diet. In the Fathala forest, young leaves and leaf buds have been recorded as major dietary items, with fruits, flowers and mature leaves of varying importance. Species most often consumed were the trees *Erythrophleum guineense* (Leguminosae, Caesalpinioideae), *Pterocarpus erinaceus* (Leguminosae, Papilionoideae) and *Ficus glumosa* (Moraceae) (Gatinot, 1977). The annual diet of the main study group in the Abuko Nature Reserve included 89 plant species; 42% of the diet was fruits and seeds, 35% young leaves and leaf buds, 11% mature leaves, and 9% flowers and flower buds. The most frequently eaten species were *Parinari excelsa* (Chrysobalanaceae), *Ficus trichopoda* (Moraceae) and *Detarium senegalense* (Leguminoase, Caesalpinioideae) (Starin, 1991)

Association with other species. In Kilimi, Sierra Leone, Harding (1984) always observed red colobus in association with black-and-white colobus (*Colobus polykomos*), although black-and-white groups were commonly observed without accompanying red colobus. In the Cantanhez Forest, Guinea-Bissau, groups of *P. b. temminckii* also were often seen in close association with groups of *Colobus polykomos* (Gippoliti and Dell'Omo, 1996).

Colobinae

Fig. 8.114: Temminck's red colobus (*Procolobus badius temminckii*), Abuko Nature Reserve, The Gambia (photo by E. D. Starin).

Predators. In the geographical region where Temminck's red colobus occurs there is a dense, long-settled human population and potential natural predators of red colobus are scarce. As colobus habitat has declined and the monkeys have taken to moving more frequently on the ground, they have been increasingly subjected to predation by dogs and spotted hyenas (Galat-Luong and Galat, 2005).

Conservation Status

Procolobus b. temminckii is listed as Endangered on the IUCN-SSC Red List. Temminck's red colobus is being badly affected by degradation and the conversion of its woodland habitat as a result of cultivation, tree cutting, cattle grazing and fire. Gallery forest in its Fathala habitat in Senegal had been reduced in 1989 to less than 25% of its 1969 area. In response, the red colobus use open habitat much more often, travel on the ground, and venture into mangrove swamps where they had not previously been observed (Galat-Luong and Galat, 2005). More recent surveys have documented a loss of many populations in the northern part of *P. b. temminckii*'s former range, with its habitat fragmented by the activities of a growing human population (and especially the spread of groundnut cultivation) and a drying climate (Galat *et al.*, 2009). Hunting of this red colobus for meat has increased to the south in Guinea-Bissau (D. Starin, pers. comm., 2010).

Temminck's red colobus occurs in several protected areas, including in Senegal the Saloum Delta National Park (within the Mab Saloum Delta Biosphere Reserve) and Niokolo Koba National Park, in The Gambia the Abuko Nature Reserve and River Gambia National Park, and in Guinea the Badiar National Park across the border from Niokolo Koba.

Where to See It

Temminck's red colobus can most readily be observed in the Abuko Nature Reserve in The Gambia, on the outskirts of the capital Banjul, and also in the small Bijilo Forest Park about 11 km from Banjul. The Fathala Forest, an important long-term study site for red colobus in Senegal, is in the Saloum Delta National Park, about 200 km south of Dakar.

Colobinae

Bay colobus
Procolobus badius badius (Kerr, 1792)

Other English: Western red colobus, Upper Guinea red colobus
French: Colobe bai
West African languages: Nduwei (Mende, Sierra Leone); Duweh
(Sapo, Liberia); Lohê (Guere, Côte d'Ivoire)

Identification (see Figs. 8.107 & 108, pp.336 –37)

This is a subspecies with two predominant colors, black and a
rich red-brown; the red-brown color is sometimes referred to as "bay"
(hence the scientific name of this taxon, *badius*, from the Latin word for
reddish-brown). The back, shoulders, upper arms, outer upper thighs,
crown and sides of the head are black, and the belly, lower limbs,
flanks, cheeks and throat are red-brown. The tail is dark maroon-red
near the base, and becomes black distally. There are grayish-white
hairs on the inner thighs and perineal area.

Similar species. It is not easy to confuse this colobus with other
species. The black-and-white colobus monkey with which it shares its
geographic range, *Colobus polykomos*, is of similar size but has no red
hair and a white rather than dark-red tail. The olive colobus monkey
has similar proportions and a similar outline to the bay colobus and in
poor light they can be confused if only glimpsed (for instance, olive
colobus mistaken for a juvenile red colobus). When seen clearly the
black back and red belly of the bay colobus are readily distinguished
from the brown back and gray belly of the olive colobus.

Geographic Range

Procolobus badius badius once occurred over much of Sierra
Leone, Liberia and the moist forest zone of western Côte d'Ivoire up
to the region of the confluence of the Bandama and Nzi rivers (Booth,
1954a, 1954b, 1958).

As noted in the description of Temminck's red colobus, red
colobus monkeys in Guinea-Bissau have pelage that is intermediate in
coloration between that of the *P. b. temminckii* population living near
the River Gambia and that of *P. b. badius*. The red colobus in northern
Sierra Leone, close to the border with the Republic of Guinea, may be
P. b. temminckii (Harding, 1984).

Colobinae

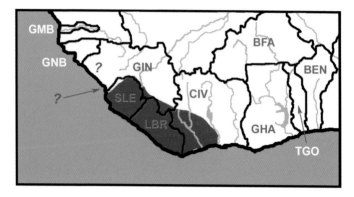

Fig. 8.115: Distribution of *Procolobus badius badius*.

Natural History

Habitat. The bay colobus is restricted to the tropical moist forest zone of the Upper Guinea region, where it is most typically associated with relatively undisturbed old-growth forest.

Field studies. Almost all information on the behavior and ecology of this monkey come from two sites: the Taï National Park in Côte d'Ivoire, and Tiwai Island Wildlife Sanctuary in Sierra Leone. In Taï, Anh Galat-Luong made comparative studies in 1979–1982 of red, olive and black-and-white colobus for her doctoral thesis (Galat-Luong, 1983; Galat and Galat-Luong, 1985), while Amanda Korstjens studied the same three species at the same site for her doctoral thesis in 1996–1999 (Korstjens, 2001; Korstjens *et al.*, 2007). Locomotion and habitat use in Taï have been studied by Scott McGraw (1996, 1998b, 1998c), and patterns of association of red colobus with Diana monkeys by Ronald Noë and students (Holenweg *et al.*, 1996; Höner *et al.*, 1997; Noë and Bshary, 1997; Wachter *et al.*, 1997). At Tiwai Island, ecological data were obtained in the course of research by George Whitesides and others (Whitesides *et al.*, 1988; Oates *et al.*, 1990b), and behavioral and ecological data were collected from an habituated group studied by A. G. Davies in 1985–1986 (Davies *et al.*, 1999).

Population. Population densities of this monkey are greatly affected by the intensity of hunting by humans; they can be very abundant in suitable habitats in the absence of hunting. At sites with little or no hunting pressure, western red colobus density has been estimated at 66–124/ km² in the Taï Forest (Galat and Galat-Luong, 1985; McGraw and Zuberbühler, 2007) and 49–70/km² at Tiwai Island (based on 1.4–2.0 groups/km² and an average group size of 35) (Whitesides *et al.*, 1988; Oates *et al.*, 1990b). In Sapo National Park, Liberia, in 1988–1989, this species was the second most frequently encountered monkey after *Cercopithecus diana* (Agooramorthy, 1989).

Habitat use. Procolobus b. badius predominantly moves and feeds in the main canopy of the forest (between 21 and 40 m), commonly using the largest branches (boughs) for support (McGraw, 1998b).

Locomotion and posture. Studies in Taï found that sitting is the dominant posture used by this monkey and the sympatric olive and black-and-white colobus (McGraw, 1998c). When moving, the red colobus differs from the other two species by engaging in more climbing and walking, and much less running; it leaps more often than the black-and-white colobus, but less than the smaller olive colobus (McGraw, 1996).

Activity pattern. The red colobus study group at Tiwai was found to spend 37% of its time feeding, 55% resting and 5% moving (from A. G. Davies, in Oates, 1994a), while a group at Taï spent 29% of its time in feeding, 16% foraging (movement during feeding), 30% resting, 19% traveling, and 6% socializing (McGraw, 1998b).

Colobinae

Fig. 8.116: Bay colobus (*Procolobus badius badius*), Taï Forest, Côte d'Ivoire (photo by W. S. McGraw).

Vocalizations. All red colobus monkeys have a repertoire of calls that grade into one another (Hill and Booth, 1957; Marler, 1970). Struhsaker (1975) recognizes nine categories of call in *P. b. badius*; some of the most common of these calls are the "chirp", "nyow" and "yelp". Females very often produce a "quaver" call during and after copulation. This is a series of exhalations and inhalations, with some of the exhalations relatively long and sounding like a moan. The length of copulation quaver bouts is longer than in other red colobus forms (Struhsaker, 2010), and these calls can be heard over distances of up to 400 m (Korstjens, 2001).

Social organization. Groups are typically large, with reported sizes of 33–90 individuals reported from Tiwai and Taï (Oates, 1994a; Korstjens, 2001; McGraw and Zuberbühler, 2007). These large groups typically contain many adult males, who form a cohesive group core and remain in the groups in which they are born while females disperse from their natal groups (Korstjens, 2001; McGraw and Zuberbühler, 2007).

Social behavior. Red colobus females in Taï were found to spend more time close to males than to other females; females groomed males as much as they groomed females, and males performed grooming infrequently; females supported males in conflicts, but males did not support females (Korstjens, 2001).

Interactions between groups. Only a small degree of overlap (6–7%) was found in the ranges of two adjacent red colobus groups in the Taï Forest. Males defended their ranges as territories against other groups, with some assistance from females (Korstjens, 2001).

Reproduction. Like Temminck's red colobus, female bay colobus display large periodic perineal swellings, described by Struhsaker (1975) as up to 13 cm deep and 14 cm wide, usually pink in appearance, and signalling female receptivity for copulation. A. G. Davies (in Oates, 1994a) found that females at Tiwai produced copulation quaver calls (associated with mating) most frequently in February–May, with births peaking six months later.

Ranging patterns. Study groups in Taï forest had average day journey lengths of 822–922 m and annual home ranges of 50 and 65 ha (Korstjens, 2001), compared with an annual range of 55 ha for a Tiwai group (A. G. Davies in Oates, 1994a).

Colobinae

Fig. 8.117: Bay colobus (*Procolobus badius badius*), Taï Forest, Côte d'Ivoire (photo by W. S. McGraw).

Diet. At Tiwai the most commonly eaten items in the red colobus diet were young leaf parts (32%), followed by seeds (25%) and mature leaf parts (20%). The most commonly eaten plant species were the trees *Funtumia africana* (Apocynaceae), *Cynometra leonensis* (Leguminoseae, Caesalpinioidea) and *Plagiosiphon emarginatus* (Caesalpinioidea) (Davies *et al.*, 1999). At Taï in Côte d'Ivoire, the diet is reported as 50% foliage, 29% fruit and 20% flowers (McGraw and Zuberbühler, 2007). Important species recorded in the diet at Taï are the large trees *Scytopetalum tieghemii* (Scytopetalaceae, a year-round staple), *Gilbertiodendron preussii* (Leguminoseae, Caesalpinioidea), *Klainedoxa gabonensis* (Irvingiaceae), *Dialium aubrevillei* (Leguminoseae, Caesalpinioidea) and *Parinari aubrevillei* (Chrysobalanaceae) (Korstjens, 2001).

Association with other species. Like most West African forest monkeys, red colobus are often observed in close proximity to other primate species. However, a study at Tiwai Island found that *P. badius badius* was not seen in association with *Cercopithecus diana* more than would be expected by chance (Whitesides, 1989). In the Taï Forest on the other hand, a red colobus group did associate significantly with a group of Diana monkeys; the two groups spending more than 62% of observation time together (Holenweg *et al.*, 1996). Holenweg *et al.* attribute this difference to the much higher predation risk experienced by red colobus in the more pristine Taï ecosystem. In Taï, red colobus are hunted less frequently by chimpanzees when they are associating with Diana monkeys than when they are on their own (Bshary, 2007).

Predators. In many parts of their range the major predator on bay colobus monkeys today is the human hunter, but in the intact ecosystem of the Taï Forest, chimpanzees, crowned eagles and leopards have all been recorded to prey upon this colobus. In the 25 km² territory of a chimpanzee study community, 125 of 150 monkeys killed annually by chimpanzees were red colobus, which are hunted particularly in the rainy season (Boesch and Boesch, 1989; Boesch and Boesch-Achermann, 2000). In studies of leopard scat in Taï Forest, red colobus hairs were found in 3.7% of 215 dung samples by Hoppe-Dominik, and in 10.5% of 200 samples by Züberbuhler and Jenny (2007). The lower frequency found by Hoppe-Dominik (1984) may be a result of sampling in the eastern part of Taï where red colobus are less abundant because of human hunting. Although crowned eagles do prey on red colobus in Taï, this predation is less frequent than would be expected based on the abundance of the colobus (Shultz and Tomsett, 2007).

Conservation Status

Procolobus b. badius is listed as Endangered on the IUCN Red List. Because of its association with mature forest habitats, its relatively large body size and conspicuousness (living in large groups, using the upper canopy, and calling frequently), *P. b. badius* is heavily impacted by humans, both from forest conversion and from hunting for bushmeat. Based on a study of restaurants and markets in the vicinity of Taï National Park, Refisch and Koné (2005b) estimated that the meat of red colobus was consumed in greater quantities than that of any other primate (68,898 kg/year out of a total for all primates of 249,229 kg/year). Almost certainly as a result of such hunting pressure, Refisch and Koné found that the best protected part of Taï supported significantly more red colobus groups than a moderately poached area.

The bay colobus occurs in several protected areas, including the Tiwai Island Wildlife Sanctuary, Gola National Park, and the Loma Mountains proposed national park in Sierra Leone, the Sapo National Park in Liberia, the Mount Nimba Strict Nature Reserve in Guinea, and the Taï National Park in Côte d'Ivoire.

Where to See It

The bay colobus can most readily be observed at Tiwai Island Wildlife Sanctuary and in the Gola North section of the proposed Gola National Park, Sierra Leone, and in primate research areas of Taï National Park in Côte d'Ivoire.

Miss Waldron's red colobus
Procolobus waldroni (Hayman, 1936)

French: Colobe bai de Waldron
West African languages: Tachié (Agni, Côte d'Ivoire); Ebene (Twi, Ghana)

Identification (see Figs. 8.107 & 108, pp.336 –37)

Like *P. b. badius*, this is a monkey with two predominant colors, black and a rich red-brown. In *P. waldroni*, however, the patterning of black and red-brown is different, and the red coloration is slightly more orangey than in *P. badius badius*. In *waldroni* the forehead is red rather than black, and there is more conspicuous red hair behind the ears. The legs of *waldroni* are entirely red, while in *badius* the upper thighs are black. The tail is black throughout its length in *waldroni*, but deep red proximally in *badius*. Black hair extends from the shoulder to the elbows on the outer surface of the arms in *waldroni*. As in *badius*, there are white hairs on the inner thighs and perineal area. The male's scrotum is white. Body size is smaller than in *P. b. badius* and there is no apparent sexual dimorphism (Groves, 2007b). Pocock (1936) has described an adult female specimen collected by W. P. Lowe in Ghana as having a large perineal swelling measuring almost 60 mm in width, with a depth of 19 mm.

Taxonomic Note

Dandelot (1971) described the nose of Miss Waldron's red colobus as being different from that of the bay colobus: in *P. waldroni* the nose is not raised on a fleshy base, as it is in *P. b. badius*. The structure of the nose, and a straight rather than rounded skull profile, led Dandelot to regard *waldroni* as a "potential" species, separate from *badius*. Groves (2007b) definitively separates *waldroni* from *badius*, noting that the differences in their color patterns are highly consistent. Ting (2008) found a relatively deep divergence in mitochondrial DNA between *waldroni* and *badius-temminckii*. Booth (1954b) argued that *badius* and *waldroni* "were clearly differentiated originally on either side of the Bandama River," but observed mixed groups just east of the Bandama-Nzi without definite proof of hybridization occurring, although he believed this was likely to occur.

Colobinae

This monkey derives its name from Miss Fanny Waldron, who was the companion of Willoughby P. Lowe on a shooting expedition he made to the Gold Coast in 1933–1934. During this expedition Lowe collected the type specimens of this colobus in Goaso (in today's Western Region of Ghana). Hayman (1936) named the monkey *Colobus badius waldroni* in Miss Waldron's honor. Groves (2001) changed *waldroni* to *waldronae* to be consistent with Miss Waldron's gender, but Brandon-Jones *et al.* (2007) have argued persuasively that the International Code of Zoological Nomenclature does not require this change and that the original spelling of the name (*waldroni*) should be preserved.

Geographic Range

Procolobus waldroni once occurred in south-eastern Côte d'Ivoire and south-western Ghana, from the Bandama River east to about 2°30'W (Booth, 1954a, 1954b, 1958a, 1958b; Grubb *et al.*, 1998). Since 1990, the only convincing evidence for the continued survival of any population has come from swamp forests in the far south-eastern corner of Côte d'Ivoire, between the Ehy Lagoon and the Tano, or Tanoé, River (McGraw and Oates, 2002; McGraw, 2005; Gonedelé Bi *et al.*, 2008).

Fig. 8.118: A skin of *Procolobus waldroni* in a village on the edge of the Tanoé Forest, southeastern Côte d'Ivoire, 2006 (photo by W. S. McGraw).

Colobinae

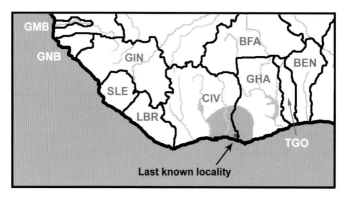

Fig. 8.119: The presumed original distribution of *Procolobus waldroni* (pink). The arrow points to the Tanoé Forest, Côte d'Ivoire (red); the last known location of a population of this monkey.

Natural History

Habitat. Most of the area where Miss Waldron's colobus once lived is in the moist forest zone, which, however, has a lower annual rainfall than the region to the west occupied by the western red colobus. Except near the coast, the area once inhabited by this monkey predominantly supports a forest type often referred to as "semi-deciduous" (Hall and Swaine, 1981; Bongers *et al.*, 2004), which has a marked dry season, during which many emergent trees shed their leaves (Booth, 1956).

Ecology and behavior. Very little information is available on the ecology and behavior of this monkey, although it seems probable that in its behavior it is similar to the western red colobus. A few notes were published by Booth (1956), who described this red colobus as using the upper canopy of the forest more than other sympatric species, including black-and-white colobus (*Colobus polykomos*). Hill and Booth (1957) noted that the vocal "capabilities" of *P. b. badius* and *P. waldroni* are closely similar. A field study of Miss Waldron's colobus was conducted in the Bia National Park, Ghana, in the 1970s by Michael Rucks, but few results from that study have been published, although a summary is provided in the book on West African forests by Claude Martin. Like Booth, Martin (1991) describes this colobus as typically using higher levels of the forest canopy than other monkeys, and notes how it makes great leaps from tree to tree. Two groups were studied at Bia, one with 34 individuals, the other with 58; the smaller group had an annual home range of 1.4 km² and the larger group a range of 1.0 km²; the diet was

Colobinae

mainly leaves, but fruits, seeds and flowers were also eaten, from more than 50 tree species and at least 15 climbers (Martin, 1991).

Conservation Status

Procolobus waldroni is listed (as *P. badius waldroni*) as Critically Endangered on the IUCN Red List. Careful surveys across the known range of Miss Waldron's red colobus in Côte d'Ivoire and Ghana from 1993 to 1999 failed to find convincing evidence for the continued survival of this monkey, leading Oates *et al.* (2000a) to suggest that it was probably extinct as a result of human hunting. Booth (1956) had predicted the extinction of red colobus in Ghana unless effective legislation was enacted to protect it. Although Bia and Nini-Suhien national parks were subsequently established (Bia in part to protect this particular monkey), anti-poaching measures in these parks lapsed (Oates, 1999).

During the 1993–1999 surveys, hunters reported the possible survival of red colobus in the swamp forests near the Ehy lagoon in the southeastern corner of Côte d'Ivoire. These reports were repeated during a follow-up survey in 2000, and in the course of subsequent visits local hunters produced a tail, skins and a photograph of red colobus from these forests, the last of these dating from 2006 (McGraw and Oates, 2002; McGraw, 2005; S. Gonedelé Bi, pers. comm.). The Ehy (or Tanoé) Forest, which covers about 60 km^2, has been under serious threat of conversion to an oil palm plantation, and logging has occurred in the northwest of the forest (Gonedelé Bi *et al.*, 2008). At the time of writing, no scientist had seen a red colobus monkey in these forests, and on recent visits hunters informed scientists that they had not seen a red colobus for some time. It is feared that Miss Waldron's red colobus is now fully exterminated.

Where to See It

Procolobus waldroni is probably extinct. The only site from which it has been reported recently, Tanoé in southeastern Côte d'Ivoire, is mostly swamp, and moving around in the forest is said to be very difficult.

Colobinae

Niger Delta red colobus
Procolobus epieni Grubb & Powell 1999

West African languages: Epieni (Ijaw, Nigeria)

Identification (see Figs. 8.120 & 121, pp.366 –67)

The back and crown of the Niger Delta red colobus monkey is dark brownish-gray, with the darkest color (almost black) on the crown and shoulders. This dark color extends down the arms, narrowing and becoming faint below the elbow. A dark gray stripe also extends down the thigh. The dark dorsal surfaces are speckled with brown, particularly on the lower back and towards the flanks. The facial skin is black and there are white cheek whiskers. The lower flanks of the trunk and legs are dull orangey-brown and there is a narrow band of orange-brown on the trailing edge of the arm. The tail is initially red-brown, becoming darker to an almost gray tip. The undersurfaces are creamy white, with the white extending to the throat and anterior surface of the upper arms. The lower arms are predominantly grayish-cream and the hands and feet black. There is a detailed description of the coat in Grubb and Powell (1999).

Similar species. Procolobus epieni is not readily confused with any other monkey species in the Niger Delta. The only other colobus species reported from the delta is the olive colobus (*Procolobus verus*). The olive colobus and red colobus have similar proportions and can sometimes be mistaken for one another if glimpsed in poor light. However, an adult olive colobus is about half the size of an adult red colobus; the red colobus has a darker back than the olive colobus and orangey-red flanks (where the olive colobus is olivey gray-brown), and the striking white chest of the red colobus contrasts with the gray chest of the olive colobus. The olive colobus is rare in the Niger Delta.

Taxonomic Note

This is the most recently described form of red colobus monkey. It was first encountered in the central Niger Delta by scientists in 1993, and was described by Grubb and Powell (1999) as a new subspecies, *Procolobus badius epieni*. Grubb *et al.* (2003) placed it as a subspecies of *P. pennantii*. Werre (2000) reports that the call repertoire of *epieni* is similar to that of *Procolobus rufomitratus tephrosceles* of East Africa, while Ting (2008) has found that *epieni* is distinctive in its

Colobinae

Niger Delta Red Colobus
Procolobus epieni

Pennant's Red Colobus
Procolobus pennantii

Preuss's Red Colobus
Procolobus preussi

Colobinae

Fig. 8.120.

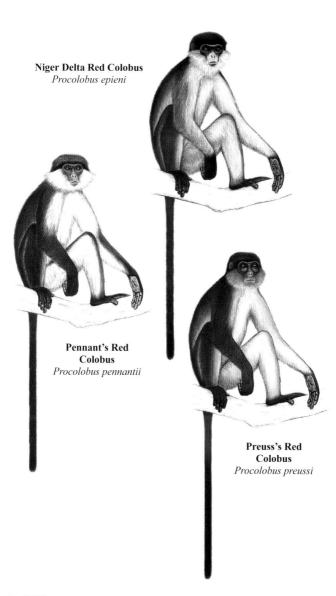

Niger Delta Red Colobus
Procolobus epieni

Pennant's Red Colobus
Procolobus pennantii

Preuss's Red Colobus
Procolobus preussi

Colobinae

Fig. 8.121.

NADH4 mitochondrial DNA gene, but groups more closely with red colobus from eastern and central Africa than with West African forms. Provisionally *epieni* is therefore treated here as a distinct species.

Geographic Range

Procolobus epieni is known only from an area of about 200 km² in Bayelsa State in the central Niger Delta, Nigeria, bounded by the Forcados River and Bomadi Creek to the north and the Sagbama, Osiama and Apoi creeks in the east (Werre, 2000).

Natural History

Habitat. The habitat of *P. epieni* is a freshwater swamp forest classified as "Marsh Forest" by Powell (1993). In this area, tidal influence dampens the effect of the annual flood of the Niger River and a high water table persists through the short dry season. Among common trees are *Uapaca* spp., *Klaineanthus gaboniae*, *Alstonia boonei* and *Hallea ledermannii,* with *Raphia* palms abundant in the understorey. In places *Ctenolophon englerianus* is the most frequent emergent tree and the upper canopy can reach heights of 45 m, although a 20 m canopy is more typical (Werre, 2000).

Field studies. After C. Bruce Powell received a skin of this monkey in 1993 from a hunter at Gbanraun in the Niger Delta, a small team made observations of groups in several forest areas near Gbanraun (Oates, 1994b). Subsequently, there has been only one long-term field study of this species, undertaken by J. Lodewijk Werre between 1994 and 1997,

Colobinae

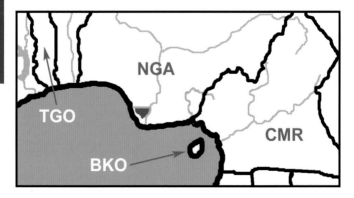

Fig. 8.122: Distribution of *Procolobus epieni*.

including intensive study of one social group near the settlement of Gbanraun in 1996–1997 (see Fig. A.8, p.461) (Werre, 2000).

Habitat use. Within Werre's Gbanraun study area there were permanently wet swampy areas, and higher ground which only flooded during heavy rain. The red colobus used both types of forest, but their main food trees appeared to be more clumped in the swamp than dryland forest (Werre, 2000). The monkeys rested at an average height of 20 m, high in the upper canopy, and fed and travelled at an average height of 15 m where there were fewer gaps in the canopy.

Activity pattern. Werre found that Gbanraun red colobus spent 37% of their time feeding, 33% inactive and 25% travelling. This is a greater proportion of time spent moving than found in other red colobus populations.

Vocalizations. The call repertoire of Niger Delta red colobus was found by Werre (2000) to be similar, surprisingly, to that described for the *tephrosceles* form of red colobus from East Africa by Struhsaker (1975). Struhsaker (2010) has analyzed recordings provided by Werre and notes "chist", "wheet", "nyow" and "convex" calls as being common.

Social organization and behavior. Werre encountered groups ranging in size from about 15 to 80 individuals at Gbanraun, all with at least two adult males. His study group contained about 60 individuals, including 7 adult males. Within this study group agonistic behaviors were most frequent among adult and subadult males. Grooming was conducted most frequently by females, and most grooming of females by adult males involved females with perineal swellings.

Interactions between groups. The ranges of groups at Gbanraun overlapped and meetings between groups were usually peaceful, but were accompanied by an increase in vocalizations. Werre's main study group showed signs of having arisen from the merger of two smaller groups.

Reproduction. Adult females develop cyclical perineal swellings averaging 12 cm long and 10 cm wide. At Gbanraun, swollen females and copulations were observed throughout the year, but copulations were most frequent in the rainy season months of April–July (Werre, 2000). Small infants were seen in all months at Gbanraun, but the highest number of sightings was in the dry-season months of December–March, possibly reflecting a birth peak at this time of year.

Colobinae

Colobinae

Fig. 8.123: Niger Delta red colobus (*Procolobus epieni*), Gbanraun, Niger Delta, Nigeria (photo by N. Rowe).

Ranging patterns. The Gbanraun study group had daily travel distances ranging from 450 m to 1,900 m (mean 1,040 m). Based on their occupancy of 0.25 ha grid cells, the group's annual range was 73 ha.

Diet. Leaf buds, young leaves and the terminal parts of stems made up 62% of the annual diet of Werre's Gbanraun group, with other important foods being seeds (12%), flowers and flower buds (10%) and leaf petioles (5%). The single most important item in the *epieni* diet was the young leaves of *Ctenolophon englerianus* (Ctenolophonaceae), making up 44% of the annual diet. Other important items were the seeds of *Uapaca* spp. (Euphorbiaceae) (6% of diet) and the seeds of *Klaineanthus gaboniae* (Euphorbiaceae) (5%).

Predators. Werre observed attacks by crowned eagles on red colobus at Gbanraun, and found colobus skulls under a crowned eagle nest within the range of his study group.

Conservation Status

Procolobus epieni (as *P. pennantii epieni*) is listed as Critically Endangered on the IUCN Red List. The swamp forest habitat of the Niger Delta red colobus has been severely damaged by uncontrolled logging, especially of *Hallea ledermannii* (Rubiaceae) (known locally as "abura") (Werre and Powell, 1997). The Ijaw people who inhabit the area occupied by this colobus are traditionally fishermen and did not hunt monkeys to a significant extent. The opening-up of the delta to the outside world, especially by the oil industry, has led to an increase in the hunting of wildlife and to trade in bushmeat. Red colobus have therefore faced an increasing threat from shotgun hunting. Werre (2000) estimated that the total population of *P. epieni* had fallen below 10,000 individuals. A conservation area between the Pennington River and Apoi Creek, southwest of Gbanraun that would provide special protection for this red colobus was being planned in the late 1990s, but the increasing instability in the Niger Delta has resulted in all such plans being frozen.

Where to See It

In the 1990s, visitors to the town of Gbanraun in the central Niger Delta could observe red colobus relatively easily in swamp forests near the town. At the time of writing, conditions in the delta are too insecure to allow safe visits by foreigners to any part of the range of *P. epieni.*

Colobinae

Pennant's red colobus
Procolobus pennantii (Waterhouse, 1838)

Other English: Bioko red colobus
French: Colobe bai de Pennant
Spanish: Colobo castaño de Pennant
West African languages: Mberi (Bubi; Bioko)

Identification (see Figs. 8.120 & 121, pp.366 –67)

The crown of the head, shoulders, back and upper thighs of
Pennant's red colobus are dark charcoal gray with a brown tinge. The
dark color extends to the upper thighs. The flanks are a rich orangey
rust-red and the outer surfaces of the limbs are a similar color or darker.
The throat, chest, belly and inner limb surfaces are creamy white, and
there are long white cheek whiskers; a fringe of white hair from the
chest extends to the upper, outer arms. The tail is dark reddish-brown,
sometimes reddening towards the tip. The hands and feet are black,
and this black color extends above the ankles. The facial skin is black.
Females display large two-lobed perineal sexual swellings (Struhsaker,
2010).

Butynski *et al.* (2009) present information suggesting that adult
female Pennant's red colobus are slightly longer in linear dimensions
than males, but not quite as heavily built; 12 males averaged about
50 cm in head and body length with 59-cm tails, while 48 females
averaged 52 cm in head and body length with 64-cm tails. One intact
male had a body weight of 11 kg, compared with one 10 kg female,
and in a large sample of eviscerated carcasses males were still slightly
heavier than females.

Similar species. Pennant's red colobus, with its unique and
distinctive coat pattern, cannot readily be confused with any other
Bioko monkey, especially if it is clearly seen in good light. However,
the black colobus, *Colobus satanas*, with which it shares its habitat, is
similar in body size and general proportions. The two colobines can be
confused if they are only glimpsed in poor light, but *C. satanas* has an
entirely black coat with markedly long hairs extending from the crown
of its head.

Colobinae

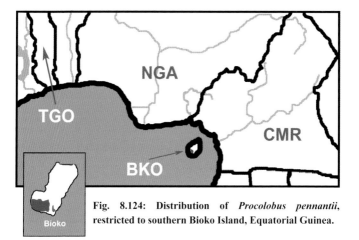

Fig. 8.124: Distribution of *Procolobus pennantii*, restricted to southern Bioko Island, Equatorial Guinea.

Taxonomic Note

This colobus is classified as *P. pennantii pennantii* by Kingdon (1997) and by Grubb *et al.* (2003). Kingdon also includes the forms *bouvieri* and *epieni* as subspecies of *P. pennantii*, while Grubb *et al.* (2003) include both those forms and *preussi*. Here, each of these monkeys is accorded species status, following Groves (2007b).

Geographic Range

Procolobus pennantii is restricted to Bioko Island, Equatorial Guinea. It probably once occurred over most of Bioko but appears today to be restricted to the south-western corner of the island. It likely survived on Pico Basilé at least until the late 1980s (Butynski and Koster, 1994).

Natural History

Habitat. Procolobus pennantii occurs from sea level forests on the southern coast of Bioko through mid-altitude forests up into montane and *Schefflera* forest at 1,800 m or above (Butynski and Koster, 1994; Gonzalez-Kirchner, 1997). This monkey therefore occurs at a higher elevation than any other form of red colobus in West Africa and, according to Gonzalez-Kirchner (1997), may prefer montane forest. The forests of southern Bioko receive very high rainfall, in places exceeding 10,000 mm per annum (Pérez de Val, 1996).

Colobinae

Field studies. There has been no field study of habituated groups and detailed information on the behavioral ecology of this monkey is therefore lacking. All observations have been from relatively short-term surveys by Butynski and Koster (1994), Gonzalez-Kirchner (1997), Struhsaker (2000), Hearn *et al.* (2006) and Butynski and Owens (2008).

Abundance. Surveys in the Gran Caldera de Luba in early 2008 encountered 0.18 groups of Pennant's red colobus per km (Butynski and Owens, 2008).

Habitat use. Gonzalez-Kirchner (1997) reports that Pennant's red colobus uses all layers of the forest canopy, with the most frequent sightings coming from the middle canopy at 18–23 m. Struhsaker (2000) occasionally saw individuals on the ground.

Social organization. Butynski and Koster (1994) report that most groups seem to have at least 20 animals and that some contained at least 30 individuals. Struhsaker (2000) obtained group counts of five to over 30 (mean of at least 14), indicating a smaller typical group size than in other West African red colobus. A high percentage of Struhsaker's observations (23.5%) were of solitary monkeys, all of them females, suggesting that females rather than males disperse from groups. Many of the 14–15 groups observed by Struhsaker had only one adult male, but at least one group contained two adult males and another contained at least three.

Predators. There are no crowned eagles, leopards or chimpanzees on Bioko. Humans are the only known predator of Pennant's red colobus. Struhsaker (2000) suggests that the absence of the crowned eagles is a major cause of the small size of Bioko red colobus groups, the frequency with which solitary individuals are observed, and the relatively low frequency (39% of observations) with which he saw them in association with monkeys of other species. Busse (1977) has speculated that the large size and multi-male structure typical of red colobus groups on the African mainland may have been selected for by chimpanzee predation.

Conservation Status

Procolobus pennnantii is listed (as *P. p. pennnantii*) as Endangered on the IUCN Red List. During the colonial period, most of the lowland forest in northern Bioko (then Fernando Po) was cleared for plantation agriculture, predominantly plantations of cacao. The extensive forest clearance presumably had a major impact on red colobus and other primates. Following independence in 1968 and the collapse of the colonial plantation economy, many abandoned plantations began to revert to forest. In 1974, shotguns were removed from most of the civilian population for security reasons, and monkey populations began to increase (Butynski and Koster, 1990, 1994). In the 1980s, shotgun hunting resumed and an active bushmeat market began to flourish in the capital city of Malabo. Pennant's red colobus, with the most restricted range of all of Bioko's primates, has been particularly threatened by this hunting. Numbers of red colobus carcasses in the Malabo market increased sharply in 2004 and estimated population decline, based on censuses in the Gran Caldera de Luba, was about

Fig. 8.125: A juvenile Pennant's red colobus (*Procolobus pennantii*), Gran Caldera de Luba, Bioko (photo by R. A. Bergl).

Fig. 8.126: Pennant's red colobus (*Procolobus pennantii pennantii*) in the Gran Caldera de Luba, Bioko Island (photo by B. Johnson).

45% from 1986 to 2006 (Hearn *et al.*, 2006). In November 2007, a ban on shotgun hunting came into force on Bioko; it is hoped that this will be effective and relieve the pressure on *P. pennantii*, but soon after the ban was announced some monkeys were appearing again in the market (Morell, 2008).

The Gran Caldera and Southern Highlands Scientific Reserve that covers approximately 600 km² of southern Bioko could provide good protection for the red colobus but has suffered from a lack of adequate patrolling and law enforcement.

Where to See It

This monkey is most readily observed in and near the Gran Caldera section of Bioko's Gran Caldera and Southern Highlands Scientific Reserve, especially in those areas kept under surveillance by the Bioko Biodiversity Protection Program of the Universidad Nacional de Guinea Ecuatorial and Drexel University, Pennsylvania. South-western Bioko, where the Gran Caldera is located, is, however, a difficult destination to reach.

Colobinae

Preuss's red colobus
Procolobus preussi (Matschie, 1900)

French: Colobe bai de Preuss (Cameroon)
West African languages: Nka'mbok (Ejagham; Cameroon, Nigeria);
Konowok (Korup; Cameroon, Nigeria); Nyanda (Oroko; Cameroon);
Soonyam (Banen and Bassa, Cameroon)

Identification (see Figs. 8.120 & 121, pp.366 –67)

The back of Preuss's red colobus is dark gray with flecks of brown
that are produced by the light brown banding on the individual hairs;
this brownish-gray color becomes darker on the nape of the neck and
crown. The dark coloration of the back extends onto the rump and
upper outer thighs. The flanks, outer limb surfaces and cheek whiskers
are orangey foxy-red with the arms tending to be a richer red than
the flanks (although there is individual variation in coloration). Red
coloration extends to the hair of the hands and feet. The tail is also
red, but of a deeper hue than the limbs and flanks, becoming darker
towards the tip. The chest, midline of the belly and inner limb surfaces
are creamy or buffy white. Struhsaker (1975) notes that females of
this colobus can exhibit very large pink sexual swellings, reaching one-
quarter to one-third of body size

Similar species. Preuss's red colobus is not easily confused with
the other monkeys in its habitat in Cameroon and eastern Nigeria. No
sympatric species has the orange-red flanks and outer limb surfaces
and white belly of *P. preussi*. *Cercopithecus pogonias*, with which
it is quite often seen in association, is considerably smaller and has
bright golden hair on its ventral surfaces. In the Korup region, no other
colobus species is present, but at least until recently *Colobus guereza*
occurred in the Makombe-Ndokbou-Ebo forest block in the southern
part of the range of Preuss's red colobus. The entirely black and white
pelage of *C. guereza* is very different from the gray-brown, red and
white coat pattern of *P. preussi*.

Taxonomic Note

Dandelot (1971) listed Preuss's red colobus as a "potential
species" but without providing a rationale for this conclusion. Based
on vocalizations, Struhsaker (1975, 1981, 2010) considers *preussi* to
fall into its own group, but one allied to *badius* and *temminckii*. Also

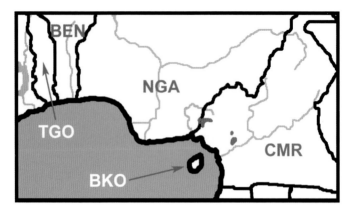

Fig. 8.127: Distribution of *Procolobus preussi*.

recognizing its distinctiveness, Kingdon (1997) and Groves (2007b) each place this monkey in its own species, which they call *Piliocolobus preussi*. However, Grubb *et al.* (2003) classify *preussi* as a subspecies of *Procolobus pennantii*, and Ting (2008) has found that *preussi* groups closely with *pennantii* of Bioko in its NADH4 mitochondrial gene, a relationship that might be expected based on geographical proximity.

Geographic Range

Preuss's red colobus monkey is known only from western Cameroon and the far southeastern corner of Nigeria. The present range in Cameroon is disjunct. One population is known from the Makombe-Ndokbou-Ebo forest block, in the hill country north and south of Yingui (4°32'N, 10°18'E) (Dowsett-Lemaire and Dowsett, 2001). Another occurs in Korup National Park and some adjacent forests (e.g., Ejagham), adjacent to the Nigerian border (Struhsaker, 1975; J. S. Gartlan in Wolfheim, 1983). In Nigeria they are known only from a limited area of the Oban Division of Cross River National Park, north of the settlement of Ekonganaku (5°06'N, 8°40'E), in forests contiguous with those of Korup in Cameroon.

Natural History

Habitat. The ecology of this monkey is poorly documented, but it appears to be largely restricted to little-disturbed high-canopy moist forest habitats. Its forest habitat in Korup is dominated by caesalpinioid legumes. In southern Korup National Park, near the park headquarters

Fig. 8.128: Preuss's red colobus (*Procolobus preussi*), Korup National Park, Cameroon (photo by J. M. Linder).

at Mundemba, caesalpinioid legumes make up an estimated 14% of tree basal area; in southern Korup the tree species with the largest basal area (8%) is *Oubanguia alata* (Scytopetalaceae). Rainfall in Korup is high, ranging from 4,000–6,000 mm annually in the south of the park to 2,500–3,000 mm in the north (Linder, 2008).

Field studies. This is a relatively poorly-known species. Apart from a short study of feeding behavior in Korup National Park, Cameroon, by Usongo and Amubode (2001), all observations have been collected in the course of surveys, or during studies on other sympatric species.

Population. In 1990, Edwards (1992) encountered 0.065 groups of Preuss's red colobus per km of transect walked in the Ikenge area of Korup, and from these encounters she derived a density estimate of 0.56 groups per km². Repeating these transect walks in 2004–2005, Linder (2008) encountered 0.05 groups per km. In the Mundemba area of southern Korup, Dunn and Okon (2003) encountered 0.06 groups per km and in 2004–2005 Linder (2008) encountered 0.05 groups per km. In the Ebo forest its distribution is patchy (B. Morgan, pers. comm.).

Vocalizations. Struhsaker (1975) recognized 18 different call variants in Preuss's red colobus, of which the most common were the "bark" and "chirp" (variants of one call), the "nyow" and the "yelp." When copulating, females produce quaver calls. Struhsaker (2010) notes that Preuss's red colobus has the most complex call repertoire of all the different forms of red colobus, and perhaps the most diverse repertoire among all nonhuman primates.

Social organization. Struhsaker (1975) estimated that seven groups encountered in southern Korup ranged in size from at least 24 to more than 80 monkeys (mean 47). Most of these groups had more than one adult male. Edwards (1992) estimated that group sizes in the Ikenge area ranged from 20 to 50, and made one complete count of a group of 64. Dunn and Okon (2003) give an average group size of 34.5 for southern Korup, but this figure is based on counts during census walks which are likely to have been underestimates of total size.

Ranging patterns. One repeatedly-observed group in Korup was estimated by Edwards (1992) to have a home range of approximately 100 ha.

Diet. From their study in Korup, Usongo and Amubode (2001) reported that 89% of feeding observations were on young leaves, and 10% were on flowers and buds. The most commonly eaten items were the young leaves of *Lecomtedoxa klaineana* (Sapotaceae), comprising 27% of all observations, and the young leaves of *Xylopia aethiopica* (Annonaceae), 22% of observations. In the Ebo Forest, young leaves of *Lophira alata* (Ochnaceae) appear to be important in the diet (B. Morgan, pers. comm.).

Association with other species. In 12 of 13 encounters (92%) with Preuss's red colobus in the Ikenge area of Korup, Edwards (1992) observed them to be in association with other monkey species, the highest such frequency among all the Korup monkey species.

Colobinae

However, only with *Cercopithecus pogonias* did this association occur at a frequency estimated to be greater than by chance.

Predators. In the Ebo Forest, chimpanzees have been seen to chase Preuss's red colobus monkeys in apparent predation attempts (B. Morgan, pers. comm.). Crowned eagles are almost certainly a predator on this colobus. Preuss's red colobus is hunted by humans wherever it occurs.

Conservation Status

Procolobus preussi is listed as Critically Endangered on the IUCN Red List. The status and trajectory of populations of Preuss's red colobus are only relatively well known for Korup National Park. In Korup, census surveys conducted in 2004–2005 by Linder (2008) encountered slightly fewer colobus than did earlier censuses at Ikenge in 1990 (Edwards, 1992) and at Mundemba in 2001–2003 (Dunn and Okon, 2003). Linder encountered no red colobus in the Bajo area immediately northeast of the park where they had been seen in small numbers in 1999–2001 by Waltert *et al.* (2002). These declines are most likely the result of shotgun hunting that is undertaken mainly to supply bushmeat markets, and which is only partially controlled in the national park (Linder, 2008). Logging is probably a factor contributing to decline outside the park (Waltert *et al.*, 2002).

Procolobus preussi occurs in the Oban Division of Cross River National Park, Nigeria, but its distribution there is patchy and it is rare. Its main surviving populations are in Cameroon, in Korup National Park and the proposed Ebo National Park.

Where to See It

Preuss's red colobus is most readily observed in the southern part of Korup National Park, Cameroon, which is accessible from park headquarters at Mundemba, located about 10 km east of the park boundary. Southern Korup has a good system of trails and campsites, and there is less hunting in this part of the park than elsewhere, making it easier to observe primates.

Colobinae

Colobus Illiger, 1811
Black-and-white, and black colobus monkeys

These are large, arboreal long-haired forest monkeys which have coats in varying patterns of black, white and (in some populations) silvery hair. *Colobus satanas* has an all-black coat. Unlike the females of the olive and red species, most black-and-white colobus do not develop perineal sexual swellings, although very small swellings have been reported in *Colobus satanas*. Young *Colobus* infants are often handled by group members other than the mother, behavior not seen in the olive and red colobus. Adult males have enlarged larynxes and produce low-pitched croaking loud calls that are delivered in long sequences. Adult males are typically about 25% heavier than adult females, contrasting with West African populations of olive and red colobus, which usually show much lower levels of dimorphism.

Kingdon (1997), Grubb *et al.* (2003) and Groves (2007b) recognize five species in this genus: *Colobus satanas*, *C. polykomos*, *C. angolensis*, *C. vellerosus*, and *C. guereza*.

Colobus polykomos geospecies

Grubb (2006b) includes all the different forms of black-and-white colobus into one geospecies, *Colobus polykomos*. However, *C. guereza* is sympatric in parts of its range in western Africa with *C. satanas*, and in the Congo basin with *C. angolensis*. Strictly, therefore, *C. guereza* should be regarded as a member of a separate geospecies to the other forms, given that Grubb notes that a zoogeographical species (or geospecies) contributes no more than one taxon to any local fauna.

Local Representatives

Four species occur in West Africa: *C. polykomos* in Guinea-Bissau, Republic of Guinea, Sierra Leone, Liberia and western Côte d'Ivoire; *C. vellerosus* in eastern Côte d'Ivoire, Ghana, Togo, Bénin and western Nigeria; *C. guereza* in eastern Nigeria and Cameroon; and *Colobus satanas* on Bioko Island.

Colobinae

White-thighed Black-and-White Colobus
Colobus vellerosus

Western Black-and-White Colobus
Colobus polykomos

Western Guereza
Colobus guereza occidentalis

Bioko Black Colobus
Colobus satanas satanas

Colobinae

Fig. 8.129.

Western black-and-white colobus
Colobus polykomos (Zimmermann, 1780)

Other English: King colobus, western pied colobus, ursine colobus,
full-bottom monkey
French: Colobe blanc et noir d'Afrique occidentale
Portuguese: Macaco-fidalgo
West African languages: Tuwai (Mende; Sierra Leone); Ka rusi
(Temne; Sierra Leone); Bo'-wah (Bassa, Liberia); Po-weh (Sapo,
Liberia); Bohê (Guere, Côte d'Ivoire)

Identification (see Fig. 8.129, p.383)

A large arboreal forest monkey that is mostly black on the body
and limbs, but with a very long pure white tail. There is long, wispy
silvery-white hair around the face and on the throat. It has epaulettes
of white or silvery-white hair on the shoulders. The ventral margins of
the ischial callosities are fringed with white hair.

Adult male *Colobus polykomos* are heavier than females, weighing
on average about 10 kg, compared with an average female weight of
7–8 kg (Delson *et al.*, 2000; Napier, 1985; Oates *et al.*, 1990b). In
linear dimensions there is less dimorphism; head and body length is
60–65 cm in males, 55–60 cm in females. Tail length in both sexes
averages about 90 cm.

Similar species. The western black-and-white colobus may be
confused with the two subspecies of western red colobus monkey
(*Procolobus badius badius* and *P. b. temminckii*) that share a major
part of its range and forest habitat. The red colobus are of similar size
and have similar postures and body proportions to the black-and-white
colobus, but the tail of the black-and-white colobus is longer. When
seen clearly, the reddish belly, flanks, cheeks and lower limbs of the red
colobus are quite distinctive. The loud roaring call of the male black-
and-white colobus does not have a parallel in the red colobus repertoire,
and the "yelp", "nyow" and "quaver" calls of the red colobus are not
heard in the black-and-white species.

Taxonomic Note

Until recently this monkey was treated as a subspecies (*C.
polykomos polykomos*) of a species extending as far east as western

Colobinae

Fig. 8.130: Western black-and-white colobus (*Colobus polykomos*), Tiwai Island, Sierra Leone (photo by R. A. Mittermeier).

Nigeria and which also included *C. p. dollmani* and *C. p. vellerosus* (Rahm, 1970; Wolfheim, 1983). Following the study by Oates and Trocco (1983), demonstrating differences between *polykomos* and *vellerosus* in the male loud call, these two forms have been widely regarded as different species (e.g., by Groves, 2007b). *Colobus p. dollmani* appears to represent a hybrid population between *polykomos* and *vellerosus*, which is best regarded as part of *C. vellerosus* (Groves *et al.*, 1993; Grubb *et al.*, 2003).

Geographic Range

Colobus polykomos occurs from the vicinity of the border of Guinea-Bissau with Senegal, south and east through Guinea-Bissau, western and southern Guinea, Sierra Leone and Liberia to the Sassandra River in Côte d'Ivoire (Booth, 1954b; Gippoliti and Dell'Omo, 2003).

Colobinae

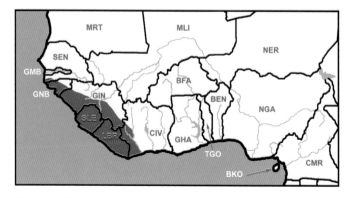

Fig. 8.131: Distribution of *Colobus polykomos.*

A map by Booth (1958b) that indicates its presence north of the Gambia River appears to be erroneous.

Natural History

Habitat. In southern Sierra Leone, Liberia and Côte d'Ivoire this is typically a monkey of the moist forest zone. In Guinea-Bissau its habitat is in a drier climatic zone and here this species may be particularly associated with gallery forests. In the Kilimi area of northwestern Sierra Leone, where the vegetation is predominantly savanna woodland, *C. polykomos* occurs in patches of dry forest and in riparian gallery forests (Harding, 1984).

Field studies. Studies of habituated groups of *C. polykomos* have been conducted in the Taï Forest, Côte d'Ivoire, by Anh Galat-Luong in 1979–1982 and by Amanda Korstjens and associates in 1993–1999 (Galat-Luong, 1983; Galat and Galat-Luong, 1985; Korstjens, 2001; Korstjens *et al.*, 2007). The species was also the subject of doctoral dissertation research by Georgina Dasilva at Tiwai Island, Sierra Leone in 1984–1986 (Dasilva, 1989, 1992, 1993; Davies *et al.*, 1999).

Population. Western black-and-white colobus have been found at densities of 5–6 groups per km² at Tiwai Island, Sierra Leone, where an average group is estimated to contain 9 individuals (Oates *et al.*, 1990b), giving a density of 45.5 individuals per km², and at a density of 36 individuals per km² in the Taï Forest, Côte d'Ivoire (McGraw and Zuberbühler, 2007).

Habitat use. This colobus prefers to use the tallest trees in its habitat. In the Taï Forest, *C. polykomos* spends more of its time (52%) in the upper part of the main canopy and in the emergent layer than any other monkey species (McGraw, 2007). Even in mature high forest the black-and-white colobus will sometimes use the ground, and in less dense habitats they will flee from humans along the ground (Harding, 1984; Gippoliti and Dell'Omo, 2003).

Locomotion and posture. Like other members of this geospecies, *C. polykomos* spends much time resting; sitting is the most common posture adopted when the monkeys are not moving (McGraw, 2007). Lying prone on branches is a characteristic posture. Although large boughs are commonly used for resting, most feeding takes place on smaller supports (McGraw, 1998c). At Tiwai, much foraging occurs in liana tangles around the boles of large trees. When travelling through the canopy, black-and-white colobus often bound along branches and make powerful leaps between tree crowns.

Activity pattern. Averaged across seasons, data collected by Dasilva (1992) at Tiwai Island show the western black-and-white colobus spending 55% of its time resting, 31% feeding and 12% travelling. The activity budget changed seasonally, with more time spent feeding in the

Fig. 8.132: Western black-and-white colobus (*Colobus polykomos*), Taï Forest, Côte d'Ivoire (photo by W. S. McGraw).

Colobinae

dry season when seeds, a high energy food source, are most abundant. In the wet season, resting increases to 60% of the activity budget, and travelling falls to 9%, perhaps to minimize energy expenditure. At the height of the wet season, sitting in hunched postures becomes frequent, while at other times of year sunbathing is common. Dasilva (1993) interprets these behaviors as contributing to thermoregulation, another component of an energy-saving strategy.

Vocalizations. Adult male *C. polykomos* produce loud "roaring" calls, which are higher pitched than those of male *C. guereza* and *C. vellerosus* (Oates and Trocco, 1983). Common calls in this species' repertoire are "snorts", "grunts" and "snuffles" (Dasilva, 1989). Snorts are alarm calls, grunts are low-level alarms and are also made by dominant animals supplanting others, and snuffles are produced by supplanted subordinates and by females approaching mothers with small infants. A "whaahah" call is sometimes heard during fights (Dasilva, 1989). Infants produce squeals. Both sexes make tongue clicks as a threat.

Social organization. Study groups of this species at Tiwai Island and in the Taï Forest contained between 9 and 19 individuals, with 1–3 fully adult males, and 4–6 adult females (Galat and Galat-Luong, 1985; Dasilva, 1989; Korstjens, 2001). These groups may have been larger than population averages. Harding reports a mean group size (including solitary animals) of 3.3 in the Kilimi area of Sierra Leone (Harding, 1984), while Gippolitti and Dell'Omo (2003) report groups of 5–6 in Guinea Bissau. At Tiwai, males and females were observed to mature in their natal groups, and there was evidence of females occasionally moving between groups (Dasilva, 1989).

Social behavior. In *C. polykomos* social groups, females form relatively strong bonds. They tend to maintain close spatial proximity and groom each other more frequently than they groom males. When more than one adult male is present in a group the males interact rarely, and appear to establish a dominance hierarchy (Dasilva, 1989; Korstjens, 2001; Korstjens *et al.*, 2007). At times when a Tiwai study group contained three adult males, all three produced roaring calls (Dasilva, 1989).

Interactions between groups. In Taï Forest, the ranges of *C. polykomos* groups overlap and there are no areas of exclusive use (Korstjens, 2001). Although some interactions between groups are peaceful, the majority are aggressive, involving chases and sometimes fights. Males are always involved in between-group aggression and females are also frequently involved. Both sexes may produce roaring calls during these encounters. Encounters are won (with losers leaving the area of the encounter) more frequently by groups when they are in the core of their range. This pattern has been interpreted by Korstjens as evidence of food resource defence.

Reproduction. Little information is available on reproduction in this species. At Tiwai in Sierra Leone, newborn infants were observed only in the dry season months of December–February and a typical interbirth interval in females appeared to be two years (Dasilva, 1989). Infants are born with an all-white coat which begins to darken after a few days. Juvenile and adult females other than the mother show great interest in young infants, and non-maternal adults attempt to handle newborns from the day after birth, sometimes holding the infant for several hours (Ormrod, 1967; Mallinson, 1968; Korstjens, 2001). The full adult coat pattern is acquired after 3.5 months (Mallinson, 1968).

Ranging patterns. Daily travel distance of a Tiwai study group averaged 830 m, with a range of 350–1,400 m (Dasilva, 1989), while in the Taï Forest one group averaged 680 m per day and another 637 m (Korstjens *et al.*, 2007). The annual home range of the Tiwai group (comprising 9–11 individuals) was only 24 ha, but the two larger Taï study groups ranged more widely, a group of 12–16 covering 83 ha and a group of 16–18 covering 72 ha.

Diet. A careful study of the diet of western black-and-white colobus at Tiwai Island by Dasilva found that seeds were the most important component of the annual diet, comprising 33% of feeding observations, followed by young foliage (30%) and mature foliage (27%) (Dasilva, 1989; Davies *et al.*, 1999); almost half of the monkeys' food came from lianas, and a majority of the seeds from leguminous plants, especially the trees *Pentaclethra macrophylla* (Mimosoideae) and *Samanea dinklagei* (Mimosoideae). *Pentaclethra macrophylla* was also heavily exploited in the Taï Forest, as was *Diospyros canaliculata* (Ebenaceae) (Korstjens, 2001).

Association with other species. The western black-and-white colobus has not been found to associate with other monkey species more than would be expected by chance.

Predators. Several of the original predators of *C. polykomos* are now rare or absent over much of its range, and humans are often the main threat to these monkeys. In the Taï Forest, where the fauna is in a relatively pristine state, this species is preyed upon by crowned eagles, leopards and chimpanzees (Hoppe-Dominik, 1984; Shultz and Tomsett, 2007; Zuberbühler and Jenny, 2007). *Colobus polykomos* is the second most frequently hunted monkey by chimpanzees in Taï, after red colobus, even though male black-and-white colobus will regularly attack hunting male chimpanzees (Boesch and Boesch-Achermann, 2000). *Colobus polykomos* is still broadly sympatric with chimpanzees across its range, so chimps may be a general threat to this species.

Conservation Status

Colobus polykomos is listed as Vulnerable on the IUCN Red List. The western black-and-white colobus has been seriously impacted by human hunting, a likely result of its large size and tendency to rest high in the forest canopy, where it is conspicuous. The male's loud call can also direct hunters to its location. However, *C. polykomos* is somewhat more cryptic in its behavior than sympatric red colobus and has been less affected by hunting as result. Black-and-white colobus meat, by weight, was found to be the second-most abundant kind of monkey meat (after red colobus) in markets and restaurants around Taï National Park in a study by Refisch and Koné (2005a, 2005b).

Loss of mature forest habitat is another serious threat to this species. It can survive in degraded habitats and small patches of forest, but its preferred habitat is undisturbed high forest (Davies, 1987; Harding, 1984; Fimbel, 1994).

Colobus polykomos occurs in many protected areas, including the Outamba-Kilimi National Park, Tiwai Island Wildlife Sanctuary, the Gola Forest National Park, and the Loma Mountains proposed national park in Sierra Leone; the Haut Niger National Park, the Mont Nimba Strict Nature Reserve, and the Ziama and Diécké biosphere reserves in Guinea; Sapo National Park in Liberia; and Taï National Park, Côte d'Ivoire. However, most of these protected areas do not provide the colobus with adequate protection against hunting.

Where to See It

The western black-and-white colobus can be most readily observed at Tiwai Island Wildlife Sanctuary, Sierra Leone, and in the primate research zone in the western part of Taï National Park, Côte d'Ivoire.

Colobinae

White-thighed black-and-white colobus
Colobus vellerosus (I. Geoffroy, 1834)

Other English: White-thighed colobus, white-thighed guereza,
ursine colobus, Geoffroy's pied colobus, Geoffroy's black-and-white
colobus, black colobus monkey
French: Colobe de Geoffroy
West African languages: Fouô (Agni, Côte d'Ivoire); Foulêh (Appolo,
Côte d'Ivoire); Efuo (Twi, Ghana); Takla (Éwé, Togo); Zin klan,
toklan (Fon, Bénin)

Identification (see Fig. 8.129, p.383)

This is a large arboreal monkey with a predominantly black body
and limbs, and a long, pure white tail. White hair surrounds the black
face, in a dense ruff-like structure that extends from below the chin up
to the temples and in a band across the brow. The ruff does not reach
the upper chest. The thighs have silvery white patches on their outer
surfaces and there is white hair on the margins of the ischial callosities.
Colobus vellerosus typically lacks the epaulettes of long white hair on
the shoulders seen in the closely-related *C. polykomos*, but it is not
uncommon to find a scattering of white shoulder hairs.

Adult *Colobus vellerosus* have a head and body length of 60–70 cm
and a tail length of 75–90 cm (Jeffrey, 1974). Adult males are heavier
than females, weighing on average about 8.5 kg, compared with an
average female weight of 7 kg (Delson *et al.*, 2000).

Similar species. This monkey once shared part of its range in Côte
d'Ivoire and Ghana with Miss Waldron's red colobus (*Procolobus
waldroni*), a monkey of similar size and body proportions, but which
has a distinctly red belly and limbs. Miss Waldron's colobus has now
disappeared from all of its range (with the possible exception of the
very far southeastern corner of Côte d'Ivoire), so that any large colobus
monkey seen in eastern Côte d'Ivoire and or western Ghana is likely
to be *C. vellerosus*. There is no similar tree-living monkey in Bénin
or Togo. The loud roaring call of the male black-and-white colobus is
distinctive.

Colobinae

Taxonomic Note

The white-thighed colobus was formerly regarded as a subspecies of *Colobus polykomos* (e.g., by Napier, 1985), but its pelage pattern is different and its male loud call, or roar, is lower-pitched and has a slower pulse rate in each roar phrase (Oates and Trocco, 1983).

Black-and-white colobus monkeys that show a mixture of *C. vellerosus* and *C. polykomos* features were seen and collected in south-central Côte d'Ivoire in the past (in the vicinity of Marahoué National Park, between the Bandama and Sassandra rivers) (Booth, 1954a, 1954b). These individuals, which have been named *C. polykomos dollmani* (Schwarz, 1927), probably represented a zone of hybridization. Groves *et al.* (1993) consider that these hybrids are best regarded as part of *C. vellerosus*. Black-and-white colobus monkeys may now be extinct in the area from which *dollmani* was described,

Fig. 8.133: White-thighed black-and-white colobus (*Colobus vellerosus*), Boabeng-Fiema Monkey Sanctuary, Ghana (photo by J. A. Teichroeb).

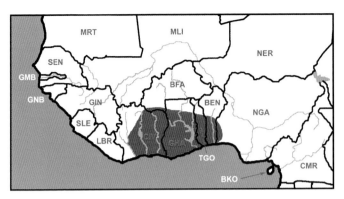

Fig. 8.134: Distribution of *Colobus vellerosus*.

but some black-and-white colobus were observed to the south-east of that area in 2004 (Gonedelé Bi *et al.*, 2006). The true affinities of those monkeys have yet to be determined at the time of writing (Oates and McGraw, 2009).

Geographic Range

Colobus vellerosus once occurred from somewhere between the Sassandra and Bandama rivers in Côte d'Ivoire eastwards through Ghana, Togo and Bénin to the western edge of Nigeria (Booth, 1954a, 1954b, 1958a, 1958b). How its range in Côte d'Ivoire is understood depends on whether *dollmani* is recognized as a distinct taxon; if *dollmani* is regarded as part of *vellerosus* then the range of *vellerosus* is probably from the Sassandra eastward. Given recent habitat loss and heavy hunting pressure it may now be very difficult to establish the original western limit of the *vellerosus* range. The distribution of *C. vellerosus* extends well north of the forest zone, reaching to about 10°N in southern Burkina Faso (Galat and Galat-Luong, 2006) and, at least in the past, northern Ghana (Grubb *et al.*, 1998). It may now be extinct in Nigeria; it should be searched for in Kainji National Park, from where it was reported in a personal communication to Happold (1987).

Natural History

Habitat. Before its populations were decimated by hunting, the white-thighed colobus could be found in a variety of forest types, ranging from moist forest near the coast, through semi-deciduous and dry forest zones to gallery forest in the woodland savanna zone. The

Colobinae

Boabeng-Fiema Monkey Sanctuary in Ghana, where most studies of this species have been conducted, is a small traditionally-protected forest in the forest-savanna transition zone, containing a mixture of old forest, regenerating forest, woodland and plantings of exotic trees (Teichroeb *et al.*, 2003).

Field studies. Habituated groups of this colobus have been studied at only two sites, both in Ghana: Bia National Park, where observations were made in the 1970s, and Boabeng-Fiema Monkey Sanctuary and nearby forest fragments, where observations have been made since 2000 by a research group at the University of Calgary, Canada, led by Pascale Sicotte. Few of the results from the Bia study have been published (however, see Olson, 1986 and Martin, 1991), but an extensive set of papers has been emerging from the Boabeng-Fiema studies (e.g., Teichroeb *et al.*, 2003; Sicotte and MacIntosh, 2004; Saj and Sicotte, 2005; Wong and Sicotte, 2006, 2007; Wong *et al.*, 2006; Saj and Sicotte, 2005, 2007; Sicotte *et al.*, 2007; Teichroeb and Sicotte, 2008a, 2008b, 2009, 2010).

Population. Martin (1991) estimated a population density of 22 individuals/km² in Bia National Park in 1978. In 1991, the 1.9-km² Boabeng-Fiema sanctuary supported about 130 colobus—a density of about 70 individuals/km², which increased to about 120 individuals/km² by 2003 (Wong and Sicotte, 2006). Small forest fragments of 3–55 ha outside the main sanctuary had densities of about 50 monkeys/km² (Wong and Sicotte, 2006). Natural predators and most potential colobus competitors are absent from Boabeng-Fiema. Surveys at other sites in Ghana since 1993 have provided encounter rates with *C. vellerosus* that have been so low as a result of hunting that densities cannot be estimated.

Habitat use. Booth (1956) notes that this colobus is most often seen in the upper layers of the forest canopy, but says that it feeds at any level from low bushes to the topmost branches of emergent trees. It will travel on the ground, especially in habitats where the forest is fragmented. Martin's (1991) studies in Bia, Ghana, in the the 1970s found that white-thighed colobus tend to keep to the middle layers of the canopy, but Olson (1986) notes that they will use crowns of emergent trees at least 50 m above ground.

Locomotion and posture. No systematic studies have been published of locomotor patterns in this species, but casual observations suggest that the white-thighed colobus is very similar to *C. polykomos* and *C. guereza*; bounding and leaping when travelling in the upper canopy, and frequently sitting at rest or lying on large branches.

Activity pattern. In Boabeng-Fiema sanctuary, 59% of activity records from three study groups were of resting animals, 24% were of feeding, 15% moving and 3% social behavior. Feeding peaks occur in the early morning and late afternoon (Teichroeb *et al.*, 2003). In small forest fragments near Boabeng-Fiema, 69% of time was spent resting, 22% feeding, 7% moving and 3% in social behavior (Wong and Sicotte, 2007).

Vocalizations and displays. One of the earliest accounts of primate vocalizations, by Hill and Booth (1957), included information on this species, which Booth had studied opportunistically in Ghana. Hill and Booth describe the loud call characteristically given by adult males as sounding like "rurr rurr rurr rurr". They note this call being given at the appearance of crowned eagles, but also in the apparent absence of external stimuli. As in other black-and-white colobus species, male roaring often occurs as a chorus close to dawn ("morning calls") among males in different groups. Hill and Booth also note an explosive, snorting alarm call given by males and females; a very soft grunting;

Colobinae

Fig. 8.135: White-thighed black-and-white colobus (*Colobus vellerosus*) in the Boabeng-Fiema Monkey Sanctuary, Ghana, where they sometimes travel along the ground (photo by J. A. Teichroeb).

and a sound like a rooting pig. Sicotte and MacIntosh (2004) note low grunts during male chases, and screams of immatures during male incursions. Excepting the grunts during male chases, these five calls appear to be equivalent to the five main call types described for *Colobus guereza* by Marler (1972): "roaring," "snorting," "purring," "cawing," and "squeaking and screaming". Oates (1977a) described *C. guereza* males producing a "loud, harsh grunting" during chases in intergroup encounters. After a male takeover and infanticide in one group at Boabeng-Fiema, adult females produced roaring calls (higher in frequency than male calls), prompting the new group male to roar (Sicotte *et al.*, 2007). While producing their roaring call, adult males often make conspicuous leaps through the canopy. Males will also display by leaping without roaring, and these displays may be combined with extending the legs stiffly and opening the mouth (Teichroeb and Sicotte, 2010).

Social organization. Group size in this species is very variable and groups with multiple adult males are common. In studies at Bia National Park, Olson (1980) observed two groups of 16 monkeys, one including 4 adult males and 6 adult females, and the other 2 males and 7 females. During the study each group increased through births, and after six months of the study the group with 4 males split into two groups, each with 2 adult males. Groups of 10–15 are reported from the gallery forests of Comoé National Park, Côte d'Ivoire (Fischer *et al.*, 2000). Fourteen groups at Boabeng-Fiema, Ghana, ranged in size from 4 to 33 (mean 14.3); one study group of 31–33 monkeys contained five adult males, one group of 7–8 had only one male, and a group of 15–16 contained seven males (Teichroeb *et al.*, 2003). Both males and females at Boabeng-Fiema have been observed to emigrate from their natal groups, but males migrate more often than females. Female emigration is correlated both with large group size and with the invasion of groups by all-male bands. Emigrant females cannot readily enter other groups, but may found new groups (Teichroeb and Sicotte, 2009).

Interactions between groups. The majority of observed encounters between different *C. vellerosus* groups at Boabeng-Fiema involved aggression, mostly directed by males at other males, but sometimes directed at females (Sicotte and MacIntosh, 2004). These encounters had a median duration of 45 minutes. During most encounters, resident males positioned themselves between members of the other group and the females and young of their own group. Females with dependent young moved away from the immediate encounter area. On two occasions during encounters, Sicotte and MacIntosh witnessed attempted copulations between females and males of other groups. Adult males also made short incursions (median duration 9 minutes) from their own bi-sexual groups into neighboring groups. In these incursions males showed aggression towards other males (e.g., by chasing them), and sometimes towards females and infants. Resident males attempted to drive away invading males. In one case a female transferred to the group from which males making a short incursion had come.

Reproduction. There is no female perineal sexual swelling in this species. In *Colobus vellerosus*, as in *C. polykomos* and *C. guereza*, infants are born with a white coat which darkens to the adult pattern in the first months of life. At Boabeng-Fiema in Ghana, births do not show a seasonal pattern but are related to the timing of male group take-overs and infanticide (Teichroeb and Sicotte, 2008a).

Male takeovers and infanticide. Sicotte and MacIntosh (2004), Saj and Sicotte (2005), Sicotte *et al.* (2007) and Teichroeb and Sicotte (2008b) report several cases of outside males (typically in all-male bands) invading the ranges of small one-male groups at Boabeng-Fiema. These invasions have been followed by attacks on the resident adult male and the disappearance and death of infants. In some cases attacks on young infants by new high-ranking males were observed; male infants seemed more likely to be attacked than females. Teichroeb and Sicotte (2008b) estimated that 38.5% of infant mortality in 2003–2005 was caused by infanticide. Interbirth intervals of Boabeng-Fiema females were shortened by these attacks.

Ranging patterns. Olson (1986) reports an annual home range size of 20–48 ha for a Bia study group of 13–18 monkeys (40 ha using data from 361 days and an analytical grid of cells with 25 m sides). The Bia group traveled a median distance of 250 m per day (range 122–675 m) in the dry season, and 306 m (range 75–752 m) in the wet season (Curtin and Olson, 1984). Based on 0.25 ha cells entered, a Boabeng-Fiema study group of 31–33 individuals had an annual range of 12 ha, and a group of 8–16 had a range of 11 ha. Day journey length for the larger group averaged 308 m (range 118–568 m) and for the smaller group 286 m (range 65–604 m) (Saj and Sicotte, 2007). Day journey lengths for groups in small forest fragments near to Boabeng-Fiema were similar, averaging 257–367 m (Wong and Sicotte, 2007).

Colobinae

Diet. Wong *et al.* (2006) found that the annual diet of white-thighed colobus groups in Boabeng-Fiema consists primarily of leaves (85–96% of records). A more limited, part-year sample from groups in nearby forest fragments recorded 70–91% of leaves in the diet. All groups also consumed flowers and most ate seed pods. Seeds have been found to comprise up to 57% of the diet in one dry-season month (Sicotte and MacIntosh, 2004). Plant species consumed varied with the composition of the forest; most seedpods eaten were from the exotic tree *Cassia siamea* (Leguminosae, Caesalpinioideae), which varied greatly in abundance. *Adansonia digitata* (Bombacacae), the baobab, was frequently eaten in all locations. Groups in forest fragments ate small numbers of insects licked or sometimes picked from the bark of trees. In Bia, Ghana, *C. vellerosus* was observed to feed on 120 plant species, of which 91 were trees, including the timber species *Entandrophragma cylindricum* and *E. utile* (Meliaceae) and *Triplochiton scleroxylon* (Sterculiaceae). Although most feeding was on leaves, fruit pulp and seeds were also eaten, including seeds of *Entandrophragma* and *Triplochiton* (Olson and Curtin, 1984).

Association with other species. Patterns of association of white-thighed colobus with other monkeys have not been reported. Only one or very few other forest monkey species are present in some of the marginal habitats where this species occurs.

Predators. No data have been published about predation on this species. Booth (1956) and Hill and Booth (1957) suggest that crowned eagles (*Stephanoaetus coronatus*) are a threat. Humans have probably been the major predator on *Colobus vellerosus* for many years.

Conservation Status

Colobus vellerosus is listed as Vulnerable on the IUCN Red List. The white-thighed colobus has been very seriously impacted by hunting for the bushmeat trade and by degradation of its habitat over most of its range. Hunting is the most serious problem faced by *C. vellerosus*. This species can flourish in small forest patches and gallery forests in the absence of hunting pressure (see, e.g., Wong and Sicotte, 2006), but is now rare or absent in many relatively large forest reserves where vegetation is intact but hunting uncontrolled (Oates *et al.*, 1997).

Even in the 1950s, Angus Booth recorded that this monkey was more affected by human hunting than any other primate in Ghana, because of demand for both its meat and its fur (Booth, 1956). In

1970, Sonia Jeffrey reported that roads built to open up forests for logging in western Ghana were providing access for farmers to clear forest, while hunting for meat was rife. *Colobus vellerosus* was killed frequently despite being completely protected by law (Jeffrey, 1970). McGraw (1998a) found that *C. vellerosus* had become rare in forest reserves in eastern Côte d'Ivoire in 1997 as a result of a combination of forest degradation and uncontrolled hunting. Surveys of Ghana's Bia National Park and Resource Reserve in 1993, where *C. vellerosus* was studied in the 1970s, failed to detect this species (Oates *et al.*, 2000a), but they were encountered once during a survey in 2006 (Oates, 2006b). Fischer *et al.* (2000) report that groups of 10–15 individuals of this species were frequently seen in Comoé National Park, Côte d'Ivoire in 1996, but that only a few small groups of 3–5 individuals were encountered in 1999, probably as a result of hunting.

Colobus vellerosus is well-protected in the Boabeng-Fiema Monkey Sanctuary in the Brong-Ahafo region of Ghana, where this species and Lowe's monkey (*Cercopithecus campbelli lowei*) are held sacred by the villagers of Boabeng and Fiema and their remnant forest habitat is preserved. The monkeys are considered to be the descendents of the patron gods of the communities (Fargey, 1992; Saj *et al.*, 2006). The sanctuary was established in 1975 when the government Department of Game and Wildlife worked with local authorities to pass a by-law prohibiting the killing of monkeys within a 3-mile radius of the villages. In 1990 a sanctuary management committee was organized, which helps to manage tourism and its revenues and oversees a ban on bush-burning and the cutting of live trees in a core area of 192 ha. Outside this core, however, the area of farmland doubled in the period 1990–2000 (Saj *et al.*, 2006). The taboo on killing monkeys is spreading to surrounding villages and there is a proposal to establish protected corridors to link the sanctuary to forest fragments in these other villages that are used by the colobus (Wong and Sicotte, 2006).

Where to See It

Colobus vellerosus is most readily observed in the Boabeng-Fiema Monkey Sanctuary in Brong-Ahafo, central Ghana. The sanctuary can be visited in a day trip from the city of Kumasi, and there is a guesthouse in Boabeng. Visitors can walk through the sanctuary to observe the colobus monkeys. The white-thighed colobus can also be seen in the gallery forests of Mole National Park (4,840 km^2), which lies 170 km west of the city of Tamale in northern Ghana; the park has suffered in the past from bushmeat hunting.

Colobinae

Guereza
Colobus guereza Rüppell, 1835

Other English: Mantled guereza, guereza colobus, Abyssinian black-
and-white colobus monkey, magistrate colobus
French: Colobe guéréza
West African languages: Biri mai roro (Hausa); Ngote (Bakossi,
Camroon); Nko (Bamileke, Cameroon); Nkeufeu (Bamoun,
Cameroon); Kendi (Gbaya, Cameroon); Mbagnie (Mvouté,
Cameroon); M'banlanrou (Foufoulbe, Cameroon)

Identification (see Fig. 8.129, p.383)

A large arboreal monkey with a very long tail. It differs from other
members of the black colobus group in having a full mantle, or veil,
of long white hair extending from the shoulders, down the flanks and
across the base of the tail. White hair surrounds the black face, but it
does not form as extended a ruff as that in *Colobus vellerosus*. The
ischial callosities are bordered with white hair—continuous in males,
divided in females. In the only subspecies found in West Africa (*C. g.
occidentalis*), the terminal two-fifths to one-third of the tail is white and
tufted. Otherwise the pelage is black.

Colobus guereza has a head and body length of about 60 cm and a
tail length of about 90 cm. Adult males are typically heavier than adult
females, weighing on average about 9 kg, compared with an average
female weight of about 7.5 kg (Delson *et al.*, 2000).

Subspecies. The only form of this widespread species to occur
in the region of this guide is the western guereza, *Colobus guereza
occidentalis* (Rochebrune, 1887). Groves (2001, 2007b) recognizes
seven other subspecies.

Similar species. In the area covered by this guide, it is hard
to confuse this monkey with any other primate. No other large,
predominantly arboreal monkey is encountered in the forests of eastern
Nigeria and western Cameroon that has a coat patterned in black and
white like the guereza; in particular the black tail with an obvious white
tuft is especially distinctive and has no parallel in other species in the
area (*Colobus vellerosus*, formerly found in far western Nigeria, has an
all-white tail). The loud roaring call of the male guereza (similar to that
of the other black colobus species) is also distinctive, especially when
produced as an early morning chorus.

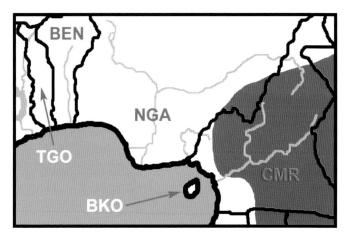

Fig. 8.136: Distribution of *Colobus guereza occidentalis* in West Africa.

Taxonomic Note

In the older literature this species is known as *Colobus abyssinicus* (e.g., Rahm, 1970) or *Colobus polykomos abyssinicus* (Schwarz, 1929).

Geographic Range

Colobus guereza ranges from northeastern Nigeria eastward across the northern part of the Congo Basin forest zone to the highlands of Kenya and northern Tanzania. *Colobus g. occidentalis* is, as its name suggests, the most westerly subspecies, occurring in Gashaka Gumti National Park and Mambilla Plateau in Adamawa and Taraba states of Nigeria, in Cameroon (excepting coastal regions), northeastern Gabon, northern and eastern Republic of Congo (including the Ituri Forest), western and southern Central African Republic, northern and northeastern Democratic Republic of Congo, southwestern Sudan and western Uganda (Oates and Trocco, 1983; Wolfheim, 1983; Groves, 2001).

Natural History

Habitat. Although this species does occur in some moist lowland forest areas, it reaches its greatest abundance (in the absence of hunting) in the deciduous forest and savanna woodland zone north of the moist

Colobinae

forest, where it flourishes in gallery forests along rivers. It can also be common in montane forest. In large blocks of lowland rain forest, this species is mostly found in riparian forest (Bocian, 1997; Gautier-Hion *et al.*, 1999).

Field studies. There is very little published information on the behavior and ecology of this colobus from field studies in West Africa. Several studies of the same subspecies found in West Africa have been conducted elsewhere, especially in Uganda's Kibale Forest (e.g., Oates, 1974, 1977a, 1977b; Harris, 2005, 2006a, 2006b; Harris and Monfort, 2003, 2006; Harris and Chapman, 2007), but also in the Budongo Forest, Uganda (Marler, 1969, 1972; Suzuki, 1979), Murchison Falls National Park, Uganda (Leskes and Acheson, 1971; Oates, 1974, 1977a, 1977b), and the Ituri Forest, DRC (Bocian, 1997). The subspecies *Colobus guereza matschiei*, very similar to *C. g. occidentalis* in appearance, has also been well-studied in the Kakamega Forest, Kenya, by Fashing (2001a, 2001b, 2001c, 2002). Many quantitative details from those studies in eastern Africa will not

Fig. 8.137: Guerezas in the Kibale Forest, Uganda (photo by N. Ting). The geographic range of the Kibale subspecies (*Colobus guereza occidentalis*) extends west across the northern Congo basin and reaches Nigeria.

be presented here because it is likely that the specifics of behavior are different in West Africa. Instead, an outline sketch of what has been found in eastern Africa will be provided, to give the user of this guide an idea of features of this monkey's natural history that are also likely to be characteristic of West African populations.

Population. *Colobus guereza* was sighted at rates of 0.48 groups per km of transect in montane forest and 0.25–0.42 in lowland gallery forest in Gashaka Gumti National Park, Nigeria by Dunn (1993). From these data, Dunn calculated densities of 2 to 3.5 groups/km² in gallery forest and 4.4 groups/km² in montane forest.

Habitat use. Guerezas typically sleep in tall tree crowns, but frequently feed in lower levels of the canopy and at forest edges. They often travel on the ground, especially in open environments where there are large gaps between trees or tree clumps.

Locomotion and posture. Like *C. polykomos* and *C. vellerosus*, guerezas have significant bounding/galloping and leaping components to their locomotion when travelling through the forest canopy. Two-thirds of the day can be spent in sitting postures; guerezas typically sit while feeding, and, when resting, they often sit or recline on large branches (Morbeck, 1977; Rose, 1978; Gebo and Chapman, 1995).

Activity pattern. In East Africa, guerezas typically spend more than half of their day resting, and often engage in early-morning sunbathing; in cool, wet conditions they adopt hunched sitting positions. Such activity patterns have been linked to their diet, which is commonly dominated by fibrous plant material with a relatively low energy content (Oates, 1974a, 1994a; Rose, 1978).

Vocalizations. Marler (1972) described five main categories of *C. guereza* call based on studies in Budongo, Uganda: "roar," "snort," "purr," "caw" and "squeaking and screaming". A sixth nonvocal sound is also common, "tongue clicking". Oates (1974) preferred the term "soft grunt" to "purr," "snuffle" (or "honk") to "caw," and "squealing" to "squeaking and screaming", and noted three other call types heard occasionally, including loud grunts made by males during chases. West African guerezas are expected to have the same vocal repertoire as those in East Africa. Adult male roars made by *C. g. occidentalis* in Gashaka Gumti are indistinguishable from those made by Ugandan animals (Oates *et al.*, 2000b). At Gashaka, as in East Africa, adult male guerezas in different groups typically produce a chorus of roars around

Colobinae

dawn. Males often accompany their roaring with ritualized jumping, with the limbs held more stiffly than in normal locomotion. East African male guerezas will jump and roar in response to the proximity of crowned eagles. Roars are sometimes heard at night.

Social organization. *Colobus guereza* social groups are generally smaller than those of other black-and-white colobus species and typically contain only a single adult male, although groups with at least two adult males are quite common at some sites. Solitary males and all-male bands have been observed. Groups of *C. g. occidentalis* with one adult male and 2–4 adult females seem to be the norm in gallery forests and forest fragments in East Africa. At Gashaka Gumti in Nigeria, Dunn (1999) reports that it is usual for groups to contain no more than 8–12 individuals, with one adult male.

Social behavior. Members of a guereza group maintain close spatial relationships. Grooming, especially among females, is common and overt agonistic interactions are infrequent.

Interactions between groups. Guereza groups typically interact antagonistically when they meet (Oates, 1977a). Adult and subadult males display to one another, using tongue clicks, extended-leg gestures, penile erections, yawns and leaps. Sometimes males chase males of the interacting group, and guttural grunts are heard. The outcome of between-group interactions has been found to vary across sites. At some sites groups usually "win" an encounter if they are in the core of their range, at other sites encounters are more influenced by dominance relationships among groups.

Reproduction. Guereza populations in eastern Africa have not been observed to have distinct birth seasons. Gestation is about 150 days (Harris and Monfort, 2006). Newborn guerezas have pure white coats and pink skin; the skin and coat start becoming gray in the third week of life. By two months of age much of the coat and skin are dark and the full adult color pattern is attained in 4–4.5 months (Oates, 1974). Young infants are very attractive to other group members, especially females, who will pull the infant away from the mother, hold the infant and groom it. Sometimes an infant passes through several hands before being reunited with its mother.

Male takeovers and infanticide. In the Kibale Forest, Uganda, adult males (in bands, or singly) have been found to invade bisexual groups with one or two adult males. An incoming male may eventually take over the group with the ouster of the original male (Oates, 1977a). These male incursions can be accompanied by infanticide (Onderdonk, 2000; Harris and Monfort, 2003).

Ranging patterns. Home range sizes for *C. guereza* in West Africa have not been measured. Range sizes vary greatly at sites in eastern Africa, from 2 to 100 ha, generally being small where forests are patchy and guereza densities are high, but larger in continuous forest with lower guereza population densities. Where ranges are large, activity is concentrated in a small core area. Daily travel distances vary greatly also, but average 500–600 m. At several East African sites, guerezas have been found to make long excursions outside their core areas (and sometimes outside their normal home range) to feed on sodium-rich vegetation, such as water plants and *Eucalyptus* bark; these resources are shared among groups without aggression (Oates, 1978; Fashing, 2001a; Harris, 2005).

Diet. In some localities guerezas have been found to be highly folivorous, with over 80% of the diet consisting of foliage, especially young leaves (e.g., Kibale, Uganda – Oates, 1977b; Harris and

Colobinae

Fig. 8.138: Western guerezas (*Colobus guereza occidentalis*), Gashaka Gumti National Park, Nigeria (photo by J. F. Oates).

Chapman, 2007). Consumption of mature foliage increases when young leaves are in short supply. At other sites, more than 30% of the diet is fruit (e.g., Naivasha, Kenya – Rose, 1978, and Kakamega, Kenya – Fashing *et al.*, 2007). Guerezas do not eat invertebrates, and make up for resultant deficiencies of minerals (especially sodium and zinc) in their diet by consuming mineral-rich water plants, tree bark and soils. Feeding habits of this species have not been studied in West Africa.

Predators. Crowned eagles and, to a lesser extent, chimpanzees are known to prey on guerezas in East African forests (Skorupa, 1989; Watts and Mitani, 2002). The guereza's habit of travelling on the ground in mosaic habitats probably makes them vulnerable to terrestrial carnivores. Its remains have been found in the feces of lions and spotted hyenas in the Faro National Park in northern Cameroon (Breuer, 2005).

Conservation Status

Colobus guereza as a species and the subspecies *occidentalis* are listed as of Least Concern on the IUCN Red List. *Colobus g. occidentalis* has a very wide distribution, but in West Africa its range is limited to the extreme east of the area covered by this guide, where it occurs mainly in the forest-savanna transition zone, especially in gallery forests. It is therefore not as badly affected by forest conversion as are strictly moist forest species (and in East Africa its numbers sometimes increase when closed forest is opened up by logging). A large portion of its range in Cameroon and Nigeria is in areas inhabited by Muslim people, who traditionally do not eat monkey meat, affording it some protection. However, throughout its range the guereza has long been hunted for its skin, used for decoration, and it suffers from bushmeat hunting in the forest zone of Cameroon (Oates, 1977c).

It is relatively well protected in Nigeria in the large Gashaka Gumti National Park (6,400 km²), and in Cameroon in both Faro National Park (3,300 km²) and Mbam & Djerem National Park (about 5,000 km²).

Where to See It

In West Africa, *Colobus guereza* can be quite readily observed in the Gashaka Gumti National Park, Nigeria, and it is widely distributed in Mbam & Djerem National Park, Cameroon.

Colobinae

Black colobus
Colobus satanas (Waterhouse, 1838)

Other English: Satanic colobus
French: Colobe satan, colobe noir
Spanish: Mono satanás
West African languages: Mmonchi (Bubi; Bioko).

Identification (see Fig. 8.129, p.383)

Bioko Island, Equatorial Guinea, is the only place in the region covered by this guide where the black colobus occurs. It is a large, entirely black monkey. Like other colobus monkeys, it differs in body proportions from sympatric guenon species in having a relatively small head, relatively long legs, and a large belly. Its entire coat is long, giving it a fluffy appearance, with especially long hair on the shoulders and forehead, giving its head a "mal coiffé" appearance (Gautier-Hion *et al.*, 1999).

Colobus satanas is the largest arboreal monkey on Bioko, with a head and body length of about 60 cm, and a tail of about 75 cm. Adult

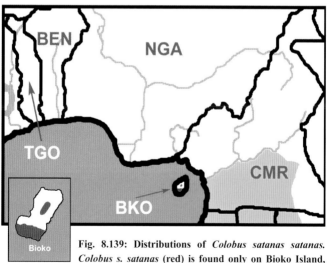

Fig. 8.139: Distributions of *Colobus satanas satanas*. *Colobus s. satanas* (red) is found only on Bioko Island, while *C. s. anthracinus* (yellow) occurs on the mainland south of the Sanaga River.

males average a little over 10 kg in weight (but can reach 13 kg), while females weigh just over 8 kg (Butynski *et al.*, 2009).

Subspecies. The Bioko subspecies of this monkey is *C. satanas satanas*. Another subspecies, *C. s. anthracinus*, occurs in mainland Equatorial Guinea, southern Cameroon, Gabon and a limited area of the Congo Republic. The island subspecies has longer hair than the mainland form, and a male loud call with a significantly slower pulse rate (Oates *et al.*, 2000b).

Similar species. Seen clearly, the black colobus is not easily confused with any other Bioko monkey. Pennant's red colobus has a similar body shape, but is slightly smaller and has a distinctive coat pattern with white on its cheeks, throat and undersurfaces, red on its flanks and outer limbs, and a dark gray back. The croaking male loud call of the black colobus is distinctive.

Geographic Range

Colobus satanas satanas occurs only on Bioko Island. Today it is restricted to the southern highlands and limited parts of Pico Basilé (Butynski and Koster, 1994).

Natural History

Habitat. Black colobus occur on Bioko from near sea level to the top of Pico Basilé (3,011 m), in lowland, mid-elevation and montane rain forest, *Schefflera* forest, and even in montane heath and grassland (Sabater Pí, 1973; Butynski and Koster, 1994; Gonzalez-Kirchner, 1997; Struhsaker, 2000).

Field studies. There has been no careful behavioral study of this species on Bioko, but there have been several studies on the mainland, in Rio Muni, Cameroon, Gabon and Congo Republic (e.g., Sabater Pí, 1970, 1973; McKey, 1978; McKey and Waterman, 1982; Harrison, 1986; Brugière, 1998; Fleury and Gautier-Hion, 1999).

Population. Butynski and Owens (2008) encountered black colobus groups at the rate of 0.18 per hour in the forests of the Gran Caldera de Luba. In unlogged forest in Gabon, densities of *C. s. anthracinus* can reach 11.3 individuals/km² (Brugière, 1998).

Habitat use. From transect surveys on Bioko, Gonzalez-Kirchner (1997) reports that the black colobus shows a diverse pattern of canopy use, being observed at all heights up to 50 m, with 30% of observations coming from above 30 m. Most resting occurred in emergent trees, and most feeding occurred in the lower canopy. At times the move and feed on the ground in grassland.

Activity pattern. Mainland groups spend 22–27% of their time feeding (Fleury and Gautier-Hion, 1999), but activity patterns on Bioko have not been studied.

Vocalizations. Like other species in the black-and-white colobus group, adult male *C. satanas* produce a loud croaking vocalization, sometimes called a "roar" (Schenkel and Schenkel-Hulliger, 1967; Marler, 1972). The call resembles the fast-paced croaking of a large frog. Each individual "croak" phrase is made up of a series of closely-spaced pulses. The pitch of a *C. satanas* croak is higher than the similar calls of other black-and-white colobus, and the call modulates (the phrase rises and falls in pitch during delivery). The pulses in the black colobus croak are also closer together than in the other black-and-white species—i.e., there is a faster pulse rate, or tempo (Oates and Trocco, 1983). In Bioko black colobus this tempo is slightly slower than in mainland populations (Oates *et al.*, 2000b). Mainland black colobus produce their roaring call in response to disturbances (including the loud calls of other monkey species), the appearance of potential predators, and calling from other black colobus groups (Gautier-Hion *et al.*, 1999). As in other black-and-white colobus species, a series of soft grunts may be given as a low-intensity alarm call (Oates, 1977a; see <http://www.bioko.org/wildlife/satanas.asp>).

Social organization. Social groups of Bioko black colobus appear to be small, especially compared to those on the mainland. Butynski and Koster (1994) counted one group with at least ten individuals, but they report that hunters claim that groups typically have 7–10 individuals. Struhsaker (2000) counted five groups, each with only two or three members. Struhsaker relates the small group size of Bioko primates in comparison with their mainland relatives to the absence on the island of natural predators, especially crowned eagles. Groups of *C. satanas* on the mainland vary in size from 7–30 with an average of 13–17 and typically contain several adult males (Sabater Pí, 1970; Oates, 1994a; Fleury and Gautier-Hion, 1999; Gautier-Hion *et al.*, 1999).

Fig. 8.140: Bioko black colobus (*Colobus satanas satanas*) in the Gran Caldera de Luba (photo by R. A. Bergl).

Colobinae

Reproduction. Little is known about reproduction in *C. satanas*. Infants have brown coats at birth (contrasting with other species in the black-and-white colobus group whose newborns all have pure white coats).

Diet and Ranging. *Colobus satanas* groups studied in Cameroon and Gabon include large quantities of seeds in their diet, together with young and mature leaves (McKey, 1978; McKey and Waterman, 1982; Harrison and Hladik, 1986; Fleury and Gautier-Hion, 1999). Home range sizes vary from about 70 ha in Douala-Edéa, Cameroon, to over 570 ha at Makandé in the Forêt des Abeilles, Gabon. The Makandé monkeys (which travelled an average of 850 m each day) are considered by Fleury and Gautier-Hion (1999) to be semi-nomadic in their ranging, a response to great temporal and spatial variation in the abundance of caesalpinioid legume seeds. The small size of Bioko black colobus groups hints at differences in the diet and ranging behavior of the island population, which lives in forests of a very different botanical structure to those on the mainland. Details on the diet and ranging of the Bioko black colobus are lacking.

Association with other species. Butynski and Koster (1994) observed this monkey in association with *Cercopithecus erythrotis*, *C. nictitans* and red colobus in Bioko forests.

Predators. The potential natural predators on this species on the mainland (chimpanzees, leopards and crowned eagles) are absent from Bioko, but, as elsewhere, black colobus on the island are targets of human hunters.

Conservation Status

Colobus satanas satanas is listed as Endangered on the IUCN Red List. Like other Bioko primates, the black colobus has been badly affected by the increase in shotgun hunting for the bushmeat market since the 1980s. Hearn *et al.* (2006) have estimated that the black colobus population declined by more than 60% between 1986 and 2006, the greatest decline of any of the Bioko monkey species. This steep decline is attributed in part to particularly heavy hunting in 2002–2006 on Pico Basilé, where the black colobus was once abundant. In November 2007, a ban on shotgun hunting came into force on Bioko, but this has not stopped all hunting. In Gabon, Brugière (1998) reports that hunting is probably the most important threat to populations of *Colobus satanas anthracinus*, which are otherwise not strongly affected by low-intensity logging.

The Pico Basilé National Park and the Gran Caldera and Southern Highlands Scientific Reserve should theoretically provide good protection for the Bioko black colobus but in practice these protected areas have suffered from a lack of adequate patrolling and law enforcement.

Where to See It

This monkey is most readily observed in the Gran Caldera de Luba in southwestern Bioko. The species is now rare elsewhere on the island (Hearn *et al.*, 2006).

FAMILY HOMINIDAE
Great apes and humans

This family needs little introduction. It comprises the living and fossil humans and their close great ape relatives. They are characterized by large body sizes, absence of an external tail, large brains, and a tendency to hold the trunk in a vertical rather than horizontal posture. With the exception of humans themselves, these primates have arms longer than their legs, and use their long arms to haul themselves around when climbing in trees. All the hominids are sexually dimorphic in size, with males being significantly larger than females.

Traditionally (see, e.g., Napier and Napier, 1967) the great apes were separated from humans into the family Pongidae, but a wealth of evidence, especially from DNA, now clearly demonstrates the close evolutionary relationship between these groups and points to the biological logic of uniting them in the single family Hominidae. Groves (2001) divides the Hominidae into the subfamilies Ponginae (for the orang utans of Southeast Asia) and Homininae for the African great apes (gorillas and chimpanzees) and humans. Molecular evidence suggests that these two subfamilies diverged about 14 MYA, that the gorilla line separated about 8 MYA, and that humans and chimpanzees had a last common ancestor 6 MYA (Raaum *et al.*, 2005).

Most current classifications place the living African great apes in the genera *Gorilla* (for the gorillas) and *Pan* (for the chimpanzees). The human genus *Homo* also has its origins in Africa.

Gorilla I. Geoffroy, 1852
Gorillas

Gorillas are the largest of all living primates and, because of the powerful effect their appearance and stories about them have on the human psyche, they are probably better known to people around the world than most other primates, with the possible exception of chimpanzees.

Gorillas first became known to science through the work of Thomas Staughton Savage, an American missionary, physician and naturalist, who stopped in Gabon in 1847 on his way back to the United States after working in Liberia. In Gabon, Savage collected skulls and other skeletal material from what he considered to be a new species of

Cross River Gorilla (female)
Gorilla gorilla diehli

Cross River Gorilla (male)
Gorilla gorilla diehli

Chimpanzee
Pan troglodytes

Fig. 8.141.

Hominidae

orang utan, and these specimens were named *Troglodytes gorilla* in a famous paper co-authored by Savage and Jeffries Wyman, a professor of anatomy at Harvard (Savage and Wyman, 1847). Groves (2001) notes that Savage alone was responsible for the name *T. gorilla* in their joint paper; *Troglodytes* as a generic name had first been used for the chimpanzee.

Gorillas were transferred to the genus *Gorilla* by Isidore Geoffroy Saint-Hilaire in 1853. Over the next 80 years, several new species of *Gorilla* and many subspecies were named, until Schwarz (1928b) reduced all described gorillas to one species, *Gorilla gorilla*, with seven subspecies. Soon after this, Coolidge (1929) undertook a thorough review and recognized only two subspecies; *G. gorilla gorilla* in western equatorial Africa and *G. g. beringei* in eastern Africa. An accumulation of morphological and genetic evidence now supports the recognition of western and eastern gorillas as two species, *Gorilla gorilla* and *Gorilla beringei*, each with two subspecies: *G. g. gorilla* and *G. g. diehli*, and *G. b. beringei* and *G. b. graueri* (Groves, 2001, and see Pilbrow, 2010). This arrangement is followed by Grubb *et al.* (2003) and in this guidebook.

Gorilla gorilla *geospecies*

Grubb (2006b) places the two gorilla species, *Gorilla gorilla* and *G. beringei*, which today occur allopatrically on either side of the Congo Basin, in the geospecies *G. gorilla*.

Local Representatives

In the region covered by this guide, populations of western gorillas (*Gorilla gorilla*) occur in two limited areas. One of these is the hills and mountains at the headwaters of the Cross River straddling the border between Nigeria and Cameroon, inhabited by the Cross River gorilla, *Gorilla gorilla diehli*. The other population occurs just north of the Sanaga River in a small mountainous area within the Ebo Forest in the Littoral Province of Cameroon; the Ebo gorillas are still poorly known, but limited evidence suggests that they are an unusual peripheral population of the western lowland gorilla *G. g. gorilla* (Morgan *et al.*, 2003; Groves, 2005).

Western gorilla
Gorilla gorilla (Savage, 1847)

French: Gorille de l'oeust

The account of western gorillas in this guidebook will focus on *G. g. diehli*, the Cross River gorilla, which has become relatively well known from a series of surveys and field studies that commenced in 1987. The Ebo population was only located in 2002; given that the taxonomic affinities of the Ebo gorillas remain in doubt, and that very little is known of their natural history, this population will be given just a short summary treatment at the end of the description of the Cross River gorilla.

Cross River gorilla
Gorilla gorilla diehli Matschie, 1904

West African languages: Echie, ichi (Boki, Nigeria); Echile (Becheve, Nigeria); Miki (Okwa, Nigeria); Meki (Denya/Anyang, Cameroon)

Identification (see Fig. 8.141, p.413)

Gorillas, like the other great apes (the orang utans and chimpanzees), have long arms and short legs, and no external tail. Gorillas have a particularly massive head, with prominent, powerful jaws and broad nostrils. Their fingers are short and broad, the skin of their face, hands and feet is black, and their ears are small. Male Cross River gorillas have a relatively shorter face than do males in other western gorilla populations, and a poorly developed sagittal crest (Sarmiento and Oates, 2000). Cross River gorillas have short hair that is predominantly dark gray, but is often lighter and browner on the back, and darker and blacker on the limbs. The brow and crown of the head are rust-red. Fully adult males have light silvery-brown backs ("silverbacks").

Few data on body dimensions are available for Cross River gorillas. Sanderson (1940) gives the length of an adult male from the crown of the head to the base of the spine as 125 cm, and from the base of the spine to the heel as 67 cm. According to Smith and Jungers (1997), adult male *G. g. gorilla* average 170 kg in weight, compared to an average adult female weight of 71.5 kg.

Gorillas have a very much more restricted range than chimpanzees in the area covered by this guide; even where they occur in eastern Nigeria and western Cameroon, gorillas are so rare that they are very unlikely to be seen. In the habitats where they still survive, evidence of their existence is provided mostly by the remains of the long-lasting nests they construct for sleeping, and by the signs of their feeding trails. The gorillas' nests (or "beds") consist of small branches, saplings or herb stems bent towards each other and knitted together to form a springy platform. Gorilla nests are not always easy to distinguish from those of chimpanzees (see next section).

Gorillas, and especially adult males, have a strong, distinctive pungent odor from which their proximity can be detected even when the apes cannot be seen or heard.

Similar species. The only other species that the gorilla may readily be confused with is the chimpanzee. A large male chimpanzee has a similar body length to a female gorilla and is only a little less bulky. Although the coat coloration of adult chimpanzees within the range of Cross River gorillas is variable (with combinations of black, brownish gray and silvery-gray hair being seen), chimpanzees predominantly have black or dark gray hair, and are less brown than gorillas. Like gorillas, adult chimpanzees in the Cross River area (belonging to the taxon *Pan troglodytes ellioti*) often have black skin on the face, hands and feet, although this skin is pinkish in young animals, and some adults have pinkish skin on the muzzle and/or around the eyes. Therefore, when glimpsed at a distance, adult chimpanzees can be confused with gorillas, especially by a novice observer.

Cross River gorillas differ from sympatric chimpanzees in that male gorillas are very much larger and more robustly built than chimpanzees. Gorillas have a more massive skull and broader nostrils than chimps. The front of the crown in *P. t. ellioti* typically has bald black skin, while Cross River gorillas typically have reddish hair at the front of the crown; and although the ears in both taxa are black these are larger in chimpanzees than in gorillas and protrude further through the coat. The fingers and toes of chimpanzees are more slender than those of gorillas, and relatively longer. Female chimpanzees cyclically display large, pink perineal swellings which are not seen in female gorillas. Young chimps have a tuft of white hair on the rump, absent in gorillas. The loud whooping calls of chimpanzees, by which they can be detected at a considerable distance, do not have a parallel in gorillas.

In their general behavior, gorillas are quieter, more undemonstrative animals than chimpanzees.

Like gorillas, chimpanzees make night sleeping nests (or beds). The nests are described by McGrew (1992a) as follows: "Each arboreal construction is a skilful inter-weaving of leafy, springy branches, large and small, with a central mattress of twigs and leaflets sometimes detached and added for lining." Gorilla nests are typically more robust than those of chimps, and are more often constructed near or on the ground; adult male (silverback) gorillas usually (but not always) make a ground nest. Chimpanzees only rarely nest on or very close to the ground. Chimp nests are commonly in smaller, more dispersed groups. If nests are fresh, the presence of the gorilla's distinctive dung in or close to a nest allows species identification. Gorilla dung is larger in diameter than chimp dung, typically contains more fibrous material, and consists of several distinct lobes of fecal material.

Hunters and other local people in southern Nigeria and Cameroon often use the name "gorilla" to describe male chimpanzees, no doubt based on the superficial similarities of these apes, and this can confuse visitors.

Fig. 8.142: Cross River gorillas (*Gorilla gorilla diehli*), Kagwene, Cameroon (photo by J. L. Sunderland-Groves). This gorilla is very difficult to observe and rarely photographed.

Hominidae

Taxonomic Note

Matschie (1904) described the species *Gorilla diehli* based on specimens collected near today's Takamanda National Park in southwestern Cameroon. Taxonomists subsequently reduced the status of this population to that of a subspecies, *G. g. diehli*, and it was sunk into *G. g. gorilla* by Coolidge (1929). Sarmiento and Oates (2000) revived *G. g. diehli*, which they called the "Cross River gorilla", based on a new analysis which found that compared to *G. g. gorilla*, *G. g. diehli* has a significantly smaller cheek tooth occlusal area, a smaller vault volume, a narrower biglenoid diameter, a narrower incisor row and a narrower palate width.

Geographic Range

The Cross River gorilla is found further north and west than any other form of gorilla. Most of its remaining populations are scattered across an area of about 4,000 km², in the northern parts of Nigeria's Cross River State and Cameroon's Southwest Region (with one subpopulation just entering the Northwest Region), from Afi Mountain in the west to Kagwene Mountain in the east. An isolated population occurs to the southeast of this area, in the Bechati-Fossimondi forests of Southwest Cameroon. The core of the gorilla's range is in the

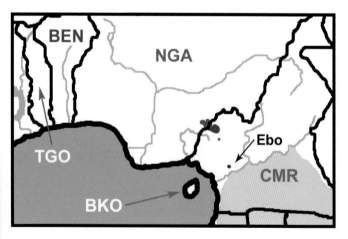

Fig. 8.143: Distribution of *Gorilla gorilla diehli* (red) and *Gorilla gorilla gorilla* (yellow) in West Africa. The isolated Ebo population (arrowed) is just north of the Sanaga River.

Takamanda National Park in Cameroon and the adjacent forests of the
Okwangwo Division of Cross River National Park in Nigeria.

Natural History

Field studies. In addition to several surveys (e.g., Harris *et al.*,
1987; Harcourt *et al.*, 1989; Oates *et al.*, 1990a; J. L. Groves, 2001;
Sunderland-Groves *et al.*, 2003b, Sunderland-Groves, 2008), there have
been long-term field studies of Cross River gorillas at Afi Mountain in
Nigeria by Kelley McFarland (Oates *et al.*, 2003; McFarland, 2007) and
at Kagwene Mountain in Cameroon by Jacqueline Sunderland-Groves
(Sunderland-Groves *et al.*, 2009), as well as a population-wide study of
population structure, genetics and habitat connectivity by Richard Bergl
(Bergl, 2006; Bergl and Vigilant, 2007; Bergl *et al.*, 2008). However,
these studies have not involved close-range observation of habituated
animals; a long history of hunting has made these gorillas very wary
of humans and therefore difficult to approach, and researchers have
also avoided habituation because of the increased risk to hunters that
tame gorillas would face. Most knowledge of wild gorilla behavior has
come from studies of eastern gorillas and particularly of the Virunga
mountain gorillas (*G. b. beringei*), starting with the classic studies
by George Schaller in 1959–1961 (Schaller, 1963), but considerable
knowledge has also been gathered on western lowland gorillas (*G. g.
gorilla*) in Central Africa (see, e.g., Williamson *et al.*, 1990; Remis,
1995; Goldsmith, 1999; Robbins *et al.*, 2004).

Habitat. Cross River gorillas occur in lowland, submontane and
montane forest. Although they are occasionally encountered in lowland
river valleys, they mostly use hill areas at elevations of 400–2,000 m.
Most of the forests where Cross River gorillas concentrate their time
are relatively mature and have not been subject to commercial logging
or recent cultivation. At higher elevations the forests are dominated
by trees of relatively low stature, and may have open areas containing
abundant herbaceous vegetation as a result of land slides and fire.
In some highland areas of their range the vegetation is a mosaic of
submontane and montane forest and anthropogenic grassland; the
gorillas will cross grassland between forest patches. Much of the Cross
River gorilla's habitat has an intense dry season, and at Afi Mountain in
Nigeria, on the western edge of this gorilla's range, little rain falls from
November through March.

Population. Even where these rare animals still occur they are
generally at low densities. Surveys suggest that between 200 and 300

Cross River gorillas remain, with population nuclei in 10–11 localities across their range (Oates *et al.*, 2007). Some of these nuclei have densities of about one gorilla/km².

Habitat use. Because Cross River gorillas have not been habituated and closely observed, the amount of time they spend on the ground and in trees has not been measured. Evidence from feeding trails suggests that, although much of their time is spent on the ground, they do climb trees, especially to get fruit. At Bai Hokou in the Central African Republic, western lowland gorillas frequently climb trees in the wet season, when fruits are most abundant; they will ascend to heights of at least 30 m (Remis, 1995).

Locomotion and posture. Gorillas travel on the ground by quadrupedal knuckle-walking, supporting the weight of the fore part of the body on the backs of middle segments of their fingers. When they climb trees they use their arms and legs for support, and typically move cautiously (large males move with especial caution). Locomotion has not been studied in Cross River gorillas, but studies at Bai Hokou in the Central African Republic show that adult males climb less than females and stay closer to the core of trees where there are substantial supports; the gorillas use lianas for support while climbing and feeding (Remis, 1995, 1999). Gorillas only stand bipedally for short periods; males will do this in particular during chest-beating displays, and females will sometimes stand bipedally when feeding in trees.

Activity pattern. Like other great apes, gorillas are only active during the day, and typically sleep in nests (or beds) at night. The activity budget of Cross River gorillas has not been measured. A western gorilla group studied in the Central African Republic on average spent 67% of the day feeding, 21% resting and 12% travelling; however, there were large seasonal variations, with more time spent feeding and less travelling in the December–February dry season when little fruit was eaten. The adult male spent less time feeding than did females and young (Masi *et al.*, 2009).

Nesting behavior. Cross River gorillas build their night-sleeping nests on the ground and in trees. At Kagwene in Cameroon, the gorillas built 55% of their night nests on the ground or on fallen trees, and the remaining 45% in trees. In the driest months, 81% of nests were on the ground, compared with 31% in the wettest months (Sunderland-Groves *et al.*, 2009). Surveys in Nigeria found 62% of nests below a height of 1 m (Oates *et al.*, 2000). Gorillas will also make less robust nests for resting during the day. At Kagwene in Cameroon, 18% of Cross River gorilla nests located were judged to have been made for day resting; they contained little or no dung (Sunderland-Groves *et al.*, 2009).

Vocalizations. Vocal communication in gorillas has been studied more in eastern than in western gorillas, and very little in Cross River gorillas. Based on a review of the literature, Estes (1991) describes 15 distinct gorilla calls along with the sound made by chest beating. Schaller (1963), on the other hand, distinguishes 22 call types in eastern mountain gorillas. The most frequent vocalizer, and emitter of the loudest calls, is the silverback male (Gautier-Hion *et al.*, 1999). Among the most notable of adult male calls is a short loud, low-pitched "roar", given in situations of stress or perceived threat (particularly from humans) and often accompanied by other aggressive, intimidating displays such as hooting calls, and charging. Another distinctive call, made by subadult males, adult females and juveniles, is the "bark", resembling the sound of a barking dog, and given as a warning call or threat (Schaller, 1963). "Staccato grunts" (also called "cough-grunts") are given by females and males during agonistic encounters and in other disturbing situations. Gorillas of all ages and both sexes practice chest beating, in which the chest is slapped rapidly with open, slightly cupped hands (usually both hands, used alternately, but sometimes just one hand); the loudest chest-beating, sounding like a hollow tree or

Fig. 8.144: Gorilla research camp at Kagwene Mountain, Cameroon (photo by J. F. Oates).

large gourd being knocked, comes from adult males in which the sound is amplified by air sacs on either side of the throat (Schaller, 1963).

Social organization. Gorillas typically live in cohesive social groups containing one or a few fully adult (silverback) males and several adult females. Western gorillas as a whole have groups ranging from 2–32, with an average of 10 individuals and most commonly just one fully adult male (Robbins *et al.*, 2004; McFarland, 2007). Solitary adult males occur, and may acquire females to found new groups. Almost all evidence on the social organization of Cross River gorillas comes from nest sites. At most sites, groups of eight or fewer nests are typical. Commonly just three or four nests are encountered (Oates *et al.*, 1990a, 2003; Sunderland-Groves *et al.*, 2003a), but occasionally 10 or more nests are found. Large nest groups. on the other hand, are the norm at Afi Mountain in Nigeria (mean nest group size 18.2) and at Kagwene Mountain in Cameroon (mean group size 12.4) (McFarland, 2007; Sunderland-Groves *et al.*, 2009). Fluctuations in the number of nests in the study group at Afi Mountain during extended group follows strongly suggest that a large group sometimes divides into smaller groups not only for foraging but also for night resting, and that at other times small numbers of animals join the main group for short periods (McFarland, 2007). Evidence from the size of dung associated with nests suggests that between one and three fully adult males were present in the Afi study group so that, when the group fissioned, each subgroup still retained at least one silverback male. Group size from day to day was most variable at times of low fruit availability. At Kagwene, nest data also suggest a flexible grouping pattern (Sunderland-Groves *et al.*, 2009). Some groups of western lowland gorillas in Central Africa have also shown evidence of splitting into foraging subgroups (Remis, 1997).

Social behavior. Because of challenges with the habituation of western compared to eastern gorillas, and poor visibility in the rain-forest understorey, little information on social behavior is available for wild groups of western gorillas. Some observational data are available from groups entering large open swampy areas (or "bais") in Central African forests, such as Mbeli Bai in the Nouabalé-Ndoki National Park, Republic of Congo, where gorillas have been observed from viewing platforms (Stokes, 2004). Among groups entering Mbeli Bai, very little affiliative behavior was seen among group members, and no grooming was observed. Agonistic interactions were more frequent; adult males approached and supplanted females, and males and females made aggressive staccato grunts. No dominance hierarchy was evident among females. No information is available on social behavior in Cross River gorillas.

Interactions between groups. Nothing is known about interactions between different groups of Cross River gorillas, but given their scattered distribution it is likely that some social groups rarely meet with others. Among Central African western lowland gorillas, group ranges overlap but groups often ignore each other when they are in proximity. Aggression between males in different groups occurs infrequently, its occurrence possibly depending on the degree of relatedness between the males (Doran-Sheehy *et al.*, 2004)

Reproduction and life history. No specific data are available on reproductive patterns in Cross River gorillas; most information on reproduction has come from studies of wild mountain gorillas or captive western lowland gorillas. Unlike the obvious perineal swellings displayed by female chimpanzees around the time of ovulation, there are no obvious external signs of ovulation in gorilla females, except for some slight labial swelling (Czekala and Sicotte, 2000). Around the time of ovulation, female gorillas will approach adult males and solicit mating. Female eastern mountain gorillas first reproduce at the age of 10 or 11, following a gestation period of about 255 days (slightly shorter than that of humans) (Harcourt *et al.*, 1980). Interbirth interval in western gorillas is 4–6 years (Robbins *et al.*, 2004). Both male and female western gorillas transfer between groups (Robbins *et al.*, 2004), and genetic evidence of the migration of individuals between Cross River gorilla subpopulations has revealed equal numbers of male and female migrants (Bergl, 2006). At least in mountain gorillas there appears to be no distinct breeding season (Schaller, 1963).

Ranging patterns. The best information on Cross River gorilla ranging patterns comes from the study by McFarland (2007) at Afi Mountain, Nigeria, in which the movements of gorillas were tracked from their feeding trails and nest sites. The Afi study group (of about 18 gorillas) travelled from 61 m to 3.7 km/day (average 1.3 km/day). The gorillas travelled furthest in the period when they ate most fruit (February–July, late dry season and early wet season). Based on the number of 100 m × 100 m quadrats entered, the group had an annual home range of at least 13 km², McFarland estimated that the actual annual range was probably about 20 km², but that over a longer period of time they might use an area of at least 30 km². At times of low fruit availability, the gorillas concentrated in areas where herbaceous vegetation was abundant and the risk from human hunters low. Groups of western lowland gorillas in Central Africa have similar daily path lengths (averaging 1.5–2.3 km/day), similar total home ranges (16–23 km²), and they also range more widely when fruit is most abundant (Remis, 1997; Cipolletta, 2004; Doran-Sheehy *et al.*, 2004).

Diet. At the time of writing, the only detailed information available on Cross River gorilla diet is from Afi Mountain, where McFarland (2007) examined 1,418 fecal samples and 4,181 feeding sites. The gorillas at Afi were found to consume at least 168 plant species, including 69 trees, 32 lianas and vines, 22 herbs and 6 shrubs. Herb pith, leaves of herbs and trees, and liana bark and pith were staple foods eaten in all weeks of the year. All fecal samples contained remains of the pith of herbs. Fruit was eaten according to availability, with fruit remains making up 35–67% of fecal weight in February–July and 1–24% in August–January. Among important fruits were those of two species of the liana *Landolphia* (Apocynaceae), of the trees *Treculia africana* and *Myrianthus arboreus*, and of figs, *Ficus* spp. (all of which are members of the Moraceae). Among important large herbs in the Afi gorilla diet were *Anchomanes difformis* (Araceae), and species of *Aframomum* (Zingiberaceae), *Palisota* (Commelinaceae) and *Megaphrynium* (Marantaceae). Bark of the trees *Milicia* (Moraceae) and *Pterocarpus* (Papilionaceae) was an important fall-back food item, eaten when other preferred foods were in short supply. No evidence was found of Afi gorillas eating insects or other animals.

Predators. There is strong circumstantial evidence that leopards are predators of western lowland gorillas (Fay *et al.*, 1995; Robbins *et al.*, 2004), but leopards are now very rare or extinct in the range of Cross River gorillas. In recent years human hunting has been the main form of predation suffered by Cross River gorillas (Oates *et al.*, 2003).

Conservation Status

Gorilla gorilla diehli is listed as Critically Endangered on the IUCN Red List. Cross River gorillas are considered Critically Endangered because of the very small number of mature individuals known to exist (estimated at <200), the fragmented structure of their population, and the continuing threats they face from habitat conversion and hunting. Some of the forests in which they live are still being eroded by subsistence farming and by fire, and although conservation programs developed since 1990 have reduced the direct targeting of these gorillas by hunters, general bushmeat hunting remains a major activity in most of the sites where they survive (Oates *et al.*, 2007). In addition to wildlife laws in Cameroon and Nigeria that prohibit gorilla hunting, Cross River gorillas occur in two formal protected areas in Nigeria (Afi Mountain Wildlife Sanctuary, and the Okwangwo Division of Cross River National Park) and two in Cameroon (the Kagwene Gorilla Sanctuary and Takamanda National Park). Despite the small size and fragmented nature of the Cross River gorilla's population, the population's level of genetic diversity remains relatively high, and quite large areas of apparently suitable habitat remain intact adjacent to the areas where subpopulations are presently concentrated (Bergl, 2006). This suggests that the population's viability can be increased by sustained protection of the animals and their habitat.

Where to See It

Visitors to the rugged hill country inhabited by Cross River gorillas should not have a high expectation of seeing these apes. Not only are they very rare, and wary of humans, but studies on these gorillas, and conservation efforts directed at protecting them, have generally avoided habituation because of the fear of increasing the gorillas' susceptibility to hunting. In the presence of an expert guide, visitors to the Afi or Mbe Mountains in Cross River State, Nigeria, or to Kagwene Mountain in Cameroon, have a good chance of seeing nests of Cross River gorillas.

Ebo Forest gorilla
Gorilla gorilla ?gorilla (Savage, 1847)

West African languages: Paki (Bassa, Cameroon); Mbes (Banen, Cameroon)

In the course of a biodiversity survey of forests in the Yabassi area of the Littoral Province of western Cameroon in December 2000–February 2001, Dowsett-Lemaire and Dowsett (2001) were shown gorilla nests in the Bekob area of the Ebo Forest, north of the Sanaga River, a locality from which gorillas were previously unknown to science. This is more than 150 km south of the nearest subpopulation of Cross River gorillas, and about 250 km away from the nearest population of western lowland gorillas known to survive south of the Sanaga River (in the Belabo region). The taxonomic affinities of the Ebo population have yet to be fully resolved, but measurements from a single adult male skull suggest affinities with western lowland gorillas (*G. g. gorilla*) from the inland plateau of Cameroon (Groves, 2005).

The Ebo Forest covers over 1,500 km² of rugged hills and mountains, between 200 and 1,200 m above sea level. Since 2002 the primates of Ebo Forest have been monitored by a team led by Bethan Morgan. This team has found evidence of one group of up to 12 weaned gorillas using a small area of about 25 km² in the northwest of the forest, together with a solitary male (Morgan *et al.*, 2003; Morgan, 2004; Morgan and Sunderland-Groves, 2006). Like some other western gorilla populations, the Ebo gorillas seem to readily climb trees, with all six nests observed in one group of day nests built >15 m above ground, including one at about 35 m; food remains and feces indicate consumption of the pith of herbs and climbing palms, leaves, and fruit (Morgan *et al.*, 2003).

The Ebo Forest is an important site for several other forest primates, including chimpanzees (*Pan troglodytes ellioti*), drills (*Mandrillus leucophaeus*), Preuss's red colobus (*Procolobus preussi*) and Preuss's monkey (*Allochrocebus preussi*), but all these primates, including gorillas, are threatened by bushmeat hunting.

Pan Oken, 1816
Chimpanzees

Chimpanzees resemble gorillas in their general body plan. Like gorillas they use quadrupedal knuckle-walking to travel on the ground, and they also employ their powerful arms (and long fingers) to clamber up and through trees. They are smaller than gorillas, and less sexually dimorphic in size. They have a coat of long, rather coarse, and predominantly black hair. Their rounded head has a prominent muzzle, prominent brows, and relatively large, prominent ears. The nostrils of chimpanzees are smaller than those of gorillas. Unlike gorillas, female chimpanzees display large, pink perineal swellings around the time of ovulation.

Chimpanzees are currently considered to belong to two species: the common or robust chimpanzee, *Pan troglodytes*, and the bonobo or gracile chimpanzee, *Pan paniscus*, sometimes known as the pygmy chimpanzee. *Pan troglodytes* occurs from Senegal east through West Africa (but not, at least today, in the Dahomey Gap) to the forests of western equatorial Africa, and from there across the north of the Congo Basin to the Western Rift Valley in East Africa. The bonobo is restricted to the Congo Basin, in forests south of the great bend of the River Congo.

Pan troglodytes geospecies

Grubb (2006b) regards both *Pan troglodytes* and *P. paniscus*, which are allopatric, as belonging to the geospecies *P. troglodytes*.

Local Representatives

Only *Pan troglodytes* occurs in the area of this guidebook, with two subspecies that are restricted to West Africa: *P. t. verus* in Upper Guinea, and *P. t. ellioti* in Nigeria and Cameroon. Differences between these two forms (and their precise distributions) will be described below. At this point the geographic boundary between *P. t. verus* and *P. t. ellioti* is not fully settled, and to the north of the Upper Sanaga River in Cameroon there is an area of hybridization between *P. t. ellioti* and *P. t. troglodytes*.

Chimpanzee
Pan troglodytes (Blumenbach, 1799)

Other English: Common chimpanzee, robust chimpanzee
French: Chimpanzé commun

In this guidebook, the two West African subspecies will each be given a separate account. Before giving those accounts, a commentary on the naming of *Pan troglodytes* and its subspecies is in order, as this has been an area of some confusion.

In addition to *Pan troglodytes*, many other Latin names have been applied to the common chimpanzee over the years, including *Simia satyrus*, *Anthropopithecus pan* and *Troglodytes niger* (see Jenkins, 1990; Groves, 2001). Napier and Napier (1967) recognized three subspecies in *Pan troglodytes*: *P. t. troglodytes* from eastern Nigeria, Cameroon and western equatorial Africa; *P. t. schweinfurthii* from the Ubangi River east to Tanzania; and *P. t. verus* in West Africa, including western Nigeria. This classification remained in very wide use until the late 1990s, when Gonder *et al.* (1997) published preliminary results from a study of mitochondrial D-loop sequences from southern Nigerian chimpanzees. This study found that the mtDNA of a sample of chimpanzees from both east and west of the Niger River was much more similar to that of *P. t. verus* than to that of *P. t. troglodytes*.

The findings of Gonder *et al.* have been largely corroborated by an analysis of a much larger sample of material from both Nigerian and Cameroonian chimpanzees. This analysis indicates that chimpanzees in eastern Nigeria and western Cameroon are a distinctive genetic form separated from *P. t. troglodytes* by the Sanaga River in Cameroon (Gonder, 2000; Gonder *et al.*, 2006). Gonder *et al.* (1997, 2006) suggested that the name *P. t. vellerosus* was appropriate for these Nigeria-Cameroon chimpanzees, based on a specimen apparently collected on Mount Cameroon in 1862 by Richard Burton (Gray, 1862). Groves (2001) and Grubb *et al.* (2003) recognized *P. t. vellerosus* as a subspecies, and this course has been supported by the study of Pilbrow (2006), who found that the molar morphology of the chimpanzees from between the Niger and Sanaga distinguishes them from all other populations. Oates *et al.* (2009) have shown that the type specimen of *P. t. vellerosus* was actually collected by Burton not on Mt. Cameroon, but in Gabon, and that chimpanzees living between the Niger and Sanaga are properly referred to as *Pan troglodytes ellioti*, the name used in this book.

Hominidae

The affinities of chimpanzees in western Nigeria have not yet been definitively settled. Depending on which evolutionary tree-building model is employed, the mtDNA of the small sample of western Nigerian chimpanzees for which genetic material is available groups either with the chimpanzees of Upper Guinea to the west, or with those of eastern Nigeria and western Cameroon (Gonder *et al.*, 2006). A small sample of molars from western Nigerian chimpanzees studied by Pilbrow (2006) also shows differences from eastern Nigerian samples. It is possible that western Nigerian chimpanzees are a distinct form (as are several other primates from this area, such as *Cercopithecus erythrogaster* and *Perodicticus potto juju*). Alternatively, all chimpanzees in West Africa from Senegal to the Sanaga River might be considered as members of one subspecies, for which the correct biological name would be *Pan troglodytes ellioti*.

Western chimpanzee
Pan troglodytes verus

Elliot's chimpanzee
Pan troglodytes ellioti

Fig. 8.145.

Hominidae

Western chimpanzee
Pan troglodytes verus Schwarz, 1934

Other English: Upper Guinea chimpanzee
French: Chimpanzé oriental
Portuguese: Chimpanzé
West African languages: Dàri (Fula, Guinea-Bissau); Demorú
(Mandingo, Guinea-Bissau); Ka watu (Temne, Sierra Leone); Ngolei
(Mende, Sierra Leone); Baboon, bamboo (Krio, Sierra Leone;
Liberian English); Gwah (Bassa, Liberia); Weh (Sapo, Liberia);
Akatia (Twi, Ghana); Amékessé (Ewe, Togo)

Identification (see Figs. 8.141 & 8.145, pp.413, 429)

The face and head of western chimpanzees have a distinctive
appearance. The muzzle is broad, fringed laterally and under the lower
jaw by an obvious beard of sparse white hairs in adults and young; this
white beard is especially well-developed in adult males. Young animals
have a generally pink face, but often with darker pigmentation around
the eyes. The face darkens with age, becoming almost entirely black
or dark gray in some individuals, but remaining mottled pink-gray on
the muzzle in others. The ears are especially large and prominent; they
are pinkish in young animals and darken with age. As they get older,
these chimpanzees lose hair on their forehead, producing a triangular
bald spot in adult males and a broader sparsely-haired area in females.
Brow ridges with bare skin are well-developed in this subspecies and
sometimes are distinctly arched. Adult males are markedly more
robust in build than females, and have shaggier body hair. For *Pan
troglodytes* as a whole, Napier and Napier (1967) give adult head and
body length as 77–93 cm in males and 70–85 cm in females. Very
little published information is available on the body weights of West
African chimpanzees; for *P. t. verus*, weights for adult male are given
as 46–49 kg and for adult females as 42 kg (Smith and Jungers, 1997;
Groves, 2001).

Similar species. It is difficult to confuse the chimpanzee with any
other primate in the forests of Upper Guinea. It is the largest primate
in this region. There is no other very large primate in the moist forests
of Upper Guinea that lacks a tail, and that has such a characteristic face
and locomotory style. In drier forests and woodlands in the western
part of West Africa, chimpanzees and baboons occur in the same
habitat, and an adult male baboon can approach the size of a young

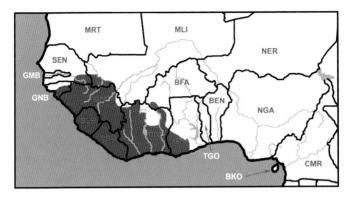

Fig. 8.146: Distribution of *Pan troglodytes verus*.

chimpanzee. However, both the Guinea baboon (*Papio papio*) and the olive baboon (*P. anubis*) have tails, brown (rather than black or black and silvery) coats, dog-like muzzles, and arms that are approximately the same length as their legs. When moving in trees, baboons move quadrupedally, rather than hauling themselves around with their arms. Chimpanzees build nests in which they sleep at night and baboons do not. Confusion can arise in Liberia and Sierra Leone because chimpanzees are often colloquially called "baboon".

Geographic Range

Pan t. verus occurs from southeastern Senegal and Guinea-Bissau, south and east through the forest and southern savanna-woodland zones to Ghana. Until at least the 1950s, chimpanzees presumed to belong to this subspecies still probably occurred in western Togo, but they are now almost certainly extinct (Cornevin, 1962; Brownell, 2003a; G. Campbell, pers. comm.).

Natural History

A useful summary of the natural history of western chimpanzees is provided by T. Humle in Kormos *et al.* (2003a).

Field studies. Some of the earliest attempts to study wild chimpanzees were conducted on *P. t. verus* in West Africa. In 1930, Henry Nissen made observations of unhabituated chimpanzees at Neribili in Guinea (Nissen, 1931), and Adriaan Kortlandt launched a series of short-term studies in the same country in 1960 (see, for example, Kortlandt, 1962; de Bournonville, 1967). The results of that early work were overshadowed by research on East African chimpanzees (*P. t. schweinfurthii*), and especially the studies begun at Gombe, Tanzania, by Jane Goodall in 1960 (e.g., Goodall, 1963, 1965, 1986). In 1976, Y. Sugiyama began studies of *P. t. verus* at Bossou in southeastern Guinea that have continued to the present day (see Sugiyama and Koman, 1979; Humle and Matsuzawa, 2001, 2002). A team from the University of Stirling later began studying the chimpanzees of Mount Assirik in the Niokolo Koba National Park, Senegal (see McGrew *et al.*, 1978, 1981; Baldwin *et al.*, 1982; Tutin *et al.*, 1983), and Christophe Boesch conducted a pilot study of the chimpanzees of the Taï forest in Côte d'Ivoire (Boesch, 1978). In 1979, Boesch launched a long-term study of the Taï chimps. This study continues and has yielded the largest body of knowledge on the behavior and ecology of wild *P. t. verus*; three well-habituated communities are observed regularly (see, for example, Boesch and Boesch, 1989; Boesch and Boesch-Achermann, 2000; Boesch *et al.*, 2006). In 2001, a new long-term study site was established by Jill Pruetz at Fongoli in the savanna zone of southeastern Senegal, east of Niokolo Koba National Park (Pruetz, 2006, 2007; Pruetz and Bertolani, 2009). Other sites where western chimpanzee natural history has been studied include Outamba-Kilimi in Sierra Leone (e.g., Alp, 1993, 1997), and Sapo, Liberia (e.g., Anderson *et al.*, 1983).

Habitat. Although human activities have greatly restricted the range of western chimpanzees over the last 50 years, they still occupy a very wide range of habitats, including mature moist closed-canopy lowland forest, montane forest, semi-deciduous and dry forest, savanna woodland and grassland with gallery forests, and agriculturally-dominated landscapes with a mosaic of secondary forest and farmland. The study sites of Taï, Bossou and Mt. Assirik provide fascinating contrasts as chimpanzee habitats. Taï is a pristine high-canopy moist forest habitat; Bossou is an agricultural landscape of cultivated fields with secondary forest at various stages of regrowth subsequent to farming; and Mt. Assirik is in the Sudanian savanna woodland zone (with gallery forests). Taï and Bossou each have an annual rainfall of around 2,000 mm with a major November-February dry season and a two-peaked wet season, while Mt. Assirik has less than 1,000 mm of rainfall and a seven-month dry season. The Fongoli habitat has many similarities to Mt. Assirik.

Population. Population densities of *P. t. verus* vary tremendously from site to site, related to the wide range of habitats they occupy, and the impact of human hunting on many populations. In the dry savanna woodlands of Niokolo Koba National Park and of the Fongoli region of Senegal, densities of 0.09-0.13/km² have been estimated (Baldwin *et al.*, 1981; Pruetz *et al.*, 2002), while the moister savanna woodland environment of the Haut Niger National Park in Guinea is estimated to have a chimpanzee density of 0.87 individuals/km² (Fleury-Brugière and Brugière, 2010). A nationwide survey of chimpanzees in Sierra Leone in 2009–2010 found that they are still widespread, but they vary greatly in density from site to site, ranging from 0.03 individuals/km² in non-protected areas to 2.7/km² in the 396-km² Loma Mountains proposed national park, one of the highest chimpanzee densities recorded in Africa (Brincic *et al.*, 2010). After a two-month survey in the southeastern part of the Sapo Forest in Liberia, Anderson *et al.* (1983) estimated a density of 0.24 chimps/km². Based on counting nests along a relatively small number of transects at many sites in Côte d'Ivoire in 1988–1989, Marchesi *et al.* (1995) estimated local densities (where nests were found) of between 0.06 and 10.3 chimpanzees/km², with a mean density of 1.6/km² in the moist forest zone and 1.1/km² in forests in the savanna zone. A resurvey of many of these sites in 2007 found a 90% decline in nest encounter rate (Campbell *et al.*, 2008a).

Fig. 8.147: Western chimpanzee (*Pan troglodytes verus*) fishing for termites, Fongoli, Senegal (photo by S. Bogart).

Hominidae

Habitat use. Chimpanzees usually sleep in trees, in specially constructed night nests (or beds), but they obtain their food both in trees and on the ground, and they travel between feeding sites and patrol their range on the ground, moving quadrupedally. The amount of time spent on the ground during the day varies between sites and seasons, depending on the distribution of food, but it is common for more than half of their time to be spent in trees. Males spend more time on the ground than females. In the Taï forest, Doran (1993) found that adult male chimpanzees spent an average of 56.5% of the day on the ground, while the smaller adult females spent an average of only 38.7% on the ground and spent more time above 20 m in the canopy than did males. In the mosaic habitat of Fongoli, consisting of open woodland, grassland, gallery forest and agricultural fields, the chimpanzees preferentially use small patches of forest, but travel across short grassland between the forest and woodland areas where they spend most of their time (Pruetz and Bertolani, 2009).

Locomotion and posture. Like gorillas, chimpanzees use quadrupedal "knuckle-walking" to travel on the ground, flexing their hands so that the backs of middle segments of the fingers are in contact with the substrate, but placing the soles of their feet on the ground. Goodall (1965) describes this travel as typically being in "a leisurely fashion." Goodall notes that Gombe chimpanzees will stand bipedally to look over long grass, with the trunk held erect and the arms held at the sides; Taï forest chimpanzees use bipedalism only rarely, and typically when carrying food for a short distance (Doran, 1993). Occasionally chimps walk and even run bipedally, and adult males typically run in the course of displays with branch waving and throwing. In trees, chimpanzees climb using their arms and legs: ascending tree trunks by placing the hands around the trunk and the feet flat against it, walking quadrupedally on large branches, and hauling themselves through the crown with their arms; in climbing and scrambling around tree crowns, the feet are used like a second pair of hands in "quadrumanous" locomotion (Doran, 1993).

Activity pattern. Chimpanzees in the Taï forest study community have been observed to spend about 43% of the day feeding, 39% resting and 12% travelling. Peaks of feeding occur in the early morning and late afternoon, and females spend more time feeding than males (Doran, 1993, 1997). Doran found that time spent feeding was lowest, and time resting highest, when figs were abundant in the wet month of May. At Fongoli in Senegal, the chimpanzees have been found to use caves during the hottest part of the dry season when maximum temperatures in their habitat exceed 35°C (Pruetz, 2007).

Nesting behavior. At Mt. Assirik, Baldwin *et al.* (1981) found that chimpanzees selected tall trees in which to nest in gallery forest, woodland and grassland, with a typical nest being 10–12 m from the ground (higher than the nests built by forest-living *Pan troglodytes troglodytes* in Rio Muni). The height of nests built by chimps in the Sapo Forest, Liberia, was similar, at 12 m, to that in Senegal, despite the very different habitat (Anderson *et al.*, 1983). At both Mt. Assirik and Sapo the great majority of nests were built above 5 m and below 20 m. At Sapo, mature forest was selected for nesting in preference to swamp forest or young secondary forest. In his initial studies in the Taï Forest, Boesch (1978) found that most nests were constructed between 3.5 and 15 m above ground. During the day, chimpanzees will sometimes construct simple beds on the ground in which to rest, and ground nests may occasionally be used at night. In the heavily farmed landscapes of Guinea and Sierra Leone, oil-palm trees (*Elaeis guineensis*) are often used for sleeping (Humle, 2003).

Fig. 8.148: Adult male western chimpanzee (*Pan troglodytes verus*), Fongoli, Senegal (photo by S. Bogart).

Hominidae

Vocalizations and drumming. Chimpanzees are the noisiest of the great apes, and parties within earshot of each other may exchange calls frequently (Goodall, 1986). They can, however, also remain silent for long periods. In addition to communicating with a broad range of gestures and calls, chimpanzees (and particularly adult males) will strike the buttress roots of large trees; the loud sounds produced by this "drumming" carry far through the forest. The complex vocal repertoire of chimpanzees includes many types of call that grade into one another, so that attempting to describe a discrete number of calls is not a straightforward matter. Building on her earliest descriptions (Goodall, 1965), and the work of Marler (1976), Goodall (1986) lists 19 kinds of calls exchanged among party members (together with other sounds such as lip smacking, yawning and coughing), and 8 additional long-distance calls. Many of these vocalizations are variations on four major call types: grunts, barks, screams and hoots. The pant-hoot (of which Goodall recognizes four different varieties) is one of the loudest and most distinctive of chimp calls; voiced during inhalation and exhalation, it commences softly as a series of "hoos" which become

Fig. 8.149: A group of western chimpanzees (*Pan troglodytes verus*) moving through a recently burned savanna woodland, Fongoli, Senegal (photo by S. Bogart).

increasingly loud and build to a climax that may include screams and barks, before subsiding to soft "hoos" again. Pant-hoots may be given upon arrival at food sources, when two parties meet, during travel, or on hearing the calls of other chimps (Goodall, 1986). Loud pant-hoots are given by adult males during encounters between communities.

Social organization. Chimpanzees live in social communities in which individuals have fluid patterns of association, forming a "fission-fusion" society. An entire community rarely comes together at the same place at the same time; instead, an observer typically encounters small "parties" of apes that are associating together temporarily in the community's range. Parties contain varying combinations of age classes and sexes, with the most common type being a mixture of male and female adults with immature offspring. Boesch and Boesch-Achermann (2000) report that the study community of chimpanzees at Taï varied in size from 29 to 82 individuals over a 16-year period, and contained 2–10 adult males and 11–27 adult females. The average size of parties observed was 10 individuals, and these parties stayed together on average for 24 minutes. For many years the Bossou community has fluctuated in size from 16–23 individuals with 1–3 adult males and 5–7 adult females. Party sizes vary greatly, but most frequently consist of between 7 and 12 independently-moving apes (Sugiyama and Koman, 1979; Humle and Matsuzawa, 2001). In 1976–1979, the chimp community studied at Mt. Assirik was estimated to contain probably 25–30 individuals, with at least 6 adult males and 5 adult females; parties ranged in size from 1–22 with a median of 4 (Tutin *et al.*, 1983). In 2005–2006, the Fongoli community had 35 members, with 10 adult males, 7 adult females and 18 immature. Dry season party size averaged 17.7 individuals, compared with 12.1 in the wet season (Pruetz and Bertolani, 2009). The high average year-round party size of 15 is larger than recorded at any other site.

Social behavior. Bonds between male chimpanzees in a community typically are closer than those between females. Males spend more time in proximity to members of their sex than do females, and there is more male-male than female-female grooming. For instance, at Taï 44% of grooming bouts observed were between adult males, while only 22% were between adult females, even though females outnumbered males in the community (Boesch and Boesch-Achermann, 2000). There is a linear dominance hierarchy among community males, leading individuals to frequently evaluate and adjust their behavior as they join different short-term social parties. The dominance hierarchy itself is dynamic and maintained by agonistic interactions, in which

Hominidae

the most dominant males typically show aggression to subordinate individuals. Males will form coalitions in attacks on other chimps. In one study period at Taï most of these coalitions involved other individuals in a partnership with either the most dominant male or the oldest male (Boesch and Boesch-Achermann, 2000). Taï chimpanzee society has been found to differ from that observed in East African chimp populations in that females quite often enter coalitions with males, and build stable, long-term alliances with other females, leading Boesch and Boesch-Achermann (2000) to refer to the society as "bi-sexually bonded."

Interactions between groups. Where more than one social community is present in an area, members of one chimpanzee community defend their ranges against other groups. This territorial behavior is a significant facet of the apes' lives. In the Taï forest, just over half of the study community's territory has been found to overlap the territories of five adjoining communities. As described by Boesch and Boesch-Achermann (2000), adult males play a primary role in territorial defence. An important component of this male territorial behavior consists of patrolling the edges of their range (and intruding into the ranges of other communities), searching for signs of their neighbors. In these patrols, small groups of males move silently through the forest, listening and smelling for signs of other chimpanzees. On detecting strangers, they may move towards them and establish visual contact; a visual encounter can be followed by an attack, and counter-attacks, accompanied by loud aggressive calling, and physical contact, including biting, can occur. Females may join males in attacks, and females with sexual swellings have been observed at Taï to briefly join males in a neighboring community and mate with them, before returning to their own community. Killing of the infants of stranger females has not been observed at Taï, as it has in East African chimpanzees.

Reproduction and life history. Female western chimpanzees have an ovulatory cycle of 36 days; their perineal skin expands in the second week of this cycle, resulting in a large pink swelling that persists for about 10 days, with ovulation occurring in the last 2-3 days of the swelling (Boesch and Boesch-Achermann, 2000). Mating occurs most frequently during the period of maximum swelling. At Taï, however, swellings have also been observed in females that are probably not ovulating (for instance, in low-status lactating mothers), and the swellings are therefore not an entirely "honest" signal of reproductive state. They may also act as a "social passport" that lowers aggression from males. Mating is sometimes promiscuous, with a swollen female being mated by several different community males without obvious signs of conflict among the males. On other occasions an estrous female forms a consortship with a particular male, moving with him for several days, away from other community members. These consortships occur especially with high-ranking males, but only a few of them result in paternity. Genetic analysis has shown that estrous females will leave their community surreptitiously and mate with males in neighboring communities. Half of 14 infants sampled in the study community had extra-group fathers (Gagneux *et al.*, 1997).

The gestation period in chimpanzees is about 230 days, and the interbirth interval of Taï chimpanzee females (if their infant does not die) averages 69 months (Boesch and Boesch-Achermann, 2000). At Taï, females leave their natal community around the time of adolescence (at an age of about 11 years), and then remain in their new host community, while males stay with the community in which they are born. Females begin to display a small sexual swelling before adolescence, and in the Taï forest they give birth for the first time at an average age of 13.7 years. Males mature more slowly, undergoing adolescence by about 15 and becoming fully grown at about 25 years. In Taï, chimpanzees may live as long as 50 years (Boesch and Boesch-Achermann, 2000).

Ranging patterns. The size of a community's range—its territory—varies greatly depending on the habitat and on relations with other communities, and it also been found to vary considerably through time. Ranging patterns are influenced by seasonal variations in food supply, the fission-fusion nature of chimpanzee society, and the movements of members of neighboring communities. Between 1982 and 1995, the main study group of chimpanzees in Taï used a territory of between 16 and 27 km²; 75% of the community's time was spent in a core area that made up 35% of the total range (Boesch and Boesch-Achermann, 2000). Boesch and Boesch-Achermann (2000) note a maximum monthly average day range for Taï chimps of 11.3 km, but individuals can also move as little as 70 m in a day (Doran, 1997). By contrast, in the poorer-quality habitat at Mt. Assirik in Senegal, the study community's total range has been estimated to be between 278 and 333 km², although actual sightings of chimpanzees and nests over a four-year period were spread over a smaller area of 72 km² (Baldwin *et al.*, 1982). Rather than being spread evenly across their very large range, the small Mt. Assirik community (averaging 28 individuals) appeared to move seasonally as a community from one part of the range

Hominidae

to another, moving silently and rapidly over long distances in large travelling parties (Tutin *et al.*, 1983). At the nearby and similarly arid Fongoli site, the chimpanzee community's total range is estimated to cover at least 65 km², with a core range of 30 km² (Pruetz, 2007; Pruetz and Bertolani, 2009). The Bossou chimp community uses about 15 km², restricting their activities to a core area of 6 km² (Humle, 2003).

Diet. Chimpanzees are omnivores whose diet is typically dominated by fruit, but leaves and a variety of animals are also eaten. Among western chimpanzees, fruits have been found to account for 62–85% of feeding observations. In the Taï forest, 85% of the overall diet is fruit, but the species eaten vary greatly from month to month. Preferred species are *Dacryodes aubrevillei* (Burseraceae), *Ficus* spp. (Moraceae), *Dialium guineense* (Leguminosae, Caesalpinioideae), *Parinari excelsa* (Chysobalanaceae), *Treculia africana* (Moraceae) and *Chysophyllum taiensis* (Sapotaceae) (Boesch *et al.*, 2006). Part of the diet of the chimps at Bossou in Guinea consists of the fruits of cultivated trees and oil palms. A one-year study of the Bossou chimps found that soft fruit made up 62% of the diet on average (based on time spent feeding), and the kernels of oil palms another 12%; leaves and herbs were eaten 14% of the time and insects 2% (Yamakoshi, 1998). In observations of feeding at Fongoli in Senegal, 63% were on fruit, 19% on leaves and pith, 11% on flowers and 5% on invertebrates (Pruetz, 2006). The seeds of four kinds of tree were found in more than 50% of feces of Fongoli chimps in more than a single month: *Adansonia digitata* (Bombacaceae), *Diospyros mespiliformis* (Ebenaceae), *Ficus* spp. (Moraceae), and *Saba senegalensis* (Apocynaceae). Figs (*Ficus* spp.) appeared to be a staple food, occurring in feces in 11 of 12 months.

Tool use. The use of tools by chimpanzees to obtain food has received much attention, with Goodall (1963) first describing the use by Tanzanian chimps of small twigs or grass stalks to extract termites from their nests, and Struhsaker and Hunkeler (1971) describing how chimpanzees in the Taï forest use stones or sticks to crack open the hard nuts of *Coula edulis* (Olacaceae) and *Panda oleosa* (Pandaceae) fruits to extract oil-rich seeds. Subsequently, evidence has emerged of nut-cracking by *P. t. verus* directed at other tree species, including *Detarium senegalensis* (Leguminosae, Caesalpinioideae), *Parinari excelsa*, *Sacoglottis gabonensis* (Humiriaceae) and the oil palm, *Elaeis guineensis*, not only in Côte d'Ivoire but also in Guinea, Liberia and Sierra Leone (Boesch and Boesch, 1983; Anderson *et al.*, 1983; Whitesides, 1985; Hannah and McGrew, 1987; Yamakoshi, 1998). Tree roots are most often used as anvils for the nut hammers, but rocks

Fig. 8.150: An anvil and hammer used by chimpanzees (*Pan t. verus*) at Putu, Liberia. Remains of hard-shelled *Panda oleosa* (Pandaceae) nuts, which have oil-rich seeds, can be seen on top of the anvil (photo by J. Decher).

may also be employed. Over the years the list of tools used by wild chimpanzees has grown, as has the purposes for which they are used, including termite-fishing by *P. t. verus* at Bossou, Mt. Assirik, the Nimba Mountains and Fongoli (McGrew, 1992b; Whiten *et al.*, 1999; Humle, 2003; McGrew *et al.*, 2005).

Hunting behavior. Another feature of chimpanzee diet that has received a great deal of attention is the hunting of mammalian prey. Again, the first evidence of this behavior was documented at Gombe by Goodall (1963) who recorded a young bushpig, a young bushbuck and an unidentified small mammal being eaten by adult male chimps. Red colobus monkeys were eventually added to this list (Goodall, 1965). Once chimpanzees became habituated for study in the Taï forest it was found that they too quite frequently eat mammalian prey, focusing their attention on monkeys, and particularly red colobus (*Procolobus badius*) and black-and-white colobus (*Colobus polykomos*) (Boesch and Boesch, 1989; Boesch and Boesch-Achermann, 2000).

Monkey hunts at Taï occur in every month of the year, but are most frequent in the wet months of September and October. Hunting

Hominidae

is undertaken predominantly by males. Taï chimpanzees occasionally hunt alone but they most frequently cooperate in groups. These hunts can last for two hours, but the average duration is 18 minutes. The Taï chimps find their monkey prey by listening for their calls (or for the whistling calls of the Diana monkeys with which red colobus often associate), approach them silently, then usually try to isolate an individual monkey in the forest canopy (blocking its escape routes), where it can be ambushed and captured. When adult colobus are captured, the chimpanzees begin eating them while they are still alive, but death follows within minutes. A prey capture is commonly followed by an outburst of screaming that attracts other chimps, and unless the carcass is small it is then almost always divided among several animals, although the captor usually retains some meat. Meat is shared with other adult males (especially dominants) and with adult females (Boesch and Boesch, 1989; Boesch and Boesch-Achermann, 2000).

At Fongoli in Senegal, western chimpanzees have been observed to select and prepare branches which are then used to extract Senegal bushbabies (*Galago senegalensis*) from their sleeping holes in trees (Pruetz and Bertolani, 2007). At nearby Mt. Assirik, McGrew *et al.* (1978) found remains of these galagos, as well as pottos, in chimp feces. Fongoli chimps also preyed on green monkeys (*Cercopithecus aethiops sabaeus*) (Pruetz, 2006). From direct observation and an analysis of fecal samples, Alp and Kitchener (1993) recorded chimpanzees in Outamba-Kilimi National Park, Sierra Leone, preying on a duiker antelope, a black-and-white colobus monkey, a guenon and a flying squirrel.

Predators. Tutin *et al.* (1983) list lion, leopard, wild dog and spotted hyaena as potential predators of chimpanzees in Niokolo Koba National Park in Senegal, but these predators are now absent at most of the woodland sites still inhabited by *P. troglodytes verus* in West Africa, and leopards are now rare or extinct in Niokolo Koba. In the rain forest, leopards prey on chimpanzees (Boesch, 1991; Boesch and Boesch-Achermann, 2000), but leopards are now very rare or absent across much of the West African forest where by far the most serious predator on many chimpanzee populations today is *Homo sapiens*. Humans hunt chimpanzees for their meat, to capture infants for sale, and for body parts used in traditional medicine and rituals. However, in some parts of West Africa, and especially in the woodland and savanna zone, their close relationship to humans is recognized, and there are religious prohibitions or other taboos against eating chimpanzees (Kormos *et al.*, 2003b). In a study of bushmeat markets in the vicinity of the Haut Niger National Park in Guinea in 2001, 14 of 9,134 carcasses were chimpanzees (Brugière and Magassouba, 2009).

Conservation Status

Pan troglodytes verus is listed as Endangered on the IUCN Red List. The western chimpanzee is considered to be Endangered because of an estimated high rate of decline across its geographical range in the last 20–30 years, with this decline projected to continue into the future. Campbell *et al.* (2008) report a 90% decline in nest encounter rate in the forests of Côte d'Ivoire between 1989–1990 and 2007, and ascribe this to an increase in human population leading to increased hunting pressure and deforestation. Similarly large declines may not have occurred in regions where these apes are not heavily hunted, and where they have long-adapted to an agricultural landscape, as in Sierra Leone. A nationwide survey of Sierra Leone by Brincic *et al.* (2010) in 2009–2010 produced a best estimate of 5,580 chimps in the country (range 2,585–10,446), compared with an estimate of 2,000 from a more limited survey by G. Teleki and L. Baldwin in 1979–1980 (Teleki, 1989). Interview surveys in western Guinea and southern Guinea-Bissau in 2003–2004 suggested that chimpanzees are still widespread and common in those areas, and that they are rarely hunted (Brugière *et al.*, 2009).

Where to See It

Wild chimpanzees are not readily seen in the rain forests of West Africa, although in areas where they have not been decimated by hunting their sleeping nests may be encountered and their calls and drumming may be heard at a distance. The best chances of direct sightings are with habituated study communities such as those at Bossou (Guinea), Taï (Côte d'Ivoire) and Fongoli (Senegal); otherwise, encounters are most likely where chimpanzees occur at relatively high densities and are not significantly targeted by hunters, such as in the Mafou forest area of Haut Niger National Park (Guinea) and the Outamba-Kilimi National Park (Sierra Leone).

Hominidae

Elliot's chimpanzee
Pan troglodytes ellioti Schwarz, 1934

Other English: Nigeria-Cameroon chimpanzee, Nigeria chimpanzee,
Gulf of Guinea chimpanzee
French: Chimpanzé du Nigeria-Cameroun
West African languages: Loki (Fon, Bénin); Etiemi, inaki, elegbede
(Yoruba, Nigeria); Osa (Bini, Nigeria); Idele (Ijaw, Nigeria); Ozor
(Igbo, Nigeria); Irua (Boki, Nigeria); Biri mai ganga (Hausa,
Nigeria—meaning "monkey with the drum"); Atieh (Denya/Anyang,
Cameroon and Nigeria); Njock (Ejagham, Nigeria and Cameroon);
Kono'w (Korup, Cameroon); Ewakou (Bakossi, Cameroon); Mouyeu
(Banen, Cameroon); Nyée (Bassa, Cameroon); Pou'koup (Bamileke,
Cameroon); Souniam (Bamoun, Cameroon); Fourdou (Foufoulbe,
Cameroon)

Identification (see Figs. 8.141 & 8.145, pp.413, 429)

Pan t. ellioti infants, like those of *P. t. verus*, have pink skin on the
face, hands and feet. As they get older, they typically develop much
more uniformly black coloration in these areas than does *P. t. verus.*
In *P. t. verus*, a lighter, freckled muzzle is common in adults, and a
black mask on a pale face in younger animals. The ears of Elliot's
chimpanzee are smaller than those of the western chimpanzee, and lie
closer to the skull, rather than sticking out prominently. The top of
the head is rounder in appearance than the more flat-topped head of
P. t. verus, the muzzle is less broad, and there is less development of a
white beard, with sparse white hairs restricted to the chin. The arched
brows of *P. t. verus* are rarely seen in *P. t. ellioti*, where the brow ridge
is typically straight. In overall build, *P. t. ellioti* is more gracile than
P. t. verus.

Similar species. Chimpanzees can be confused with gorillas but, if
they are clearly seen, not with any other primates. In a small part of the
Cameroon-Nigeria border region, and in the Lebialem and Ebo Forests
of western Cameroon, *P. t. ellioti* occurs sympatrically with gorillas. A
large male chimpanzee rivals the dimensions of a female gorilla, but
is less heavily built. In particular, gorillas have a more massive head
and broader nostrils than chimpanzees. Chimpanzees typically have
a longer, fluffier, blacker coat than the gorillas found in West Africa,
and chimpanzees have larger, protruding ears. Unlike young gorillas,
whose exposed skin is black, juvenile chimpanzees have pinkish skin

on their faces (especially the muzzle), ears, hands and feet, sparse white hair on the chin, and a distinctive tuft of white hair on the rump. The chimpanzee's exposed skin darkens with age. Western gorillas typically have reddish hair at the front of the crown, where in *P. t. ellioti* there is typically bald black skin. Gorilla females do not have the large cyclical perineal swellings displayed by chimpanzee females.

Even when they cannot be seen, chimpanzees can often be identified at a distance by their very loud whooping calls, whereas gorillas are sometimes heard at closer range from barks or male chest-beats. The sleeping nests (or beds) of chimpanzees and gorillas are much more frequently encountered than the apes themselves. Chimpanzee nests in West African forests are usually constructed in trees from leafy branches, bent over to make a springy platform. Gorilla nests are usually larger and, although they may also be constructed in trees, they are often made quite close to the ground or, in the case of adult males, on the ground. Chimpanzees also sometimes construct ground nests, particularly for short daytime rests.

Confusion between chimpanzees and gorillas sometimes arises in southern Nigeria and Cameroon because hunters and other local people often use the name "gorilla" to describe male chimpanzees.

Geographic Range

Pan t. ellioti occurs in the forests of southern Nigeria and western Cameroon. The type specimen was collected near Basho, Cameroon, in the vicinity of what is now the Takamanda National Park (Oates *et*

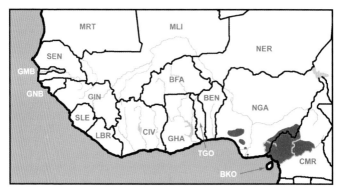

Fig. 8.151: Distribution of *Pan troglodytes ellioti*.

Hominidae

al., 2009). The southern boundary of the range of *P. t. ellioti* is the lower Sanaga River, south of which chimpanzees group genetically with *P. t. troglodytes*. North of the Upper Sanaga, in the vicinity of the Mbam & Djerem National Park, there are mtDNA genotypes that group with both *P. t. ellioti* and *P. t. troglodytes* (Gonder, 2000). The western boundary of the range of *P. t. ellioti* is not yet fully resolved; as discussed above, some evidence groups the chimpanzees west of the lower Niger River with *P. t. ellioti*, but they also group with *P. t. verus* in other analyses. In the past (perhaps until the 1960s), the chimpanzee population of western Nigeria probably extended into the forests of southeastern Bénin Republic, but chimpanzees are almost certainly now extinct in Bénin (Sayer and Green, 1984; Brownell, 2003b).

Natural History

Field studies. Relatively little is known about the ecology and behavior of Elliot's chimpanzee, which was only revived as a distinct taxon in 1997 (and referred to initially as *P. t. vellerosus*). At the time of writing, several surveys had been conducted across the range of the subspecies, but only two long-term efforts at studying its natural history were underway. One of these was in the Kwano area of the Gashaka Gumti National Park in northeastern Nigeria. Those studies, which began in 2000, have been organized by Volker Sommer, but the Gashaka chimps are not habituated (see, for example, Sommer *et al.*, 2004; Hohmann *et al.*, 2006; Fowler and Sommer, 2007). The other long-term study site is in Cameroon's Ebo Forest, where research organized by Bethan Morgan began in 2005 (Morgan and Abwe, 2006; Abwe and Morgan, 2008).

Habitat. The range of habitats occupied by *P. t. ellioti* is similar to that used by *P. t. verus*: moist lowland closed-canopy forest, montane forest, dry forest, and savanna woodlands and grasslands with gallery forests. Possibly because of heavier hunting pressure on these apes than is found in the western part of the range of *P. t. verus*, *P. t. ellioti* less often survives in agricultural landscapes with high human population densities. The Kwano study site in Nigeria supports a vegetation mosaic of savanna woodland and dry forest with gallery forest along watercourses, while the vegetation of the Ebo study site in Cameroon is a mixture lowland and sub-montane forest on rocky terrain

Population. Population densities of *P. t. ellioti* vary tremendously across the subspecies' range due to the combined influence of habitat variation and the varying intensity of hunting pressure. For instance, in surveys at many forest sites in southwest Cameroon, M. Eno Nku (unpublished reports to the Wildlife Conservation Society, 2003–2004) encountered 0.14–1.4 chimpanzee nests per km of transect surveyed, while at five sites spread across one limited area of southwest Cameroon—the Takamanda Forest Reserve and neighboring hills—Sunderland-Groves *et al.* (2003b) encountered 0–3.7 nests/km. Only one site within the range of *P. t. ellioti*, the 667-km² Banyang-Mbo Wildlife Sanctuary in southwest Cameroon, has been subject to an intensive transect-based census of its chimpanzees. From observations of nests, this 2006–2007 census produced an estimate of 1.1–1.7 individuals/km² (Greengrass and Maisels, 2007). In the best-studied population of Elliot's chimpanzee, in the Gashaka Gumti National Park, Nigeria, a density of 1.3/km² has been estimated within the range of the main study community (Sommer *et al.*, 2004).

Habitat use, locomotion and activity patterns. Few quantitative data on these topics are available for Elliot's chimpanzee, but available observations suggest that their behavior resembles that of other chimps, including *P. t. verus* (described above). When first encountered at Gashaka, chimpanzees were travelling on 42% of occasions, resting on 22% and foraging on 36% (Sommer *et al.*, 2004).

Nesting behavior. Nests observed in the Afi, Mbe and Okwangwo forests in Nigeria were built in trees at heights of 3 m to over 20 m above the ground, with almost all nests between 4 and 15 m (Oates *et al.*, 1990a). Of 232 nests recorded in a survey of Banyang-Mbo Wildlife Sanctuary, Cameroon, 7% were constructed on the ground and 46% were above a height of 12 m. The Banyang-Mbo chimpanzees showed a preference for building nests on steep slopes and cliffs (Greengrass and Maisels, 2007). In the Ebo Forest 24 (11%) of 222 nests recorded on transects in 2006–2007 were ground nests, but only six were judged to have been constructed for night resting. As in Banyang-Mbo, most beds were on steep slopes in rugged terrain, probably as a protection against human hunters (Abwe and Morgan, 2008).

Vocalizations and drumming. The communicative repertoire of *P. t. ellioti* is probably broadly similar to that of other chimpanzee subspecies, but has yet to be carefully studied. At Gashaka, chimpanzees have been heard calling or drumming most frequently in the dry season and least often at the wettest time of year (July–September); pure vocalizations made up 87% of these acoustic bouts, vocalizations and drumming 8%, and drumming alone 5%. Peaks of sound production occur in the early morning and late afternoon (Sommer *et al.*, 2004).

Greengrass and Maisels (2007) note hearing pant-hoots and screams from chimps at Banyang-Mbo.

Social organization and reproduction. Available evidence suggests that Elliot's chimpanzee lives in "fission-fusion" societies similar to those of other chimpanzees, with individual members of a community associating together for short periods of time in variable parties. At Gashaka in Nigeria (the only site for which observational data are available on this subspecies), the study community was estimated to contain a minimum of 35 individuals in 2000–2001, with a ratio of 0.9 adult males to 1 adult female in well-observed parties. Average party size was 3.7 and maximum 17, whereas the average number of nests in nest clusters was 5.7 with a range of 1–23 (Sommer *et al.*, 2004). Nest clusters do not always contain nests built on the same night. At Banyang-Mbo, Cameroon, average nest group size was 3.5, also with a range of 1-23 (Greengrass and Maisels, 2007). No detailed information is available on the social and reproductive behavior of Elliot's chimpanzee, nor on its life history patterns.

Ranging patterns. Evidence of chimpanzees was found over a 26 km² area around the Kwano site in Gashaka, leading Sommer *et al.* (2004) to believe that this area constituted the core of the study community's range.

Diet. Information on the diet of *P. t. ellioti* has come mostly from an analysis of feces and from signs of feeding activity, in the absence of habituated animals. In an examination of fecal remains, Hohmann *et al.* (2006) found great variation in the species of fruit consumed each month by chimpanzees at Gashaka. Fruit from the liane *Landolphia* (Apocynaceae) was found in feces in five different months, and in two months made up more than 50% of remains. Undigested folded leaves of *Desmodium gangeticum* (Leguminosae, Papilionoidae) have been found in the feces of *P. t. ellioti* at Gashaka; in some cases small nematode worms were found on the hairy surfaces of these leaves, leading Fowler *et al.* (2007) to conclude that these leaves were ingested by the chimpanzees as an anthelminthic medication. In the Ebo Forest, Cameroon, chimpanzees have been observed pursuing red colobus monkeys in apparent predation attempts (B. Morgan, pers. comm.).

Tool use. The use of tools in obtaining food is one of the best documented aspects of the natural history of *P. t. ellioti*. Fowler and Sommer (2007) record the use of a variety of sticks by chimpanzees at Gashaka to extract honey from bees' nests, to extract ants from their nests, and to "fish" forf termites. Army, or driver ants (*Dorylus* spp.) are a major item of diet for chimpanzees at this site, with 42% of 381 chimpanzee fecal samples being found to contain remains of these ants; a much higher frequency than found in any other chimpanzee population (Schöning *et al.*, 2006). In the Ebo Forest of Cameroon, Morgan and Abwe (2006) have recorded *P. t. ellioti* cracking open *Coula edulis* nuts with stone hammers, in a similar fashion to *P. t. verus* in the Upper Guinea forests to the west. Tools have also been found at this site that the chimpanzees have used to fish for termites and to dip into bees' nests for honey (B. Morgan, pers. comm.).

Predators. As in the case of *P. t. verus*, the heaviest predation on Elliot's chimpanzee today is by humans, who shoot wild chimpanzees for their meat, to capture infants for sale, and to obtain body parts for use in traditional medicine. Leopards were probably a significant predator on these chimpanzees in the past, but these cats are now extinct or very

Hominidae

Fig. 8.152: Elliot's chimpanzee (*Pan troglodytes ellioti*), Drill Ranch Afi Mountain, Cross River State, Nigeria (photo by A. Idoiaga).

rare in most parts of the range of *P. t. ellioti*. Leopards are still present at Gashaka, where other potential chimpanzee predators are lions, wild dogs and spotted hyenas (Sommer *et al.*, 2004).

Conservation Status

Pan troglodytes ellioti is listed as Endangered on the IUCN Red List. It has the smallest remaining population of any of the chimpanzee subspecies, probably numbering less than 9,000 individuals in total. It is hunted throughout its range, although the level of hunting is probably lower in areas with a largely Muslim human population. The range of *P. t. ellioti* overlaps with some of the densest human populations in Africa, especially in southern Nigeria. Not only has human hunting decimated chimp populations, but indiscriminate logging and the conversion of forest to agricultural land has degraded large areas of chimp habitat. In the last 20–30 years it is likely, therefore, that populations of *P. t. ellioti* have declined by at least 50% (Greengrass, 2009; Morgan *et al.*, 2011). Although chimpanzees are protected by law in Cameroon and Nigeria from hunting and trade, the laws have been only weakly enforced, even in national parks. In addition to occurring in many forest reserves (but in small numbers, because these reserves offer little protection from hunting), *P. t. ellioti* occurs in Nigeria in the Okomu, Cross River and Gashaka Gumti national parks and in the Afi Mountain Wildlife Sanctuary in Nigeria, and in Cameroon in the Korup, Takamanda and Mount Cameroon national parks, the Banyang-Mbo Wildlife Sanctuary, and the proposed Ebo National Park. The largest remaining population is probably in the Gashaka Gumti National Park (at least 6,500 km²), where more than 1,000 chimpanzees may occur (Sommer *et al.*, 2004). The park contains several human settlements (or "enclaves"), however, and suffers from the effects of overgrazing and fire, as well as poaching.

Where to See It

In most localities where this chimpanzee occurs in southern Nigeria and western Cameroon a short-term visitor will be quite fortunate to see the sleeping nests of chimpanzees, or perhaps some feeding signs, and may hear calling in the distance. Catching sight of a wild chimpanzee is a rare occurrence, even during weeks of field work. The best chance of seeing *P. t. ellioti* in the wild is in the Kwano area of Gashaka Gumti National Park in Nigeria, where visitors have a reasonable chance of encountering chimpanzees if they spend three half-days trekking in the park (see <http://www.ucl.ac.uk/gashaka/visiting/>).

APPENDIX

KEY SITES FOR WATCHING AND CONSERVING PRIMATES IN WEST AFRICA

Along with the descriptions of particular species and subspecies in this field guide, notes have been provided about sites at which there is a good chance of observing these primates. This appendix summarizes information on some of the more important of these sites, and how they may be reached by visitors. Information is also given on a number of other sites which are important for their potential for long-term conservation, even though it may be difficult to see primates there at the present time, or difficult (and in some cases dangerous) to visit them. Indeed, a majority of the sites in this list are not easily accessed and, because many parts of West Africa have yet to develop good facilities for tourism, most do not have full-service accommodation located nearby for visitors.

Taken together, the sites described here contain every primate species and subspecies known to occur in West Africa. However, this is by no means a complete list of all the places in West Africa where a visitor may view wild primates, and it is somewhat biased towards those sites with which the author is most familiar. Readers are encouraged to explore beyond the relatively limited selection of sites described in this appendix, keeping in mind that West Africa is full of surprises!

Abuko Nature Reserve, Bijilo Forest Park, and Baboon Islands, The Gambia

Abuko Nature Reserve is a 107-ha protected area on the southeastern outskirts of the Greater Banjul urban area. Part of the reserve was first fenced in 1916 to protect a water supply. The vegetation is a mosaic of wooded savanna and forest, with a nature trail and scenic pools. Abuko is an excellent place to view Temminck's red colobus (*Procolobus badius temminckii*) and green monkeys (*Chlorocebus sabaeus*). The Senegal bushbaby (*Galago senegalensis*) also occurs here and patas (*Erythrocebus patas*) are occasionally encountered. The same primate species are also found in the Bijilo Forest Park, a 51-ha area of coastal *Borassus* palm forest, on the western side of the Banjul metropolis near the Senegambia beach. Abuko includes a small orphanage for rescued animals and a conservation education center.

Fig. A.1: Coastal *Borassus* palm forest, Bijilo Forest Park (photo by E. D. Starin).

Problems have been created in both reserves, but especially at Bijilo, through tourists feeding the green monkeys, despite notices warning against such behavior. This has caused these monkeys to become semi-dependent on people, and sometimes to behave aggressively towards them. For visitors to Abuko and Bijilo, good hotel accommodation is available at Banjul's beach resorts.

Outside Banjul, Temminck's red colobus, green monkeys and Guinea baboons (*Papio papio*) can also be seen in the River Gambia National Park, also known as Baboon Islands. In addition to the wild monkeys on the islands there is a population of more than 80 chimpanzees, descended from orphaned animals and unwanted captives released there since 1979. To reach the islands, it is necessary to take a ferry from Banjul across the river to Barra, from which it is a 3 to 4 hour road journey to the village of Kuntaur. A Chimpanzee Rehabilitation Project boat can collect visitors from a jetty at Kuntaur and take them to a camp with tents and guesthouses on the south bank of the river, near the islands. Primates can be viewed in boat excursions from the camp.

Akpugoeze, Nigeria

Akpugoeze in Enugu State, south-eastern Nigeria, is one of three sites where local people regard Sclater's monkey (*Cercopithecus sclateri*) as sacred, and where these primates (found only between the Niger and Cross Rivers) can therefore be quite readily observed. The other sites are Lagwa in Imo State and Ikot Uso Akpan in Akwa Ibom State.

Akpugoeze is a settlement of seven villages embedded in a landscape of farmland and palm-bush in which there are around a dozen groves of tall trees. There are (or were) shrines to traditional deities in several of these groves. Two of these shrines are regarded as "owning" the monkeys, and these monkeys are therefore held to be sacred. Because of this tradition, most people have not harmed the monkeys, which are relatively unafraid of humans and can even be pests around the villages, raiding farms and house compounds for food. Akpugoeze is home to about 200 Sclater's guenons, organized into some 20 social groups when last censused. However, traditions protecting the tree groves and monkeys have been fading, and the forested area has been declining.

There are a similar number of Sclater's monkeys in Lagwa, but the sacred groves in this town are much smaller and the monkeys here

Fig. A.2: Sclater's monkeys feeding in a red silk cotton tree (*Bombax buonopozense*, Bombacaceae), Akpugoeze, Nigeria (photo by J. F. Oates).

Fig. A.3: Oil-palm bush with forest grove in background, Akpugoeze, Nigeria (photo by J. F. Oates).

spend much of their time in farmbush, farmland and gardens. At Ikot Uso Akpan several groups of the monkeys use five small sacred tree groves embedded in palm-bush and farmland.

No hotel accommodation is available in Akpugoeze, but it can be visited in a day trip from the large city of Enugu, 60 km to the northeast, where there are several hotels. Lagwa lies just 20 km east of the city of Owerri, and Ikot Uso Akpan is north of the city of Uyo. At the time of writing, expatriates faced a risk of kidnapping in this part of Nigeria.

Ankasa Conservation Area and Kakum National Park, Ghana

The Ankasa Conservation Area is located on hilly terrain in the southwestern corner of Ghana, not far from the border with Côte d'Ivoire. It consists of the Ankasa Resource Reserve (349 km²) and the adjacent Nini-Suhien National Park (175 km²), created in 1976; the resource reserve and national park are the southern and northern sections of the former Ankasa River Forest Reserve, and are separated by the Suhien River. This area has the highest rainfall in Ghana, and the natural vegetation of Ankasa is wet evergreen forest. Southern parts of the forest were subjected to some selective logging in the past, but otherwise the forest habitat is little disturbed, with a rich diversity of plants including a high density of rare species. All Ghana's forest primates (typical of the Upper Guinea East forest subregion) once occurred in Ankasa, including the white-naped mangabey (*Cercocebus lunulatus*), the roloway monkey (*Cercopithecus diana roloway*), Lowe's monkey (*C. campbelli lowei*), the eastern spot-nosed monkey (*C. p. petaurista*), the olive colobus (*Procolobus verus*), Miss Waldron's red colobus (*P. waldroni*), the white-thighed colobus (*Colobus vellerosus*), and the western chimpanzee (*Pan troglodytes verus*). Ankasa is potentially a very important primate conservation area, but its wildlife has suffered from years of poorly-controlled hunting, and populations of larger mammals are now at low densities. Only Lowe's monkey and the spot-nosed monkey can be fairly reliably encountered; most of the other monkey species and the chimpanzee are rare and very difficult to see; Miss Waldron's colobus is almost certainly extinct in the reserve, and the roloway monkey may be extinct. Bosman's potto (*Perodicticus potto potto*) can be observed on night walks with a headlamp.

Simple visitor accommodation is available at Nkwanta in the center of Ankasa, managed by the Wildlife Division; at the time of writing the dirt road to Nkwanta from the Swodazim junction to the south can only be reached in a 4-wheel-drive vehicle. The city of Sekondi-Takoradi, which has several hotels, is about 120 km away on the coast to the east, on a paved road, and about 360 km from Accra. There are several small resort hotels for tourists along the coast between Takoradi and Ankasa.

Fig. A.4: Visitor accommodation in Ankasa, Ghana (photo by J. F. Oates).

Fig. A.5: Canopy walkway, Kakum National Park, Ghana (photo by J. F. Oates).

More accessible than Ankasa is Kakum National Park (375 km²), which has an adjacent visitor center that can be reached by driving on a paved road about 30 km north from the coastal city of Cape Coast (about 165 km from Accra). On the edge of the park, across the road from the visitor center, is a 330-m forest-canopy walkway from which monkeys can occasionally be seen, especially very early in the morning. The canopy walkway was launched in 1995, and was one element of an initiative of Conservation International, in collaboration with national institutions, to make the park an attractive tourist destination, which included, besides the visitor's center, an educational exhibition, which highlights the cultural connections of the indigenous Akan people of southern Ghana to the natural world. Monkeys found in Kakum are *Cercopithecus campbelli lowei*, *C. p. petaurista*, *Procolobus verus* and *Colobus vellerosus*.

Boabeng-Fiema Monkey Sanctuary, Ghana

The Boabeng-Fiema Monkey Sanctuary (BFMS) is in the Brong-Ahafo Region of central Ghana. The main sanctuary is a 1.9-km² area of high semi-deciduous and secondary forest together with woodland, surrounding the two villages of Boabeng and Fiema that are about 1 km apart. The sanctuary forests are linked by narrow riparian forest to several smaller surrounding forest patches. There is a small sacred grove in the sanctuary. The white-thighed black-and-white colobus (*Colobus vellerosus*) and Lowe's monkeys (*Cercopithecus campbelli lowei*) living in these forests have been protected from harm by the traditional taboos of the local people, who consider them to be descendants of patron deities.

Since 1975, the Ghana Department of Game and Wildlife (now the Wildlife Division of the Forestry Commission) assisted the village communities in creating a formal sanctuary. A committee manages the

Fig. A.6: Boabeng village (above) and the Boabeng-Fiema Monkey Sanctuary, Ghana (photos by J. F. Oates).

forest, along with a simple guesthouse for visitors, and organizes guides for tourists. Because of the long-standing taboos against harming the Boabeng-Fiema monkeys, they are easy to observe at close range. In addition, Demidoff's galagos (*Galagoides demidovii*) can often be seen on night walks in secondary forest near the guesthouse. Since 2000, the University of Calgary has had a research program focused on the colobus monkeys of BFMS.

The nearest large town to BFMS is Techiman, on the main road from Kumasi to Tamale, about 120 km north of Kumasi. From Techiman, a paved road runs 25 km east to Nkoranza, and BFMS is a further 20 km north down dirt roads from Nkoranza.

Ebo Forest, Cameroon

The Ebo forest is located in the Littoral Region, Cameroon, and covers more than 1,400 km² of hilly terrain just north of the lower Sanaga River; the southeastern edge of the forest is less than 50 km from the large port city of Douala. Elevations in Ebo range from 200 to 1,200 m, and the natural vegetation is predominantly lowland moist forest, with submontane forest on the higher hills. The forest is bisected north-south by the Ebo River, which, over much of its length, runs over rapids through a steep-sided valley.

Ebo has a very rich primate fauna, including 11 diurnal species: red-capped mangabey (*Cercocebus torquatus*), drill (*Mandrillus leucophaeus*), Preuss's monkey (*Allochrocebus preussi*), mona monkey (*Cercopithecus mona*), crowned monkey (*C. pogonias*), red-eared monkey (*C. erythrotis*), putty-nosed monkey (*C. nictitans*), Preuss's red colobus (*Procolobus preussi*), guereza (*Colobus guereza*), Elliot's chimpanzee (*Pan troglodytes ellioti*) and gorilla (*Gorilla gorilla*). The Preuss's red colobus population is one of very few remaining, while the small gorilla population in the northeastern part of the forest appears to be a unique relic. The Ebo gorillas may be most closely related to the western lowland subspecies (*Gorilla gorilla gorilla*), the nearest population of which occurs over 100 km away across the Sanaga River. There has not been a confirmed sighting of *C. guereza* at Ebo since 2003. The nocturnal prosimians of Ebo have not yet been carefully studied.

The forest on the western side of the Ebo River suffered some selective logging in the 1970s, while the forest east of the river is peppered with the remains of abandoned villages. The eastern forest therefore has a vegetation mosaic, including extensive areas of old secondary forest and stands of oil palm. Much of Ebo is subject to commercial hunting for the bushmeat trade, but efforts are underway to classify 1,100 km² as a national park. The Zoological Society of San Diego has had three permanently staffed research stations in the Ebo Forest since 2005, and these have played an active role in combating the hunting of protected species, awaiting the time that staff of the Ministry of Forestry and Wildlife (MINFOF) can take over management of a national park.

There are currently no accommodation facilities for visitors in Ebo. To organize a trip to the forest, intended visitors are advised to contact the MINFOF Divisional Delegation based at the town of Yabassi, approximately 60 km to the west of Ebo. Yabassi has basic accommodation in an auberge. It is also possible to camp at one of the villages surrounding Ebo, with the village chief's permission, and arrange a trip into the forest from there. In order to stand a good chance of viewing primates, however, visitors should be expected to trek for at least four hours, and logistical issues, such as crossing the large Dibamba River in the wet season (if entering from the western side), have to be carefully considered.

Gashaka Gumti National Park, Nigeria

Gashaka Gumti is Nigeria's largest protected area, covering 6,700 km² in the northeastern states of Taraba and Adamawa, adjacent to the Cameroon border. The vegetation grades from savanna woodland in the north to montane forest in the south, where the peak of Chappal Waddi (or Gangirwal) reaches 2,420 m. Gallery forest grows along rivers in the lowlands. This habitat mosaic supports a rich and diverse fauna of forest, savanna, lowland and montane species. Primates found in Gashaka Gumti are Thomas's dwarf galago (*Galagoides thomasi*), Senegal bushbaby (*Galago senegalensis*), Milne-Edwards' potto (*Potto edwardsi*), olive baboon (*Papio anubis*), patas (*Erythrocebus patas*), tantalus monkey (*Chlorocebus aethiops tantalus*), mona monkey (*Cercopithecus mona*), putty-nosed monkey (*C. nictitans*), guereza (*Colobus guereza*), and Elliot's chimpanzee (*Pan troglodytes ellioti*). A few sightings of gray-cheeked mangabeys (*Lophocebus albigena*) have also been made in the park. The park's chimpanzees are probably the largest surviving population of *P. t. ellioti*.

The primates of Gashaka Gumti are relatively easy to observe because they have not been heavily hunted, although the chimpanzees

Fig. A.7: Mosaic habitat (above), and Gashaka River (below), Gashaka Gumti National Park, Nigeria (photos by R. Lodge (above) and J. F. Oates).

remain wary of humans. The park does suffer some poaching, however, and enclaved settlements of cattle herders and farmers have led to extensive vegetation damage, especially in highland areas, through overgrazing, fire and cultivation.

Gashaka Gumti is in a remote part of Nigeria. The park can be reached from Abuja by road in about nine hours, via Takum. There are also flights to the city of Yola in Adamawa State from Abuja, and from Yola it is about 350 km by surfaced road via Jalingo to the park headquarters in the town of Serti in Taraba State, where visitor accommodation is available. There is simple, self-catering accommodation at Gashaka village, on the River Gamgam on the edge of the park, 25 km from Serti. Campsites (without facilities) are available in the park, including at the site of the abandoned village of Kwano, where the Gashaka Primate Project has a field base.

Gbanraun, Nigeria

Gbanraun is a small town in the heart of the Niger Delta in Bayelsa State, Nigeria. Patches of swamp forest near the town are some of the few places where, until recently, the Niger Delta red colobus monkey (*Procolobus epieni*) could be quite readily observed. One of these forests, where the colobus were studied in 1996–1997, has been proposed as a 500-ha conservation area, but this plan had not been formalized at the time of writing. Red colobus were still present at this Gbanraun study site in 2009. The habitat and its wildlife are still threatened by hunting and logging, but there has been less human impact than in other forests in this part of the Delta. Other primates in this forest are dwarf galagos (*Galagoides*, species unconfirmed), potto (*Perodicticus potto*, subspecies unconfirmed), red-capped mangabey (*Cercocebus torquatus*), mona monkey (*Cercopithecus mona*), white-throated monkey (*C. erythrogaster pococki*), putty-nosed monkey (*C. nictitans*) and olive colobus (*Procolobus verus*). No special visitor facilities are available at Gbanraun, which can be reached by boat from

Fig. A.8: Lodewijk Werre at his Niger Delta red colobus study site, Gbanraun, Nigeria (photo by J. F. Oates).

the state capital of Yenagoa. Continuing insecurity in the Niger Delta makes visits by foreigners inadvisable at this time.

Haut Niger National Park, Guinea

This national park was constituted in 1997 from the *forêts classées* of Mafou (554 km²) and Kouya (674 km²) in central Guinea not far to the east of the Sierra Leone border. Together with these core protected areas, there is a gazetted buffer zone around the Mafou forest, giving a total area under management of more than 7,000 km². The vegetation of the core areas is a mosaic of wooded savanna, more open savanna grassland, dry forest, and gallery forest along watercourses. The Mafou section lies on the south bank of the Upper Niger River, giving the park its name.

Primates found in the park are a dwarf galago (probably *Galagoides thomasi*), Senegal bushbaby (*Galago senegalensis*), Guinea baboon (*Papio papio*), patas monkey (*Erythrocebus patas*), green monkey (*Chlorocebus aethiops sabaeus*), western black-and-white colobus (*Colobus polykomos*) and western chimpanzee (*Pan troglodytes verus*). The chimpanzee population is the largest in a protected area in Guinea.

Fig. A.9: Haut Niger National Park, Guinea (photo courtesy of the Chimpanzee Conservation Center).

Fig. A.10: Radio-tracking released chimpanzees from a boat on the Niger River in Haut Niger National Park, Guinea (photo courtesy of the Chimpanzee Conservation Center).

The town of Faranah, about 400 km by paved road from Conakry, lies at the southwest corner of the Mafou buffer zone. From Faranah there is a dirt road (passable by 4-wheel-drive vehicle) to the park headquarters at Sidakoro, about 50 km from Faranah, and Mafou itself is another 25 km from Sidakoro. In the past, simple accommodation was available at Sidakoro.

The Chimpanzee Conservation Centre sanctuary for orphaned and rescued chimpanzees is located at Somoria on the western edge of the Mafou core area. In 2008, 12 chimpanzees were released from the sanctuary into the Mafou core.

Korup National Park, Cameroon

Korup is one of the most important rain forest national parks in Africa. It was established in 1986, and protects 1,260 km² of evergreen high forest on undulating terrain in the coastal lowlands of Cameroon's South West Region. The highest elevation is reached at Mt. Yuhan (1,079 m) in the central part of the park. The rich primate fauna includes Demidoff's and Thomas's dwarf galagos (*Galagoides demidovii* and *G. thomasi*), Talbot's needle-clawed galago (*Euoticus pallidus talboti*), Allen's galago (*Sciurocheirus alleni cameronensis*), angwantibo (*Arctocebus calabarensis*), Milne-Edwards's potto (*Perodicticus edwardsi*), red-capped mangabey (*Cercocebus torquatus*), drill (*Mandrillus leucophaeus*), mona monkey (*Cercopithecus mona*), crowned monkey (*C. pogonias*), red-eared monkey (*C. erythrotis camerunensis*), putty-nosed monkey (*C. nictitans ludio*), Preuss's red colobus (*Procolobus preussi*), and Elliot's chimpanzee (*Pan troglodytes ellioti*).

Korup has been spared from logging and large-scale farming, but poaching remains a big problem over much of the park, fuelled particularly by a demand for bushmeat in neighboring Nigeria, as well as the larger Cameroonian cities such as Douala. There are plans for a large new oil-palm plantation close to the national park; if this plantation is developed it is likely to have consequences for the long-term effectiveness of the park.

The park headquarters are in the town of Mundemba, 10 km east of the boundary of the southernmost part of the protected area. Mundemba, where simple guest-house accommodation is available, can be reached by dirt road from the larger town of Kumba, some 120 km to the southeast; this road can be difficult to navigate in the rains. In the past, some people have reached the park by boat from the coastal town of Idenau (travelling to Bulu Harbour, 10 km south of Mundemba). The most southerly part of Korup has a good system of trails, and less hunting pressure than other areas of the park, making this the best area to observe primates; however, the monkeys are shy of people and chimpanzees very rarely seen. In the past, this area had a set of good campsites with screened shelters, but these have been destroyed; rehabilitation is planned. The northern part of the park is less easily reached, but there is a bush road from near the town of Nguti on the Kumba-Mamfe highway. Korup is adjacent to the Oban Division of Nigeria's Cross River National Park.

Lama Forest, Bénin

Lama is a 162-km² *"forêt classée"* (i.e., forest reserve) located in the Lama depression of southern Bénin and administered by the Office National du Bois. It is also known as the Forêt de Ko. Much of the reserve consists of tree plantations (particularly of teak), farmland and secondary growth, but a specially protected 48-km² core (*"Noyau Central"*) includes a 19-km² remnant of the original dry forest that probably once covered a much larger area of this region of the "Dahomey Gap" (see Section 2). Parts of this core become waterlogged in the wet season.

Fig. A.11: Rainforest in Korup National Park, Cameroon (photo by J. F. Oates).

Fig. A.12: Ferdinand Namata at the entrance to Korup National Park, Cameroon, in 2000. Namata assisted Thomas Struhsaker with his forest primate studies in the 1960s, and subsequently worked with several other primatologists in Cameroon.

Lama is especially important because the forest of its *Noyau Central* contains what is probably the largest surviving population of the red-bellied monkey (*Cercopithecus erythrogaster erythrogaster*). However, patience is needed to see this primate; it is secretive in its behavior, and much less abundant than the mona monkey (*C. mona*). Other primates found in Lama are Thomas's galago (*Galagoides thomasi*), Senegal bushbaby (*Galago senegalensis*), tantalus monkey (*Chlorocebus aethiops tantalus*), olive colobus (*Procolobus verus*), and white-thighed black-and-white colobus (*Colobus vellerosus*). The two colobus species are rare. The habitat of the *Noyau Central* is well protected, but some hunting occurs.

Fig. A.13: Isabelle Faucher and Reiko Matsuda in 1995 on a newly constructed visitor walkway in the Lama Forest, Bénin (photo by J. F. Oates).

The eastern edge of the Lama Forest touches the main highway that runs from Cotonou to the north of the country. It is about 25 km south of the town of Bohicon, which is itself 10 km east of the historic city of Abomey (former capital of the Kingdom of Dahomey), where there is hotel accommodation.

Loma Mountains, Sierra Leone

The Loma Mountains in northern Sierra Leone contain West Africa's highest peak west of the Cameroon Highlands and Bioko; this is Mt. Bintumani (1,947 m). A forest reserve covering about 350 km² of the mountains and their surrounding lowlands was created in 1952; this was upgraded to the status of non-hunting forest reserve in 1972 to give special protection to Loma's important wildlife. At the time of writing, efforts were in progress to declare a major portion of the reserve as a national park. The lower elevations of the reserve are mostly covered by moist forest, with savanna woodland in eastern areas. In upland areas above around 1,000 m there is submontane forest and shrubland, and montane grassland; the upland landscape is spectacular. Farms have encroached on the reserve, especially in the east, but these areas may be excluded from the national park when it is created.

The Loma Mountains have a rich and diverse fauna and flora, including several endemic plant species. These primates are known to be present: Demidoff's dwarf galago (*Galagoides demidovii*), Senegal bushbaby (*Galago senegalensis*), Bosman's potto (*Perodicticus potto potto*), sooty mangabey (*Cercocebus atys*), olive baboon (*Papio anubis*), Diana monkey (*Cercopithecus diana diana*), Campbell's monkey (*C. campbelli campbelli*), western spot-nosed monkey (*C. petaurista buettikoferi*), bay colobus (*Procolobus badius badius*), western black-and-white colobus (*Colobus polykomos*) and western chimpanzee (*Pan troglodytes verus*). Thomas's dwarf galago (*Galagoides thomasi*) and the green monkey (*Chlorocebus aethiops sabaeus*) probably also occur there. Chimpanzee population density in the Loma forests is one of the highest in West Africa, and this is therefore a very important site for their conservation.

Although hunting is prohibited by law at Loma, law enforcement has not occurred and poaching is a problem that improved management must address. At present the primates are wary of humans. Access to Loma is difficult because of the lack of good roads in the immediate vicinity of the reserve; at least in the rains, several tracks to the reserve boundary are generally only passable on foot or by motorcycle. The

Fig. A.14: Mt. Bintumani in the Loma Mountains, Sierra Leone (photo by J. F. Oates). This is the highest mountain in West Africa, to the west of Pico Basilé on Bioko.

nearest large town is Kabala, which can be reached on a highway via Makeni from the Sierra Leonean capital Freetown. From Kabala, there is a dirt road southeast for about 65 km through Koinadugu to the village of Banda Karafaia close to the northwestern corner of the reserve, from which a track leads on to Sinikoro on the reserve boundary. Another access route is via Yifin and Konombaia, which is a 1.5 h trek to the reserve boundary. No special accommodation is presently available in or close to the reserve, but it is possible to camp, or stay in nearby villages.

Mbam & Djerem National Park, Cameroon

This park, created in 2000, lies in the center of Cameroon in a zone that is transitional both ecologically and zoogeographically. At 4,200 km², Mbam & Djerem is the largest national park in Cameroon, and it is ecologically and biologically very diverse. It lies on the boundary between the semi-deciduous forest and savanna woodland zones; there is closed-canopy forest in the south of the park and savanna in the north, with transitional vegetation in between; gallery forest grows along the park's rivers. The Djerem River that flows through the park is the largest tributary of the Sanaga. The lower Sanaga River acts as a geographical boundary between West and Central Africa for many primate species or subspecies, and there is a mixing of these two faunas in the region of Mbam & Djerem.

Savanna habitats of Mbam & Djerem are home to olive baboons (*Papio anubis*), patas monkeys (*Erythrocebus patas*) and tantalus monkeys (*Chlorocebus aethiops tantalus*), while in the forests are found gray-cheeked mangabeys (*Lophocebus albigena*), northern talapoins (*Miopithecus ogouensis*), De Brazza's monkeys (*Cercopithecus neglectus*), mona monkeys (*C. mona*), mustached monkeys (*C. cephus*), putty-nosed monkeys (*C. nictitans nictitans*), guerezas (*Colobus guereza*), and chimpanzees (*Pan troglodytes*). Crowned monkeys (*Cercopithecus pogonias*) may be present, but have not yet been confirmed. The prosimians of the park have not been systematically studied, but galagos and pottos (*Perodicticus edwardsi*) occur. This is the only site in our region where there is a good chance of observing, in gallery forests, the gray-cheeked mangabey, the talapoin and De Brazza's monkey. Among the large mammal fauna of the park are elephant, buffalo, hippopotamus, and giant forest hog.

There is a large human population (about 30,000 people) living around Mbam & Djerem Park, and poaching for bushmeat has seriously affected populations of larger mammals, especially in eastern areas where a railway provides an outlet for the sale of meat.

The park can be reached by road from the Cameroon capital Yaoundé (or the commercial capital, Douala), via Bafoussam, Foumban and Tibati, although the journey is more than 500 km and can take two days. Alternatively there is a journey of about 800 km (of which 600 km are surfaced) from Yaoundé via Bertoua and Ngaoundal. Four-wheel-drive vehicles can also reach Tibati on a minor road from Ntui (north of Yaoundé) via Yoko, where the park headquarters are located. Another option for access is to take the railway from Yaoundé to Ngaoundal and then arrange for road transport for the 110 km to Tibati.

From Tibati there is a road south for 35 km to the small town of Mbakou, where the park has its sub-headquarters and where the Wildlife Conservation Society (WCS) has a base. A dirt road leads further south to Miyere at the entrance to the park where WCS has built a training center and an eco-lodge. From Miyere one can enter the park on foot, or by taking a boat down the Djerem River (which is the best way to see some of the forest primates). There are small hotels (inns) in Tibati, and it is possible to camp in the national park.

Niokolo Koba National Park, Senegal

Niokolo Koba is one of the oldest and largest national parks in West Africa. The park was established in the savanna zone of southeastern Senegal in 1954 and enlarged during the 1960s; it now covers 9,130 km². Niokolo Koba adjoins the 382-km² Badiar National Park of northern Guinea, which was created in 1985 and is now incorporated into the 2,843 km² Badiar Biosphere Reserve. Niokolo Koba and Badiar have recently been designated as components of the "Complexe écologique du Niokolo-Badiar" which covers a total area of more than 15,000 km² (see Galat et al., 1997).

The Gambia River and some of its major tributaries flow through Niokolo Koba, which lies near the boundary between Guinean and Sudanian savanna woodland zones. In addition to woodland, scrubland, wooded grassland and marsh, the park has important areas of gallery forest along watercourses and in ravines. Primates recorded in Niokolo Koba are the Senegal bushbaby (Galago senegalensis), Bosman's potto (Perodicticus potto potto), Guinea baboon (Papio papio), patas monkey (Erythrocebus patas), green monkey (Chlorocebus aethiops sabaeus), Temminck's red colobus (Procolobus badius temminckii), and western chimpanzee (Pan troglodytes verus). The Guinea baboon population is the largest found in a protected area.

Until recently, Niokolo Koba contained one of the most pristine remaining large-mammal faunas of the West African savanna zone, including elephant, giraffe, western giant eland and a full complement of predators (including wild dog, lion and leopard). However, the park has been badly degraded since the late 1990s. A road from Tambacounda to Kedougou on the Guinea border passes through the park, and commercial poaching has decimated the large mammal fauna; elephants were wiped out and had to be reintroduced, and leopards are now rare or absent. The natural vegetation has been damaged by agricultural encroachment, livestock grazing and fire. The Parc National de Niokolo Koba became a World Heritage Site in 1981, and in 2007 was added to the UNESCO World Heritage List in Danger.

Park headquarters are in the city of Tambacounda, 400 km from Dakar and about 50 km north of the park. Tambacounda can be reached from Dakar by air, road and rail. There is a hotel in the park at Simenti on the Gambia River. Additional accommodation is available at the settlement of Niokolo Koba where the road to Kedougou crosses the Niokolo Koba River, and there is tourist accommodation in thatched

La rivière Niokolo Koba

Nouvel univers que celui de cet affluent de la Gambie, le Niokolo Koba, en Malinké, la grande rivière du Niokolo, une ancienne province, et non la rivière du Koba (Hippotrague en peul). Il offre des paysages plus contrastés et son relief est plus accidenté. La rivière est, elle aussi, soumise au rythme des saisons : très violente pendant les crues, elle s'épuise pendant l'année pour se réduire à quelques trous d'eau. Elle est fréquentée par des antilopes, des buffles, des singes. Le Niokolo Koba est encaissé en gorges d'une beauté exceptionnelle. Sous la roche rougeâtre et dure de la cuirasse latéritique, vous observerez des sols de couleur rose à blanche. Çà et là, la falaise est percée d'orifices. Ce sont les nids des guêpiers, oiseaux au plumage vert, bleu, jaune ou rouge. Approcher vous avec précaution du bord de la falaise. Vous verrez de grands blocs de cuirasse qui se sont effondrés en contrebas. L'érosion verticale est très active, et certains

Fig. A.15: The Niokolo Koba River in the Niokolo Koba National Park. An illustration from a guidebook for visitors to the Niokolo-Badiar Ecological Complex, written by Galat *et al.* (1997). The illustration is by Thanh Minh and Godefroy Luong. Reproduced with permission from the authors.

Fig. A.16: Visitor accomodation in the Niokolo Koba National Park, Simenti, Senegal (photo by G. Galat).

rondavels at Wassadou, on the northern edge of the park. Tracks in the park are best navigated with a 4-wheel-drive vehicle.

Oban Hills, Nigeria

The Oban Division of Cross River National Park (CRNP) is in Cross River State. The southeastern extremity of the park adjoins the southwestern part of Cameroon's Korup National Park. At around 3,000 km², this is the largest remaining area of rain forest in Nigeria. Formerly the Oban Group of forest reserves, it was promulgated as a national park in 1991, along with the Boshi and Okwangwo Forest Reserves to the north (which form the park's Okwangwo Division). Oban is the name of a town on the road that runs northeast from Calabar to the Cameroon border. The road bisects the park, whose forests are tenuously connected north of Oban town. The rugged Oban Hills lie to the west of this road, and the Ikpan section of the park (adjacent with Korup) to the east.

Most of the forest in the Oban Division of CRNP has not recently been farmed or logged, and is therefore closed-canopy high forest. The primate fauna is the same as that of Korup (although the crowned guenon and Preuss's red colobus may be largely restricted to eastern areas). This is, therefore, a potentially very important primate conservation site, and its hills and rivers make an attractive landscape. However, hunting pressure has been even more intense in Oban than in

Fig. A.17: Rhoko camp of CERCOPAN (above) and Rhoko forest, on the edge of the Oban Hills, Cross River State, Nigeria (photos by J. F. Oates).

Korup, so it is difficult for a visitor to the park to see any of the diurnal primates, which are rare and shy.

The Centre for Education, Research and Conservation of Primates and Nature (CERCOPAN) supports a primate research and education facility at Rhoko, in the Iko Esai community forest area adjacent to the northeastern boundary of the national park. Iko Esai is reached on a dirt road that branches east off the main Calabar-Ikom highway at Ibogo, 90 km north of Calabar. It is 18 km from Ibogo to Iko Esai and a further 8 km to the Rhoko camp. Simple accommodation is available at Rhoko, but it is best for visitors to make arrangements in advance at the CERCOPAN headquarters in Calabar. Wild monkeys can be observed in the Rhoko forests, and a group of captive red-capped mangabeys (deriving from rescued animals) can be viewed in a large electrified enclosure. Rhoko is a good site at which to observe many of the nocturnal prosimians of the Korup-Oban forest complex: *Galagoides demidovii*, *G. thomasi*, *Euoticus pallidus*, *Sciurocheirus alleni* and *Perodicticus potto*. *Arctocebus calabarensis* also occurs there, but is not common.

Okomu, Nigeria

The Okomu Forest Reserve lies in Edo State, south-western Nigeria, between the Siluko and Osse Rivers; its western boundary is only about 20 km west of historic Benin City. The reserve was gazetted in 1935 and once covered about 1,200 km², much of which supported moist forest vegetation with a very uneven tree canopy, along with large areas of swamp forest near the boundary rivers, and some enclaved farmlands. The terrain has little relief. Okomu was rich in mahoganies and was selectively logged for much of the 20th century. From 1979, large areas of the forest reserve were given out for oil-palm and rubber plantations. Concerned about the destruction of an important ecosystem, conservationists worked with the state government to create a wildlife sanctuary of 67 km² in an area of relatively lightly logged forest in the center of the reserve; this was gazetted in 1985, and a 49 km² buffer zone was added in 1990. In 1999 the sanctuary came under the management of the Nigeria National Parks Service and is now widely referred to as Okomu National Park, while other parts of the original forest remain under the control of the state government.

Although poaching remains a problem, Okomu National Park has suffered less from hunting than other forests in southwestern Nigeria, and consequently its monkeys are more abundant and less wary of humans

Fig. A.18: View over one of the park's shallow swampy lakes, Okomu National Park, Edo State, Nigeria (photo by J. F. Oates).

Fig. A.19: Entrance to Okomu National Park, Nigeria, in 2009 (photo by S. K. Bearder). On the right is Alfred Ohenhen, who first assisted the author with primate surveys in Okomu in 1982.

than at most other sites in this region. Mona monkeys (*Cercopithecus mona*) are common, and this is the best site at which to observe white-throated monkeys (*C. erythrogaster pococki*). Red-capped mangabeys (*Cercocebus torquatus*) are often heard, and can sometimes be seen. Putty-nosed monkeys (*Cercopithecus nictitans insolitus*) are rare, but occasionally observed; chimpanzees (*Pan troglodytes ellioti*) are present, but hardly ever seen. During night walks, Demidoff's and Thomas's dwarf galagos (*Galagoides demidovii* and *G. thomasi*), and Benin pottos (*Perodicticus potto juju*) can be spotted with head lamps. Among other wildlife, Okomu supports forest buffalo, a small population of forest elephants, and a very rich bird fauna.

Okomu can be reached by paved road from Lagos or Benin City via the town of Udo, close to the reserve's northern boundary. From Udo, a dirt road runs south into the forest towards the settlement of Nikrowa and a branch of this road leads to visitor accommodation at the A.P. Leventis Conservation Centre at Arakhuan, on the eastern edge of the park; this facility is now managed by Nigeria National Parks. Paths, one of them motorable, run west from the Udo-Nikrowa road through the forest to marshy lakes which are overlooked by tree platforms.

The Omo Forest Reserve (1,325 km²) in Ogun State, Nigeria, has the same primate fauna as Okomu and has also been heavily degraded, both by farming and by the conversion of natural forest to plantations (especially of *Gmelina* trees). About 230 km² of logged natural forest remain in Omo, and efforts are underway to make this area into a wildlife sanctuary. Hunting has occurred at high levels in this forest, so monkeys are quite difficult to observe. Omo is only about 130 km from Lagos by road.

Okwangwo, Nigeria, and Takamanda, Cameroon

The forests of the Okwangwo-Takamanda landscape on the Nigeria-Cameroon border are very important as a primate conservation site; however, due to high levels of hunting it is hard for a short-term visitor to see wild primates here, other than the small nocturnal prosimians. From west to east, this landscape consists (in Nigeria) of the Afi River Forest Reserve (including the Afi Mountain Wildlife Sanctuary), the Mbe Mountains community forest and the Okwangwo Division of Cross River National Park (CRNP), and (in Cameroon) of Takamanda National Park and the Mawambi Hills community forest. These sites form a forest block with a total area of about 1,800 km². Okwangwo and Takamanda themselves are essentially one forested ecosystem, through which runs the international boundary, but the forest connection between the hills of Afi and Mbe has become tenuous.

This forest block lies at the headwaters of the Cross River on generally rugged terrain. Elevations are between 100 m in southern valleys to 1,500 m in the north, where the forest borders on the high-altitude Obudu grass plateau. Apart from some enclaves of settlement and farming, the Okwangwo-Takamanda vegetation is mostly closed-canopy lowland and submontane forest. Most of the forest has not recently been logged, except in Afi River.

This landscape has a rich fauna and flora. In terms of its primates it is perhaps most important as a stronghold of Cross River gorillas (*Gorilla gorilla diehli*), which also occur further east in Cameroon in the Mone River Forest Reserve, Mbulu Hills, Kagwene Gorilla Sanctuary and Lebialem Highlands. Other primates present in the Okwangwo-Takamanda forests are the drill (*Mandrillus leucophaeus*), Preuss's monkey (*Allochrocebus preussi*) found especially in submontane areas, mona monkey (*Cercopithecus mona*), crowned monkey (*C. pogonias*) probably confined to Takamanda, red-eared monkey (*C. erythrotis camerunensis*), putty-nosed monkey (*C. nictitans ludio*) and Elliot's chimpanzee (*Pan troglodytes ellioti*). The red-capped mangabey (*Cercocebus torquatus*) and gray-cheeked mangabey (*Lophocebus*

Fig. A.20: View of habitats of Cross River gorillas from the Obudu Plateau, Nigeria, across the forests of Okwangwo to the Mbe (left) and Afi Mountains (right) on the horizon (photo by J. F. Oates).

Fig. A.21: Northern uplands of the Okwangwo Division, Cross River National Park, Nigeria (photo by J. F. Oates).

albigena) have been recorded from Takamanda in the past, but have not been seen in the last 20–30 years. The nocturnal prosimians occurring in Okwangwo-Takamanda are Demidoff's and Thomas's dwarf galagos (*Galagoides demidovii* and *G. thomasi*), Talbot's needle-clawed galago (*Euoticus pallidus talboti*), Allen's galago (*Sciurocheirus alleni cameronensis*) and Milne-Edwards's potto (*Perodicticus edwardsi*). The angwantibo (*Arctocebus calabarensis*) is probably present, but has not yet been definitively recorded from the area.

The most accessible parts of this landscape are on the Nigerian side of the border. A paved highway from Calabar to Obudu via Ikom in Cross River State runs along the eastern edge of Afi River Forest Reserve, between Afi and Mbe; Calabar may be reached by air from Lagos and Abuja. A dirt road branches off on the western side of this highway to the settlement of Buanchor at the foot of Afi Mountain, and close to Buanchor is the "Drill Ranch Afi Mountain" facility of the Pandrillus Foundation where groups of rehabilitated captive drills and chimpanzees can be viewed in electric-fenced enclosures, and where there is simple visitor accommodation; arrangements for a visit should be made in advance with Pandrillus's Drill Ranch in Calabar. Hiking trails lead to Afi Mountain from Buanchor. Permission to enter the wildlife sanctuary needs to be obtained from the Cross River State Forestry Commission.

On the eastern side of the Ikom-Obudu road are the Kanyang villages, from which footpaths lead to the Mbe Mountains; about 25 km north of Kanyang a dirt road branches east to the divisional headquarters of CRNP at Butatong, from which hiking trails lead into the Boshi-Okwangwo forests of the park. Just before Obudu town on the highway another paved road branches east and leads via a mountain road with many hairpin bends (switchbacks) to the Obudu Mountain Resort at 1,575 m on the Obudu Plateau, where there is a good hotel with comfortable accommodation. Putty-nosed monkeys and Preuss's monkeys can sometimes be glimpsed in gallery forests on the plateau, but these forests have been badly damaged by cultivation and fire. On the western edge of the plateau are the forests of the Okwangwo Division of CRNP, and to the south is the northernmost part of Takamanda National Park; special permission is needed to enter these forests. At present there is no road access to Takamanda from within Cameroon.

Sapo National Park, Liberia

Sapo National Park in Sinoe County, south-eastern Liberia, was established in 1983 to protect 1,308 km² of little-disturbed lowland moist forest that contained important populations of all the large mammals typical of the Upper Guinea West forest subregion. Additional areas of forest to the north and northeast were added in 2003, bringing the park's total area to 1,800 km². The Sinoe River (the northern boundary before the 2003 extension) flows through the park. Most of the terrain is flat or gently undulating, with large areas of swamp.

The primates of Sapo are the sooty mangabey (*Cercocebus atys*), Diana monkey (*Cercopithecus diana diana*), Campbell's monkey (*Cercopithecus campbelli campbelli*), western spot-nosed monkey (*Cercopithecus petaurista buettikoferi*), olive colobus (*Procolobus verus*), bay colobus (*Procolobus badius badius*), western black-and-white colobus (*Colobus polykomos*) and western chimpanzee (*Pan troglodytes verus*). Prosimians have not been carefully evaluated, but probably present are Demidoff's dwarf galago (*Galagoides demidovii*), Thomas's dwarf galago (*G. thomasi*) and Bosman's potto (*Perodicticus potto potto*). Reports of the presence of Stampfli's putty-nosed monkey (*Cercopithecus nictitans stampflii*) in Sapo may not be accurate and may result from confusion with *C. petaurista*. Among other mammals of Sapo are forest elephant, pygmy hippopotamus, zebra duiker, Jentink's duiker, giant forest hog, and leopard.

Fig. A.22: Sapo National Park, Liberia (photo by J. Martin).

The Liberian civil conflicts (1989–1996, 1999–2003) led to an inevitable breakdown of management in Sapo. Infrastructure was destroyed, and (especially towards the end of the second period of conflict) thousands of settlers moved into the park, including many artisanal gold miners. Along with these incursions there has been an increase in hunting pressure on the park's fauna, including its primates, reversing a situation in the early stages of the conflict when bushmeat hunting (which has been a major threat to wildlife populations in Liberia for many years) reportedly eased and mammal populations increased. At the time of writing, efforts were underway to evict the settler communities from the park.

Sapo can be reached from the Liberian capital Monrovia in a 350-km road journey via the coastal city of Buchanan. The park is managed by the Liberian Forestry Development Authority (FDA), and intending visitors should register with the FDA in Monrovia before entering the park. Park headquarters are at Jalay's Town, which lies near the western boundary of the park about 10 km from the town of Juarzon. At present there is no special accommodation for visitors at Jalay's town and no developed network of trails inside the park. However, guides can lead naturalists into the forest, where all of the monkey species can, with patience, be observed.

Several other national parks in the forest zone of Liberia have been planned since the 1980s but none has yet been legalized.

Southern Highlands, Bioko

The Southern Highlands and Gran Caldera Scientific Reserve covers about 600 km² of the wet and rugged terrain of the southern part of Bioko Island, Equatorial Guinea. This is the one part of Bioko where all of the island's primates can still be found; this book regards each of these primates as either an endemic subspecies or (in the case of the red colobus monkey) endemic species. Along with the southern foothills of Mt. Cameroon, this is the wettest region in all of Africa, with rainfall on the south coast reaching 10,000 mm per annum. Much of the reserve is forested, with "monsoon" forest in the lowlands giving way at higher elevations first to submontane forest and then to montane forest and *Schefflera* woodland. The most striking geomorphological feature in the Southern Highlands is the Gran Caldera Volcanica de Luba, the remains of an extinct volcano whose walls reach to an elevation of 2,261 m.

The primates of the Southern Highlands and Gran Caldera are Demidoff's dwarf galago (*Galagoides demidovii*), Thomas's dwarf

Fig. A.23: Wall of the Gran Caldera de Luba, Bioko, Equatorial Guinea (photo by R. A. Bergl).

galago (*G. thomasi*), needle-clawed galago (*Euoticus pallidus pallidus*), Allen's galago (*Sciurocheirus alleni alleni*), drill (*Mandrillus leucophaeus poensis*), Preuss's monkey (*Allochrocebus preussi insularis*), crowned monkey (*Cercopithecus pogonias pogonias*), red-eared monkey (*C. erythrotis erythrotis*), putty-nosed monkey (*C. nictitans martini*), Pennant's red colobus (*Procolobus pennantii*) and black colobus (*Colobus satanas satanas*). The monkeys occur at high densities in the Gran Caldera, the crater of which can be entered on a foot trail leading up from the island's south coast; however, the putty-nosed and Preuss's monkeys are much less frequently encountered than the other species. The range of forest types and its spectacular terrain make this crater a very special place in West Africa in which to view primates.

All parts of Bioko suffer from hunting to feed a large and active bushmeat market in the capital, Malabo, on the island's north coast. Because the monkeys are a major part of the mammalian biomass of the Bioko forests they are one of the main targets for bushmeat hunters and their populations have declined significantly over much of the island in the last 20 years. The Gran Caldera monkey populations have been less affected by hunting than those elsewhere on the island, partly because of the Caldera's inaccessibility but also because of a research and conservation program established there by the Bioko Biodiversity Protection Program (BBPP) run by Drexel University in the USA and Universidad Nacional de Guinea Ecuatorial. While the Caldera monkeys are somewhat wary of humans, the hilly terrain and relatively short stature of the forest (especially at higher elevations) make it relatively easy to see most of the species.

The BBPP organizes a once-a-year survey of primates in the Gran Caldera, in which overseas students and volunteers participate (see <www.bioko.org>). Other visitors must obtain special permits from the government to enter this area. No housing is available in the Gran Caldera or its immediate vicinity; participants on the annual survey expedition camp at several sites on the ascent trail and southern coast.

On the northern edge of the Southern Highlands and Gran Caldera Reserve is the settlement of Moka at an elevation of 1,200 m. Moka, which has long been a stronghold of the island's indigenous people, the Bubi, can be reached from Malabo on a paved road. The forest in the immediate vicinity of Moka has been cleared for farmland and cattle pasture, but undisturbed forest on deeply dissected terrain can be seen on treks south and west of the town. At Moka the BBPP has

Fig. A.24: Streams cascade into the steep valley of the Iladyi River (above); and montane forest (below), Southern Highlands, Bioko Island, Equatorial Guinea (photos by J. F. Oates).

established a Wildlife Research Center that hosts visiting scientists; the center contains educational exhibits, and a guesthouse is planned.

It is sometimes possible to arrange accommodation with local residents of Moka. Several of the Bioko monkeys (especially *Cercopithecus erythrotis* and *C. pogonias*) can be encountered in treks into the forest from there, and galagos can be seen at night with a head lamp. On a long trek, it is possible to reach the Gran Caldera via the southern coast.

Taï National Park, Côte d'Ivoire

Taï, created in 1972 from part of an existing faunal and floral reserve, is the oldest rain-forest national park in West Africa and, at 3,300 km², the largest in the Upper Guinea forest region. It is in south-western Côte d'Ivoire, just to east of the Cavally River which forms the boundary with Liberia. The vegetation of Taï is high, closed-canopy moist forest, with no recent history of farming or logging except at the periphery. The terrain is generally flat or gently undulating, with the highest elevation being Mt. Niénokoué (623 m) in the south. Taï has been a World Heritage Site since 1982.

Fig. A.25: Sign for Taï National Park, Côte d'Ivoire (photo by W. S. McGraw).

Taï is home to all the primates of the Upper Guinea West forest subregion: Demidoff's and Thomas's dwarf galagos (*Galagoides demidovii* and *G. thomasi*), Bosman's potto (*Perodicticus potto potto*), sooty mangabey (*Cercocebus atys*), Diana monkey (*Cercopithecus diana diana*), Campbell's monkey (*C. campbelli campbelli*), eastern spot-nosed monkey (*C. petaurista petaurista*), Stampfli's putty-nosed monkey (*C. nictitans stampflii*), olive colobus (*Procolobus verus*), bay colobus (*P. badius badius*), western black-and-white colobus (*Colobus polykomos*) and western chimpanzee (*Pan troglodytes verus*). The putty-nosed monkey once occurred only in the northern section of the park but appears to be extending its range southward.

Taï has long been recognized as a key site for the conservation of the Upper Guinea rain forest and its primates, and primate research has been carried out there since 1976. However, since the park was created the human population in the surrounding area has grown dramatically, as a result both of migration from other parts of Côte d'Ivoire, and of an influx of refugees from Liberia. This population increase has been accompanied by an increase in poaching in the national park to supply the bushmeat trade, and this has had a devastating impact on large mammals across much of the park; among the primates, red and black-and-white colobus monkeys have been particularly seriously affected. The presence of scientists and support staff has led to low levels of hunting in the research areas of the Taï Chimpanzee Project and the Taï Monkey Project near the field station of the Institut d'Ecologie Tropicale (IET), established in 1977 on the western edge of the park near the town of Taï. Primates can be readily observed in these research areas. Farming appears to be expanding in the park's buffer zone and is encroaching on the forest.

The Parc national de Taï may be reached in a long road journey from the Ivorian capital Abidjan. Tourists can stay at an eco-lodge near Djiroutou, close to the southwestern corner of the park. Djiritou lies on the road that runs close to the Liberian border between the town of Guiglo on the Nzo River northwest of the park, and Tabou, on the coast. At the time of writing, this road was said to be in bad condition, especially to the south of the town of Taï, and Djiritou may therefore best be approached from Tabou via San Pedro, about 115 km to the east. From the lodge it is possible to hike into the forest with a guide. Diana monkeys, bay and black-and-white colobus, and chimpanzees may be encountered. Visits by tourists to the research areas near the IET station (near the town of Taï) are not encouraged and require special permission from the ministry of Eaux et Forêts and from research project managers.

Tanoé Forest, Côte d'Ivoire

The Tanoé Forest lies in the far south-eastern corner of Côte d'Ivoire, between the Ehy Lagoon and the Tano (or Tanoé) River, which forms the boundary with Ghana. This is a difficult site to reach, particularly in the rains between April and November. It has no visitor facilities and no permanent research base, but it is potentially a very important site for primate conservation. Tanoé was the last confirmed location (based on skins from animals reportedly killed by hunters in 2001 and 2006) of a surviving population of Miss Waldron's red colobus monkey (*Procolobus waldroni*), and the only place where roloway monkeys (*Cercopithecus diana roloway*) have been seen in recent years by scientists. Other primates recorded from Tanoé include the white-naped mangabey (*Cercocebus lunulatus*), Lowe's monkey (*Cercopithecus campbelli lowei*), eastern spot-nosed monkey (*C. petaurista petaurista*), olive colobus (*Procolobus verus*), and white-thighed black-and-white colobus (*Colobus vellerosus*). Local people also claim that chimpanzees (*Pan troglodytes verus*) occur here, but this has not been confirmed.

Most of the Tanoé forest, which has the status of a *forêt classée* and covers about 120 km², grows on swampy ground, making it very difficult to penetrate. However, hunters (many coming from Ghana)

Fig. A.26: Searching for primates in the Tanoé Forest, Côte d'Ivoire (photo by I. Koné).

have not been deterred by the difficult conditions, and have likely driven Miss Waldron's colobus to extinction. The forest has also been subjected to logging in some peripheral areas and much of it was recently threatened with conversion to oil-palm plantation; however, an international campaign led to the abandonment of the plantation plans in 2009. Efforts are underway to create a community-managed conservation area at Tanoé.

The nearest large town to Tanoé is Aboisso, which can be reached on a surfaced road from Abidjan; from Aboisso it is about 60 km on country roads to the small town of Nouamou on the Ehy Lagoon, and 4 km from there to the edge of the forest on a road constructed by the oil-palm company. The forest can also be reached by canoe on the lagoon from Nouamou, or from the village of Kadja Gnanzoukro on the Tano River.

Tiwai Island and Gola National Park, Sierra Leone

Based on an agreement between local chiefdoms and the government's Forestry Division, Tiwai Island Wildlife Sanctuary in south-eastern Sierra Leone was officially gazetted as a protected area in 1987, the first area in the country to be set aside for wildlife conservation. Prior to this, the 12 km^2 island had, since 1982, been the site of a field station for primate research. Tiwai lies in one of Sierra Leone's largest rivers, the Moa, about 5 km northeast of the western part of the Gola Forest National Park. The low-lying island, on sandy soils, is covered by a mosaic of old secondary forest, younger secondary forest, and palm swamp. Until 1990, parts of the island had small rice farms.

Probably because of the combined effect of the vegetation mosaic and a history of lower levels of hunting than occurs over much of southern Sierra Leone, Tiwai has both a high density and a high diversity of primates. The diurnal species are the same as those in other protected areas in the Upper Guinea West Forest subregion: sooty mangabey (*Cercocebus atys*), Diana monkey (*Cercopithecus diana diana*), Campbell's monkey (*Cercopithecus campbelli campbelli*), western spot-nosed monkey (*Cercopithecus petaurista buettikoferi*), olive colobus (*Procolobus verus*), bay colobus (*Procolobus badius badius*), western black-and-white colobus (*Colobus polykomos*) and western chimpanzee (*Pan troglodytes verus*). Green monkeys (*Chlorocebus aethiops sabaeus*) are occasionally seen in riparian forest. At night Demidoff's dwarf galago (*Galagoides demidovii*) and

Fig. A.27: Moa River with Tiwai Island behind (above), and original visitor center, in 1988, Tiwai Island, Sierra Leone (below) (photos by J. F. Oates).

Bosman's potto (*Perodicticus potto potto*) can be spotted with head lamps; Thomas's dwarf galago (*G. thomasi*) is probably also present. The beautiful Diana monkey has been the subject of several long-term field studies at Tiwai, and is usually quite readily observed in old forest areas. Another important component of the fauna of Tiwai, and the Moa River downstream, is the pygmy hippopotamus.

Tiwai is reached by road from Freetown via the towns of Bo, Bandajuma and Potoru. After Bandajuma the road is not surfaced. From just north of Potoru you take a narrow dirt road (best navigated by 4-wheel-drive, east for about 13 km to the village of Kambama on the west bank of the Moa River, adjacent to the island. The road journey from Freetown can take up to one day, depending on the transport used. Tiwai Island has simple facilities for visitors at a special campsite, Kikihun, reached by boat from Kambama. Kikihun has tents on elevated platforms and from there visitors can make guided or non-guided tours of the forest. These visitor facilities are managed by local communities in conjunction with the Freetown-based Environmental Foundation for Africa.

There is a long-standing plan for a landscape conservation program that would connect Tiwai and other Moa islands to the south with the Gola Forest National Park (748 km^2). The rain forests of Gola support the same set of primate species as Tiwai, and Diana monkeys are common in some areas. Gola is reached on the highway from Freetown via Bo to Kenema; from Kenema you go south across the Moa River to Joru on a dirt road. There is hotel accommodation in Kenema, and community-run guest houses at Lalehun and Belebu, close to the edge of the northern section of the Gola Forest National Park. Accommodation is also available at the Sileti campsite in southern Gola, close to the Zimmi road. Permits are needed to enter the forest and can be obtained from Gola Forest Programme headquarters in Kenema.

The Gola Forest Reserves became a national park in 2011; the park is managed by the Sierra Leone Forestry Division in partnership with the Conservation Society of Sierra Leone and the Royal Society for the Protection of Birds. A separate, related programme spearheaded by BirdLife International is working to establish a "Transboundary Peace Park" that will link Gola to Tiwai Island and to forests across the border in Liberia.

"W" Transboundary Park, Bénin, Burkina Faso and Niger

The Parcs nationaux du W du Niger were established in 1954 in the French West African territories of Dahomey (today the Republic of Bénin), Haute Volta (today Burkina Faso) and Niger, upgrading the status of existing reserves in the area. This regional park takes its name from W-shaped bends in the River Niger, the park's northern boundary. The total area of the three national parks that form the regional complex is over 10,000 km^2, with about half of this area lying in Bénin. Although there are hills in the south (at the northern end of the Atakora Mountains), much of the terrain is flat and low-lying. The vegetation is predominantly Sudanian savanna woodland.

There are no rare, restricted-range or endangered primates in the "W" park complex, but this is a good location to observe typical species of the eastern savanna region of West Africa: the Senegal bushbaby (*Galago senegalensis senegalensis*), the olive baboon (*Papio anubis*), the patas (*Erythrocebus patas*), and the tantalus monkey (*Chlorocebus aethiops tantalus*). This is also one of the last refuges for the cheetah in West Africa.

The Niger section of the "W" park complex became a World Heritage Site in 1996. This is the most accessible area of the park and can be reached in a 150-km journey by road from the Nigerien capital Niamey via Say and Tamou (after Tamou the road is dirt, and a 4-wheel-drive vehicle is recommended). The park headquarters are at Tapoa, where there is a hotel. The Tapoa Hotel is open between November and May, and a dedicated shuttle bus service runs between Niamey and the hotel.

Only about 20 km southwest of the southern edge of this park in Bénin is the Pendjari National Park (2,755 km²), which has the same primate fauna. Pendjari and "W", together with Arli Faunal Reserve in Burkina Faso and several outlying game safari areas, form the "Complex écologique régional WAP." The nearest town to Pendjari is Tanguieta.

References

Abernethy, K. A., White, L. J. T. and Wickings, E. J. 2002. Hordes of mandrills (*Mandrillus sphinx*): extreme group size and seasonal male presence. *Journal of Zoology, London* 258: 131–137.

Abwe, E. E. and Morgan, B. J. 2008. The Ebo forest: four years of preliminary research and conservation of the Nigeria-Cameroon chimpanzee (*Pan troglodytes vellerosus*). *Pan African News* 51: 26–29.

Agoramoorthy, G. 1989. Survey of rain forest primates in Sapo National Park, Liberia. *Primate Conservation* (10): 71–73.

Ajayi, S. S. 1971. Wildlife as a source of protein in Nigeria: some priorities for development. *Nigerian Field* 36: 115–127.

Alp, R. 1993. Meat eating and ant dipping by wild chimpanzees in Sierra Leone. *Primates* 34: 463–468.

Alp, R. 1997. "Stepping-sticks" and "seat-sticks": new types of tools used wild chimpanzees (*Pan troglodytes*) in Sierra Leone. *American Journal of Primatology* 41: 45–52.

Alp, R. and Kitchener, A. C. 1993. Carnivory in wild chimpanzees, *Pan troglodytes verus*, in Sierra Leone. *Mammalia* 57: 273–274.

Altmann, J. 1974. Observational study of behavior: sampling methods. *Behaviour* 49: 227–265.

Ambrose, L. 1999. Species Diversity in West and Central African Galagos (Primates, Galagonidae): The Use of Acoustic Analysis. PhD Thesis, Oxford Brookes University, Oxford, UK.

Ambrose, L. 2002. *A Survey of Prosimians in the National Parks and Forest Reserves of Uganda*. Nocturnal Primate Research Group, Oxford Brookes University, Oxford, UK.

Ambrose, L. 2003. Three acoustic forms of Allen's galagos (Primates; Galagonidae) in the Central African region. *Primates* 44: 25–39.

Ambrose, L. and Perkin, A. W. 2000. A survey of nocturnal prosimians at Moca on Bioko Island, Equatorial Guinea. *African Primates* 4: 4–10.

Anadu, P. A. and Oates, J. F. 1988. The olive colobus monkey in Nigeria. *Nigerian Field* 53: 31–34.

Anadu, P. A., Elamah, P. O. and Oates, J. F. 1988. The bushmeat trade in southwestern Nigeria: a case study. *Human Ecology* 16: 199–208.

Anderson, J. R. and McGrew, W. C. 1984. Guinea baboons (*Papio papio*) at a sleeping site. *American Journal of Primatology* 6: 1–14.

Anderson, J. R., Williamson, E. A. and Carter, J. 1983. Chimpanzees of Sapo Forest, Liberia: density, nests, tools and meat-eating. *Primates* 24: 594–601.

Anderson, M. J. 1998. Comparative morphology and speciation in galagos. *Folia Primatologica* 69 (supplement 1): 325–331.

Arnold, K. and Zuberbühler, K. 2006. The alarm calling system of adult male putty-nosed monkeys, *Cercopithecus nictitans martini*. *Animal Behaviour* 72: 643–653.

Asibey, E. O. A. 1978. Primate conservation in Ghana. Pp.55–74 in D. J. Chivers and W. Lane-Petter (eds.), *Recent Advances in Primatology, Volume 2, Conservation*. Academic Press, London.

Astaras, C., Mühlenberg, M. and Waltert, M. 2008. Note on drill (*Mandrillus leucophaeus*) ecology and conservation status in Korup National Park, Southwest Cameroon. *American Journal of Primatology* 70: 306–310.

Astaras, C., Krause, S., Mattner, L., Rehse, C. and Waltert, M. 2011. Associations between the drill (*Mandrillus leucophaeus*) and sympatric monkeys in Korup National Park, Cameroon. *American Journal of Primatology* 73: 127–134.

Aubréville, A. 1949. *Contribution à la Paleohistoire des forêts de l'Afrique tropicale*. Société d'Editions Géographiques, Maritimes et Coloniales, Paris.

Baker, L. R. 2005. Distribution and Conservation Status of the Sclater's Guenon (*Cercopithecus sclateri*) in Southern Nigeria. Conservation Biology Graduate Program, University of Minnesota, Minneapolis, MN.

Baker, L. R. and Olubode, O. S. 2008. Correlates with the distribution and abundance of endangered Sclater's monkeys (*Cercopithecus sclateri*) in southern Nigeria. *African Journal of Ecology* 46: 365–373.

Baker, L. R., Tanimola, A. A., Olubode, O. S. and Garshelis, D. L. 2009. Distribution and abundance of sacred monkeys in Igboland, southern Nigeria. *American Journal of Primatology* 71: 574–586.

Baker, L. R., Arnold, T. W., Olubode, O. S. & Garshelis, D. L. 2011. Considerations for using occupancy surveys to monitor forest primates: a case study with Sclater's monkey (*Cercopithecus sclateri*). *Population Ecology* 53(4). In press.

Baldwin, P. J., Sabater Pí, J., McGrew, W. C. and Tutin, C. E. G. 1981. Comparisons of nests made by different populations of chimpanzees (*Pan troglodytes*). *Primates* 22: 474–486.

Baldwin, P. J., McGrew, W. C. and Tutin, C. E. G. 1982. Wide-ranging chimpanzees at Mt. Assirik, Senegal. *International Journal of Primatology* 3: 367–385.

Barnett, A., Prangley, M., Hayman, P. V., Diawara, D. and Koman, J. 1994. A preliminary survey of Kounounkan Forest, Guinea, West Africa. *Oryx* 28: 269–275.

Basilio, A. 1962. *La Vida Animal en la Guinea Español*. 2nd edition. Instituto de Estudios Africanos, Cosejo Superior de Investigaciones Cientificas, Madrid.

Baudenon, P. 1949. Contribution à la connaissance du potto de Bosman dans le Togo-sud. *Mammalia* 13: 76–99.

Bearder, S. K. and Doyle, G. A. 1974. Ecology of bushbabies *Galago senegalensis* and *Galago crassicaudatus*, with some notes on their behaviour in the field. Pp.109–130 in R. D. Martin, G. A. Doyle and A. C. Walker (eds.), *Prosimian Biology*. Duckworth, London.

Bearder, S. K. and Honess, P. E. 1992. A Survey of Nocturnal Primates and Other Mammals in the Korup National Park, Cameroon. Report to Wildlife Conservation International, New York.

Bearder, S. K. and Martin, R. D. 1980. *Acacia* gum and its use by bushbabies, *Galago senegalensis* (Primates: Lorisidae). *International Journal of Primatology* 1: 103–128.

Bearder, S. K. and Oates, J. F. 2009a. A Survey of Nocturnal Primates in Rhoko Forest, Nigeria, 14–18 January 2009. Report to CERCOPAN. Oxford Brookes University, Oxford, UK.

Bearder, S. K. and Oates, J. F. 2009b. Report on a Survey of Nocturnal Primates in Okomu National Park and Forest Reserve, 21–26 January 2009. Report to the A.P. Leventis Conservation Foundation. Oxford Brookes University, Oxford, UK.

Bearder, S. K., Honess, P. E. and Ambrose, L. 1995. Species diversity among galagos with special reference to mate recognition. Pp.331–352 in L. Alterman, G. A. Doyle and M. K. Izard (eds.), *Creatures of the Dark: The Nocturnal Prosimians*. Plenum Press, New York.

Bearder, S. K., Ambrose, L., Harcourt, C., Honess, P., Perkin, A., Pimley, E., Pullen, S. and Svoboda, N. 2003. Species-typical patterns of infant contact, sleeping site use and social cohesion among nocturnal primates in Africa. *Folia Primatologica* 74: 337–354.

Beeson, M., Tame, S., Keeming, E. and Lea, S. E. G. 1996. Food habits of guenons (*Cercopithecus* spp.) in Afro-montane forest. *African Journal of Ecology* 34: 202–210.

Benefit, B. R. 1993. The permanent dentition and phylogenetic position of *Victoriapithecus* from Maboko Island, Kenya. *Journal of Human Evolution* 25: 83–172.

Benefit, B. R., McCrossin, M., Boaz, N. T. and Pavlakis, P. 2008. New fossil cercopithecoids from the late Miocene of As Sahabi, Libya. *Garyounis Scientific Bulletin*, Special Issue 5: 265–282.

Bergl, R. A. 2006. Conservation Biology of the Cross River Gorilla (*Gorilla gorilla diehli*). PhD thesis, City University of New York, New York.

Bergl, R. A. and Vigilant, L. 2007. Genetic analysis reveals population structure and recent migration within the highly fragmented range of the Cross River gorilla (*Gorilla gorilla diehli*). *Molecular Ecology* 16: 501–516.

Bergl, R. A., Bradley, B. J., Nsubuga, A. M. and Vigilant, L. 2008. Genetic effects of habitat fragmentation, population size and demographic history on primate populations: the Cross River gorilla in a comparative context. *American Journal of Primatology* 70: 848–859.

Berry, J. 1970. Language systems and literature. Pp.80–98 in J. N. Paden and E. W. Soja (eds.), *The African Experience, Vol. 2.* Heineman Educational, London.

Bitty, E. A. and McGraw, W. S. 2007. Locomotion and habitat use of Stampfli's putty-nosed monkey (*Cercopithecus nictitans stampflii*) in the Taï National Park, Ivory Coast. *American Journal of Physical Anthropology* 134: 383–391.

Blackwell, K. F. and Menzies, J. I. 1968. Observations on the biology of the potto (*Perodicticus potto*, Miller). *Mammalia* 32: 447–451.

Bloch, J. I., Silcox, M. T., Boyer, D. M. and Sargis, E. J. 2007. New Paleocene skeletons and the relationship of plesiadapiforms to crown-clade primates. *Proceedings of the National Academy of Sciences USA* 104: 1159–1164.

Bocian, C. M. 1997. Niche Separation of Black-and-White Colobus Monkeys (*Colobus angolensis* and *C. guereza*) in the Ituri Forest. PhD thesis, City University of New York, New York.

Böer, M. 1987. Beobachtungen zur Fortpflanzung und zum Verhalten des Drill (*Mandrillus leucophaeus* Ritgen, 1824) im Zoo Hannover. *Zeitschrift für Säugertierkunde* 52: 265–281.

Boesch, C. 1978. Nouvelles observations sur les chimpanzés de la forêt de Taï, Côte d'Ivoire. *La Terre et la Vie* 32: 195–201.

Boesch, C. 1991. The effect of leopard predation on grouping patterns in forest chimpanzees. *Behaviour* 117: 220–242.

Boesch, C. and Boesch, H. 1983. Optimisation of nut-cracking with natural hammers by wild chimpanzees. *Behaviour* 83: 265–286.

Boesch, C. and Boesch, H. 1989. Hunting behavior of wild chimpanzees in the Taï National Park. *American Journal of Physical Anthropology* 78: 547-573.

Boesch, C. and Boesch-Achermann, H. 2000. *The Chimpanzees of the Taï Forest: Behavioural Ecology and Evolution.* Oxford University Press, Oxford.

Boesch, C., Goné Bi, Z. B., Anderson, D. and Stahl, D. 2006. Food choice in Taï chimpanzees: are cultural differences present? Pp.183–201 in G. Hohmann, M. M. Robbins and C. Boesch (eds.), *Feeding Ecology in Apes and Other Primates.* Cambridge University Press, Cambridge, UK.

Boese, G. K. 1975. Social behavior and ecological considerations of West African baboons (*Papio papio*). Pp.205–230 in R. H. Tuttle (ed.), *Socioecology and Psychology of Primates.* Mouton, The Hague.

Bongers, F., Poorter, L. and Hawthorne, W. D. 2004. The forests of Upper Guinea: gradients in large species composition. Pp.41–52 in L. Poorter, F. Bongers, F. Y. N'. Kouamé and W. D. Hawthorne (eds.), *Biodiversity of West*

African Forests: An Ecological Atlas of Woody Plant Species. CABI Publishing, Wallingford, UK.

Booth, A. H. 1954a. The Dahomey Gap and the mammalian fauna of the West African forests. *Revue de Zoologie et de Botanique africaines* 50: 305–314.

Booth, A. H. 1954b. A note on the colobus monkeys of the Gold and Ivory Coasts. *Annals and Magazine of Natural History*, 12th series 7: 857–860.

Booth, A. H. 1955. Speciation in the mona monkeys. *Journal of Mammalogy* 36: 434–449.

Booth, A. H. 1956. The distribution of primates in the Gold Coast. *Journal of the West African Science Association* 2: 122–133.

Booth, A. H. 1957. Observations on the natural history of the olive colobus monkey, *Procolobus verus* (van Beneden). *Proceedings of the Zoological Society of London* 129: 421–430.

Booth, A. H. 1958a. The Niger, the Volta and the Dahomey Gap as geographic barriers. *Evolution* 12: 48–62.

Booth, A. H. 1958b. The zoogeography of West African primates: a review. *Bulletin de l'Institut français de l'Afrique noire* (A) 20: 587–622.

Booth, A. H. 1960. *Small Mammals of West Africa*. Longmans, London.

Bowen-Jones, E. and Pendry, S. 1999. The threat to primates and other mammals from the bushmeat trade in Africa, and how this threat could be diminished. *Oryx* 33: 233–246.

Bourlière, F., Hunkeler, C. and Bertrand, M. 1970. Ecology and behavior of Lowe's guenon (*Cercopithecus campbelli lowei*) in the Ivory Coast. Pp.297–350 in J. R. Napier and P. H. Napier (eds.), *Old World Monkeys: Evolution, Systematics, and Behavior*. Academic Press, New York.

Brandon-Jones, D., Duckworth, J. W., Jenkins, P. D., Rylands, A. B. and Sarmiento, E. E. 2007. The genitive of species-group scientific names formed from personal names. *Zootaxa* 1541: 41–48.

Breuer, T. 2005. Diet choice of large carnivores in northern Cameroon. *African Journal of Ecology* 43: 97–106.

Brincic, T. T., Amarasekaran, B. and McKenna, A. 2010. *Sierra Leone National Chimpanzee Census*. Tacugama Chimpanzee Sanctuary, Freetown, Sierra Leone.

Brown, A. 2008. 505: Lower Niger-Benue. In: *Freshwater Regions of the World*. World Wildlife Fund (WWF) and the Nature Conservancy, Washington, DC. Website: <http://www.feow.org/ecoregion_details.php?eco=505>. Accessed: 13 July 2010.

Brownell, A. 2003a. Togo. Pp.117–118 in R. Kormos, C. Boesch, M. I. Bakarr and T. M. Butynski (eds.), *West African Chimpanzees: Status Survey and Conservation Action Plan*. IUCN, Gland, Switzerland.

Brownell, A. 2003b. Benin. Pp.119–120 in R. Kormos, C. Boesch, M. I. Bakarr and T. M. Butynski (eds.), *West African Chimpanzees: Status Survey and Conservation Action Plan*. IUCN, Gland, Switzerland.

Brugière, D. 1998. Population size of the black colobus monkey *Colobus satanas* and the impact of logging in the Lopé reserve, Central Gabon. *Biological Conservation* 86: 15–20.

Brugière, D. and Gautier, J.-P. 1999. Status and conservation of the sun-tailed guenon *Cercopithecus solatus*, Gabon's endemic monkey. *Oryx* 33: 67–74.

Brugière, D. and Magassouba, B. 2009. Pattern and sustainability of the bushmeat trade in the Haut Niger National Park, Republic of Guinea. *African Journal of Ecology* 44: 630–639.

Brugière, D., Gautier, J.-P., Moungazi, A. and Gautier-Hion, A. 2002. Primate diet and biomass in relation to vegetation composition and fruiting phenology in a rain forest in Gabon. *International Journal of Primatology* 23: 999–1024.

Brugière, D., Badjinca, I., Silva, C. and Serra, A. 2009. Distribution of chimpanzees and interactions with humans in Guinea-Bissau and western Guinea, West Africa. *Folia Primatologica* 80: 353–358.

Brunet, M. *et al.* 2002. A new hominid from the Upper Miocene of Chad, Central Africa. *Nature* 418: 145–151.

Bshary, R. 2007. Interactions between red colobus and chimpanzees. Pp.155–170 in W. S. McGraw, K. Zuberbühler and R. Noë (eds.), *Monkeys of the Taï Forest: An African Primate Community*. Cambridge University Press, Cambridge, UK.

Burgess, N., Hales J. D'A., Underwood, E. and Dinerstein, E. 2004. *Terrestrial Ecoregions of Africa and Madagascar: A Conservation Assessment.* Island Press, Washington, DC.

Busse, C. D. 1977. Chimpanzee predation as a possible factor in the evolution of red colobus monkey social organization. *Evolution* 31: 907–911.

Butler, H. 1966. Some notes on the distribution of primates in the Sudan. *Folia Primatologica* 4: 416–423.

Butler, H. 1967. Seasonal breeding of the Senegal galago (*Galago senegalensis senegalensis*) in the Nuba Mountains, Republic of the Sudan. *Folia Primatologica* 5: 165–175.

Butynski, T. M. 1988. Guenon birth seasons and correlates with rainfall and food. Pp.284–322 in A. Gautier-Hion, F. Bourlière, J.-P. Gautier and J. Kingdon (eds.), *A Primate Radiation: Evolutionary Biology of the African Guenons*. Cambridge University Press, Cambridge, UK.

Butynski, T. M. and de Jong, Y. A. 2007. Distribution of the potto *Perodicticus potto* (Primates: Lorisidae) in eastern Africa, with a description of a new subspecies from Mount Kenya. *Journal of East African Natural History* 96: 113–147.

Butynski, T. M. and Koster, S. H. 1990. The Status and Conservation of Forests and Primates on Bioko Island (Fernando Poo), Equatorial Guinea. Impenetrable Forest Conservation Project, Kampala, Uganda.

Butynski, T. M. and Koster, S.H. 1994. Distribution and conservation status of primates in Bioko island, Equatorial Guinea. *Biodiversity and Conservation* 3: 893–909.

Butynski, T. M. and Owens, J. R. 2008. Mammals and Birds Encountered in the Gran Caldera de Luba during January 2008. Report of the Bioko Biodiversity Protection Program, Drexel University, Philadelphia, PA, and Universidad Nacional de Guinea Ecuatorial (UNGE), Malabo, Equatorial Guinea.

Butynski, T. M., de Jong, Y. A. and Hearn, G. W. 2009. Body measurements for the monkeys of Bioko Island, Equatorial Guinea. *Primate Conservation* (24): 99–105.

Butynski, T. M., Kingdon, J. and Kalina, J. (eds.). 2011. *The Mammals of Africa*, Vol. II. University of California Press, Berkeley. In press.

Buzzard, P. J. 2004. Interspecific Competition Among *Cercopithecus campbelli*, *C. petaurista*, and *C. diana* at Taï Forest, Côte d'Ivoire. PhD thesis, Columbia University, New York.

Buzzard, P. J. 2006a. Ecological partitioning of *Cercopithecus campbelli, C. petaurista,* and *C. diana* in the Taï Forest. *International Journal of Primatology* 27: 529–558.

Buzzard, P. J. 2006b. Ranging patterns in relation to seasonality and frugivory among *Cercopithecus campbelli, C. petaurista,* and *C. diana* in the Taï Forest. *International Journal of Primatology* 27: 559–573.

Buzzard, P. J. and Eckardt, W. 2007. The social systems of the guenons. Pp.51–71 in W. S. McGraw, K. Zuberbühler and R. Noë (eds.), *Monkeys of the Taï Forest: An African Primate Community.* Cambridge University Press, New York.

Byrne, R. W. 1981. Distance vocalizations of Guinea baboons (*Papio papio*) in Senegal: an analysis of function. *Behaviour* 78: 283–312.

Cable, S. and Cheek, M. 1998. *The Plants of Mount Cameroon: A Conservation Checklist.* Royal Botanic Gardens, Kew, UK.

Campbell, G., Kuehl, H., Kouamé, P. N'G. and Boesch, C. 2008a. Alarming decline of West African chimpanzees in Côte d'Ivoire. *Current Biology* 18: R903–R904.

Campbell, G., Teichroeb, J. and Paterson, J. D. 2008b. Distribution of diurnal primate species in Togo and Bénin. *Folia Primatologica* 79: 15–30.

Carles, A. and Petrella, E. 2009. *World Water Atlas.* European Parliament Working Document DT.4.2009.EN, Brussels.

Carpenter, C. R. 1965. The howlers of Barro Colorado Island. Pp.250–291 in

I. DeVore (ed.), *Primate Behavior: Field Studies of Monkeys and Apes*. Holt, Rinehart and Winston, New York.

Castelo, R. 1994. Biogeographical considerations of fish diversity in Bioko. *Biodiversity and Conservation* 3: 808–827.

Central Intelligence Agency. 2009. *The World Factbook 2009*. Central Intelligence Agency, Washington, DC.

Chaber, A.-L., Allebone-Webb, S., Lignereux, Y., Cunningham, A. A. and Rowcliffe, J. M. 2010. The scale of illegal meat importation from Africa to Europe via Paris. *Conservation Letters* 3: 317–321.

Chalmers, N. R. 1968a. Group composition, ecology, and daily activities of free living mangabeys in Uganda. *Folia Primatologica* 8: 247–262.

Chalmers, N. R. 1968b. The social behavior of free living mangabeys in Uganda. *Folia Primatologica* 8: 263–281.

Chalmers, N. R. 1968c. The visual and vocal communication of free living mangabeys in Uganda. *Folia Primatologica* 9: 258–280.

Charles-Dominique, P. 1966a. Naissance et croissance d'*Arctocebus calabarensis* en captivité. *Biologica Gabonica* 2: 331–345.

Charles-Dominique, P. 1966b. Analyse de contenus stomacaux d'*Arctocebus calabarensis, Perodicticus potto, Galago alleni, Galago elegantulus, Galago demidoffi*. *Biologica Gabonica* 2: 347–353.

Charles-Dominique, P. 1971. Eco-éthologie des prosimiens du Gabon. *Biologica Gabonica* 7: 121–228.

Charles-Dominique, P. 1977. *Ecology and Behaviour of Nocturnal Primates: Prosimians of Equatorial West Africa*. Duckworth, London.

Chism, J. and Rowell, T. E. 1988. The natural history of patas monkeys. Pp.412–438 in A. Gautier-Hion, F. Bourlière, J.-P. Gautier and J. Kingdon (eds.), *A Primate Radiation: Evolutionary Biology of the African Guenons*. Cambridge University Press, Cambridge, UK.

Chivers, D. J. and Hladik, C. M. 1980. Morphology of the gastrointestinal tract in primates: comparisons with other mammals in relation to diet. *Journal of Morphology* 166: 337–386.

Cipolletta, C. 2004. Effects of group dynamics and diet on the ranging patterns of a western gorilla group (*Gorilla gorilla gorilla*) at Bai Hokou, Central African Republic. *American Journal of Primatology* 64: 193–205.

Clark, P. U., Dyke, A. S., Shakun, J. D., Carlson, A. E., Clark, J., Wohlfarth, B., Mitrovica, J. X., Hostetler, S. W. and McCabe, A. M. 2009. The last glacial maximum. *Science* 325: 710–714.

Clutton-Brock, T. H. 1974. Activity patterns of red colobus (*Colobus badius tephrosceles*). *Folia Primatologica* 21: 161–187.

Colyn, M., Hulselmans, J., Sonet, G., Oudé, P., de Winter, J., Natta, A., Nagy, Z. T. and Verheyen, E. 2010. Discovery of a new duiker species (Bovidae: Cephalophinae) from the Dahomey Gap, West Africa. *Zootaxa* (2637): 1–30.

Cooke, C. 2005. The cercopithecid community of Sette Cama, Gabon: a preliminary study. *American Journal of Primatology* 66 (supplement 1): 151–152.

Cooke, C. and McGraw, W. S. 2007. Ranging and foraging behavior of red-capped mangabeys, *Cercocebus torquatus*, in Sette Cama, Gabon. *American Journal of Physical Anthropology* 132 (supplement 44): 90.

Cooke, C., Ibessa, R. M. and McGraw, W. S. 2009. New information on the feeding and grouping behavior of *Cercocebus torquatus*, the red-capped mangabey, from southwestern Gabon. *American Journal of Physical Anthropology* 138 (supplement 48): 108–109.

Coolidge, H. J. 1929. A revision of the genus *Gorilla*. *Memoirs of the Museum of Comparative Zoology* 50: 291–381.

Cornevin, R. 1962. *Histoire du Togo*. Éditions Berger-Levrault, Paris.

Couvreur, T. L. P., Chatrou, L. W., Sosef, M. S. M. and Richardson, J. E. 2008. Molecular phylogenetics reveal multiple tertiary vicariance origins of the African rain forest trees. *BMC Biology* 6: 54.

Cowlishaw, G., Mendelson, S. and Rowcliffe, J. M. 2005. Structure and operation of a bushmeat commodity chain in southwestern Ghana. *Conservation Biology* 19: 139–149.

Cracraft, J. 1983. Species concepts and speciation analysis. *Current Ornithology* 1: 159–187.

Curtin, S. H. 2002. Diet of the roloway monkey, *Cercopithecus diana roloway*, in Bia National Park, Ghana. Pp.351–371 in M. E. Glenn and M. Cords (eds.), *The Guenons: Diversity and Adaptation in African Monkeys*. Kluwer Academic/ Plenum, New York.

Curtin, S. H. and Olson D. K. 1984. Ranging patterns of black-and-white colobus and diana monkeys in Bia National Park, Ghana. Paper presented at 53rd Annual Meeting of American Association of Physical Anthropologists, Philadelphia, PA.

Czekala, N. and Sicotte, P. 2000. Reproductive monitoring of free-ranging female mountain gorillas by urinary hormone analysis. *American Journal of Primatology* 51: 209–215.

Dandelot, P. 1971. Classification of African Anthropoidea. In J. Meester and H. W. Setzer (eds.), *The Mammals of Africa: An Identification Manual. Part 3.* Smithsonian Institution Press, Washington, DC.

Dasilva, G. L. 1989. The Ecology of the Western Black and White Colobus (*Colobus polykomos polykomos* Zimmerman 1780) on a Riverine Island in South-eastern Sierra Leone. DPhil. thesis, University of Oxford. Oxford.

Dasilva, G. L. 1992. The western black-and-white colobus as a low-energy strategist: activity budgets, energy expenditure and energy intake. *Journal of Animal Ecology* 61: 79–91.

Dasilva, G. L. 1993. Postural changes and behavioural thermoregulation in *Colobus polykomos*: the effect of climate and diet. *African Journal of Ecology* 31: 226–241.

Davenport, T. R. B., Stanley, W.T., Sargis, E. J., De Luca, D. W., Mpunga, N. E., Machaga, S. J. and Olson, L. E. 2006. A new genus of African monkey, *Rungwecebus*: morphology, ecology, and molecular phylogenetics. *Science* 312: 1378–1381.

Davies, A. G. 1987. Conservation of primates in the Gola Forest Reserves, Sierra Leone. *Primate Conservation* (8): 150–153.

Davies, A. G. and Oates, J. F. (eds.). 1994. *Colobine Monkeys: Their Ecology, Behaviour and Evolution*. Cambridge University Press, Cambridge, UK.

Davies, A. G., Oates, J. F. and Dasilva, G. L. 1999. Patterns of frugivory in three West African colobine monkeys. *International Journal of Primatology* 20: 327–357.

de Bournonville, D. 1967. Contribution à l'étude du chimpanzé en République de Guinée. *Bulletin de l'Institut français de l'Afrique noire* (A) 29: 1188–1269.

Defler, T. R. 2004. *Primates of Colombia*. Conservation International, Bogotá, Colombia.

Delson, E. 1994. Evolutionary history of the colobine monkeys in paleoenvironmental perspective. Pp.11–43 in A. G. Davies and J. F. Oates (eds.), *Colobine Monkeys: Their Ecology, Behaviour and Evolution*. Cambridge University Press, Cambridge, UK.

Delson, E., Terranova, C. J., Jungers, W. L., Sargis, E. J., Jablonski, N. G. and Dechow, P. C. 2000. Body mass in Cercopithecidea (Primates, Mammalia): estimation and scaling in extinct and extant taxa. *Anthropological Papers of the American Museum of Natural History* (83): 159pp.

deMenocal, P. B. 2004. African climate change and faunal evolution during the Pliocene-Pleistocene. *Earth and Planetary Science Letters* 220: 3–24.

Depew, L. A. 1983. Ecology and Behaviour of Baboons (*Papio anubis*) in the Shai Hills Game Production Reserve, Ghana. MSc thesis, University of Cape Coast, Ghana.

DeVore, I. and Hall, K. R. L. 1965. Baboon ecology. Pp.20–52 in I. DeVore (ed.), *Primate Behavior: Field Studies of Monkeys and Apes*. Holt, Rinehart and Winston, New York.

Diouck, D. 2001. Adaptations of western red colobus (*Colobus badius temmincki*) in Senegal. *Folia Primatologica* 72: 115–127.

Disotell, T. R. 2000. Molecular systematics of the Cercopithecidae. Pp.29–56 in P. F. Whitehead and C. J. Jolly (eds.), *Old World Monkeys*. Cambridge University Press, Cambridge, UK.

Disotell, T. R. and Raaum, R. L. 2002. Molecular timescale and gene tree incongruence in the guenons. Pp.27–36 in M. E. Glenn and M. Cords (eds.), *The Guenons: Diversity and Adaptation in African Monkeys*. Kluwer Academic/ Plenum, New York.

Doran, D. 1993. Sex differences in adult chimpanzee positional behavior: the influence of body size on locomotion and posture. *American Journal of Physical Anthropology* 91: 99–115.

Doran, D. 1997. Influence of seasonality on activity patterns, feeding behavior, ranging, and grouping patterns in Taï chimpanzees. *International Journal of Primatology* 18: 183–206.

Doran-Sheehy, D. M., Greer, D., Mongo, P. and Schwindt, D. 2004. Impact of ecological and social factors on ranging in western gorillas. *American Journal of Primatology* 64: 207–222.

Dorst, J. and Dandelot, P. 1970. *A Field Guide to the Larger Mammals of Africa*. Collins, London.

Douady, C. J., Catzeflis, F., Raman, J., Springer, M. S. and Stanhope, M. J. 2003. The Sahara as a vicariant agent, and the role of Miocene climatic events, in the diversification of the mammalian order Macroscelidea (elephant shrews). *Proceedings of the National Academy of Sciences USA* 100: 8325–8330.

Dowsett, R. J. and Dowsett-Lemaire, F. 1989. Larger mammals observed in the Gotel Mts and on the Mambilla Plateau, eastern Nigeria. *Tauraco Research Report* 1: 38–41.

Dowsett-Lemaire, F. and Dowsett, R. J. 2001. A new population of gorillas *Gorilla gorilla* and other endangered primates in western Cameroon. *African Primates* 5: 3–7.

Drake, N. and Bristow, C. 2006. Shorelines in the Sahara: geological evidence for an enhanced monsoon from palaeolake Megachad. *The Holocene* 16: 901–911.

Dunbar, R. I. M. 1974. Observations on the ecology and social organization of the green monkey, *Cercopithecus sabaeus*, in Senegal. *Primates* 15: 341–350.

Dunbar, R. I. M. 1988. *Primate Social Systems*. Cornell University Press, Ithaca, NY.

Dunbar, R. I. M. and Nathan, M. F. 1972. Social organization of the Guinea baboon, *Papio papio*. *Folia Primatologica* 17: 321–334.

Dunn, A. 1991. *A Study of the Relative Abundance of Primate and Duiker Populations in Liberia: the Findings of a National Survey 1989–90*. World Wide Fund for Nature, and Forestry Development Authority, Liberia.

Dunn, A. 1993. *The Large Mammals of Gashaka Gumti National Park, Nigeria:*

Line Transects Surveys from Forest and Savannah. Nigerian Federal Ministry of Agriculture, Water Resources and Rural Development, Nigerian Conservation Foundation, and World Wide Fund for Nature, UK.

Dunn, A. 1999. *Gashaka Gumti National Park: A Guide Book*. Nigerian Conservation Foundation, Nigeria National Parks, and World Wide Fund for Nature, UK.

Dunn, A. and Okon, D. 2003. Monitoring the Abundance of Diurnal Primates and Duikers in Korup National Park, Cameroon, 2001–2003. Report from the Korup Project, Cameroon.

Dupuy, A. R. 1971. Statut actuel des primates au Sénégal. *Bulletin de l'Institut Fondamental d'Afrique noire (A)* 33: 467–478.

Dutrillaux, B., Muleris, M. and Couturier, J. 1988. Chomosomal evolution of Cercopithecinae. Pp.150–159 in A. Gautier-Hion, F. Bourlière, J.-P. Gautier and J. Kingdon (eds.), *A Primate Radiation: Evolutionary Biology of the African Guenons*. Cambridge University Press, Cambridge, UK.

Dutton, J. 1994. Introduced mammals in São Tomé and Príncipe: possible threats to biodiversity. *Biodiversity and Conservation* 3: 927–938.

Eagles, G. and Koenig, M. 2008. A model of plate kinematics in Gondwana breakup. *Geophysical Journal International* 173: 703–717.

Eck, S. 1996. Die palaearktischen Vögel - Geospezies und Biospezies. *Zoologisch Abhandlungen, Staatlichen Museum für Tierkunde Dresden* 49 (supplement): 1–103.

Eckardt, W. and Zuberbühler, K. 2004. Cooperation and competition in forest monkeys. *Behavioral Ecology* 15: 400–412.

Edwards, A. E. 1992. The Diurnal Primates of Korup National Park, Cameroon: Abundance, Productivity and Polyspecific Associations. MSc thesis, University of Florida, Gainesville.

Eisentraut, M. 1973. *Der Wirbeltierfauna von Fernando Poo und Westkamerun. Bonner Zoologische Monographien no. 3*. Zoologisches Forschungsinstitut und Museum Alexander Koenig, Bonn.

Elliot, D. G. 1907. Descriptions of apparently new species and subspecies of mammals belonging to the families Lemuridae, Cebidae, Callitrichidae, and Cercopithecidae in the collection of the Natural History Museum. *Annals and Magazine of Natural History*, 7th series 20: 185–196.

Elliot, D. G. 1913. *A Review of the Primates*. Vol. 3. American Museum of Natural History, New York.

Enstam, K. L. and Isbell, L. A. 2002. Comparison of responses to alarm calls by patas (*Erythrocebus patas*) and vervet (*Cercopithecus aethiops*) monkeys in relation to habitat structure. *American Journal of Physical Anthropology* 119: 3–14.

Estes, R. D. 1991. *The Behavior Guide to African Mammals*. University of California Press, Berkeley.

Fa, J. E. 2000. Hunted animals in Bioko Island, West Africa: sustainability and future. Pp.168–198 in J. G. Robinson and E. L. Bennett (eds.), *Sustainability of Hunting in Tropical Forests*. Columbia University Press, New York.

Fa, J. E., Juste, J., Del Val, J. P. and Castroviejo, R. 1995. Impact of market hunting on mammal species in Equatorial Guinea. *Conservation Biology* 9: 1107–1115.

Fa, J. E., Garcia Yuste, J. E. and Castelo, R. 2000. Bushmeat markets on Bioko Island as a measure of hunting pressure. *Conservation Biology* 14: 1602–1613.

Fa, J. E., Seymour, S., Dupain, J., Amin, R., Albrechtsen, L. and Macdonald, D. 2006. Getting to grips with the magnitude of exploitation: bushmeat in the Cross-Sanaga rivers region, Nigeria and Cameroon. *Biological Conservation* 129: 497–510.

Fage, J. D. 1962. *An Introduction to the History of West Africa*. 3rd Edition. Cambridge University Press, Cambridge, UK.

Fahr, J., Vierhaus, H., Hutterer, R. and Kock, D. 2002. A revision of the *Rhinolophus maclaudi* species group with the description of a new species from West Africa (Chiroptera: Rhinolophidae). *Myotis* 40: 95–126.

FAO. 2005. *Global Forest Resources Assessment 2005*. Food and Agriculture Organization of the United Nations, Rome. Website: <http://www.fao.org/forestry/fra/fra2005/en/>. Accessed: 14 September 2010.

Fargey, P. J. 1992. Boabeng-Fiema Monkey Sanctuary—an example of traditional conservation in Ghana. *Oryx* 26: 151–156.

Fashing, P. J. 2001a. Activity and ranging patterns of guerezas in the Kakamega Forest: intergroup variation and implications for intragroup feeding competition. *International Journal of Primatology* 22: 549–577.

Fashing, P. J. 2001b. Feeding ecology of guerezas in the Kakamega Forest, Kenya: the importance of Moraceae fruit in their diet. *International Journal of Primatology* 22: 579–609.

Fashing, P. J. 2001c. Male and female strategies during intergroup encounters in guerezas (*Colobus guereza*): evidence for resource defense mediated through males and a comparison with other primates. *Behavioral Ecology and Sociobiology* 50: 219–230.

Fashing, P. J. 2002. Population status of black and white colobus monkeys (*Colobus guereza*) in Kakamega Forest, Kenya: are they really on the decline? *African Zoology* 37: 119–126.

Fashing, P. J., Dierenfeld, E. S. and Mowry, C. B. 2007. Influence of plant and soil chemistry on food selection, ranging patterns, and biomass of *Colobus guereza* in Kakamega Forest, Kenya. *International Journal of Primatology* 28: 673–703.

Fay, J. M., Carroll, R., Peterhans, J. C. K. and Harris, D. 1995. Leopard attack on and consumption of gorillas in the Central African Republic. *Journal of Human Evolution* 29: 93–99.

Fedigan, L. and Fedigan, L. M. 1988. *Cercopithecus aethiops*: a review of field studies. Pp.389–411 in A. Gautier-Hion, F. Bourlière, J.-P. Gautier and J. Kingdon (eds.), *A Primate Radiation: Evolutionary Biology of the African Guenons*. Cambridge University Press, Cambridge.

Fimbel, C. 1994. The relative use of abandoned farm clearings and old forest habitats by primates and a forest antelope at Tiwai, Sierra Leone, West Africa. *Biological Conservation* 70: 277–286.

Fischer, F., Gross, M. and Kunz, B. 2000. Primates of the Comoé National Park, Ivory Coast. *African Primates* 41: 10–15.

Fischer, F., Gross, M. and Linsenmair, K. E. 2002. Updated list of the larger mammals of the Comoé National Park, Ivory Coast. *Mammalia* 66: 83–92.

Fleagle, J. G. and McGraw, W. S. 1999. Skeletal and dental morphology supports diphyletic origin of baboons and mandrills. *Proceedings of the National Academy of Sciences USA* 96: 1157–1161.

Fleury, M.-C. and Gautier-Hion, A. 1999. Seminomadic ranging in a population of black colobus (*Colobus satanas*) in Gabon and its ecological correlates. *International Journal of Primatology* 20: 491–509.

Fleury-Brugière, M.-C. and Brugière, D. 2010. High population density of the western chimpanzee *Pan troglodytes verus* in the Haut Niger National Park, Republic of Guinea: implications for local and regional conservation. *International Journal of Primatology* 31: 383–392.

Fowler, A. and Sommer, V. 2007. Subsistence technology of Nigerian chimpanzees. *International Journal of Primatology* 28: 997–1023.

Fowler, A., Koutsioni, Y. and Sommer, V. 2007. Leaf-swallowing in Nigerian chimpanzees: evidence for assumed self-medication. *Primates* 48: 73–76.

Frade, F. and Silva, J. A. 1980. Mamíferos de Guiné (colecção do Centro de Zoologia). *Garcia de Orta, Série de Zoologia* 9: 1–12.

Freeland, W. J. 1979. Mangabey *Cercocebus albigena* social organization and population density in relation to food use and availability. *Folia Primatologica* 32: 108–124.

Gadsby, E. L. and Jenkins, P. D. 1998. The drill—integrated *in situ* and *ex situ* conservation. *African Primates* 3: 12–18.

Gagneux, P., Woodruff, D. S. and Boesch, C. 1997. Furtive mating in female chimpanzees. *Nature* 387: 358–359.

Galat, G. and Galat-Luong, A. 1976. La colonisation de la mangrove par *Cercopithecus aethiops sabaeus* au Senegal. *Revue d'Ecologie Appliquée (la Terre et la Vie)* 30: 3–30.

Galat, G. and Galat-Luong, A. 1977. Demographie et regime alimentaire d'une troupe de *Cercopithecus aethiops sabaeus* en habitat marginal au nord Senegal. *Revue d'Ecologie Appliquée (la Terre et la Vie)* 31: 557–577.

Galat, G. and Galat-Luong, A. 1978. Diet of green monkeys in Senegal. Pp.257–258 in D. J. Chivers and J. Herbert (eds.), *Recent Advances in Primatology, Volume 1, Behaviour.* Academic Press, London.

Galat, G. and Galat-Luong, A. 1985. La communauté de primates diurnes de la fôret de Taï, Côte-d'Ivoire. *Revue d'Ecologie Appliquée (la Terre et la Vie)* 40: 3–32.

Galat, G. and Galat-Luong, A. 2006. Hope for the survival of the critically endangered white-naped mangabey *Cercocebus atys lunulatus*: a new primate species for Burkina Faso. *Oryx* 40: 355–357.

Galat, G., Galat-Luong, A. and Pichon, G. 1997. *Niokolo-Badiar: Guide à l'Usage des Visiteurs du Complexe Écologique du Niokolo-Badiar*, FED No 4213/REG & ORSTOM (eds.). Projet Niokolo-Badiar. Belancor, Rueil-Malmaison, Paris. 20pp.

Galat, G., Galat-Luong, A. and Keita, Y. 2000. Régression de la distribution et statut actuel du babouin *Papio papio* en limite d'aire répartition au Senegal. *African Primates* 4: 69–70.

Galat, G., Galat-Luong, A. and Nizinski, G. 2009. Increasing dryness and regression of the geographical range of the northernmost western red colobus *Procolobus badius temminckii*. *Mammalia* 73: 65–68.

Galat-Luong, A. 1983. Socio-écologie de Trois Colobes Sympatriques, *Colobus badius, C. polykomos* et *C. verus* du Parc National de Taï. Doctoral thesis, Université Pierre et Marie Curie, Paris 6, France.

Galat-Luong, A. 1988. Monkeys in the Pirang forest. Pp.187–199 in H. Ellenberg, A. Galat-Luong, H.-J. von Maydell, M. Mühlenberg, K. F. Panzer, R. Schmidt-Lorenz, M. Sumser and T. W. Szolnoki (eds.), *Pirang: Ecological Investigations in a Forest Island in the Gambia*. Stiftung Walderhaltung in Afrika and Bundesforschungsanstalt für Forst- und Holzwirtschaft, Hamburg.

Galat-Luong, A. and Galat, G. 1978. *Abondance Relative et Associations Plurispecifiques des Primates Diurnes du Parc National de Taï, Côte d'Ivoire.* ORSTOM, Abidjan, Côte d'Ivoire.

Galat-Luong, A. and Galat, G. 1979. Consequences comportementales de perturbations sociales repetées sur une troupe de mones de Lowe *Cercopithecus campbelli lowei* de Côte d'Ivoire. *Revue d'Ecologie Appliquée (la Terre et la Vie)* 33: 49–58.

Galat-Luong, A. and Galat, G. 2003. Régression du babouin de Guinée, *Papio papio*, en Afrique de l'Ouest. *Bulletin de la Société Francophone de Primatologie* 17: 10.

Galat-Luong, A. and Galat, G. 2005. Conservation and survival adaptations of Temminck's red colobus (*Procolobus badius temminckii*), in Senegal. *International Journal of Primatology* 26: 585–603.

Galat-Luong, A., Galat, G., Durand, J.-P. and Pourrot, X. 1996. Sexual weight dimorphism and social organization in green and patas monkeys in Senegal. *Folia Primatologica* 67: 92–93.

Galat-Luong, A., Galat, G. and Hagell, S. 2006. The social and ecological flexibility of Guinea baboons: implications for Guinea baboon social organization and male strategies. Pp.105–121 in L. Swedell and S. R. Leigh (eds.), *Reproduction and Fitness in Baboons: Behavioral, Ecological, and Life History Perspectives*. Springer, New York.

Gartlan, J. S. 1970. Preliminary notes on the ecology and behavior of the drill, *Mandrillus leucophaeus* Ritgen, 1824. Pp.445–480 in J. R. Napier and P. H. Napier (eds.), *Old World Monkeys: Evolution, Systematics, and Behavior*. Academic Press, New York.

Gartlan, J. S. 1975. The African coastal rain forest and its primates—threatened resources. Pp.67–82 in G. Bermant and D. G. Lindburg (eds.), *Primate Utilization and Conservation*. John Wiley, New York.

Gartlan, J. S. and Brain, C. K. 1968. Ecology and social variability in *Cercopithecus aethiops* and *C. mitis*. Pp.253–292 in P. Jay (ed.), *Primates: Studies in Adaptation and Variability*. Holt, Rinehart and Winston, New York.

Gartlan, J. S. and Struhsaker, T. T. 1972. Polyspecific associations and niche separation of rain-forest anthropoids in Cameroon, West Africa. *Journal of Zoology, London* 168: 221–266.

Gatinot, B. L. 1974. Précisions sur la répartition du colobe bai (*Colobus badius temmincki* Kuhl, 1820) et de la mone de Campbell (*Cercopithecus mona campbelli* Waterhouse, 1838) en Sénégambie. *Mammalia* 40: 1–12.

Gatinot, B. L. 1976. Le milieux fréquentés par le colobe bai d'Afrique de l'Ouest (*Colobus badius temmincki* Kuhl, 1820) en Sénégambie. *Mammalia* 40: 1–12.

Gatinot, B. L. 1977. Le régime alimentaire par le colobe bai au Sénégal. *Mammalia* 41: 373-402.

Gatti, S. 2010. *Status of Primate Populations in Protected Areas Targeted by the Community Forest Biodiversity Project*. West African Primate Conservation Action, Accra, Ghana.

Gautier, J.-P. 1973. Influence éventuelle de la vie en associations polyspécifiques sur l'apparition d'un type habituel d'émission sonore chez les males adultes de *C. nictitans*. *Mammalia* 37: 371–378.

Gautier, J.-P., Moysan, F., Feistner, A. T. C., Loireau, J.-N. and Cooper, R. W. 1992. The distribution of *Cercopithecus (lhoesti) solatus*, an endemic guenon of Gabon. *Terre et la Vie* 47: 367–381.

Gautier, J.-P., Drubbel, V. R. and Deleporte, P. 2002. Phylogeny of the *Cercopithecus lhoesti* group revisited: combining multiple character sets.

Pp.37–48 in M. E. Glenn and M. Cords (eds.), *The Guenons: Diversity and Adaptation in African Monkeys*. Kluwer Academic/Plenum, New York.

Gautier-Hion, A. 1966. L'écologie et l'éthologie du talapoin (*Miopithecus talapoin talapoin*). *Biologica Gabonica* 2: 311–329.

Gautier-Hion, A. 1968. Étude du cycle annuel de reproduction du talapoin (*Miopithecus talapoin*) dans le nord-est du Gabon. *Biologica Gabonica* 4: 163–173.

Gautier-Hion, A. 1971. L'écologie du talapoin du Gabon. *La Terre et la Vie* 25: 427–490.

Gautier-Hion, A. 1973. Social and ecological features of talapoin monkey – comparisons with sympatric cercopithecines. Pp.147–170 in R. P. Michael and J. H. Crook (eds.), *Comparative Ecology and Behaviour of Primates*. Academic Press, London.

Gautier-Hion, A. 1978. Food niches and coexistence in sympatric primates in Gabon. Pp.269–286 in D. J. Chivers and J. Herbert (eds.), *Recent Advances in Primatology, Volume 1, Behaviour*. Academic Press, London.

Gautier-Hion, A. 1980. Seasonal variations of diet related to species and sex in a community of *Cercopithecus* monkeys. *Journal of Animal Ecology* 49: 237–269.

Gautier-Hion, A. and Gautier, J.-P. 1974. Les association polyspécifiques des cercopithèques du Plateau de M'passa, Gabon. *Folia Primatologica* 26: 165–184.

Gautier-Hion, A. and Gautier, J.-P. 1978. Le singe de Brazza: une stratégie originale. *Zeitschrift für Tierpsychologie* 46: 84–104.

Gautier-Hion, A., Gautier, J.-P. and Quris, R. 1981. Forest structure and fruit availability as complementary factors influencing habitat use by a troop of monkeys (*Cercopithecus cephus*). *Terre et la Vie* 35: 511–536.

Gautier-Hion, A., Colyn, M. and Gautier, J.-P. 1999. *Histoire Naturelle des Primates d'Afrique Centrale*. ECOFAC, Libreville, Gabon.

Gebo, D. L. and Chapman, C. A. 1995. Positional behavior in five sympatric Old World monkeys. *American Journal of Physical Anthropology* 97: 49–76.

Gippoliti, S. and Dell'Omo, G. 1996. Primates of the Cantanhez Forest and the Cacine Basin, Guinea-Bissau. *Oryx* 30: 74–80.

Gippoliti, S. and Dell'Omo, G. 2003. Primates of Guinea-Bissau, West Africa: distribution and conservation status. *Primate Conservation* (19): 73–77.

Gisolfi, C. V., Sato, K., Wall, P. T. and Sato, F. 1982. In vivo and in vitro characteristics of eccrine sweating in patas and rhesus monkeys. *Journal of Applied Physiology* 53: 425–431.

Glenn, M. E. 1997. Group size and group composition of the mona monkey (*Cercopithecus mona*) on the island of Grenada. *American Journal of*

Primatology 43: 167–173.

Glenn, M. E. 1998. Population density of *Cercopithecus mona* on the Caribbean island of Grenada. *Folia Primatologica* 69: 167–171.

Glenn, M. E., Matsuda, R. and Bensen, K. J. 2002. Unique behavior of the mona monkey (*Cercopithecus mona*): all-male groups and copulation calls. Pp.133–145 in M. E. Glenn and M. Cords (eds.), *The Guenons: Diversity and Adaptation in African Monkeys*. Kluwer Academic/Plenum, New York.

Goldsmith, M. L. 1999. Ecological constraints on the foraging effort of western gorillas (*Gorilla gorilla gorilla*) at Bai Hokou, Central African Republic. *International Journal of Primatology* 20: 1–24.

Gonder, M. K. 2000. Evolutionary Genetics of Chimpanzees (*Pan troglodytes*) in Nigeria and Cameroon. PhD Thesis, City University of New York, New York, NY.

Gonder, M. K., Oates, J. F., Disotell, T. R., Forstner, M. R. J., Morales, J. C. and Melnick, D. J. 1997. A new west African chimpanzee subspecies? *Nature* 388: 337.

Gonder, M. K., Disotell, T .R. and Oates, J.F. 2006. New genetic evidence on the evolution of chimpanzee populations and implications for taxonomy. *International Journal of Primatology* 27: 1103–1127.

Gonedelé Bi, S., Zinner, D., Koné, I., Goné Bi, Z., Akpatou, B. K., Béné, J.-C. K., Sangaré, A. and Boesch, C. 2006. A West African black-and-white colobus monkey, *Colobus polykomos dollmani* Schwarz, 1927, facing extinction. *Primate Conservation* (21): 55–61.

Gonedelé Bi, S., Koné, I., Béné, J.-C. K., Bitty, A. E., Akpatou, B. K., Goné, B. Z., Ouattara, K. and Koffi, D. A. 2008. Tanoé forest, south-eastern Côte-d'Ivoire identified as a high priority site for the conservation of critically endangered primates in West Africa. *Tropical Conservation Science* 1: 263–276.

Gonzalez-Kirchner, J. P. 1996. Notes on habitat use by the russet-eared guenon (*Cercopithecus erythrotis* Waterhouse 1838) on Bioko Island, Equatorial Guinea. *Tropical Zoology* 9: 297–304.

Gonzalez-Kirchner, J. P. 1997. Behavioural ecology of two sympatric colobines on Bioko Island, Equatorial Guinea. *Folia Zoologica* 46: 97–104.

Gonzalez-Kirchner, J. P. 2004. Habitat preference of the Preuss's guenon (*Cercopithecus preussi*) on Bioko Island, Equatorial Guinea. *Human Evolution* 19: 239–246.

Gonzalez-Kirchner, J. P. and de la Maza, M. S. 1996. Preliminary notes on the ecology of the drill (*Mandrillus leucophaeus*) on Bioko Island, Republic of Equatorial Guinea. *Garcia de Orta, Série de Zoologia* 21: 1–5.

Goodall, J. 1963. Feeding behaviour of wild chimpanzees: a preliminary report. Pp.39–48 in J. Napier and N. A. Barnicot (eds.), *The Primates.* Symposia of the Zoological Society of London, no. 10. Zoological Society of London, London.

Goodall, J. 1965. Chimpanzees of the Gombe Stream Reserve. Pp.425–473 in I. DeVore (ed.), *Primate Behavior: Field Studies of Monkeys and Apes*. Holt, Rinehart and Winston, New York.

Goodall, J. 1986. *The Chimpanzees of Gombe: Patterns of Behavior*. Harvard University Press, Cambridge, MA.

Goodwin, R. M. 2007. Behavior and Ecology of the Mona Monkey (*Cercopithecus mona* Schreber, 1774) in the Seasonally Dry Lama Forest, Republic of Bénin, West Africa. PhD thesis, City University of New York, New York.

Gornitz, V. 2007. Sea level rise, after the ice melted, and today. *Science Briefs*, Goddard Institute for Space Studies, National Aeronautics and Space Administration. Website: <http://www.giss.nasa.gov/research/briefs/gornitz_09/>. Accessed: 7 September 2010.

Grand, T., Duro, E. and Montagna, W. 1964. Observations on the development of a potto born in captivity. *American Journal of Physical Anthropology* 22: 329–332.

Gray, J. E. 1862. List of Mammalia from the Camaroon Mountains, collected by Capt. Burton, H.M. Consul, Fernando Po. *Proceedings of the Zoological Society of London* (1862): 180–181.

Gray, J. E. 1863. Revision of the species of lemuroid animals, with the description of some new species. *Proceedings of the Zoological Society of London* (1863): 129–152.

Gray, J. E. 1866. Notice of a new West-African monkey living in the gardens of the Society. *Proceedings of the Zoological Society of London* (1866): 168–169.

Gray, J. E. 1872. Notes on *Propithecus*, *Indris*, and other lemurs (Lemurina) in the British Museum. *Proceedings of the Zoological Society of London* (1872): 846–860.

Greengrass, E. J. and Maisels, F. 2007. Conservation of the Nigerian-Cameroon Chimpanzee *P. t. vellerosus* (and other mammals) in and around the Banyang-Mbo Wildlife Sanctuary, South-west Province, Cameroon. Limbe, Cameroon. Wildlife Conservation Society, New York.

Greengrass, E. J., 2009. Chimpanzees are close to extinction in southwest Nigeria. *Primate Conservation* (24): 77–83.

Groves, C. P. 1978. Phylogenetic and population systematics of the mangabeys (Primates: Cercopithecoidea). *Primates* 19: 1–34.

Groves, C. P. 1989. *A Theory of Human and Primate Evolution*. Oxford University Press, Oxford.

Groves, C. P. 2001. *Primate Taxonomy*. Smithsonian Institution Press, Washington, DC.

Groves, C. P. 2004. The what, why and how of primate taxonomy. *International*

Journal of Primatology 25: 1105–1126.

Groves, C. P. 2005. A note on the affinities of the Ebo Forest gorilla. *Gorilla Journal* 31: 19–21.

Groves, C. P. 2007a. The endemic Uganda mangabey, *Lophocebus ugandae*, and other members of the *albigena*-group (*Lophocebus*). *Primate Conservation* (22): 123–128.

Groves, C. P. 2007b. The taxonomic diversity of the Colobinae in Africa. *Journal of Anthropological Sciences* 85: 7–34.

Groves, C. P., Angst, R. and Westwood, C. R. 1993. The status of *Colobus polykomos dollmani* Schwarz. *International Journal of Primatology* 14: 573–586.

Groves, J. L. 2001. Gorillas of Takamanda, Mone and Mbulu forest, Cameroon. *Gorilla Journal* 22: 27–29.

Grubb, P. J. 1973. Distribution, divergence and speciation of the drill and mandrill. *Folia Primatologica* 20: 161–177.

Grubb, P. J. 1978a. Patterns of speciation in African mammals. *Bulletin of the Carnegie Museum of Natural History*. 6: 152–167.

Grubb, P. J. 1978b. The potto (*Perodicticus potto*: Primates, Lorisidae) in Nigeria and adjacent territories. *Bulletin de l'Institut français de l'Afrique noire* (A) 40: 909–913.

Grubb, P. J. 1982. Refuges and dispersal in the speciation of African forest mammals. Pp.537–553 in G. T. Prance (ed.), *Biological Diversification in the Tropics*. Columbia University Press, New York.

Grubb, P. J. 1990. Primate geography in the Afro-tropical forest biome. Pp.187–214 in G. Peters and R. Hutterer (eds.), *Vertebrates in the Tropics*. Museum Alexander Koenig, Bonn.

Grubb, P. J. 2001. Endemism in African rain forest mammals. Pp. 88–100 in W. Weber, L. J. T. White, A. Vedder and L. Naughton-Treves (eds.), *African Rain Forest Ecology and Conservation: An Interdisciplinary Perspective*. Yale University Press, New Haven, CT.

Grubb, P. J. 2006a. English common names for subspecies and species of African primates. *Primate Conservation* (20): 65–73.

Grubb, P. J. 2006b. Geospecies and superspecies in the African primate fauna. *Primate Conservation* (20): 75–78.

Grubb, P. J. and Powell, C. B. 1999. Discovery of red colobus monkeys (*Procolobus badius*) in the Niger Delta with the description of a new and geographically isolated subspecies. *Journal of Zoology, London* 248: 67–73.

Grubb, P. J., Jones, T. S., Davies, A. G., Edberg, E., Starin, E. D. and Hill, J. E. 1998. *Mammals of Ghana, Sierra Leone and the Gambia*. Trendrine Press, St. Ives, England.

Grubb, P. J., Oates, J. F., White, L. J. T. and Tooze, Z. 2000. Monkeys recently added to the Nigerian faunal list. *The Nigerian Field* 65: 149–158.

Grubb, P. J., Butynski, T. M., Oates, J. F., Bearder, S. K., Disotell, T. R., Groves, C. P. and Struhsaker, T. T. 2003. Assessment of the diversity of African primates. *International Journal of Primatology* 24: 1301–1357.

Grünmeir, R. 1990. Pollination by bats and non-flying mammals of the African tree *Parkia bicolor* (Mimosaceae). *Memoirs of the New York Botanical Garden* 55: 83–104.

Gunderson, V. 1977. Some observation on the ecology of *Colobus badius temmincki*, Abuko Nature Reserve, The Gambia, West Africa. *Primates* 18: 305–314.

Gust, D. A., Busse, C. D. and Gordon, T. P. 1990. Reproductive parameters in the sooty mangabey (*Cercocebus torquatus atys*). *American Journal of Primatology* 22: 241–250.

Haddow, A. J. and Ellice, J. M. 1964. Studies on bush-babies (*Galago* spp.) with special reference to the epidemiology of yellow fever. *Transactions of the Royal Society of Tropical Medicine and Hygiene* 58: 521–538.

Haffer, J. 1969. Speciation in Amazonian forest birds. *Science* 165: 131–137.

Hall, J. B. and Swaine, M. D. 1981. *Distribution and Ecology of Vascular Plants in a Tropical Rain Forest: Forest Vegetation in Ghana*. W. Junk, The Hague.

Hall, K. R. L. 1965. Behaviour and ecology of the wild patas monkey, *Erythrocebus patas*, in Uganda. *Journal of Zoology, London* 148: 15–87.

Hall, K. R. L. and DeVore, I. 1965. Baboon social behavior. Pp.53–110 in I. DeVore (ed.), *Primate Behavior: Field Studies of Monkeys and Apes*. Holt, Rinehart and Winston, New York.

Ham, R. M. 1994. Behaviour and Ecology of Grey-cheeked Mangabeys (*Cercocebus albigena*) in the Lopé Reserve, Gabon. PhD thesis, University of Stirling, Stirling, UK.

Hannah, A. C. and McGrew, W. C. 1987. Chimpanzees using stones to crack open oil palm nuts in Liberia. *Primates* 28: 31–46.

Happold, D. C. D. 1973. The red crowned mangabey, *Cercocebus torquatus*, in Western Nigeria. *Folia Primatologica* 20: 423–428.

Happold, D. C. D. 1987. *The Mammals of Nigeria*. Oxford University Press, New York.

Harcourt, A. H., Fossey, D., Stewart, K. J. and Watts, D. P. 1980. Reproduction in wild gorillas and some comparisons with chimpanzees. *Journal of Reproduction and Fertility*, Supplement 28: 59–70.

Harcourt, A. H., Stewart, K. J. and Inaharo, I. M. 1989. Gorilla quest in Nigeria. *Oryx* 23: 7–13.

Harding, R. S. O. 1976. Ranging patterns of a troop of baboons (*Papio anubis*) in Kenya. *Folia Primatologica* 25: 143–185.

Harding, R. S. O. 1977. Patterns of movement in open country baboons. *American Journal of Physical Anthropology* 47: 349–353.

Harding, R. S. O. 1984. Primates of the Kilimi area, northwest Sierra Leone. *Folia Primatologica* 42: 96–114.

Harding, R. S. O. and Olson, D. 1986. Patterns of mating among male patas monkeys (*Erythrocebus patas*) in Kenya. *American Journal of Primatology* 11: 343–358.

Harris, D., Fay, J. M. and MacDonald, N. 1987. Report of gorillas from Nigeria. *Primate Conservation* (8): 40.

Harris, T. R. 2005. Roaring, Intergroup Aggression, and Feeding Competition in Black and White Colobus Monkeys (*Colobus guereza*) at Kanyawara, Kibale National Park, Uganda. Ph.D. Thesis, Yale University, New Haven, CT.

Harris, T. R. 2006a. Between-group contest competition for food in a highly folivorous population of black and white colobus monkeys (*Colobus guereza*). *Behavioral Ecology and Sociobiology* 61: 317–329.

Harris, T. R. 2006b. Within- and among-male variation in roaring by black and white colobus monkeys (*Colobus guereza*): what does it reveal about function? *Behaviour* 143: 197–218.

Harris, T. R. and Chapman, C. A. 2007. Variation in diet and ranging of black and white colobus monkeys in Kibale National Park, Uganda. *Primates* 48: 208–221.

Harris, T. R. and Monfort, S. L. 2003. Behavioral and endocrine dynamics associated with infanticide in a black and white colobus monkey (*Colobus guereza*). *American Journal of Primatology* 61: 135–142.

Harris, T. R. and Monfort, S. L. 2006. Mating behavior and endocrine profiles of wild black and white colobus monkeys (*Colobus guereza*): toward an understanding of their life history and mating system. *American Journal of Primatology* 68: 383–396.

Harrison, M. J. S. 1982. The Behavioural Ecology of Green Monkeys, *Cercopithecus sabaeus*, at Mt. Assirik, Senegal. PhD thesis, University of Stirling, Stirling, UK.

Harrison, M. J. S. 1983a. Patterns of range use by the green monkey, *Cercopithecus sabaeus*, at Mt. Assirik, Senegal. *Folia Primatologica* 41: 157–179.

Harrison, M. J. S. 1983b. Age and sex differences in the diet and feeding strategies of the green monkey, *Cercopithecus sabaeus*. *Animal Behaviour* 31: 969–977.

Harrison, M. J. S. 1983c. Territorial behaviour in the green monkey,

Cercopithecus sabaeus: seasonal defense of local food supplies. *Behavioral Ecology and Sociobiology* 12: 85–94.

Harrison, M. J. S. 1984. Optimal foraging strategies in the diet of the green monkey, *Cercopithecus sabaeus*, at Mt. Assirik, Senegal. *International Journal of Primatology* 5: 435–471.

Harrison, M. J. S. 1985. Time budget of the green monkey, *Cercopithecus sabaeus*: some optimal strategies. *International Journal of Primatology* 6: 351–376.

Harrison, M. J. S. 1986. Feeding ecology of black colobus, *Colobus satanas*, in central Gabon. Pp.31–37 in J. G. Else and P. C. Lee (eds.), *Primate Ecology and Conservation.* Cambridge University Press, Cambridge, UK.

Harrison, M. J. S. 1988. A new species of guenon (*Cercopithecus*) from Gabon. *Journal of Zoology, London* 215: 561–575.

Harrison, M. J. S. and Hladik, C. M. 1986. Un primate granivore: le colobe noir dans le forêt du Gabon; potentialité d'évolution du comportement alimentaire. *Revue d'Ecologie* 41: 281–298.

Hart, J. A., Hart, T. B. and Thomas, S. 1986. The Ituri Forest of Zaire: primate diversity and prospects for conservation. *Primate Conservation* (7): 42–44.

Harvey, P. H., Martin, R. D. and Clutton-Brock, T. H. 1987. Life histories in comparative perspective. Pp.181–196 in B. B. Smuts, D. L. Cheney, R. M. Seyfarth, R. W. Wrangham, and T. T. Struhsaker (eds.), *Primate Societies*. The University of Chicago Press, Chicago.

Hayman, R. W. 1936. On a collection of mammals from the Gold Coast. *Proceedings of the Zoological Society of London (*1935): 915–937.

Hearn, G., Morra, W. A. and Butynski, T. M. 2006. *Monkeys in Trouble: The Rapidly Deteriorating Conservation Status of the Monkeys on Bioko Island, Equatorial Guinea.* Arcadia University Bioko Biodiversity Protection Program, Glenside, PA.

Henschel, P., Abernethy, K. A. and White, L. J. T. 2005. Leopard food habits in the Lopé National Park, Gabon, Central Africa. *African Journal of Ecology* 43: 21–28.

Higham, J. P., Heistermann, M., Ross, C., Semple, S. and MacLarnon, A. 2008a. The timing of ovulation with respect to sexual swelling detumescence in wild olive baboons. *Primates* 49: 295–299.

Higham, J. P., MacLarnon, A., Ross, C., Heistermann, M. and Semple, S. 2008b. Baboon sexual swellings: Information content of size and color. *Hormones and Behavior* 53: 452–462.

Hill, C. M. 1991. A Study of Territoriality in *Cercopithecus diana*. Do Females Take an Active Part in Territorial Defence? PhD thesis, University of London, London.

Hill, W. C. O. 1952. The external and visceral anatomy of the olive colobus monkey (*Procolobus verus*). *Proceedings of the Zoological Society of London* 122: 127–186.

Hill, W. C. O. 1953. *Primates: Comparative Anatomy and Taxonomy. I. Strepsirhini*. Edinburgh University Press, Edinburgh.

Hill, W. C. O. 1966. *Primates: Comparative Anatomy and Taxonomy. VI. Catarrhini, Cercopithecoidea, Cercopithecinae*. Edinburgh University Press, Edinburgh.

Hill, W. C. O. 1970. *Primates: Comparative Anatomy and Taxonomy. VIII. Cynopithecinae*. Papio, Mandrillus, Theropithecus. Edinburgh University Press, Edinburgh.

Hill, W. C. O. 1974. *Primates: Comparative Anatomy and Taxonomy. VII. Cynopithecinae*. Cercocebus, Macaca, Cynopithecus. Edinburgh University Press, Edinburgh.

Hill, W. C. O. and Booth, A. H. 1957. Voice and larynx in African and Asiatic Colobidae. *Journal of the Bombay Natural History Society* 54: 309–321.

Hill, W. C. O. and Meester, J. 1971. *The Mammals of Africa: An Identification Manual. Part 3.2, Suborder Prosimii, Infraorder Lorisiformes*. Smithsonian Institution Press, Washington, DC.

Hoare, R. 2005. WorldClimate. Website: <http://www.worldclimate.com>. 5 January, 2005. v271. Accessed: 24 February, 2011.

Hockings, K. J., Anderson, J. R. and Matsuzawa, T. 2009. Use of wild and cultivated foods by chimpanzees at Bossou, Republic of Guinea: feeding dynamics in a human-influenced environment. *American Journal of Primatology* 71: 636–646.

Hohmann, G., Fowler, A., Sommer, V. and Ortmann, S. 2006. Frugivory and gregariousness of Salonga bonobos and Gashaka chimpanzees: the influence of abundance and nutritional quality of fruit. Pp.123–159 in G. Hohmann, M. M. Robbins and C. Boesch (eds.), *Feeding Ecology in Apes and Other Primates: Ecological, Physical, and Behavioral Aspects*. Cambridge University Press, Cambridge, UK.

Holenweg, A. K., Noë, R. and Schabel, M. 1996. Waser's gas model applied to associations between red colobus and Diana monkeys in the Taï National Park, Ivory Coast. *Folia Primatologica* 67: 125–136.

Höner, O. P., Leumann, L. and Noë, R. 1997. Dyadic associations of red colobus and Diana monkey groups in the Taï National Park, Ivory Coast. *Primates* 38: 281–291.

Hopkins, B. 1974. *Forest and Savanna: An Introduction to Tropical Terrestrial Ecology with Special Reference to West Africa*. 2nd Edition. Heinemann, London.

Hoppe-Dominik, B. 1984. Étude du spectre des proies de la panthère, *Panthera pardus*, dans le Parc National de Taï en Côte d'Ivoire. *Mammalia* 48: 477–487.

Howard, R. 1977. Niche Separation Among Three Sympatric Species of *Cercopithecus* Monkeys. PhD thesis, University of Texas, Austin, TX.

Horrocks, J. A. 1986. Life-history characteristics of a wild population of vervets (*Cercopithecus aethiops sabaeus*) in Barbados, West Indies. *International Journal of Primatology* 7: 31–47.

Howell, J. H. 1968. The Borgu Game Reserve of Northern Nigeria, part 2. *Nigerian Field* 33: 147–165.

Hugueny, B. and Lévêque, C. 1994. Freshwater fish zoogeography in West Africa: faunal similarities between river basins. *Environmental Biology of Fishes* 39: 365–380.

Humle, T. 2003. Behavior and ecology of chimpanzees in West Africa. Pp.13–19 in R. Kormos, C. Boesch, M. I. Bakarr and T. M. Butynski (eds.), *West African Chimpanzees: Status Survey and Action Plan*. IUCN, Gland, Switzerland.

Humle, T. and Matsuzawa, T. 2001. Behavioural diversity among the wild chimpanzee populations of Bossou and neighbouring areas, Guinea and Côte d'Ivoire, West Africa. *Folia Primatologica* 72: 57–68.

Humle, T. and Matsuzawa, T. 2002. Ant-dipping among the chimpanzees of Bossou, Guinea, and some comparisons with other sites. *American Journal of Primatology* 58: 133–148.

Imong, I., Mengnjo, C. and Okeke, F. 2009. Gorilla census of Boshi Extension and Okwa Hills, Cross River National Park, Nigeria. Wildlife Conservation Society, Calabar, Nigeria.

Isbell, L. A. 1998. Diet for a small primate: insectivory and gummivory in the (large) patas monkey (*Erythrocebus patas pyrrhonotus*). *American Journal of Primatology* 45: 381–398.

Isbell, L. A., Cheney, D. L. and Seyfarth, R. M. 2002. Why vervet monkeys (*Cercopithecus aethiops*) live in multimale groups. Pp.173–187 in M. E. Glenn and M. Cords (eds.), *The Guenons: Diversity and Adaptation in African Monkeys*. Kluwer Academic/Plenum, New York.

Isbell, L. A. and Chism, J. 2007. Distribution and abundance of patas monkeys (*Erythrocebus patas*) in Laikipia, Kenya, 1979–2004. *American Journal of Primatology* 69: 1223–1235.

Isbell, L. A., Young, T. P., Jaffe, K. E., Carlson, A. A. and Chancellor, R. L. 2009. Demography and life histories of sympatric patas monkeys, *Erythrocebus patas*, and vervets, *Cercopithecus aethiops*, in Laikipia, Kenya. *International Journal of Primatology* 30: 103–124.

IUCN, UNEP and WWF. 1980. *World Conservation Strategy: Living Resources for Sustainable Development*. IUCN, Gland, Switzerland.

Izard, M. K. and Nash, L. T. 1988. Contrasting reproductive parameters in *Galago senegalensis braccatus* and *G. s. moholi*. *International Journal of Primatology* 9: 519–527.

Jeffrey, S. M. 1970. Ghana's forest wildlife in danger. *Oryx* 10: 240–243.

Jeffrey, S. M. 1974. Primates of the dry high forest of Ghana. *Nigerian Field* 39: 117–127.

Jenkins, P. D. 1987. *Catalogue of Primates in the British Museum (Natural History) and Elsewhere in the British Isles; Part IV: Suborder Strepsirrhini, including the Subfossil Madagascan Lemurs and Family Tarsiidae.* British Museum (Natural History), London.

Jenkins, P. D. 1990. *Catalogue of Primates in the British Museum (Natural History) and elsewhere in the British Isles; Part V: The Apes, Superfamily Hominoidea.* The Natural History Museum, London.

Jewell, P. A. and Oates, J. F. 1969a. Breeding activity in prosimians and small rodents in West Africa. *Journal of Reproduction and Fertility*, Supplement 6: 23–28.

Jewell, P. A. and Oates, J. F. 1969b. Ecological observations on the lorisoid primates of African lowland forest. *Zoologica Africana* 4: 231–248.

Johnston, H. 1906. *Liberia.* Hutchinson, London.

Jolly, C. J. 1993. Species, subspecies, and baboon systematics. Pp.67–107 in W. H. Kimbel and L. B. Martin (eds.), *Species, Species Concepts, and Primate Evolution.* Plenum Press, New York.

Jones, C. 1969. Notes on ecological relationships of four species of lorisids in Rio Muni, West Africa. *Folia Primatologica* 11: 255–267.

Jones, C. and Sabater Pi, J. 1968. Comparative ecology of *Cercocebus albigena* (Gray) and *Cercocebus torquatus* (Kerr) in Rio Muni, West Africa. *Folia Primatologica* 9: 99–113.

Jones, T. S. 1998. The Sierra Leone monkey drives. Appendix II (pp. 214–219) in P. J. Grubb, T. S. Jones, A. G. Davies, E. Edberg, E. D. Starin and J. E. Hill, *Mammals of Ghana, Sierra Leone and The Gambia.* Trendrine Press, St. Ives, UK.

Kaplin, B. A. 2001. Ranging behavior of two species of guenons (*Cercopithecus lhoesti* and *C. mitis doggetti*) in the Nyungwe Forest Reserve, Rwanda. *International Journal of Primatology* 22: 521–548.

Kaplin, B. A. 2002. Terrestriality and the maintenance of the disjunct geographical distribution in the *lhoesti* group. Pp.49–59 in M. E. Glenn and M. Cords (eds.), *The Guenons: Diversity and Adaptation in African Monkeys.* Kluwer Academic/Plenum, New York.

Kavanagh, M. 1977. Some Inter-population Variation in the Behavioural Ecology of *Cercopithecus aethiops tantalus.* DPhil thesis, University of Sussex, Brighton, UK.

Kavanagh, M. 1978. The diet and feeding behaviour of *Cercopithecus aethiops tantalus.* *Folia Primatologica* 30: 30–63.

Kavanagh, M. 1980. The invasion of the forest by an African savannah monkey: behavioural adaptations. *Behaviour* 73: 238–260.

Kavanagh, M. 1981. Variable territoriality among tantalus monkeys in Cameroon. *Folia Primatologica* 36: 76–98.

Kingdon, J. S. 1980. The role of visual signals and face patterns in African forest monkeys (guenons) of the genus *Cercopithecus*. *Transactions of the Zoological Society of London* 35: 431–475.

Kingdon, J. S. 1990. *Island Africa: The Evolution of Africa's Rare Animals and Plants*. Collins, London.

Kingdon, J. S. 1997. *The Kingdon Field Guide to African Mammals*. Academic Press, London.

Kingdon, J. S. 2004. *The Kingdon Pocket Guide to African Mammals*. Princeton University Press, Princeton, NJ.

Klop, E., Lindsell, J. and Siaka, A. 2008. Biodiversity of Gola Forest, Sierra Leone. Report to Royal Society for the Protection of Birds (RSPB), Conservation Society of Sierra Leone, and Government of Sierra Leone.

Koné, I. and Akpatou, B. K. 2004. Identification des sites abritant encore *Cercopithecus diana roloway, Cercocebus atys lunulatus* et *Piliocolobus badius waldronae* en Côte d'Ivoire. Report, University of Wisconsin, Madison, WI.

Kormos, R., Boesch, C., Bakarr, M. I. and Butynski, T. M. (eds.). 2003a. *West African Chimpanzees: Status Survey and Action Plan*. IUCN, Gland, Switzerland.

Kormos, R., Bakarr, M.I., Bonnéhin, L. and Hanson-Alp, R. 2003b. Bushmeat hunting as a threat to chimpanzees in West Africa. Pp.151–155 in R. Kormos, C. Boesch, M. I. Bakarr and T. M. Butynski (eds.), *West African Chimpanzees: Status Survey and Action Plan*. IUCN, Gland, Switzerland.

Korstjens, A. H. 2001. The Mob, the Secret Sorority, and the Phantoms. An Analysis of the Socio-ecological Strategies of the Three Colobines of Taï. PhD thesis, Utrecht University, Utrecht, Netherlands.

Korstjens, A. H. and Noë, R. 2004. The mating system of an exceptional primate, the olive colobus (*Procolobus verus*). *American Journal of Primatology* 62: 261–273.

Korstjens, A. H. and Schippers, E. P. 2003. Dispersal patterns among olive colobus in Taï National Park. *International Journal of Primatology* 24: 515–540.

Korstjens, A. H., Bergman, K., Deffernez, C., Krebs, M., Nijssen, E. C., van Oirschot, B. M. A., Paukert, C. and Schippers, E. P. 2007. How small-scale differences in food competition lead to different social systems in three closely related sympatric colobines. Pp.72–108 in W. S. McGraw, K. Zuberbühler and R. Noë (eds.), *Monkeys of the Taï Forest: An African Primate Community*. Cambridge University Press, Cambridge.

Kortlandt, A. 1962. Observing chimpanzees in the wild. *Scientific American* 206(5): 128–138.

Koster, S. H. 1985. Food habits of a free ranging patas monkey (*Erythrocebus patas*) in "W" National Park, Niger. *Mammalia* 49: 589–591.

Kuhn, H.-J. 1964. Zur Kenntnis von Bau und Funktion des Magens der Schlankaffen (Colobinae). *Folia Primatologica* 2: 193–221.

Kuhn, H.-J. 1967. Zur Systematik der Cercopithecidae. Pp. 25–46 in D. Starck, R. Schneider and Kuhn, H.J. (eds.), *Neue Ergebnisse der Primatologie*. Gustav Fischer, Stuttgart.

Kuhn, H.-J. 1972. On the perineal organ of male *Procolobus badius*. *Journal of Human Evolution* 1: 371–378.

Kunz, B. K. and Linsenmair, K. E. 2007. Changes in baboon feeding behavior: maturity-dependent fruit and seed size selection within a food plant species. *International Journal of Primatology* 28: 819–835.

Kunz, B. K. and Linsenmair, K. E. 2008a. The disregarded west: diet and behavioural ecology of olive baboons in the Ivory Coast. *Folia Primatologica* 79: 31–51.

Kunz, B. K. and Linsenmair, K. E. 2008b. Seed size selection by olive baboons. *Primates* 49: 239–245.

Lawson, G. W. 1966. *Plant Life in West Africa*. Oxford University Press, Oxford.

Lernould, J.-M. 1988. Classification and geographical distribution of guenons: a review. Pp.54–78 in A. Gautier-Hion, F. Bourlière, J.-P. Gautier and J. Kingdon (eds.), *A Primate Radiation: Evolutionary Biology of the African Guenons*. Cambridge University Press. Cambridge, UK.

Leskes, A. and Acheson, N. H. 1971. Social organization of a free-ranging troop of black and white colobus monkeys (*Colobus abyssinicus*). Pp.22–31 in *Proceedings of the 3rd International Congress of Primatology, Zurich 1970*. Karger, Basel.

Lewis, A. R., Marchant, D. R., Ashworth, A. C., Hedenäs, L., Hemming, S. R., Johnson, J. V., Leng, M. J., Machlus, M. L., Newton, A. E., Raine, J. I., Willenbring, J. K., Williams, M. and Wolfe, A. P. 2008. Mid-Miocene cooling and the extinction of tundra in continental Antarctica. *Proceedings of the National Academy of Sciences USA* 105: 10676–10680.

Lieberman, D., Hall, J. B., Swaine, M. D. and Lieberman, M. 1979. Seed dispersal by baboons in the Shai Hills, Ghana. *Ecology* 60: 65–75.

Linder, J. M. 2008. The Impact of Hunting on Primates in Korup National Park, Cameroon: Implications for Primate Conservation. PhD Thesis, City University of New York, New York.

Loireau, J.-N. and Gautier-Hion, A. 1988. Olfactory marking behaviour in guenons and its implications. Pp.246–253 in A. Gautier-Hion, F. Bourlière, J.-P.

Gautier and J. Kingdon (eds.), *A Primate Radiation: Evolutionary Biology of the African Guenons*. Cambridge University Press, Cambridge, UK.

Loy, J. 1974. Changes in facial color associated with pregnancy in patas monkeys. *Folia Primatologica* 22: 251–257.

Machado, A. de B. 1969. Mamíferos de Angola ainda não citados ou pouco conhecidos. *Publicações Culturais da Companhia de Diamantes de Angola* 46: 93–232.

MacKinnon, J., MacKinnon, K., Child, G. and Thorsell, J. 1986. *Managing Protected Areas in the Tropics*. IUCN, Gland, Switzerland.

Maestripieri, D., Leoni, M., Raza, S. S., Hirsch, E. J. and Whitman, J. C. 2005. Female copulation calls in Guinea baboons. *International Journal of Primatology* 26: 737–758.

Maestripieri, D., Mayhew, J., Carlson, C.I., Hoffman, C. L. and Radtke, J. M. 2007. One-male harems and female social dynamics in Guinea baboons. *Folia Primatologica* 78: 56–68.

Magnuson, L. E. 2002. Distribution and Habitat Use of the Roloway Guenon (*Cercopithecus diana roloway*) in Ghana, West Africa. MSc thesis, Humboldt State University, Arcata, CA.

Maisels, F., Keming, E., Kemei, M. and Toh, C. 2001. The extirpation of large mammals and implications for montane forest conservation: the case of the Kilum-Ijim Forest, North-west Province, Cameroon. *Oryx* 35: 322–331.

Maisels, F., Ambahe, R., Ambassa, E. and Fotso, R. 2006. New northwestern range limit of the northern talapoin, Mbam et Djerem National Park, Cameroon. *Primate Conservation* (21): 89–91.

Maisels, F., Bout, N., Inkamba-Inkulu, C., Pearson, L., Aczel, P., Ambahe, R., Ambassa, E. and Fotso, R. 2007a. New northwestern and southwestern range limits of De Brazza's monkey, Mbam et Djerem National Park, Cameroon, and Bateke Plateau, Gabon and Congo. *Primate Conservation* (22): 107–110.

Maisels, F., Makaya, Q.P. and Onononga, J.-R. 2007b. Confirmation of the presence of the red-capped mangabey (*Cercocebus torquatus*) in Mayumba National Park, southern Gabon, and Conkouati-Douli National Park, southern Republic of Congo. *Primate Conservation* (22): 111–115.

Malbrant, R. and Maclatchy, A. 1949. *Faune de l'Equateur Africain Français, Tome II, Mammifères*. Paul Lechevalier, Paris.

Maley, J. 1996. The African rain forest—main characteristics of changes in vegetation and climate from the Upper Cretaceous to the Quaternary. *Proceedings of the Royal Society of Edinburgh* 104B: 31–73.

Maley, J. 2001. The impact of arid phases on the African rain forest through geological history. Pp.68–87 in W. Weber, L. J. T. White, A. Vedder and L. Naughton-Treves (eds.), *African Rain Forest Ecology and Conservation: An Interdisciplinary Perspective*. Yale University Press, New Haven, CT.

Mallinson, J. J. C. 1968. Breeding group of the ursine black and white colobus. Pp.22–25 in *Fifth Annual Report*, Jersey Wildlife Preservation Trust, Jersey.

Manley, G. H. 1966. Reproduction in lorisoid primates. *Symposium of the Zoological Society of London* 15: 493–509.

Manley, G. H. 1974. Functions of the external genital glands of *Perodicticus* and *Arctocebus*. Pp.313–329 in R. D. Martin, G. A. Doyle and A. C. Walker (eds.), *Prosimian Biology*. Duckworth, London.

Manning, P. 2006. Slavery and slave trade in West Africa, 1450–1930. Pp. 99–117 in E. K. Akyeampong (ed.), *Themes in West Africa's History*. Ohio University Press, Athens, OH.

Marchesi, P., Marchesi, N., Fruth, B. and Boesch, C. 1995. Census and distribution of chimpanzees in Côte d'Ivoire. *Primates* 36: 591–607.

Marler, P. 1969. *Colobus guereza*: territoriality and group composition. *Science* 163: 93–95.

Marler, P. 1970. Vocalizations of East African monkeys. I. Red colobus. *Folia Primatologica* 13: 81–91.

Marler, P. 1972. Vocalizations of East African monkeys. II. Black and white colobus. *Behaviour* 42: 175–197.

Marler, P. 1976. Social organization, communication, and graded signals: the chimpanzee and the gorilla. Pp.239–280 in P. P. G. Bateson and R. A. Hinde (eds.), *Growing Points in Ethology*. Cambridge University Press, Cambridge.

Martin, C. 1976. Report on a Survey of the Ankasa River Forest Reserve. Department of Game and Wildlife, Accra, Ghana.

Martin, C. 1991. *The Rainforests of West Africa: Ecology—Threats— Conservation*. Birkhäuser, Basel.

Martin, G. H. G. 1983. Bushmeat in Nigeria as a natural resource with environmental implications. *Environmental Conservation* 10: 125–132.

Marty, J. S., Higham, J. P., Gadsby, E. L. and Ross, C. 2009. Dominance, coloration, and social and sexual behavior in male drills *Mandrillus leucophaeus*. *International Journal of Primatology* 30: 807–823.

Masi, S., Cipolletta, C. and Robbins, M. M. 2009. Western lowland gorillas (*Gorilla gorilla gorilla*) change their activity patterns in response to frugivory. *American Journal of Primatology* 71: 91–100.

Mason, P. F. 1940. A brief faunal survey of north-western Benin. I. Mammals. *Nigerian Field* 9: 17–22.

Masters, J. C. 1998. Speciation in the lesser galagos. *Folia Primatologica* 69 (supplement 1): 357–370.

Masters, J. C., Boniotto, M., Crovella, S., Roos, C., Pozzi, L. and Delpero, M. 2007. Phylogenetic relationships among the Lorisoidea as indicated by craniodental morphology and mitochondrial sequence data. *American Journal of Primatology* 69: 6–15.

Maté, C. and Colell, M. 1995. Relative abundance of forest cercopithecines in Arihá, Bioko Island, Republic of Equatorial Guinea. *Folia Primatologica* 64: 49–54.

Matschie, P. 1904. Bermerkungen uber die Gattung gorilla. *Sitzungsberichte der Gesselschaft Naturforschender Freunde zu Berlin* 1904: 45–53.

Matschie, P. 1914. Neue Affen aus Mittelafrika. *Sitzungsberichte der Gesellschaft Naturforschender Freunde zu Berlin* 1914: 323–342.

Mayr, E. 1940. Speciation phenomena in birds. *American Naturalist* 74: 249–278.

Mayr, E. 1942. *Systematics and the Origin of Species*. Columbia University Press, New York.

McFarland, K. L. 2007. Ecology of Cross River Gorillas (*Gorilla gorilla diehli*) on Afi Mountain, Cross River State, Nigeria. PhD thesis, City University of New York, New York.

McGraw, W. S. 1996. Cercopithecid locomotion, support use, and support availability in the Taï Forest, Ivory Coast. *American Journal of Physical Anthropology* 100: 507–522.

McGraw, W. S. 1998a. Three monkeys nearing extinction in the forest reserves of eastern Côte d'Ivoire. *Oryx* 32: 233–236.

McGraw, W. S. 1998b. Comparative locomotion and habitat use of six monkeys in the Taï Forest, Ivory Coast. *American Journal of Physical Anthropology* 105: 493–510.

McGraw, W. S. 1998c. Posture and support use of Old World Monkeys (Cercopithecidae): the influence of foraging strategies, activity patterns, and the spatial distribution of preferred food items. *American Journal of Primatology* 46: 229–250.

McGraw, W. S. 2000. Positional behavior of *Cercopithecus petaurista*. *International Journal of Primatology* 21: 157–182.

McGraw, W. S. 2005. Update on the search for Miss Waldron's red colobus monkey. *International Journal of Primatology* 26: 605–619.

McGraw, W. S. 2007. Positional behavior and habitat use of Taï forest monkeys. Pp.223–253 in W. S. McGraw, K. Zuberbühler and R. Noë (eds.), *Monkeys of the Taï Forest: An African Primate Community*. Cambridge University Press, Cambridge.

McGraw, W. S. and Bshary, R. 2002. Association of terrestrial mangabeys (*Cercocebus atys*) with arboreal monkeys: experimental evidence for the effects of reduced ground predator pressure on habitat use. *International Journal of Primatology* 23: 311–325.

McGraw, W. S. and Oates, J. F. 2002. Evidence for a surviving population of Miss Waldron's red colobus. *Oryx* 36: 223–226.

McGraw, W. S. and Zuberbühler, K. 2007. The monkeys of the Taï forest: an introduction. Pp. 1–48 in W. S. McGraw, K. Zuberbühler and R. Noë (eds.), *Monkeys of the Taï Forest: An African Primate Community*. Cambridge University Press, Cambridge, UK.

McGraw, W. S., Monah, I. T. and Abedi-Lartey, M. 1998. Survey of endangered primates in the forest reserves of eastern Côte d'Ivoire. *African Primates* 3: 22–25.

McGraw, W. S., Zuberbühler, K. and Noë, R. (eds.). 2007. *Monkeys of the Taï Forest: An African Primate Community*. Cambridge University Press, Cambridge, UK.

McGrew, W. C. 1992a. *Chimpanzee Material Culture: Implications for Human Evolution*. Cambridge University Press, Cambridge, UK.

McGrew, W. C. 1992b. Tool-use by free-ranging chimpanzees: the extent of diversity. *Journal of Zoology, London* 228: 689–694.

McGrew, W. C., Tutin, C. E. G., Baldwin, P. J., Sharman, M. J. and Whiten, A. 1978. Primates preying upon vertebrates: new records from West Africa. *Carnivore* 1(3): 41–45.

McGrew, W. C., Baldwin, P. J. and Tutin, C. E. G. 1981. Chimpanzees in a hot, dry and open habitat: Mt. Assirik, Senegal, West Africa. *Journal of Human Evolution* 10: 227–244.

McGrew, W. C., Pruetz, J. D. and Fulton, S. J. 2005. Chimpanzees use tools to harvest social insects at Fongoli, Senegal. *Folia Primatologica* 76: 222–226.

McIntosh, S. K. 2006. The Holocene prehistory of West Africa. Pp.11–32 in E. K. Akyeampong (ed.), *Themes in West Africa's History*. Ohio University Press, Athens, OH.

McKey, D. B. 1978. Soils, vegetation, and seed-eating by black colobus monkeys. Pp.423–437 in G. G. Montgomery (ed.), *The Ecology of Arboreal Folivores*. Smithsonian Institution Press, Washington, DC.

McKey, D. B. and Waterman, P. G. 1982. Ranging behaviour of a group of black colobus (*Colobus satanas*) in the Douala-Edea Reserve, Cameroon. *Folia Primatologica* 39: 264–304.

Menzies, J. I. 1970. An eastward extension to the known range of the olive colobus monkey (*Colobus verus*, Van Beneden). *Journal of the West African Science Association* 15: 83–84.

Mitani, M. 1989. *Cercocebus torquatus*: adaptive feeding and ranging behaviors related to seasonal fluctuations of food resources in the tropical rain forest of south-western Cameroon. *Primates* 30: 307–323.

Mittermeier, R. A, Tattersall, I, Konstant, W. R., Meyers, D. M. and Mast, R.

B. 1994. *Lemurs of Madagascar*. Conservation International, Washington, DC.

Mittermeier, R. A., Myers, N., Thomsen, J., da Fonseca, G. A. B. and Olivieri, S. 1998. Biodiversity hotspots and major tropical wilderness areas: approaches to setting conservation priorities. *Conservation Biology* 12: 516–520.

Molez, N. 1976. Adaptation alimentaire du galago d'Allen aux milieux forestiers secondaires. *Terre et la Vie* 30: 210–228.

Monard, A. 1938. Résultats de la mission scientifique du Dr Monard en Guinée Portugaise 1937–1938. 1. Primates. *Arquivos do Museu Bocage* 9: 121–149.

Morbeck, M. E. 1977. Positional behavior, selective use of habitat substrate and associated non-positional behavior in free-ranging *Colobus guereza* (Ruppël, 1835). *Primates* 18: 35–58.

Morell, V. 2008. Island ark: a threatened African treasure. *National Geographic* 214(2): 68–91.

Morgan, B. J. 2004. The gorillas of the Ebo Forest, Cameroon. *Gorilla Journal* 28: 12–14.

Morgan, B. J. and Abwe, E. E. 2006. Chimpanzees use stone hammers in Cameroon. *Current Biology* 16: 632–633.

Morgan, B. J. and Sunderland-Groves, J. L. 2006. The Cross-Sanaga gorillas: the northernmost gorilla populations. *Gorilla Journal* 32: 16–18.

Morgan, B. J., Wild, C. and Ekobo, A. 2003. Newly discovered gorilla population in the Ebo Forest, Littoral Province, Cameroon. *International Journal of Primatology* 24: 1129–1137.

Morgan, B. J., Adeleke, A., Bassey, T., Bergl. R., Dunn, A., Fotso. R., Gadsby, E., Gonder, K., Greengrass, E., Koutou Koulagna, D., Mbah, G., Nicholas, A., Oates, J., Omeni, F., Saidu, Y., Sommer, V., Sunderland-Groves, J., Tiebou, J. and Williamson, E. 2011. *Regional Action Plan for the Conservation of the Nigeria-Cameroon Chimpanzee* (Pan troglodytes ellioti). IUCN/SSC Primate Specialist Group, Arlington, VA.

Mwenja, I. 2007. A new population of de Brazza's monkey in Kenya. *Primate Conservation* (22): 117–122.

Myers, N. 1980. *Conversion of Tropical Moist Forests*. National Academy of Sciences, Washington, DC.

Nakagawa, N. 1989. Activity budget and diet of patas monkeys in the Kala Maloue National Park, Cameroon: a preliminary report. *Primates* 30: 27–34.

Nakagawa, N. 1992. Distribution of affiliative behaviors among adult females within a group of wild patas monkeys in a nonmating, nonbirth season. *International Journal of Primatology* 12: 73–96.

Nakagawa, N. 1999. Differential habitat utilization by patas monkeys (*Erythrocebus patas*) and tantalus monkeys (*Cercopithecus aethiops tantalus*) living sympatrically in northern Cameroon. *American Journal of Primatology*

49: 243–264.

Nakagawa, N. 2000a. Foraging energetics in patas monkeys (*Erythrocebus patas*) and tantalus monkeys (*Cercopithecus aethiops tantalus*): implications for reproductive seasonality. *American Journal of Primatology* 52: 169–185.

Nakagawa, N. 2000b. Seasonal, sex, and interspecific differences in activity time budgets and diets of patas monkeys (*Erythrocebus patas*) and tantalus monkeys (*Cercopithecus aethiops tantalus*), living sympatrically in northern Cameroon. *Primates* 41: 161–174.

Nakagawa, N., Ohsawa, H. and Muroyama, Y. 2003. Life-history parameters of a wild group of West African patas monkeys (*Erythrocebus patas patas*). *Primates* 44: 281–290.

Nakatsukasa, M., Mbua, E., Sawada, Y., Sakai, T., Nakaya, H., Yano, W. and Kunimatsu, Y. 2010. Earliest colobine skeletons from Nakali, Kenya. *American Journal of Physical Anthropology* 143: 365–382.

Napier, J. R. and Napier, P. H. 1967. *A Handbook of Living Primates: Morphology, Ecology and Behaviour of Nonhuman Primates*. Academic Press, London.

Napier, P. H. 1981. *Catalogue of Primates in the British Museum (Natural History) and Elsewhere in the British Isles; Part II: Family Cercopithecidae, Subfamily Cercopithecinae*. British Museum (Natural History), London.

Napier, P. H. 1985. *Catalogue of Primates in the British Museum (Natural History) and elsewhere in the British Isles. Part III: Family Cercopithecidae, Subfamily Colobinae*. British Museum (Natural History), London.

Nash, L. T. and Whitten, P. L. 1989. Preliminary observations on the role of *Acacia* gum chemistry in *Acacia* utilization by *Galago senegalensis* in Kenya. *American Journal of Primatology* 17: 27–39.

Nash, L. T., Bearder, S. K. and Olson, T. R. 1989. Synopsis of galago species characteristics. *International Journal of Primatology* 10: 57–80.

Nichol, J. E. 1999. Geomorphological evidence and Pleistocene refugia in Africa. *Geographical Journal* 165: 79–89.

Nissen, H. W. 1931. A field study of the chimpanzee. Observations of chimpanzee behavior and environment in western French Guinea. *Comparative Psychology Monographs* 8(1): 1–122.

Nku, M. E. 2004. Large mammal reconnaissance surveys of Lake Barombi Mbo and Southern Bakundu Forest Reserves, SW Province. Wildlife Conservation Society, Cameroon-Nigeria Transboundary Survey Project, Limbe, Cameroon.

Nobimè, G. and Sinsin, B. 2003. Les stratégies de survie du singe à ventre rouge (*Cercopithecus erythrogaster erythrogaster*) dans la forêt classée de la Lama au Bénin. *Biogeographica* 79: 153–166.

Nobimè, G., Sinsin, B. and Lernould, J.-M. 2009. Ecological factors determining the distribution of the red-bellied guenon *Cercopithecus e. erythrogaster* in Benin and Togo. *International Journal of Biological and Chemical Sciences* 3: 606–611.

Noë, R. and Bshary, R. 1997. The formation of red colobus-diana monkey associations under predation pressure from chimpanzees. *Proceedings of the Royal Society of London* B. 264: 253–259.

Oates, J. F. 1969. The lower primates of eastern Nigeria. *African Wild Life* 23: 321–332.

Oates, J. F. 1974. The Ecology and Behaviour of the Black-and-White Colobus Monkey (*Colobus guereza* Rüppell) in East Africa. PhD thesis, University of London, London.

Oates, J. F. 1977a. The social life of a black-and-white colobus monkey. *Zeitschrift für Tierpsychologie* 45: 1–60.

Oates, J. F. 1977b. The guereza and its food. Pp.275–321 in T. H. Clutton-Brock (ed.), *Primate Ecology: Studies of Feeding and Ranging Behaviour in Lemurs, Monkeys and Apes*. Academic Press, London.

Oates, J. F. 1977c. The guereza and man. Pp.419–467 in Prince Rainier III and G.H. Bourne (eds.), *Primate Conservation*. Academic Press, New York.

Oates, J. F. 1978. Water-plant and soil consumption by guereza monkeys (*Colobus guereza*): a relationship with minerals and toxins in the diet? *Biotropica* 10: 241–253.

Oates, J. F. 1981. Mapping the distribution of West African rain-forest monkeys: issues, methods and preliminary results. *Annals of the New York Academy of Sciences* 376: 53–64.

Oates, J. F. 1982. In search of rare forest primates in Nigeria. *Oryx* 16: 431–436.

Oates, J. F. 1984. The niche of the potto, *Perodicticus potto*. *International Journal of Primatology* 5: 51–61.

Oates, J. F. 1985. The Nigerian guenon, *Cercopithecus erythrogaster*: ecological, behavioral, systematic and historical observations. *Folia Primatologica* 45: 25–43.

Oates, J. F. 1986a. African primate conservation: general needs and specific priorities. Pp.21–29 in K. Benirschke (ed.), *Primates: The Road to Self-Sustaining Populations*. Springer, New York.

Oates, J. F. 1986b. *Action Plan for African Primate Conservation: 1986–90*. IUCN/SSC Primate Specialist Group, Gland.

Oates, J. F. 1988a. The distribution of *Cercopithecus* monkeys in West African forests. Pp.79–103 in A. Gautier-Hion, F. Bourlière, J.-P. Gautier and J. Kingdon (eds.), *A Primate Radiation: Evolutionary Biology of the African Guenons*. Cambridge University Press, Cambridge, UK.

Oates, J. F. 1988b. The diet of the olive colobus monkey, *Procolobus verus*, in

Sierra Leone. *International Journal of Primatology* 9: 457–478.

Oates, J. F. 1994a. The natural history of African colobines. Pp. 75–128 in A. G. Davies and J. F. Oates (eds.), *Colobine Monkeys: Their Ecology, Behaviour and Evolution*. Cambridge University Press, Cambridge, UK.

Oates, J. F. 1994b. The Niger Delta's red colobus monkey: a new subspecies? *African Wildlife Update* 1994 (March–April): 4.

Oates, J. F. 1996a. Survey of *Cercopithecus erythrogaster* populations in the Dahomey Gap. *African Primates* 2(1): 9–11.

Oates, J. F. 1996b. *African Primates: Status Survey and Conservation Action Plan*. Revised edition. IUCN Gland, Switzerland.

Oates, J. F. 1999. *Myth and Reality in the Rain Forest: How Conservation Strategies are Failing in West Africa*. University of California Press, Berkeley.

Oates, J. F. 2006a. Conservation, development and poverty alleviation: time for a change in attitudes. Pp.277–284 in D. M. Lavigne (ed.), *Gaining Ground: In Pursuit of Ecological Sustainability*. International Fund for Animal Welfare, Guelph, Canada.

Oates, J. F. 2006b. Primate Conservation in the Forests of Western Ghana: Field Survey Results, 2005–2006. Report to the Wildlife Division, Forestry Commission, Accra, Ghana.

Oates, J. F. and Anadu, P.A. 1989. A field observation of Sclater's guenon (*Cercopithecus sclateri* Pocock, 1904). *Folia Primatologica* 52: 93–96.

Oates, J. F. and Jewell, P. A. 1967. Westerly extent of the range of three African lorisoid primates. *Nature* 215: 778–779.

Oates, J. F. and Korstjens, A. H. 2012. *Procolobus verus* (olive colobus). In: T. M. Butynski, J. Kingdon and J. Kalina (eds.), *The Mammals of Africa*, Vol. II. University of California Press, Berkeley. In press.

Oates, J. F. and McGraw, W. S. 2009. A comment on the status of "*Colobus polykomos dollmani*" in Côte d'Ivoire. *Primate Conservation* (24): 73–76.

Oates, J. F. and Trocco, T. F. 1983. Taxonomy and phylogeny of black-and-white colobus monkeys: inferences from an analysis of loud call variation. *Folia Primatologica* 40: 83–113.

Oates, J. F. and Whitesides, G. H. 1990. Association between olive colobus (*Procolobus verus*), Diana guenons (*Cercopithecus diana*), and other forest monkeys in Sierra Leone. *American Journal of Primatology* 21: 129–146.

Oates, J. F., White, D., Gadsby, E. L. and Bisong, P. O. 1990a. Conservation of gorillas and other species. Appendix 1 to J. O. Caldecott, J. F. Oates and H. J. Ruitenbeek, *Cross River National Park (Okwangwo Division): Plan for Developing the Park and Its Support Zone*. World Wide Fund for Nature, Godalming, UK.

Oates, J. F., Whitesides, G. H., Davies, A. G., Waterman, P. G., Green, S. M.,

Dasilva, G. L. and Mole, S. 1990b. Determinants of variation in tropical forest primate biomass: new evidence from West Africa. *Ecology* 71: 328–343.

Oates, J. F., Anadu, P. A., Gadsby, E. L. and Werre, J. L. 1992. Sclater's guenon: A rare Nigerian monkey threatened by deforestation. *National Geographic Research and Exploration* 8(4): 476–491.

Oates, J. F., Davies, A. G. and Delson, E. 1994. The diversity of living colobines. Pp.45–73 in A. G. Davies and J. F. Oates (eds.), *Colobine Monkeys: Their Ecology, Behaviour and Evolution*. Cambridge University Press, Cambridge, UK.

Oates, J. F., Struhsaker, T. T. and Whitesides, G. H. 1997. Extinction faces Ghana's red colobus monkey and other locally endemic subspecies. *Primate Conservation* (17): 138–144.

Oates, J. F., Abedi-Lartey, M., McGraw, W. S., Struhsaker, T. T. and Whitesides, G. H. 2000a. Extinction of a West African red colobus monkey. *Conservation Biology* 14: 1526–1532.

Oates, J. F., Bocian, C. M. and Terranova, C. J. 2000b. The loud calls of black-and-white colobus monkeys: the adaptive and taxonomic significance in light of new data. Pp.431–452 in P. F. Whitehead and C. J. Jolly (eds.), *Old World Monkeys*. Cambridge University Press, Cambridge, UK.

Oates, J. F., McFarland, K. L., Groves, J. L., Bergl, R. A., Linder, J. M. and Disotell, T. R. 2003. The Cross River gorilla: natural history and status of a neglected and critically endangered subspecies. Pp.472–497 in A. B. Taylor and M. L. Goldsmith (eds.), *Gorilla Biology: A Multidisciplinary Perspective*. Cambridge University Press, Cambridge, UK.

Oates, J. F., Bergl, R. A. and Linder, J. M. 2004. Africa's Gulf of Guinea forests: biodiversity patterns and conservation priorities. *Advances in Applied Conservation Biology*, Volume 6. Conservation International, Washington, DC.

Oates, J. F., Sunderland-Groves, J., Bergl, R., Dunn, A., Nicholas, A., Takang, E., Omeni, F., Imong, I., Fotso, R., Nkembi, L. and Williamson, E. A. (eds.). 2007. *Regional Action Plan for the Conservation of the Cross River Gorilla* (Gorilla gorilla diehli). IUCN-SSC Primate Specialist Group and Conservation International, Arlington, VA.

Oates, J. F., Groves, C. P. and Jenkins, P. D. 2009. The type locality of *Pan troglodytes vellerosus* (Gray, 1862), and implications for the nomenclature of West African chimpanzees. *Primates* 50: 78–80.

Off, E. C., Isbell, L. A. and Young, T. P. 2008. Population density and habitat preferences of the Kenya lesser galago (*Galago senegalensis braccatus*) along the Ewaso Nyiro River, Laikipia, Kenya. *Journal of East African Natural History* 97: 109–116.

Ohsawa, H., Inoue, M. and Takenaka, O. 1993. Mating strategy and reproductive success of male patas monkeys (*Erythrocebus patas*). *Primates* 34: 533–544.

Ojo, O. 1977. *The Climates of West Africa*. Heinemann, London.

Oliver, R. 1991. *The African Experience*. Weidenfeld and Nicolson, London.

Olson, D. K. 1980. Male interactions and troop split among black-and-white colobus monkeys (*Colobus polykomos vellerosus*). Paper presented at VIIIth Congress of the International Primatological Society, Florence, Italy.

Olson, D. K. 1986. Determining range size for arboreal monkeys: methods, assumptions, and accuracy. Pp.212–227 in D. M. Taub and F. A. King (eds.), *Current Perspectives in Primate Social Dynamics*. Van Nostrand Reinhold, New York.

Olson, D. K. and Curtin, S. 1984. The role of economic timber species in the ecology of black-and-white colobus and Diana monkeys in Bia National Park, Ghana. *International Journal of Primatology* 5: 371.

Olson, L. E., Sargis, E. J., Stanley, W. T., Hildebrandt, K. B. P. and Davenport, T. R. B. 2008. Additional molecular evidence strongly supports the distinction between the recently described African primate *Rungwecebus kipunji* (Cercopithecidae, Papionini) and *Lophocebus*. *Molecular Phylogenetics and Evolution* 48: 789–794.

Olson, T. R. 1979. Studies on Aspects of the Morphology and Systematics of the Genus *Otolemur* Coquerel, 1859 (Primates: Galagidae). PhD thesis, University of London, London.

Olson, T. R. and Nash, L. T. 2003. Galago (Galagidae) body measurements and museum collections data. *African Primates* 6: 50–53.

Olupot, W. 1998. Long-term variation in mangabey (*Cercocebus albigena johnstoni* Lyddeker) feeding in Kibale National Park, Uganda. *African Journal of Ecology* 36: 96 101.

Olupot, W. 2000. Mass differences among male mangabey monkeys inhabiting logged and unlogged forest compartments. *Conservation Biology* 14: 833–843.

Olupot, W. and Waser, P. M. 2001. Correlates of intergroup transfer in male grey-cheeked mangabeys. *International Journal of Primatology* 22: 169–187.

Olupot, W. and Waser, P. M. 2005. Patterns of male residency and intergroup transfer in male mangabeys (*Lophocebus albigena*). *American Journal of Primatology* 66: 331–349.

Olupot, W., Chapman, C. A., Brown, C. and Waser, P. M. 1994. Mangabey ranging patterns and group structure: A twenty-year comparison. *American Journal of Primatology* 32: 197–205.

Olupot, W., Chapman, C. A., Waser, P. M. and Isabirye-Basuta, G. 1997. Mangabey (*Cercocebus albigena*) ranging patterns in relation to fruit availability and the risk of parasite infection in Kibale National Park, Uganda. *American Journal of Primatology* 43:65–78.

Olupot, W., Waser, P. M. and Chapman, C. A. 1998. Fruit finding by mangabeys

(*Lophocebus albigena*): are monitoring of fig trees and use of sympatric frugivore calls possible strategies? *International Journal of Primatology* 19: 339–353.

Onderdonk, D. A. 2000. Infanticide of a newborn black-and-white colobus monkey (*Colobus guereza*) in Kibale National Park, Uganda. *Primates* 41: 209–212.

Ormrod, S. A. 1967. Ursine or black colobus. Pp.6–9 in *Fourth Annual Report*, Jersey Wildlife Preservation Trust, Jersey.

Pakenham, T. 1991. *The Scramble for Africa*. Abacus, London.

Pavy, J.-M. 1993. *Mali. Bafing Faunal Reserve. Biodiversity and Human Resource: Survey and Recommendations*. Report. Cheverly, MD.

Pearce, J. and Ammann, K. 1995. *Slaughter of the Apes*. World Society for the Protection of Animals, London.

Peignot, P., Fontaine, B. and Wickings, E. J. 1999. Habitat exploitation, diet and some data on reproductive behaviour in a semi-free-ranging colony of *Cercopithecus lhoesti solatus*, a guenon species recently discovered in Gabon. *Folia Primatologica* 70: 29–36.

Pérez del Val, J. 1996. *Las Aves de Bioko: Guia de Campo*. Edilsa, Léon, Spain.

Peterson, D. 2006. *Jane Goodall: The Woman Who Redefined Man*. Houghton Mifflin, Boston, MA.

Pilbrow, V. 2006. Population systematics of chimpanzees using molar morphometrics. *Journal of Human Evolution* 51: 646–662.

Pilbrow, V. 2010. Dental and phylogeographic patterns of variation in gorillas. *Journal of Human Evolution* 59: 16-34.

Pimley, E. R. 2002. The Behavioural Ecology and Genetics of Two Nocturnal Prosimians: Pottos (*Perodicticus potto edwardsi*) and Allen's Bushbabies (*Galago alleni cameronensis*). PhD thesis, University of Cambridge, Cambridge, UK.

Pimley, E. R., Bearder, S. K. and Dixson, A. F. 2005a. Social organization of the Milne-Edward's potto. *American Journal of Primatology* 66: 317–330.

Pimley, E. R., Bearder, S. K. and Dixson, A. F. 2005b. Home range analysis of *Perodicticus potto edwardsi* and *Sciurocheirus cameronensis*. *International Journal of Primatology* 26: 191–206.

Pocock, R. I. 1936. The external characters of a female red colobus monkey (*Procolobus badius waldroni*). *Proceedings of the Zoological Society of London* (1935): 939–944.

Poché, R. M. 1976. Notes on primates in Parc National du W du Niger, West Africa. *Mammalia* 40: 187–198.

Poorter, L., Bongers, F., Kouamé, F. N'. and Hawthorne, W. D. (eds.) 2004.

Biodiversity of West African Forests: An Ecological Atlas of Woody Plant Species. CABI, Wallingford, UK.

Poulsen, J. R. and Clark, C. J. 2001. Predation on mammals by the grey-cheeked mangabey *Lophocebus albigena. Primates* 42: 391–394.

Poulsen, J. R., Clark, C. J. and Smith, T. B. 2001a. Seasonal variation in the feeding ecology of the grey-cheeked mangabey (*Lophocebus albigena*) in Cameroon. *American Journal of Primatology* 54: 91–105.

Poulsen, J. R., Clark, C. J. and Smith, T. B. 2001b. Seed dispersal by a diurnal primate community in the Dja Reserve, Cameroon. *Journal of Tropical Ecology* 17: 787–808.

Powell, C. B. 1993. Sites and Species of Conservation Interest in the Central Axis of the Niger Delta (Yenagoa, Sagbama, Ekeremor and Southern Ijo Local Government Areas). Report to the National Resources Conservation Council (NARESCON), Nigeria.

Pozzi, L., Hodgson, J. A., Bergey, C. and Disotell, T. R. 2010. Dating the primate tree: new insights on primate origins from complete mitochondrial genomes. Paper presented at *XXII Congress of the International Primatological Society*, Kyoto, Japan.

Pruetz, J. D. 2006. Feeding ecology of savanna chimpanzees (*Pan troglodytes verus*) at Fongoli, Senegal. Pp.161–182 in C. Hohmann, M. M. Robbins and C. Boesch (eds.), *Feeding Ecology in Apes and Other Primates: Ecological, Physical and Behavioral Aspects.* Cambridge University Press, Cambridge, UK.

Pruetz, J. D. 2007. Evidence of cave use by savanna chimpanzees (*Pan troglodytes verus*) at Fongoli, Senegal: implications for thermoregulatory behavior. *Folia Primatologica* 48: 316–319.

Pruetz, J. D. and Bertolani, P. 2007. Savanna chimpanzees, *Pan troglodytes verus*, hunt with tools. *Current Biology* 17: 412–417.

Pruetz, J. D. and Bertolani, P. 2009. Chimpanzee (*Pan troglodytes verus*) behavioral responses to stresses associated with living in a savanna-mosaic environment: implications for hominin adaptations to open habitats. *PaleoAnthropology* 2009: 252–262.

Pruetz, J. D., Marchant, L. F., Arno, J. and McGrew, W. C. 2002. Survey of savanna chimpanzees (*Pan troglodytes verus*) in southeastern Sénégal. *American Journal of Primatology* 58: 35–43.

Pruetz, J. D., Socha, A. and Kante, D. 2010. New range record for the lesser spot-nosed guenon (*Cercopithecus petaurista*) in southeastern Senegal. *African Primates* 7: 64–66.

Pullen, S. L., Bearder, S. K. and Dixson, A. F. 2000. Preliminary observations on sexual behavior and the mating system in free-ranging lesser galagos (*Galago moholi*). *American Journal of Primatology* 51: 79–88.

Raaum, R. L., Sterner, K. N., Noviello, C. M., Stewart C.-B. and Disotell,

T. R. 2005. Catarrhine primate divergence dates estimated from complete mitochondrial genomes: concordance with fossil and nuclear DNA evidence. *Journal of Human Evolution* 48: 237–257.

Rahm, U. H. 1960. Quelques notes sur le potto de Bosman. *Bulletin de l'Institut français de l'Afrique noire* (A) 22: 331–342.

Rahm, U. H. 1970. Ecology, zoogeography, and systematics of some African forest monkeys. Pp.589–626 in J. R. Napier and P. H. Napier (eds.), *Old World Monkeys: Evolution, Systematics, and Behavior*. Academic Press, New York.

Range, F. and Fischer, J. 2004. Vocal repertoire of sooty mangabeys (*Cercocebus torquatus atys*) in the Taï National Park. *Ethology* 110: 301–321.

Range, F., Förderer, T., Storrer-Meystre, Y., Benetton, C. and Fruteau, C. 2007. The structure of social relationships among sooty mangabeys in Taï. Pp.109–130 in W. S. McGraw, K. Zuberbühler and R. Noë (eds.), *Monkeys of the Taï Forest: An African Primate Community*. Cambridge University Press, Cambridge.

Range, F. and Noë, R. 2002. Familiarity and dominance relations in female sooty mangabeys in the Taï National Park. *American Journal of Primatology* 56: 137–153.

Redford, K. H. 1992. The empty forest. *BioScience* 42: 412–422.

Refisch, J. 1988. Evaluation écologique intégrée de la forêt naturelle de la Lama en République du Bénin. Report for ECO-Consult to ONAB/KfW/GTZ, Cotonou, République du Bénin.

Refisch, J. and Koné, I. 2005a. Impact of commercial hunting on monkey populations in the Taï region, Côte d'Ivoire. *Biotropica* 37: 136–144.

Refisch, J. and Koné, I. 2005b. Market hunting in the Taï region, Côte d'Ivoire and implications for monkey populations. *International Journal of Primatology* 26: 621–629.

Remis, M. J. 1995. Effects of body size and social context on the arboreal activities of lowland gorillas in the Central African Republic. *American Journal of Physical Anthropology* 97: 413–433.

Remis, M. J. 1997. Ranging and grouping patterns of a western lowland gorilla group at Bai Hokou, Central African Republic. *American Journal of Primatology* 43: 111–133.

Remis, M. J. 1999. Tree structure and sex differences in arboreality among western lowland gorillas (*Gorilla gorilla gorilla*) at Bai Hokou, Central African Republic. *Primates* 40: 383–396.

Richards, P. W. 1952. *The Tropical Rain Forest: An Ecological Study*. Cambridge University Press, Cambridge, UK.

Richards, P. W. 1996. *The Tropical Rain Forest: An Ecological Study*. 2nd Edition. Cambridge University Press, Cambridge, UK.

Robbins, M. M., Bermejo, M., Cipolletta, C., Magliocca, F., Parnell, R. J. and

Stokes, E. 2004. Social structure and life-history patterns in western gorillas (*Gorilla gorilla gorilla*). *American Journal of Primatology* 64: 145–159.

Robinson, L. 1994. Survey of Diurnal Primates, Okomu Wildlife Sanctuary, Nigeria. Report to the People's Trust for Endangered Species, London. 11pp.

Robinson, P. T. 1971. Wildlife trends in Liberia and Sierra Leone. *Oryx* 23: 117–122.

Rose, M. D. 1978. Feeding and associated positional behavior of black and white colobus monkeys (*Colobus guereza*). Pp.253–262 in G. G. Montgomery (ed.), *The Ecology of Arboreal Folivores*. Smithsonian Institution Press, Washington, DC.

Ross, C., Warren, Y., Maclarnon, A. M. and Higham, J. P. 2010. How different are Gashaka's baboons? Forest and open country populations compared. Pp.385–411 in V. Sommer and C. Ross (eds.), *Primates of Gashaka*. Springer, New York.

Roure, G. 1966. *Animaux Sauvages du Togo et de l'Afrique Occidentale*. Service des Eaux et Forêts, Ministère de l'Economie Rurale, Lomé, Togo.

Rowe, N. 1996. *The Pictorial Guide to the Living Primates*. Pogonias Press, East Hampton, NY.

Rowell, T. E. 1966. Forest living baboons in Uganda. *Journal of Zoology*, London. 147: 344–364.

Rowell, T. E. 1988 .The social systems of guenons, compared with baboons, macaques and mangabeys. Pp.439–451 in A. Gautier-Hion, F. Bourlière, J.-P. Gautier and J. Kingdon (eds.), *A Primate Radiation: Evolutionary Biology of the African Guenons*. Cambridge University Press, Cambridge, UK.

Sabater Pí, J. 1970. Aportación a la ecología de los *Colobus polykomos satanas*, Waterhouse, 1838, de Río Muni (República de Guinea Ecuatorial). *Publicaciones del Instituto de Biologia Aplicada* 48: 17–32.

Sabater Pí, J. 1973. Contribution to the ecology of *Colobus polykomos satanas* (Waterhouse, 1838) of Rio Muni (Republic of Equatorial Guinea). *Folia Primatologica* 19: 193–207.

Saj, T. L. and Sicotte, P. 2005. Male takeover in *Colobus vellerosus* at Boabeng-Fiema Monkey Sanctuary, central Ghana. *Primates* 46: 211–214.

Saj, T. L. and Sicotte, P. 2007. Scramble competition among *Colobus vellerosus* at Boabeng-Fiema, Ghana. *International Journal of Primatology* 28: 337–355.

Saj, T. L., Mather, C. and Sicotte, P. 2006. Traditional taboos in biological conservation: the case of *Colobus vellerosus* at the Boabeng-Fiema Monkey Sanctuary, Central Ghana. *Social Science Information* 45: 285–310.

Sanderson, I. T. 1940. The mammals of the North Cameroons forest area. Being the results of the Percy Sladen Expedition to the Mamfe Division of the British Cameroons. *Transactions of the Zoological Society of London* 24: 623–725.

Sapolsky, R. M. 2001. *A Primate's Memoir: A Neuroscientist's Unconventional Life Among the Baboons*. Scribner, New York.

Sargis, E. J., Terranova, C. J. and Gebo, D. L. 2008. Evolutionary morphology of the guenon postcranium and its taxonomic implications. Pp.361–372 in E. J. Sargis and M. Dagosto (eds.), *Mammalian Evolutionary Morphology: A Tribute to Frederick S. Szalay*. Springer, Dordrecht, The Netherlands.

Sarmiento, E. E. and Oates, J. F. 2000. The Cross River gorillas: a distinct subspecies, *Gorilla gorilla diehli* Matschie 1904. *American Museum Novitates* 3304: 1–55.

Savage, T. S. and Wyman, J. 1847. Notice of the external characters and habits of *Troglodytes gorilla*, a new species of orang from the Gaboon River; osteology of the same. *Boston Journal of Natural History* 5: 417–443.

Sayer, J. A. and Green, A.A. 1984. The distribution and status of large mammals in Benin. *Mammal Review* 14: 37–50.

Schaaf, C. D., Butynski, T. M. and Hearn, G. W. 1990. The drill (*Mandrillus leucophaeus*) and other primates in the Gran Caldera Volcanica de Luba: results of a survey conducted March 7–22, 1990. Report to the Government of Equatorial Guinea.

Schaefer, J. M., Denton, G. H., Barrell, D. J. A., Ivy-Ochs, S., Kubik, P. W., Andersen, B. G., Phillips, F. M., Lowell, T. V. and Schlüchter. 2006. Near-synchronous interhemispheric termination of the last glacial maximum in mid-latitudes. *Science* 312: 1510–1513.

Schaller, G. B. 1963. *The Mountain Gorilla: Ecology and Behavior*. The University of Chicago Press, Chicago.

Schenkel, R. and Schenkel-Hulliger, L. 1967. On the sociology of free-ranging colobus (*Colobus guereza caudatus* Thomas, 1885). Pp.185–194 in D. Starck, R. Schneider and H.-J. Kuhn (eds.), *Neue Ergebnisse der Primatologie*. Karger, Basel.

Schipper, J. *et al.* 2008. The status of the world's land and marine mammals: diversity, threat, and knowledge. *Science* 322: 225–230.

Schlossman, T. 2006. The Effects of Altitude and Vegetation Type on *Galago* Distribution at Moka, Bioko Island, Equatorial Guinea. Report to Bioko Biodiversity Protection Program, Drexel University, Philadelphia, PA, and Universidad Nacional de Guinea Ecuatorial (UNGE), Malabo, Equatorial Guinea.

Schöning, C., Ellis, D., Fowler, A. and Sommer, V. 2006. Army ant availability and consumption by chimpanzees (*Pan troglodytes vellerosus*) at Gashaka (Nigeria). *Journal of Zoology* 271: 125–133.

Schwarz, E. 1927. A new black-and-white guereza from the Ivory Coast. *Annals and Magazine of Natural History*, 9th series 19: 155.

Schwarz, E. 1928a. The species of the genus *Cercocebus*, E. Geoffroy. *Annals and Magazine of Natural History*, 10th series 1: 664–670.

Schwarz, E. 1928b. Die Sammlung afrikanischer Affen in Congo-Museum. *Revue de Zoologie et Botanique Africaine* 16: 1–48.

Schwarz, E. 1929. On the local races and distribution of the black and white colobus monkeys. *Proceedings of the Zoological Society of London* (1929): 585–598.

Schwarz, E. 1931. On the African long-tailed lemurs or galagos. *Annals and Magazine of Natural History* 10th series 7: 41–66.

Seiffert, E. R. 2010. The fossil record of early primate evolution in Africa: implications for primate origins. Paper presented at *XXII Congress of the International Primatological Society*, Kyoto, Japan.

Shah, N. F. 2003. Foraging Strategies in Two Sympatric Mangabey Species (*Cercocebus agilis* and *Lophocebus albigena*). PhD thesis, Stony Brook University, Stony Brook, NY.

Sharman, M. 1981. Feeding, Ranging and Social Organisation of the Guinea Baboon. PhD thesis, University of St. Andrews, St. Andrews, UK.

Shipman, P., Bosler, W. and Davis, K. L. 1981. Butchering of giant geladas at an Acheulian site. *Current Anthropology* 22: 257–268.

Shultz, S. 2002. Population density, breeding chronology and diet of crowned eagles *Stephanoaetus coronatus* in Taï National Park, Ivory Coast. *Ibis* 144: 135–138.

Shultz, S. and Tomsett, S. 2007. Interactions between African crowned eagles and their prey community. Pp.171–193 in W. S. McGraw, K. Zuberbühler and R. Noë (eds.), *Monkeys of the Taï Forest: An African Primate Community*. Cambridge University Press, Cambridge, UK.

Shultz, S., Noë, R., McGraw, W. S. and Dunbar, R. I. M. 2004. A community-level evaluation of the impact of prey behavioural and ecological characteristics on predator diet composition. *Proceedings of the Royal Society of London, Series B* 271: 725–732.

Sicotte, P. and MacIntosh, A. J. 2004. Inter-group encounters and male incursions in *Colobus vellerosus* in central Ghana. *Behaviour* 141: 533–553.

Sicotte, P., Teichroeb, J. A. and Saj, T. L. 2007. Aspects of male competition in *Colobus vellerosus*: preliminary data on male and female loud calling, and infant deaths after a takeover. *International Journal of Primatology* 28: 627–636.

Sigé, B., Jaeger, J.-J., Sudre, J. and Vianey-Liaud, M. 1990. *Altiatlasius koulchii* n. gen. et sp., primate omomyidé du Paléocène supérieur du Maroc, et les origines des euprimates. *Palaeontographica* Abt. A, 214: 31–56.

Simons, E. L. 1990. Discovery of the oldest known anthropoidean skull from the paleogene of Egypt. *Science* 247: 1567–1569.

Simons, E. L., Plavcan, J. M. and Fleagle, J. G. 1999. Canine sexual dimorphism in Egyptian Eocene anthropoid primates: *Catopithecus* and *Proteopithecus*. *Proceedings of the National Academy of Sciences USA* 96: 2559–2562.

Sinsin, B., Nobimè, G., Téhou, A., Bekhuis, P. and Tchibozo, S. 2002. Past and present distribution of the red-bellied monkey *Cercopithecus erythrogaster erythrogaster* in Benin. *Folia Primatologica* 73: 116–123.

Skorupa, J. P. 1989. Crowned Eagles *Stephanoaetus coronatus* in rain forest: observations on breeding chronology and diet at a nest in Uganda. *Ibis* 131: 294–298.

Smith, A. 1833. African zoology. Part 1. Mammalia. *South African Quarterly Journal* 2: 17–32.

Smith, R. J. and Jungers, W. L. 1997. Body mass in comparative primatology. *Journal of Human Evolution* 32: 173–182.

Smuts, B. B. 1985. *Sex and Friendship in Baboons*. Aldine, Hawthorne, NY.

Smuts, B. B., Cheney, D. L., Seyfarth, R. M., Wrangham, R. W. and Struhsaker, T. T. (eds.). 1987. *Primate Societies*. The University of Chicago Press, Chicago.

Sommer, V., Adanu, J., Faucher, I. and Fowler, A. 2004. Nigerian chimpanzees (*Pan troglodytes vellerosus*) at Gashaka: two years of habituataion efforts. *Folia Primatologica* 75: 295–316.

Starin, E. D. 1981. Monkey moves. *Natural History* 90: 36–43.

Starin, E. D. 1988. Gestation and birth-related behaviors in Temminck's red colobus. *Folia Primatologica* 51: 161–164.

Starin, E. D. 1991. Socioecology of the Red Colobus Monkey in The Gambia with Particular Reference to Female-Male Differences and Transfer Patterns. PhD thesis, City University of New York, New York.

Starin, E. D. 2009. Contemplating colobus. *Philosophy Now*, March/April 2009: 52–54.

Steiner, C., Waltert, M. and Mühlenberg, M. 2003. Hunting pressure on the drill *Mandrillus leucophaeus* in Korup project area, Cameroon. *African Primates* 6: 10–19.

Steiper, M. E. and Young, N. M. 2006. Primate molecular divergence dates. *Molecular Phylogenetics and Evolution* 41: 384–394.

Stewart, C.-B. and Disotell, T.R. 1998. Primate evolution—in and out of Africa. *Current Biology* 8(16): R582–R588.

Steiper, M. E. and Young, N. M. 2009. Primates (Primates). Pp.482–486 in S. B. Hedges and S. Kumar (eds.), *The Timetree of Life*. Oxford University Press, New York.

Stokes, E. J. 2004. Within-group social relationships among females and adult males in wild western lowland gorillas (*Gorilla gorilla gorilla*). *American Journal of Primatology* 64: 233–246.

Struhsaker, T. T. 1967a. Behavior of vervet monkeys (*Cercopithecus aethiops*). *University of California Publications in Zoology* 82: 1–74.

Struhsaker, T. T. 1967b. Auditory communication among vervet monkeys (*Cercopithecus aethiops*). Pp.281–324 in S. A. Altmann (ed.), *Social Communication among Primates*. The University of Chicago Press, Chicago.

Struhsaker, T. T. 1967c. Ecology of vervet monkeys (*Cercopithecus aethiops*) in the Masai-Amboseli Game Reserve, Kenya. *Ecology* 48: 891–904.

Struhsaker, T. T. 1969. Correlates of ecology and social organization among African cercopithecines. *Folia Primatologica* 11: 80–118.

Struhsaker, T. T. 1970a. Phylogenetic implications of some vocalizations of *Cercopithecus* monkeys. Pp.367–444 in J. R. Napier and P. H. Napier (eds.), *Old World Monkeys: Evolution, Systematics, and Behavior*. Academic Press, New York.

Struhsaker, T. T. 1970b. Notes on *Galagoides demidovii* in Cameroon. *Mammalia* 34: 207–211.

Struhsaker, T. T. 1971a. Social behaviour of mother and infant vervet monkeys (*Cercopithecus aethiops*). *Animal Behaviour* 19: 233–250.

Struhsaker, T. T. 1971b. Notes on *Cercocebus a. atys* in Senegal, West Africa. *Mammalia* 35: 343–344.

Struhsaker, T. T. 1972. Rain-forest conservation in Africa. *Primates* 13: 103–109.

Struhsaker, T. T. 1975. *The Red Colobus Monkey*. The Chicago University Press, Chicago.

Struhsaker, T. T. 1981. Vocalizations, phylogeny and palaeogeography of red colobus monkeys (*Colobus badius*). *African Journal of Ecology* 19: 265–283.

Struhsaker, T. T. 1997. *Ecology of an African Rain Forest: Logging in Kibale and the Conflict Between Conservation and Exploitation*. University Press of Florida, Gainesville.

Struhsaker, T. T. 2000. The effects of predation and habitat quality on the socioecology of African monkeys: lessons from the islands of Bioko and Zanzibar. Pp.393–430 in P. F. Whitehead and C. J. Jolly (eds.), *Old World Monkeys*. Cambridge University Press, Cambridge, UK.

Struhsaker, T. T. 2010. *The Red Colobus Monkeys: Variation in Demography, Behavior, and Ecology of Endangered Species*. Oxford University Press, New York.

Struhsaker, T. T. and Gartlan, J. S. 1970. Observations on the behaviour and ecology of the patas monkey (*Erythrocebus patas*) in the Waza Reserve, Cameroon. *Journal of Zoology, London* 161: 49–63.

Struhsaker, T. T. and Hunkeler, P. 1971. Evidence of tool-using by chimpanzees in the Ivory Coast. *Folia Primatologica* 15: 212–219.

Struhsaker, T. T. and Leakey, M. 1990. Prey selectivity by crowned hawk-eagles on monkeys in the Kibale Forest, Uganda. *Behavioral Ecology and Sociobiology* 26: 435–443.

Struhsaker, T. T. and Leland, L. 1979. Socioecology of five sympatric monkey species in the Kibale Forest, Uganda. *Advances in the Study of Behavior* 9: 159–228.

Struhsaker, T. T. and Oates, J. F. 1995. The biodiversity crisis in south-western Ghana. *African Primates* 1: 5–6.

Strum, S. C. 1987. *Almost Human: A Journey into the World of Baboons*. Random House, New York.

Stump, D. P. 2005. Taxonomy of the Genus *Perodicticus*. PhD thesis, University of Pittsburgh, Pittsburgh, PA.

Sugiyama, Y. and Koman, J. 1979. Social structure and dynamics of wild chimpanzees at Bossou, Guinea. *Primates* 20: 323–339.

Sunderland-Groves, J. L. 2008. Population, Distribution and Conservation Status of the Cross River Gorilla (*Gorilla gorilla diehli*) in Cameroon. MPhil thesis, University of Sussex, Brighton, UK.

Sunderland-Groves, J. L. and Maisels, F. 2003. Large mammals of Takamanda Forest Reserve, Cameroon. Pp.111–127 in J. A. Comiskey, T. C. H. Sunderland and J. L. Sunderland-Groves (eds.), *Takamanda: The Biodiversity of an African Rainforest*. Smithsonian Institution Press, Washington, DC.

Sunderland-Groves, J. L., Ekinde, A. and Mboh, H. 2003a. Nesting behavior of *Gorilla gorilla diehli* at Kagwene Mountain, Cameroon: implications for assessing group size and density. *International Journal of Primatology* 30: 253–266.

Sunderland-Groves, J. L., Maisels, F. and Ekinde, A. 2003b. Surveys of the Cross River gorilla and chimpanzee populations in Takamanda Forest Reserve, Cameroon. Pp.129–140 in J. A. Comiskey, T. C. H. Sunderland and J. L. Sunderland-Groves (eds.), *Takamanda: The Biodiversity of an African Rainforest*. Smithsonian Institution Press, Washington, DC.

Sunderland-Groves, J. L., Ekinde, A. and Mboh, H. 2009. Nesting behavior of *Gorilla gorilla diehli* at Kagwene Mountain, Cameroon: implications for assessing group size and density. *International Journal of Primatology*. 30: 253–266.

Suzuki, A. 1979. The variation and adaptation of social groups of chimpanzees and black and white colobus monkeys. Pp.153–173 in I. S. Bernstein and E. O. Smith (eds.), *Primate Ecology and Human Origins*. Garland STPM Press, New York.

Tabuce, R., Marivaux, L., Lebrun, R., Adaci, M., Bensalah, M., Fabre, P.-H., Fara, E., Rodrigues, H. G., Hautler, L., Jaeger, J.-J., Lazzari, V., Mebrouk, F., Peigné, S., Sudre, J., Tafforeau, P., Valentin, X. and Mahboubi, M. 2009.

Anthropoid *versus* strepsirhine status of the African Eocene primates *Algeripithecus* and *Azibius*: craniodental evidence. *Proceedings of the Royal Society* B 276: 4087–4094.

Tahiri-Zagrët, C. 1976. Les Cercopithecidae de Côte d'Ivoire. *Bulletin de l'Institut français de l'Afrique noire* (A) 38: 206–230.

Teichroeb, J. A. and Sicotte, P. 2008a. Social correlates of fecal testosterone in male ursine colobus monkeys (*Colobus vellerosus*): the effect of male reproductive competition in aseasonal breeders. *Hormones and Behavior* 54: 417–423.

Teichroeb, J. A. and Sicotte, P. 2008b. Infanticide in ursine colobus monkeys *Colobus vellerosus* in Ghana: new cases and a test of the existing hypothesis. *Behaviour* 145: 727–755.

Teichroeb, J. A. and Sicotte, P. 2009. Female dispersal patterns in six groups of ursine colobus monkeys (*Colobus vellerosus*): infanticide avoidance is important. *Behaviour* 146: 551–582.

Teichroeb, J. A. and Sicotte, P. 2010. The function of male displays in ursine colobus monkeys (*Colobus vellerosus*): male competition, female mate choice or sexual selection? *Ethology* 116: 366–380.

Teichroeb, J. A., Saj, T. L., Paterson, J. D. and Sicotte, P. 2003. Effect of group size on activity budgets of *Colobus vellerosus* in Ghana. *International Journal of Primatology* 24: 743–758.

Teleki, G. 1989. Population status of wild chimpanzees (*Pan troglodytes*) and threats to survival. Pp. 312–353 in P. G. Heltne and L. A. Marquardt (eds.), *Understanding Chimpanzees*. Harvard University Press, Cambridge, MA.

Thorington, R. W. and Groves, C. P. 1970. An annotated classification of the Cercopithecoidea. Pp 629–647 in J. R. Napier and P. H. Napier (eds.), *Old World Monkeys: Evolution, Systematics, and Behavior*. Academic Press, New York.

Ting, N. 2008. Molecular Systematics of Red Colobus Monkeys (*Procolobus* [*Piliocolobus*]): Understanding the Evolution of an Endangered Primate. PhD thesis, City University of New York, New York.

Ting, N., Astaras, C., Hearn, G., Corush, J., Burrell, A. S., Phillips, N., Morgan, B. J., Gadsby, E. L. and Roos, C. 2011. Genetic signatures of a Late Pleistocene collapse in an Endangered forest dwelling primate (*Mandrillus leucophaeus*). *American Journal of Physical Anthropology* 144: 295.

Tooze, Z. 1995. Update on Sclater's guenon *Cercopithecus sclateri* in southern Nigeria. *African Primates* 1: 38–42.

Tosi, A. J. 2008. Forest monkeys and Pleistocene refugia: a phylogeographic window onto the disjunct distribution of the *Chlorocebus lhoesti* species group. *Zoological Journal of the Linnean Society* 154: 408–418.

Tosi, A. J., Melnick, D. J. and Disotell, T. R. 2004. Sex chromosome phylogenetics indicate a single transition to terrestriality in the guenons (tribe

Cercopithecini). *Journal of Human Evolution* 46: 223–237.

Tosi, A. J., Detwiler, K. M. and Disotell, T. R. 2005. X-chromosomal window into the evolutionary history of the guenons (Primates: Cercopithecini). *Molecular Phylogenetics and Evolution* 36: 58–66.

Tutin, C. E .G., McGrew, W. C. and Baldwin, P. J. 1983. Social organization of savanna-dwelling chimpanzees, *Pan troglodytes verus*, at Mt. Assirik, Senegal. *Primates* 24: 154–173.

Tutin, C. E. G., Ham, R. M., White, L. J. T. and Harrison, M. J. S. 1997. The primate community of the Lopé Reserve, Gabon: diets, responses to fruit scarcity, and effects on biomass. *American Journal of Primatology* 42: 1–24.

United Nations General Assembly. 2000. *Resolution 55/2: United Nations Millennium Declaration*. United Nations, New York.

United Nations Secretariat. 2008. *World Population Prospects: The 2008 Revision*. Population Division, Department of Economic and Social Affairs, United Nations Secretariat, New York. Website: <http://esa.un.org/unpp>. Accessed: 28 July, 2010.

Usongo, L. and Amubode, F. O. 2001. Nutritional ecology of Preuss's red colobus monkey (*Colobus badius preussi* Rahm 1970) in Korup National Park, Cameroon. *African Journal of Ecology* 39: 121–125.

Usongo, L. and Fimbel, C. 1995. Preliminary survey of arboreal primates in Lobeke Forest Reserve, South-east Cameroon. *African Primates* 1: 46–48.

Vanzolini, P. E. 1973. Paleoclimates, relief, and species multiplication in equatorial forests. Pp.255–258 in B. J. Meggers, E. S. Ayensu and W. D. Duckworth (eds.) *Tropical Forest Ecosystems in Africa and South America: A Comparative Review*. Smithsonian Institution Press, Washington, DC.

Verschuren, J. 1982. Hope for Liberia. *Oryx* 16: 421–427.

Vincent, F. 1969. Contribution á l'Étude des Prosimiens Africains. Le Galago de Demidoff. Reproduction (Biologie, Anatomie, Physiologie) et Comportement. Thèse de Doctorat d'État, University of Paris, Paris.

Vollmert, P., Fink, A. H. and Besler, H. 2003. "Ghana Dry Zone" und "Dahomey Gap": Ursachen für eine Niederschlagsanomalie im tropischen Westafrika. *Erde* 134: 375–393.

Wachter, B., Schabel, M. and Noë, R. 1997. Diet overlap and polyspecific associations of red colobus and Diana monkeys in the Taï National Park, Ivory Coast. *Ethology* 103: 514–526.

Waitkuwait, W. E. 2001. Report on the Establishment of a Community-based Bio-monitoring Programme in and around Sapo National Park, Sinoe County, Liberia. Report to the Society for the Conservation of Nature of Liberia, Forestry Development Authority (Liberia), and Fauna and Flora International.

Walker, A. 1969. The locomotion of the lorises, with special reference to the potto. *East African Wildlife Journal* 7: 1–5.

Wallis, S. J. 1978. The Sociology of *Cercocebus albigena johnstoni* (Lyddeker), an Arboreal Forest Monkey. PhD thesis, University College London, London.

Wallis, S. J. 1983. Sexual behaviour and reproduction of *Cercocebus albigena johnstonii* in Kibale Forest, Western Uganda. *International Journal of Primatology* 4: 153–166.

Waltert, M., Lien, Faber, K. and Mühlenberg, M. 2002. Further declines of threatened primates in the Korup Project Area, south-west Cameroon. *Oryx* 36: 257–265.

Warren, Y. 2003. Olive Baboons (*Papio cynocephalus anubis*): Behaviour, Ecology and Human Conflict in Gashaka Gumti National Park, Nigeria. PhD thesis, University of Surrey, Roehampton, UK.

Waser, P. M. 1975. Monthly variations in feeding and activity patterns of the mangabey, *Cercocebus albigena*. *East African Wildlife Journal* 13: 249–263.

Waser, P. M. 1976. *Cercocebus albigena*: site attachment, avoidance, and intergroup spacing. *American Naturalist* 110: 911–935.

Waser, P. M. 1977a. Feeding, ranging and group size in the mangabey (*Cercocebus albigena*). Pp.183–222 in Clutton-Brock, T. H. (ed.), *Primate Ecology: Studies of Feeding and Ranging Behaviour in Lemurs, Monkeys and Apes*. Academic Press, London.

Waser, P. M. 1977b. Individual recognition, intragroup cohesion, and intergroup spacing: evidence from sound playback to forest monkeys. *Behaviour* 60: 28–74.

Waser, P. M. 1980. Polyspecific associations of *Cercocebus albigena*: geographic variation and ecological correlates. *Folia Primatologica* 33: 57–76.

Waser, P. M. 1982. Primate polyspecific associations: do they occur by chance? *Animal Behaviour* 30: 1–8.

Waterhouse, G. R. 1838. Characters of a new *Galago* (*G. alleni*) and a new *Pteromys* (*P. horsfieldii*), in the Society's collection. *Proceedings of the Zoological Society of London* (for 1837): 87–88.

Watts, D. P. and Mitani, J. C. 2002. Hunting behavior of chimpanzees at Ngogo, Kibale National Park, Uganda. *International Journal of Primatology* 23: 1–28.

Webster, J. B. and Boahen, A. A. 1967. *The Growth of African Civilisation. The Revolutionary Years: West Africa since 1800*. Longman, London.

Werre, J. L. R. 2000. Ecology and Behavior of the Niger Delta Red Colobus (*Procolobus badius epieni*). PhD thesis, City University of New York, New York.

Werre, J. L. R. and Powell, C. B. 1997. The Niger Delta colobus – discovered in 1993 and now in danger of extinction. *Oryx* 31: 7–9.

White, F. 1983. *The Vegetation of Africa*. UNESCO, Paris.

White, H. and Berry, F. 2000. Krokosua Hills Forest Reserve Primate Survey July-Sept., 1999. Unpublished report, University of Aberdeen and University of Newcastle, UK.

White, L. J. T. 1994. Biomass of rain forest mammals in the Lopé Reserve, Gabon. *Journal of Animal Ecology* 63: 499–512.

White, L. J. T. and Oates, J. F. 1999. New data on the history of the plateau forest of Okomu, southern Nigeria: an insight into how human disturbance has shaped the African rain forest. *Global Ecology and Biogeography Letters* 8: 355–361.

Whiten, A., Goodall, J., McGrew, W. C., Nishida, T., Reynolds, V., Sugiyama, Y., Tutin, C. E. G., Wrangham, R. W. and Boesch, C. 1999. Culture in chimpanzees. *Nature* 399: 682–685.

Whitesides, G. H. 1985. Nut cracking by wild chimpanzees in Sierra Leone. *Primates* 26: 91–94.

Whitesides, G. H. 1989. Interspecific associations of Diana monkeys, *Cercopithecus diana*, in Sierra Leone, West Africa: Biological significance or chance? *Animal Behaviour* 37: 760–776.

Whitesides, G. H. 1991. Patterns of foraging, ranging, and interspecific associations of Diana monkeys (*Cercopithecus diana*) in Sierra Leone, West Africa. PhD thesis, University of Miami, Florida.

Whitesides, G. H., Oates, J. F., Green, S. M. and Kluberdanz, R. P. 1988. Estimating primate densities from transects in a West African rain forest: a comparison of techniques. *Journal of Animal Ecology* 57: 345–367.

Wickings, E. J., Ambrose, L. and Bearder, S. K. 1998. Sympatric populations of *Galagoides demidoff* and *Galagoides thomasi* in the Haut-Ogooué Region of Gabon. *Folia Primatologica* 69 (Supplement 1): 389–393.

Wild, C., Morgan, B. J. and Dixson, A. 2005. Conservation of drill populations in Bakossiland, Cameroon: historical trends and current status. *International Journal of Primatology* 26: 759–773.

Williamson, E. A., Tutin, C. E. G., Rogers, M. E. and Fernandez, M. 1990. Composition of the diet of lowland gorillas at Lopé in Gabon. *American Journal of Primatology* 21: 265–277.

Williamson, K. and Blench, R. M. 2000. Niger-Congo. Pp.11–42 in B. Heine and D. Nurse (eds.), *African Languages: An Introduction*. Cambridge University Press, Cambridge, UK.

Wolfheim, J. H. 1983. *Primates of the World: Distribution, Abundance, and Conservation.* University of Washington Press, Seattle.

Wong, S. N. P. and Sicotte, P. 2006. Population size and density of *Colobus vellerosus* at the Boabeng-Fiema Monkey Sanctuary and surrounding forest fragments in Ghana. *American Journal of Primatology* 68: 465–476.

Wong, S. N. P. and Sicotte, P. 2007. Activity budget and ranging patterns of *Colobus vellerosus* in forest fragments in central Ghana. *Folia Primatologica* 78: 245–254.

Wong, S. N. P., Saj, T. L. and Sicotte, P. 2006. Comparison of habitat quality and diet of *Colobus vellerosus* in forest fragments in Ghana. *Primates* 47: 365–373.

Wood, K. L., Gadsby, E. L. and Brault, S. 2008. Reproductive parameters of forest-dwelling captive drill monkeys *Mandrillus leucophaeus* in Nigeria. *Paper presented at XXIIth Congress of the International Primatological Society*, Edinburgh, UK.

World Weather Information Service. 2010. World Meteorological Organization, Geneva, Switzerland. Website: <http://worldweather.wmo.int/>. Accessed: 25 August 2010.

Yamakoshi, G. 1998. Dietary responses to fruit scarcity of wild chimpanzees at Bossou, Guinea: possible implications for ecological importance of tool use. *American Journal of Physical Anthropology* 106: 283–295.

Zalmout, I. S., Sanders, W. J., MacLatchy, L. M., Gunnell, G. F., Al-Mufarreh, Y. A., Ali, M. A., Nasser, A.-A. H., Al-Masari, A. M., Al-Sobhi, S. A., Nadhra, A. O., Matari, A. H., Wilson, J. A. and Gingerich, P. D. 2010. New Oligocene primate from Saudi Arabia and the divergence of apes and Old World monkeys. *Nature* 466: 360–364.

Ziegler, S., Nikolaus, G. and Hutterer, R. 2002. High mammalian diversity in the newly established National Park of Upper Niger, Republic of Guinea. *Oryx* 36: 73–80.

Zimmermann, E., Bearder, S. K., Doyle, G. A. and Andersson, A. B. 1988. Variations in vocal patterns of Senegal and South African lesser bushbabies and their implications for taxonomic relationships. *Folia Primatologica* 51: 87–105.

Zinner, D., Buba, U., Nash, S. and Roos, C. 2010. Pan-African voyagers: the phylogeography of baboons. Pp.319–358 in V. Sommer and C. Ross (eds.), *Primates of Gashaka*. Springer, New York.

Zuberbühler, K. 2000. Referential labelling in Diana monkeys. *Animal Behaviour* 59: 917–927.

Zuberbühler, K. 2001. Predator-specific alarm calls in Campbell's monkeys, *Cercopithecus campbelli*. *Behavioral Ecology and Sociobiology* 50: 414–422.

Zuberbühler, K. 2007. Monkey alarm calls. Pp.194–220 in W. S. McGraw, K. Zuberbühler and R. Noë (eds.), *Monkeys of the Taï Forest: An African Primate Community*. Cambridge University Press, Cambridge, UK.

Zuberbühler, K. and Jenny, D. 2007. Interaction between leopard and monkeys. Pp.133–154 in W. S. McGraw, K. Zuberbühler and R. Noë (eds.), *Monkeys of the Taï Forest: An African Primate Community*. Cambridge University Press, Cambridge, UK.

Zuberbühler, K., Noë, R. and Seyfarth, R. M. 1997. Diana monkey long-distance calls: messages for conspecifics and predators. *Animal Behaviour* 53: 589–604.

Index: West African Primates and Their Predators

For species and subspecies of primates, all page numbers are under scientific (Latin) names. Subspecies (trinomials) are listed as subheadings of the binomial species name. Page numbers in bold = the main species or subspecies account; in italics = photograph; with "pl" = illustration; with "m" = distribution map; with "t" = table.

YOUR PERSONAL
WEST AFRICAN PRIMATE
LIFE-LIST

SCIENTIFIC NAME	LOCALITY	DATE
Galagoides demidovii		
Galagoides thomasi		
Galago senegalensis senegalensis		
Euoticus pallidus pallidus		
Euoticus pallidus talboti		
Sciurocheirus alleni alleni		
Sciurocheirus alleni cameronensis		
Arctocebus calabarensis		
Perodicticus potto potto		
Perodicticus potto juju		
Perodicticus edwardsi		
Cercocebus atys		
Cercocebus lunulatus		
Cercocebus torquatus		
Mandrillus leucophaeus leucophaeus		
Mandrillus leucophaeus poensis		
Lophocebus albigena		
Papio papio		

SCIENTIFIC NAME	LOCALITY	DATE
Papio anubis		
Miopithecus ogouensis		
Erythrocebus patas		
Chlorocebus aethiops sabaeus		
Chlorocebus aethiops tantalus		
Allochrocebus preussi preussi		
Allochrocebus preussi insularis		
Cercopithecus diana diana		
Cercopithecus diana roloway		
Cercopithecus neglectus		
Cercopithecus campbelli campbelli		
Cercopithecus campbelli lowei		
Cercopithecus mona		
Cercopithecus pogonias pogonias		
Cercopithecus pogonias ssp.		
Cercopithecus petaurista petaurista		
Cercopithecus petaurista buettikoferi		
Cercopithecus erythrogaster erythrogaster		
Cercopithecus erythrogaster pococki		
Cercopithecus sclateri		
Cercopithecus erythrotis erythrotis		

SCIENTIFIC NAME	LOCALITY	DATE
Cercopithecus erythrotis camerunensis		
Cercopithecus cephus		
Cercopithecus nictitans stampflii		
Cercopithecus nictitans insolitus		
Cercopithecus nictitans ludio		
Cercopithecus nictitans martini		
Cercopithecus nictitans nictitans		
Procolobus verus		
Procolobus badius temminckii		
Procolobus badius badius		
Procolobus waldroni		
Procolobus epieni		
Procolobus pennantii		
Procolobus preussi		
Colobus polykomos		
Colobus vellerosus		
Colobus guereza		
Colobus satanas satanas		
Gorilla gorilla diehli		
Pan troglodytes verus		
Pan troglodytes ellioti		

NOTES

NOTES

REQUESTS FOR INFORMATION

We would welcome hearing from you if you see primates in unusual places or in unusual circumstances. If you think you have seen something of scientific value, please contact one of us at the addresses below. You may have made an observation worthy of publication in *African Primates*, the newsletter of the IUCN/SSC Primate Specialist Group's Africa Section, see <http://journals.sfu.ca/afrprims/index.php/AfricanPrimates>, or another primatological journal.

Of particular interest are the following kinds of data:

1. Sightings outside the geographical ranges given in this book (please provide place names and GPS coordinates where possible).

2. Photographs or videotape of the animal(s) sighted to assist us in confirming identifications.

3. Cases in which primates have been kept as pets, or captured or shot for food. This would include situations in which entire carcasses or body parts (skins, meat, skulls, etc.) are being sold in markets or shops, or are being kept in private homes (again, photographs would be helpful).

4. Sites not mentioned in this book where primates are especially abundant or where observation conditions are particularly good. We would like to add such sites to future editions of this guide.

5. Any other information that you think might be useful in improving our knowledge of biology of the West African primates and their conservation.

Please write to:

Russell A. Mittermeier, President, Conservation International, 2011 Crystal Drive, Suite 500, Arlington, VA 22202, USA
E-mail: <r.mittermeier@conservation.org>

Galagidae

Lorisidae

Cercopithecinae

Colobinae

Hominidae

Dwarf Galagos
Galagoides
Pp.85 - 100

Lesser Galagos, Bushbabies
Galago
Pp.102 - 120

Allen's Galagos
Sciurocheirus
Pp.119 - 128

Needle-clawed Galagos
Euoticus
Pp.110 - 118

Angwantibo
Arctocebus
Pp.131 - 136

Pottos
Perodicticus
Pp.137 - 150

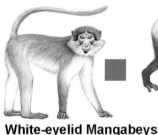

Drills, Mandrill
Mandrillus
Pp.174 - 183

White-eyelid Mangabeys
Cercocebus
Pp.153 - 173

Crested Mangabeys
Lophocebus
Pp.185 - 195

Baboons
Papio
Pp.196 - 210